Foreword

Increasing amounts of municipal solid waste, declining landfill capacity, public opposition to all types of management facilities, concerns about the risks associated with waste management, and rising costs are common problems facing communities across the Nation. As a result, there is increasing awareness about the need to prevent municipal waste from being generated in the first place and to better manage what is generated. Many communities, States, businesses, and public interest groups are undertaking a variety of activities to address these needs. The challenge to improve the situation ranges from actions by individuals to supportive policies at the Federal level.

This study on MSW was requested by the House Committee on Energy and Commerce, the House Committee on Science, Space, and Technology, and the Senate Committee on Environment and Public Works in anticipation of the reauthorization of the Resource Conservation and Recovery Act. As part of the assessment, OTA issued a background paper on *Issues in Medical Waste Management* (October 1988).

Our report discusses options for a national policy based on the dual strategies of MSW prevention and better management. It also presents options to address immediate problems such as increased interstate shipments of MSW and unfinished Federal guidelines for landfills and incinerators.

OTA is grateful for the considerable assistance provided by our advisory panel, workshop participants, contractors, reviewers, and other contributors during the course of the assessment. These individuals helped OTA obtain and examine the enormous amount of available information. OTA, however, remains solely responsible for the contents of this report.

JOHN H. GIBBONS
Director

Municipal Solid Waste Advisory Panel

Joseph Sax, *Chair*
University of California

John Bazin
Anheuser-Busch Cos., Inc.

Gordon Boyd
Schillinger, Salerni, and Boyd

Paul Connett
Saint Lawrence University

Randall Curlee
Oak Ridge National Laboratory

Dana Duxbury
Dana Duxbury & Associates

Rodney Edwards
American Paper Institute

Jeffrey Hahn
Ogden Projects, Inc.

Michael Herz
Benjamin Cardozo School of Law

Walter Johnson
St. Paul Metropolitan Waste Control Commission

Richard Kattar
New England CRInc.

Raymond Naar
General Electric Plastics

Lorie Parker
Seattle Solid Waste Utility

Glenrose Pitt
Citizens' Environmental Advisory Committee
Louisiana Department of Environmental Quality

Neil Seldman
Institute for Local Self-Reliance

Barry Scher
Giant Food, Inc.

Peter Vardy
Waste Management, Inc.

Irvin White
New York State Energy Research and
    Development Authority

NOTE: OTA appreciates the valuable assistance and thoughtful critiques provided by the advisory panel members. The views expressed in this OTA report, however, are the sole responsibility of the Office of Technology Assessment. Participation on the advisory panel does not imply endorsement of the report.

OTA Project Staff—Municipal Solid Waste

John Andelin, *Assistant Director, OTA*
Science, Information, and Natural Resources Division

Robert W. Niblock, *Oceans and Environment Program Manager*

Howard Levenson, *Project Director*

Kathryn D. Wagner, *Assistant Project Director*

Judy Kowalski, *Analyst*

Joan Harn, *Analyst*

Administrative Staff

Kathleen A. Beil

Sally W. Van Aller

Workshop on State and Local MSW Programs, March 17-18, 1988

William Apgar
Pennsylvania Bureau of Waste
  Management

Jerome Balter
Public Interest Law Center

David Buckner
Illinois Department of Energy and
  Natural Resources

Fred Clinton
Michigan Department of Natural
  Resources

David Colbert
House Committee on Energy and
  Commerce

Hershel Cutler
Institute of Scrap Recycling
  Industries

Michael Downs
Oregon Department of Environmental
  Quality

Shelley Dresser-Gagnon
Council of State Governments

Dana Duxbury
Dana Duxbury & Associates

George Eowan
California Waste Management Board

Randall Franke
Marion County Board of
  Commissioners

Joseph Gilson
Camden County Office of Solid
  Waste Management

Janet Keller
Rhode Island Department of
  Environmental Management

Linda King
Citizen's Clearinghouse for
  Hazardous Wastes

Carolyn Konheim
Konheim & Ketcham, Inc.

Ruth Lampi
Environmental Task Force

Gerry Lederer
U.S. Conference of Mayors

Lynne Markus
Missouri Department of Natural
  Resources

Cassandra Maurer
Land-of-Sky Regional Council

Hector Mendieta
Texas Division of Solid Waste
  Management

Theodore O'Neill
Cape May County Municipal
  Utilities Authority

John Reindl
Wisconsin Department of
  Natural Resources

Ken Rosenbaum
Office of Congressman Ron Wyden

Neil Seldman
Institute for Local Self-Reliance

Jere Sellers
Franklin Associates, Ltd.

Mary Sheil
New Jersey Department of
  Environmental Protection

Don Silva
Science & Engineering
  Associates, Inc.

Gary Sondermeyer
New Jersey Department of
  Environmental Protection

Nancy VandenBerg
Markets for Recycled Products

Mary Wiard
Ohio Department of Natural
  Resources

Elliott Zimmermann
Illinois Department of Energy and
  Natural Resources

Workshop on Markets for Recycled Materials, June 8, 1988

Victor Bell
North East Recycling
  Association

Leroy Cooper
California Office of Procurement

Tom Couling
Great Lakes Recycling Coalition

John Gleason
New York State Office of
  Procurement

Jim Grove
Miami Paper Co.

David Jeans
American Iron and Steel Institute

John P. Josephs
Garden State Paper Co.

Steve Levetan
Institute of Scrap Recycling
  Industries

Stanton Moss
Stanton A. Moss, Inc.

Frank Reid
Anchor Glass Container

Paul Relis
Gildea Resource Center

Andy Stephens
Eaglebrook

Doug Stewart
Montana Recycling

Al Troglio
General Services Administration

Workshop on Incineration/Waste-to-Energy Issues, June 28, 1988

Donald Barnes
U.S. EPA Science Advisory Board

Marjorie Clarke
INFORM

Thomas Constable
Environment Canada

Richard Cook
Kalamazoo College

Richard Denison
Environmental Defense Fund

Keith Forester
Wheelabrator Environmental Systems

Michael Gough
Resources for the Future

Warren Gregory
Smith-Barney

Jeffrey Hahn
Ogden Projects, Inc.

Walter Shaub
CORRE

Jim Sears
Marion County Department of Solid Waste

Allan Smith
University of California

Workshop on MSW Reduction, July 14-15, 1988

Judd Alexander
James River Corp.

Mary Amini
General Foods Technical Center

John Burke
James River Corp.

Ron Catlett
Dow Consumer Products, Inc.

Dana Duxbury
Dana Duxbury & Associates

Rolf Faste
Stanford University

Harry Fatkin
Polaroid Corp.

Ed Fox
Proctor & Gamble Co.

Marc Goldberg
Safer, Inc.

Erica Guttman
Rhode Island Solid Waste
    Management Corp.

Roy C. Herndon
Florida State University

Ken Hunnibell
Rhode Island School of Design

Bruce L. Kline
Pentapco Inc.

Ruth Lampi
Environmental Action Foundation

Wayne Martin
DuPont

Merilyn Reeves
League of Women Voters of the
    United States

Shelby Yastrow
McDonald's Corp.

Contents

Chapter 1

Findings and Policy Options

CONTENTS

Boxes

Figures

Table

Findings and Policy Options

OVERVIEW

"Waste not, want not"—a notion that helped carve a Nation out of a wilderness, but increasingly an ignored concept. It is time to revisit this notion, reassess our attitudes about MSW, and plan a wise policy to guide the Nation into the next century.

Today we find ourselves facing growing mounds of trash and the label "throw-away society." In the United States, we generate over 160 million tons of municipal solid waste (MSW) each year—more than one-half ton per person—and the amount is rising steadily (box 1-A; figure 1-1 shows the estimated portions of materials and products in MSW, by weight). In 1986, only about 10 percent of all MSW was recycled and 10 to 15 percent was incinerated (mostly with energy recovery), while almost 80 percent—about 130 million tons—was disposed of in landfills (figure 1-2).

Landfilling has been the most available disposal method, but many areas of the country are experiencing shortfalls of permitted landfill capacity and rising landfill costs. The Environmental Protection Agency (EPA) estimates that 80 percent of existing permitted landfills will close within 20 years (figure 1-3).[1] Landfill capacity is declining primarily because of three interrelated trends: 1) older landfills are reaching the end of their expected lives; 2) environmental requirements are being strengthened by some States and local governments (which has resulted in the closure of substandard landfills, but which also ensures that future landfills will be more environmentally sound); and 3) siting new landfills is difficult, in part due to public opposition.[2] This opposition results primarily from previous experiences with poorly performing facilities, concerns

over potential health and environmental risks, "Not In My Backyard" (NIMBY) attitudes, and the failure of public officials to involve the public adequately at the beginning of the decisionmaking process.

The private sector and local non-profit organizations have practiced recycling for decades, both for profit and to conserve natural resources. Many activities to increase the collection, processing, and marketing of recyclable materials are being undertaken by citizen groups, communities, States, and businesses, and it is likely that recycling of MSW will increase in the next few years. Incineration also has been used for many decades, but only recently has it been coupled with energy recovery. Its use has increased during the last decade, and additional capacity is being constructed or planned. Predicting the extent to which recycling or incineration will increase is impossible, however, because of factors such as the volatility of markets for recyclable materials and public opposition to incineration.[3] Even if we attempt to recycle or incinerate all MSW, landfills will still be needed for managing the residuals from these methods.

In areas where landfill capacity is declining or exhausted, and where other management capacity such as recycling and incineration cannot be increased sufficiently in the short term, one of the options being pursued is to transport MSW to other jurisdictions within a State or to other States. Localities receiving these transported wastes express concern about additional risks to human health and the environment and the strain on their own MSW management capacity. Yet their legal leverage to restrict such shipments is limited.

---

[1]This estimate was made before EPA proposed its new landfill guidelines, which could further increase the number of closures. As the proposed guidelines are now written, if existing landfills close within 2 1/2 years of their adoption, the landfill owner will be exempt from costly requirements for closing and cleaning up the facility. Substandard landfills are likely to close to avoid these costs.

[2]Siting is not only a problem for landfills, but also for other MSW management facilities, such as incinerators and recycling facilities.

[3]The intensity of public opposition is reflected in the suggestion by some spokespersons that incineration should be banned to force dramatic changes in the way our society consumes materials and products.

Box 1-A—MSW Definition and Data Needs[1]

MSW is solid waste generated at residences, commercial establishments (e.g., offices, retail shops, restaurants), and institutions (e.g., hospitals and schools). This waste may be categorized as materials (e.g., glass, paper) or products (e.g., appliances, containers, tires). For purposes of this report, MSW does *not* include construction or demolition debris or automobile scrap. Medical wastes were addressed by OTA in another report (54).

Solid waste is defined more broadly in RCRA (Sec. 1004 (27)) as ''any garbage, refuse, sludge from a waste treatment plant, water supply treatment plant, or air pollution control facility and other discarded material, including solid, liquid, semisolid, or contained gaseous material resulting from industrial, commercial, mining, and agricultural operations, and from community activities. . .''

Estimates of MSW Generation

EPA has estimated that total MSW generation in the United States is over 160 million tons in 1986, and that it is rising at a rate of slightly over 1 percent each year. These estimates are based on a materials flow model (referred to here as the EPA/Franklin model). Figure 1-1 shows the model's estimates of the composition of MSW by weight, in terms of different materials and products.

Most of the increase in the generation rate is attributable to population growth. However, each person also appears to be generating more waste on average. The EPA/Franklin model estimates that each person in the United States generated 3.6 pounds of garbage per day in 1986; this is expected to grow to 3.9 pounds by 2000.

Determining actual MSW generation rates is difficult. Some evidence indicates that the average generation rate per person may be higher than the model's estimates. Different studies report widely different rates, and use different definitions. For example, it often is not clear whether industrial waste and demolition debris are included in calculations.[2] This lack of consistent definitions and procedures for measuring, calculating, or reporting MSW data makes it difficult to aggregate existing local and State data or to compare them with the EPA/Franklin estimates.

Problems caused by inconsistent definitions and data collection techniques also make it difficult to compare generation rates among countries. It is often stated that U. S. citizens produce more MSW per person than citizens of other industrialized countries. This may be true—after all, the United States has high rate of purchasing products—but the magnitude of such differences cannot be reliably estimated with current data.

National estimates of total MSW generation in the United States also are not particularly useful for local decisionmaking. **From a local perspective, information about the generation and composition of MSW in communities is much more critical for making decisions about capacity needs and management options.** For example, overall generation in a given area affects what size of landfill or incinerator is needed; the types of products and materials in the MSW influence planning for recovery of materials for recycling; and variations in composition can affect incinerator design.

Data and Research Gaps

Underlying Factors—Many potentially important underlying factors that affect MSW generation have not been investigated extensively. Few studies have looked at how degree of urbanization, socioeconomic status, or family size affect generation and composition. Little has been done to document trends in the production of single-use, disposable items, or to document the relative contributions from the residential, commercial, and institutional sectors. Without more detailed analyses of such factors, it will be difficult to focus educational efforts to change consumption patterns and reduce MSW generation rates.

Weight and Volume—Better data on the weight of MSW components are needed to make decisions about recycling and incineration. For example, prices for secondary materials are usually quoted on a weight basis, so officials who have data on individual components can estimate potential revenues. On a national basis, the largest categories of MSW by weight are estimated to be paper products, yard waste, and food waste.

Data on volume are useful for evaluating landfill capacity, collection vehicle capacity, and the feasibility of quantity reduction. **Unfortunately, most studies have not gathered data on the volumes of different materials in MSW prior to disposal**. Excavation studies at several landfills have provided some data on MSW volume after it has been landfilled for several years; these excavations show that paper and plastics are the largest components by volume.

Calculating Recycling Rates—Calculating recycling rates for the Nation is also problematic. EPA's estimate that about 10 percent of MSW is recycled excludes materials and products such as demolition debris and automobiles. Some observers contend that these should be included, which would raise the overall recycling rate considerably. For example, approximately 12 million tons of steel were recycled from automobiles in 1983; this would almost double the EPA/Franklin estimate of tonnage recycled.

---

[1]This box is drawn primarily from ch. 3.

[2]For example, industrial waste might make up 10 percent or more of all waste received at MSW landfills. As new regulations (under RCRA) regarding the

Figure 1-1—Estimated Portions of Materials and Products in MSW, 1986, by Weight

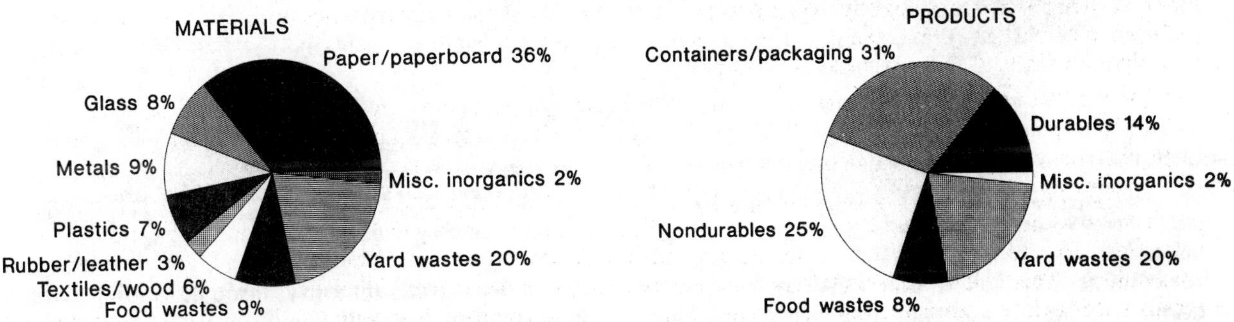

MATERIALS

Paper/paperboard 36%
Glass 8%
Metals 9%
Plastics 7%
Rubber/leather 3%
Textiles/wood 6%
Food wastes 9%
Misc. inorganics 2%
Yard wastes 20%

PRODUCTS

Containers/packaging 31%
Durables 14%
Misc. inorganics 2%
Nondurables 25%
Yard wastes 20%
Food wastes 8%

Durables=major appliances, furniture, rubber tires, miscellaneous.
Nondurables=newspapers, books, magazines, tissue paper, office and commercial paper, clothing, footware, miscellaneous.
SOURCE: Franklin Associates, Ltd., *Characterization of Municipal Solid Waste in the United States, 1960 to 2000 (Update 1988)*, final report, prepared for the U.S. Environmental Protection Agency (Prairie Village, KS: March 1988).

The costs of MSW management are rising steeply, driven in part by these factors (ch. 2). Per-person MSW costs are still relatively low, but the rate of increase already is causing financial problems for some communities. Further, as proper management of MSW becomes more expensive, the likelihood of illegal disposal will increase.

The regional and national implications of these problems are becoming evident, yet the Nation lacks a clearly articulated Federal policy for MSW. Consequently, State and local authorities receive little guidance to help them address their MSW problems. **Although primary responsibility for MSW management rests with State and local governments, the Federal Government can help in two areas: first, by addressing some immediate** **problems and second, by addressing the longer term issue of how society uses and disposes of materials and products.**

The Federal Government could help address the most pressing problems by:

- resolving the uncertainty created by unfinished Federal guidelines on landfills and incinerators;

- addressing issues associated with increased interstate shipments of MSW; and

- providing better information to local and State governments, businesses, and citizens about technical capabilities, comparative costs, and risks of different MSW management methods.

Figure 1-2—Estimated Use of MSW Management Methods, 1986

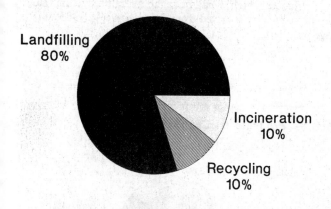

- Landfilling 80%
- Incineration 10%
- Recycling 10%

SOURCE: Franklin Associates, Ltd., *Characterization of Municipal Solid Waste in the United States, 1960 to 2000 (Update 1988)*, final report, prepared for the U.S. Environmental Protection Agency (Prairie Village, KS: March 1988).

Figure 1-3—Estimated Decline in Existing Permitted Landfills

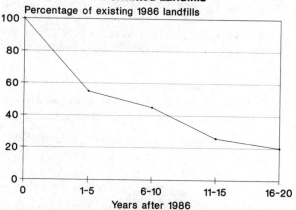

Percentage of existing 1986 landfills

NOTE: Based on estimate of 6,034 landfills; data for years 1-5 include an estimated 535 closings in 1986-87.

SOURCE: U.S. Environmental Protection Agency, *Report to Congress, Solid Waste Disposal in the United States, Volume II*, Office of Solid Waste and Emergency Response, EPA/530-SW-88-011B (Washington, DC: October 1988).

One immediate action that EPA could take to accomplish these goals, possibly with additional congressional guidance, would be to complete regulations for all types of MSW management facilities. This would involve finishing the revision of the landfill regulations, adopting regulations for MSW incinerators, and developing regulations for emissions and residues from composting and recycling facilities (some of which currently are unregulated at the Federal level). These actions would reduce uncertainties regarding requirements for new facilities and could help better protect human health and the environment. If increased Federal regulation of MSW management is to occur, it should be accompanied by strengthened Federal enforcement provisions. States would also need to increase enforcement action against improper management.

Congress could also address the issue of ensuring sufficient management capacity for MSW. For example, Congress could require each State to guarantee management capacity for a specified percentage of MSW generated within its borders—a "capacity assurance" provision. Even with such congressional action, States and localities still may have problems siting the facilities needed to meet their capacity requirements. To address this problem, EPA could develop model siting and dispute resolution procedures. These procedures could sug-

gest how a State authority, through binding arbitration or other methods, could resolve siting disputes that cannot otherwise be settled at the local level.

In addition to addressing these immediate problems, the broader issue of how our society uses materials—from manufacturing through subsequent distribution and disposal (figure 1-4)—should be considered. **A clear national policy on MSW that addresses the use of materials is essential for providing a broader context in which specific MSW programs can be developed and implemented.** This has important implications not only for MSW, but also for other environmental issues such as global warming, natural resource conservation, and pollution abatement. These issues are all interconnected. Leaders of countries around the world now recognize that changes in the way we use resources and materials are needed if we are to achieve sustainable economic development without harming the environment (61). MSW offers everyone an opportunity to work toward these goals.

A national MSW policy that reflects these ideas should be based on the dual strategies of waste prevention and better materials management. It is important to make a clear distinction between *prevention* and *management* activities to ensure that

Photo credit: Office of Technology Assessment

About 80 percent of MSW is managed by keeping it mixed together and sending it to a landfill. Declining landfill capacity, environmental risks, and rising costs, however, are causing communities around the Nation to examine other management methods.

adequate attention is focused on each.[4] Prevention refers to activities by manufacturers (e.g., modifying products, including packaging, to reduce the toxicity or quantity of products *before* they are manufactured) and by consumers (e.g., modifying purchasing decisions to buy products that are less toxic or more durable).[5] The motivation for promoting MSW prevention is strong and simple. Reducing toxicity would make all management methods safer and could restore public confidence in waste management policies and programs. For example, reducing the amounts and types of organic chemicals in landfills would mean less air pollution (e.g., from

volatile organic chemicals) and less toxic leachate. Quantity reduction would mean that the useful life of existing and future waste management facilities would be extended and new replacement capacity could be developed at a slower rate.

OTA cannot predict the extent to which waste prevention will occur, but this approach offers important potential benefits that are worth pursuing. If Congress includes prevention as part of its national policy for MSW, there is widespread consensus that a vigorous Federal role will be needed to pursue these opportunities. This is in part

---

[4]This differs from the concept of "integrated waste management" espoused by EPA and others, because that concept includes prevention **within** a hierarchy of management options.

[5]Product modification also has implications for the management of products discarded as MSW (e.g., the recyclability of a product). It should also be noted that OTA includes **backyard** composting of yard and food wastes as a form of quantity reduction because no public or private sector management is involved.

Figure 1-4—Waste Prevention and Materials Management in the Context of Materials Use

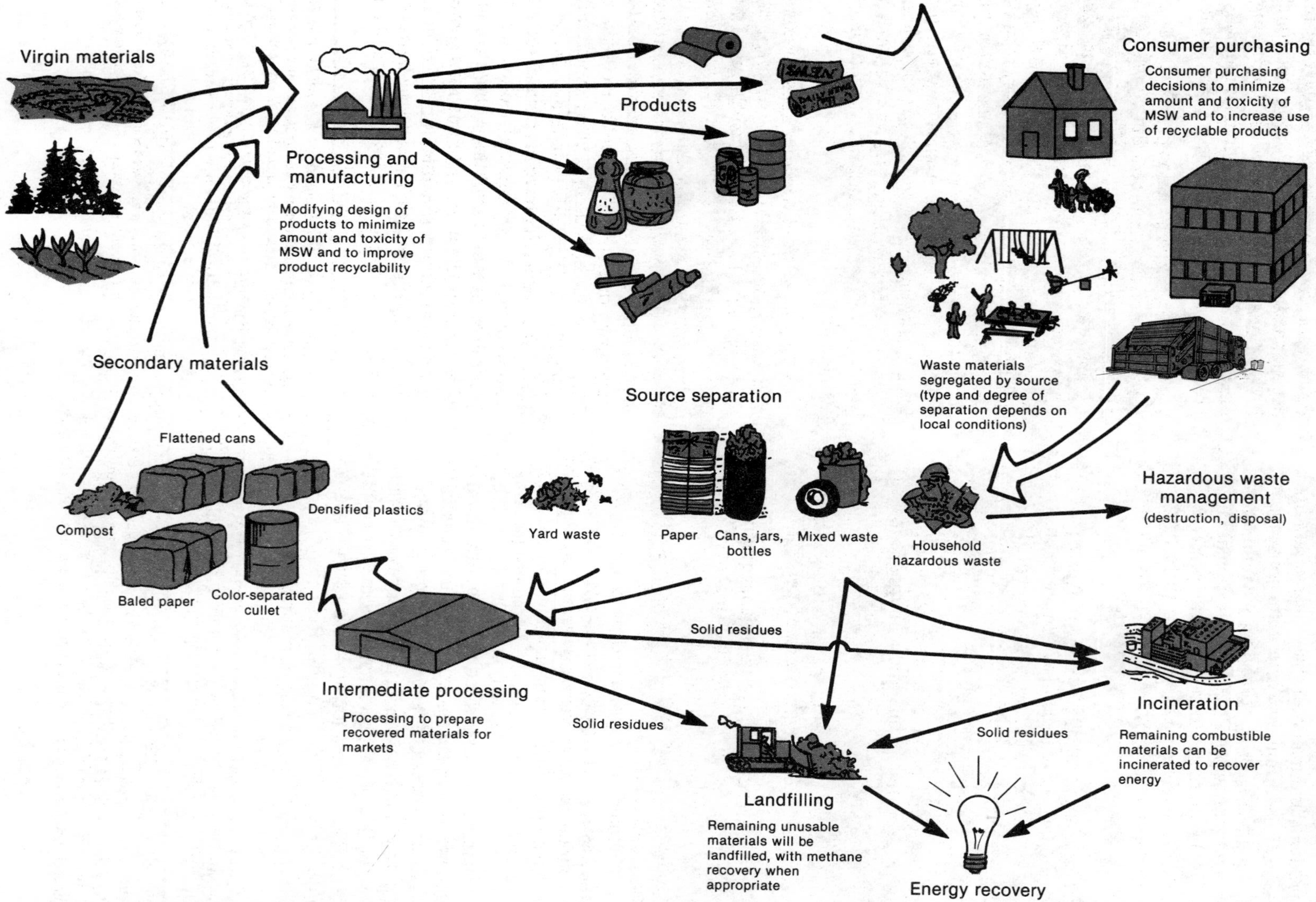

Consumer purchasing

Consumer purchasing decisions to minimize amount and toxicity of MSW and to increase use of recyclable products

Hazardous waste management

(destruction, disposal)

Incineration

Remaining combustible materials can be incinerated to recover energy

Waste materials segregated by source (type and degree of separation depends on local conditions)

Household hazardous waste

Solid residues

Energy recovery

Products

Source separation

Mixed waste

Cans, jars, bottles

Paper

Solid residues

Landfilling

Remaining unusable materials will be landfilled, with methane recovery when appropriate

Yard waste

Solid residues

Solid residues

Processing and manufacturing

Modifying design of products to minimize amount and toxicity of MSW and to improve product recyclability

Intermediate processing

Processing to prepare recovered materials for markets

Secondary materials

Densified plastics

Flattened cans

Color-separated cullet

Baled paper

Compost

Virgin materials

SOURCE: Office of Technology Assessment, 1989.

because the Federal Government has the potential to affect products and materials that move across State boundaries. In addition, one important consequence of a national MSW prevention policy would be that the government would become responsible for leadership in putting the policy into practice. To date, MSW prevention has received little congressional attention and EPA has not had the resources or political motivation to promote it.[6]

Even assuming notable progress in waste prevention, communities will continue to generate large amounts of MSW requiring management. In addition, unless prevention efforts successfully reduce the toxicity of all products, toxic constituents will remain in MSW, either because some products are toxic per se (e.g., pesticides) or contain substances that can be harmless in the product but pose toxicity problems during waste management (e.g., cadmium in some plastics). For these reasons, a comprehensive MSW strategy must consider not only prevention, but also better "materials management."

OTA suggests that "materials management" has two aspects. First, the manufacturing of products should be coordinated with the needs of different management methods (e.g., by designing products for recyclability) (figure 1-4). Second, MSW management should be approached on a material-by-material basis, in which discarded materials (including discarded products, yard waste, etc.) are diverted to the most appropriate management method based on their physical and chemical characteristics.[7]

To establish a framework for deciding how to manage MSW when it is generated, OTA considers materials and energy conservation (already stated as objectives in the Resource Conservation and Recovery Act, or RCRA) to be national goals, and assumes that each management method is designed to ensure

the safety of human health and the environment. The framework developed by OTA suggests that local decisionmakers consider recycling (and composting) first, followed by incineration and landfilling, recognizing that all of these management methods may be viable and complementary in a given situation.[8]

Recycling is given the top priority based on: 1) its materials conservation benefits compared with incineration and landfilling; and 2) its energy savings, at least for some materials such as aluminum, compared with manufacturing using virgin materials. Further, assuming that adequate regulations exist for both primary and secondary manufacturing facilities, recycling may produce fewer pollutants when the entire MSW system is considered.[9] Incineration of combustible wastes is given preference over landfilling because it destroys pathogens and organic materials, decreases the volume of waste destined for landfills, and often can recover energy economically.[10]

At the local level, communities should use this framework to decide how to manage particular materials *in light of local conditions*. This entails considering factors such as: human health and environmental risks, management costs (including capital, operating, and collection/transportation costs), availability of technologies, market conditions for secondary materials, and public acceptance of various alternatives. Although many communities have explicitly or implicitly adopted a MSW "hierarchy," they generally have not considered all of these factors (ch. 8). A national policy of materials management would encourage more complete consideration of them. A materials management strategy should also be flexible, so that MSW management methods can be chosen on the basis of regional and local variations and limitations, and changes in these conditions over time.

---

[6]There are signs of change at EPA, however—for example, a proposed policy statement on pollution prevention (54 *Federal Register* 3845, Jan. 26, 1989). Various pollution control associations also have endorsed this concept (e.g., 59). How applicable these policy statements will be to MSW, as opposed to hazardous waste, remains to be seen. However, a recent EPA report devoted to MSW stressed the idea of MSW prevention (57).

[7]The materials management approach builds on materials use concepts that have been discussed for many years (e.g., refs. 2,24,35,46). In fact, many communities practiced a form of materials management prior to the 1960s, when they routinely separated discarded materials for management. Only in recent decades have most communities collected mixed MSW, a trend that was encouraged, for example, by the advent of collection trucks that compact MSW.

[8]Although the term "hierarchy" is often applied to MSW, OTA does not use the term because it suggests a rigid, linear approach to decisionmaking.

[9]Primary manufacturing refers to production with virgin materials; secondary manufacturing uses materials recovered from waste. If recycled products replace products made from virgin materials, potential pollution savings may result from the avoidance of manufacturing and subsequent disposal of replacement products made from virgin materials (ch. 5).

[10]Energy also can be recovered from landfills, in the form of methane gas.

Implementing a materials management approach at the local level will require MSW to be thought about in terms of its components instead of as an indistinguishable mixture. This means that residences and commercial establishments will have to keep some waste materials separate to make subsequent management safer and more economical.[11] For example, keeping yard waste separate for backyard or municipal composting can reduce, to some extent, leachate from landfills and nitrogen oxide emissions from incinerators (chs. 5, 6, and 7). Separating recyclable materials before they are mixed with other waste results in cleaner, more uniform commodities, thus making them easier to market.

Implementing a national policy that emphasizes MSW prevention and materials management inherently requires strong Federal leadership. Congress can provide the basis for such leadership during the reauthorization of RCRA, the primary Federal authority regarding MSW (box 1-B).

Chapters 2 through 8 present discussions of the MSW system and factors affecting management costs, amounts and composition of MSW, prevention, recycling, incineration, landfilling, and government programs. The remainder of this chapter presents specific policy options for Congress to consider. Each policy option is discussed in the context of the technical material presented throughout the report.

POLICY OPTIONS

Introduction

Decisions about how to manage MSW today and tomorrow are becoming increasingly difficult, particularly for the local governments that have primary responsibility for MSW management. The Federal Government respects State and local primacy in MSW issues and to date has assumed a limited role in MSW management. EPA has primarily focused on developing guidelines for Subtitle D landfills and for procurement of products containing recycled materials. During the late 1970s, EPA also encouraged the development and implementation of Solid Waste Management Plans by States (box 1-B). In

Photo credit: Office of Technology Assessment

Separating MSW into different components, such as the green glass in this bin, is only the first step in a long recycling chain. The separated "secondary" materials then must be processed into forms that can be reused as raw materials for new products. Markets for secondary materials are highly dynamic and represent the key to recycling's future.

general, Federal attention to MSW lapsed during the 1980s, primarily because the Nation focused instead on hazardous waste. Some States and communities, even without Federal involvement, have developed noteworthy programs promoting recycling and requiring that new incinerators and landfills use the best technologies available (ch. 8).

EPA's recent *Agenda for Action* (57), which outlines goals for the Nation and future MSW activities at EPA, signifies increased attention to MSW at the Federal level (box 1-C). The success of EPA's efforts, as well as other activities within the public and private sectors, will in part depend on how Congress addresses MSW issues in the upcoming reauthorization of RCRA.

At least two important MSW concerns are driving the Federal Government to reexamine its role with respect to MSW issues. The first is the decline in existing landfill capacity, along with the inability of many local governments to site new MSW facilities of any type. Indeed, grass-roots opposition to new landfills and incinerators has driven, at least in part, the development of recycling programs and adoption

---

[11]Separation can occur, for example, at drop-off centers, through curbside collection, or in centralized facilities. The merits and costs of some of these separation modes are discussed in chs. 2 and 5. The choice is not always clear, even on a technical basis.

Box 1-B—The Resource Conservation and Recovery Act (RCRA)

RCRA is the major Federal statutory authority addressing solid waste, including MSW.[1] Key solid waste management provisions of RCRA are described here, but it should be noted that many of these programs were not implemented or have not been functional since the early 1980s (ch. 8).

A major focus of Subtitle D (Subch. IV) of RCRA is to encourage the *development of State solid waste management plans* and to foster intergovernmental (Federal, State, and local) and public/private cooperation (Sec. 4001). Federal technical and financial assistance are offered to States and localities as incentives for them to develop plans (Secs. 4002-4003, Secs. 4006-4008).

Another major focus of Subtitle D is *the improvement of landfills.*[2] EPA is authorized to promulgate regulations containing criteria to classify types of sanitary landfills (Sec. 4004), to facilitate the closing or upgrading of existing open dumps (Sec. 4005), and to provide assistance for these activities to rural communities (Sec. 4009). HSWA directed EPA to survey solid waste management facilities across the Nation and evaluate whether current guidelines and standards are adequate to protect human health and the environment, as well as to revise the landfill guidelines.

RCRA also contains *a substantial research, development, demonstration and information subtitle* (Subch. VIII). In addition to establishing broad research authorities for EPA, alone or after consultation with the Secretary of Energy (Sec. 8001), this subtitle identifies special studies to be supported (e.g., on glass, plastics, tires, waste composition, small-scale technology, and source separation) (Sec. 8002). Section 8003 identifies a comprehensive list of topics for which EPA is to "develop, collect, evaluate and coordinate information." This includes information on methods to reduce the amount of solid waste generated, the availability of markets for energy and materials recovered, methods and costs of collection and management practices, and research and development projects for solid waste management.

A central reference library was to be established and maintained to house this information and other relevant data on the performance and cost-effectiveness of various waste management and resource conservation technologies and systems (Sec. 8003(b)). *Full-scale demonstration facilities and grants* for resource recovery systems and "improved solid waste disposal facilities" programs also were to be established (Secs. 8004-8006).

Procurement guidelines are to be prepared by EPA, after consultation with the Administrator of General Services, the Secretary of Commerce, and the Public Printer (RCRA, Subch. IV). The guidelines should designate items produced with recovered materials that must be procured by Federal agencies; recommend practices for the procurement and certification of such items; and provide information on the availability, relative price, and performance of such items (Sec. 6002(e)). EPA was required to prepare guidelines for paper and three other product categories, including tires, by 1985. In addition, each procuring Federal agency is required to establish a procurement program (Sec. 6002(i)).

In addition to EPA, the other Federal agency given major responsibilities under RCRA is the Department of Commerce (Subch. V). Four special areas of responsibilities are delineated: 1) to develop accurate specifications for recovered materials; 2) to stimulate and develop markets for recovered materials; 3) to evaluate and promote proven energy and materials recovery technologies; and 4) to establish a forum for the exchange of technical and economic data relating to resource recovery facilities (Secs. 5001-5005).

---

[1]Public Law 94-580 (1976). Congress first established a Federal role in solid waste issues in the Solid Waste Disposal Act of 1965 (Public Law 89-272; as amended by the Resource Recovery Act of 1970, Public Law 91-512). RCRA was revised most recently by the Hazardous and Solid Waste Amendments of 1984 (Public Law 98-616) and is in the process of further revision and reauthorization (ch. 8 Appendix).

of more stringent State regulations for landfills and incinerators. Second, several issues have arisen with consequences that extend far beyond any one community, and these seem most feasible for the Federal Government to address. One such issue, for example, is the need to encourage manufacturers to

consider the MSW management implications of their products (e.g., in terms of volume, toxicity, or recyclability) as they are designed.

The policy options discussed in this chapter focus on possible congressional actions. Options that can

Box 1-C—EPA's Agenda for Action

EPA's report, *The Solid Waste Dilemma: An Agenda for Action,* concluded that "to the extent practical, source reduction and then recycling are the preferred options for closing the gap [between waste generation and management capacity] and reducing the amount and toxicity of waste that must be landfilled or combusted" (57). In the report, EPA set a national goal of achieving 25 percent source reduction and recycling by 1992, and estimated that incineration would handle about 20 percent and landfilling about 55 percent of MSW at that time. EPA also developed specific objectives and outlined its future activities, as briefly described here:

- Increase information:
—develop educational and technical materials
—sponsor national conference on research and development
—establish a clearinghouse for information
—establish a peer matching program
- Encourage increased planning:
—help States develop strategies (workshops, selected State plan reviews)
- Encourage increased source reduction activities:
—promote toxicity reduction (e.g., studies, testing guidelines, options regarding lead and cadmium)
—promote quantity reduction (studies, corporate recognition, workshops)
—procurement of products with source reduction attributes
—study source reduction policies
- Participate in and encourage increased recycling:
—stimulate markets (e.g., studies on markets and incentives, guidelines for composting, Federal Task Group for implementing procurement)
—promote better separation and processing (model training and education programs, options for batteries and appliances, interagency work group)
—facilitate formation of a national advisory council
—review hazardous waste liability issue
- Help reduce the risks of combustion:
—upgrade combustor performance standards and ash management
—decide whether to develop model operator certification program
—provide information on problem wastes
- Help reduce the risks of landfilling:
—operator certification (training, State certification guidance)
—issue final criteria on design and operation
—technical guidance on revised criteria
—provide information on problem wastes

be undertaken independently by or in coordination with other entities (e.g., State and local governments, Federal agencies, and the private sector) also are noted. Specific actions regarding MSW are likely to be more effective if they are delineated in the context of a coherent, comprehensive approach for the Nation, and this can only be done if a national policy for MSW is established. **Congress can provide strong leadership by stating a clear national policy for MSW,** one that contains clearly articulated goals and sets priorities for action. Such a national policy could set the stage for moving toward a balanced, long-term approach to MSW problems. Appropriate goals might be:

- set MSW prevention as a national priority (i.e., reducing MSW toxicity and quantity);

- set the development of sufficient MSW management capacity throughout the Nation as a national priority;

- promote the use of management methods that provide materials and energy recovery benefits; and

• regulate MSW management methods so that each ensures adequate protection of human health and the environment, and vigorously enforce these regulations.

Policy options are discussed here in two major sections. The first section discusses options related to the Federal role in enhancing the institutional framework for MSW (e.g., aiding planning and coordination, ensuring capacity). The second section consists of four parts analyzing options for programs and activities specific to prevention, recycling, incineration, and landfilling. Many of the options are related in that they all are oriented toward implementing the goals stated above and an institutional framework for MSW. Table 1-1 lists these options.

Enhancing the Institutional Framework

The system that generates and manages MSW includes a range of participants that manufacture, distribute, consume, and dispose of materials and products. The evolving nature of this system is discussed in chapter 2, while box 1-D highlights leverage points at which specific options might be applied most effectively. The institutional framework includes the governmental entities that affect the interactions between these participants. Five categories of options to enhance the institutional framework for prevention and better MSW management are discussed: improving integration (planning and coordination), ensuring capacity, promoting enforcement, improving information flow, and devising funding mechanisms for Federal activities.

Integration: Planning and Coordination

A coherent strategy will be required to avoid the piecemeal approach of past MSW policies. Cooperative efforts already are increasing, especially between States and local governments and between these levels of government and the private sector (ch. 8). In many cases, however, there is a critical lack of teamwork between affected groups, particularly with respect to waste prevention and recycling (chs. 4, 5, and 8). As the Federal Government further defines its role in MSW issues, the limits of its authority need to be delineated and the implications of this authority for actions by State and local governments need to be considered carefully.

Option 1: Require State MSW Management Plans

Careful planning is crucial to the development of effective MSW programs, especially given the time and resources required for implementation. It is an open question what the Federal role should be in MSW planning. The Federal program for State Solid Waste Plans (RCRA Sec. 4002) essentially has been inoperative since 1980 (ch. 8). Some States have continued to develop their own plans, but the content and utility of these plans varies. Because all State plans are not comprehensive in their approach to MSW, **Congress could require States to submit plans to EPA and specify particular issues that must be addressed.**

State plans, for example, could be required to provide: 1) programs to encourage prevention and administer materials management; 2) coordination mechanisms among State and local agencies and the private sector; 3) specific information on the amounts and composition of MSW generated; and 4) assessments of how adequate management capacity will be made available for MSW generated in the State. In addition, Congress could provide specified Federal funds to States with approved plans and/or withhold funds from those whose plans were not submitted or could not be approved.

Although States currently are not required to submit Solid Waste Plans, RCRA does list a number of requirements which must be met if submitted plans are to be approved (RCRA Sec. 4003). For example, one requirement is that the plan evaluate the size of waste-to-energy facilities (i.e., incinerators that generate electricity) in relation "to the present and reasonably anticipated future needs of the recycling and resource recovery interest within the area encompassed by the planning process" (RCRA Sec. 4003(d)). Some of the RCRA requirements need modification, however. Some specified requirements may no longer be relevant and new issues may warrant inclusion. For example, because recycling cannot provide a consistent level of management due to fluctuations in market prices, it might be useful if plans were required to address procedures for how MSW will be managed during periods when market prices for secondary materials drop below a certain level.

Table 1-1—Potential Policy Options and Activities for MSW

Category	Issue	Option
Enhance Institutional Framework	Integration: Planning and Coordination	Require State MSW Management Plans
		Improve Interagency Coordination
	Ensuring Capacity: Siting, Interstate Transportation	Allow Barriers to be Imposed on MSW Imports
		Require States to Ensure Adequate Management Capacity
		Develop Model Siting Procedures
	Enforcement	Define Stronger Role for EPA in Enforcement
	Improving Flow of Information	Information Clearinghouse
		Education
		Increase Federal Research
	Funding	Product Fees
		User or Waste-End Fee
		National Income Tax
Waste Prevention	Developing National Goals and Assuring Them High Priority	Goals to Reduce Quantity
		Goals to Reduce Toxicity
		Assure High Priority in Federal Agencies
	Providing Economic and Other Incentives	Grant Fund
		High-Visibility Awards
		Federal Procurement
	Improving Information Flow	Develop Labeling With Reduction Information
		Data on MSW Generation
	Banning Specific Products and Substances	Bans
	Increasing Information and Education	Improve Collection, Dissemination of Information
		Increase Education
		Awards for Product Design and Labeling
Recycling	Research and Development	Funding for Research
	Standardized Definitions, Labeling, and Avoided Cost Calculations	Standardize Definitions and Testing Procedures
		Standardize Guidelines for Labeling
		Standardize Avoided Cost Calculations
	Regulations for Recycling Facilities	Ensure Adequate Regulation of Recycling Facilities
		Resolve Conflicts with Hazardous Waste Regulations
	Market Development	Procurement Programs
		Direct Subsidies
		Economic Development
		Building Export Markets
	Fees and Pricing Policies	Rate of Progress Fees on Manufacturers
		Increase Cost of Alternatives
		Product Charges
		Deposit Legislation
	Requiring Secondary Materials Recovery and Reprocessing	Require Use of Secondary Materials
		Require Source Separation Programs
		Bans
		National Stockpile of Secondary Materials
Incineration	Clarifying Ash Management	Clarify Household Waste Exclusion
		Decide How to Manage Ash Under Subtitle D
	Clarifying Emissions Regulation	Choose Standards Based on BACT or on Risks
Landfills	Giving Additional Direction to EPA's Regulatory Effort	Establish Policies Regarding Existing Facilities
		Specify How Landfills Should be Regulated
		Extend Corrective Action and Closure Requirements
	Clarifying Liability Provisions	Clarify Superfund Listing Policy

SOURCE: Office of Technology Assessment, 1989.

Box 1-D—The MSW "System"

The "system" that produces MSW is complex and dynamic, and different parts of it are linked together in ways that are not always clear. Illustrating the elements of the system can help identify leverage points at which strategies can be developed and options applied most effectively.

1. Materials/products lifecycle:
- products: design, production, distribution, purchase, use, discard
- non-product materials (yard and food waste): generation, discard
- management: collection, processing, treatment/disposal, etc.

2. Actors that touch materials and products:
- designers, manufacturers, distributors, retailers, etc.
- waste managers (haulers, landfills, incinerators, recyclers)
- citizens (purchasing, generation, siting decisions)

3. Private infrastructure:
- collection system, reclamation/other processing (e.g., scrap industry)
- landfills, incinerators, recycling facilities
- vertical integration of waste management industry
- structure and dynamics of materials industries:
  —dynamics of prices and disposal costs
  —international aspects
- financial sector

4. Public institutional structure:
- local decisionmaking, collection programs
- government programs:
  —dynamics of Federal and State roles and plans
  —subsidies and incentives (PURPA, tax credits, etc.)
  —effects on private sector

5. Social attitudes:
- value judgments, perspectives affect how potential options are viewed
- resource policies:
  —extent to which Federal Government is involved
  —how the Nation deals with materials and energy policies
- siting of facilities, degree of acceptable risks

Option 2: Interagency Coordination

To ensure that a more coherent and coordinated Federal effort is developed, **Congress could require that EPA and other Federal agencies establish an action-oriented interagency task force to review and coordinate Federal activities and policies that affect MSW generation and management.** A task force also could develop methods to compare the effectiveness of different programs. The primary difficulty facing such a task force, however, would be ensuring that its recommendations are implemented or at least considered seriously. Congress could require that the recommendations be reviewed and plans for implementing them be made by EPA and other agencies, unless there are demonstrable reasons for not doing so.

Ensuring Capacity: Siting, Interstate Transportation

Citizen opposition to the siting of new facilities remains widespread in many areas, even when the facilities would meet strict standards, but some new incinerators, landfills, and recycling facilities are being built. Siting a new facility can take 5 years or more, and an additional 2 to 3 years to obtain a permit and construct the facility.[12] Various studies indicate that if the public is involved *early* and *substantively* in the process of selecting, evaluating, and locating facilities, the chances of successful siting are improved significantly (ch. 8).

Interim solutions will be needed to meet immediate capacity needs in areas that will exhaust their current permitted capacity within a few years and that have been unable to site new facilities. The most common interim solutions are increased transportation of MSW to other jurisdictions and expansion of existing landfills. Shipping the waste elsewhere often is the only option. Many communities with available capacity, however, are increasingly unwilling to accept MSW from other jurisdictions. Some States have enacted bans or restrictions on waste from out-of-State (or localities have enacted such restrictions against other localities within a given State). Some of these restrictions have been invalidated when the courts have determined that the bans unduly constrain interstate commerce.[13]

Option 1: Compacts or Barriers Regarding Interstate Transportation

One alternative for addressing jurisdictional problems is to provide a mechanism for cooperation in interstate MSW transportation. For example, interstate compacts have been used to deal with issues such as low-level radioactive waste disposal, navigation and flood control, water pollution control, community development, and crime prevention (25). In fact, provisions exist in RCRA (Secs. 4002(a) and 4006(c)) that encourage interstate regional planning to facilitate MSW management. These provisions have not been implemented, but could provide a basis for allowing States to enter into agreements on MSW issues such as transportation of wastes, disposal fees, or development of new management facilities. Instead of erecting a barrier,

this would allow wastes to move unimpeded across State lines, but in an orderly manner.

Alternatively, assuming compliance with the Commerce Clause, which allows the Federal Government to regulate interstate commerce, **Congress could allow States to impose fees or other legal barriers on MSW imports.** Or, Congress itself could impose fees on MSW transported across State borders or adopt other mechanisms to discourage interstate shipments. These choices have important implications. Not least, they would represent a major change in the Federal approach to both interstate transportation and MSW management. In addition, although some States may want authority to restrict MSW shipments to their jurisdictions, other States (particularly some with adequate available capacity) may oppose attempts to restrict interstate transportation of MSW.[14]

Option 2: Require State Planning for Adequate Management Capacity

As part of the State Solid Waste Plan provision in RCRA, **Congress also could require "capacity assurance" for MSW—that is, require States to have a planning process for the development of adequate management capacity within specified time periods.**[15] "Adequate" could be defined as the ability to manage a specified percentage of the MSW generated within a State's borders. One mechanism to encourage the development of new capacity would be to require that permits to expand existing landfills only be in effect for a limited time and include an enforceable timetable for providing new capacity. Federal funding (e.g., Superfund money or highway funds) to States could be contingent on meeting this and other State planning requirements.

Option 3: Develop Model Siting Procedures

Another option is to establish better procedures for siting facilities. **Congress could direct EPA to develop guidelines for State siting procedures.** Such procedures could, for example, require binding

---

[12]In the future, with new siting procedures, it may be possible to reduce the time required to site facilities. See ch. 8 for further discussion of siting issues.

[13]See ch. 8 and ref. 26 for discussions of the relevant court decisions.

[14]If such barriers on interstate transportation are allowed, care should be taken not to disrupt the transportation of secondary materials to processing facilities.

[15]A capacity assurance provision, for example, is included in the Comprehensive Environmental Response, Compensation, and Liability Act and the Low-Level Radioactive Waste Policy Amendments Act. Implementing such a provision for MSW would require a different approach, however (ch. 8).

arbitration by a State authority when siting conditions cannot otherwise be negotiated successfully. Similarly, the Federal or State Government could provide resource or mediation teams to help local communities resolve siting disputes. To enforce these requirements, Congress could withhold Federal funds from States that did not meet the capacity requirement, or it could provide supplemental funds to States that meet siting goals or adopt a siting process.

Enforcement

RCRA does not include any specific enforcement procedures for MSW. This is not surprising, given the currently limited Federal role in this policy area. The only existing mechanism in RCRA for Federal action against improper disposal of MSW is Section 7003 (42 U.S.C. 6973), which grants EPA broad authority to bring suits for action against any entity (as defined by the Act) whose "past or present handling, treatment, transportation or disposal of any solid waste [including MSW] or hazardous waste may present an imminent and substantial endangerment to health or the environment."

Such suits might help States or localities bring about necessary, but politically difficult, actions (e.g., denying a permit to expand a landfill known to be hazardous, but which offers the only readily available capacity), or might correct State actions inconsistent with the stated goals of RCRA. To date, EPA has made limited use of this authority, consistent with its general deference to States on MSW issues.[16]

Option 1: Define a Stronger Enforcement Role for EPA

Congress could define a stronger enforcement role for EPA by requiring that Federal permits be issued for the handling, treatment, and disposal of MSW. If Congress were to choose this option, it would also need to address how to coordinate Federal enforcement efforts with those of State and local governments. This option has several implications. First, it raises the question of how a Federal permitting program would be structured. For exam-

ple, EPA's air and water programs are designed so EPA delegates the actual permitting and enforcement authority to the States but reserves the right to oversee the permitting process, take enforcement actions, and take over programs that are not functioning properly. Substantial resources would be needed for EPA to enter the MSW arena and develop standards and guidelines, administer the programs, and undertake vigorous enforcement actions.

Congress also could address the levels of civil and/or criminal penalties that can be assessed for violations of existing and future Federal requirements. Some States are increasing the civil and criminal penalties for improper waste management and are placing high priority on enforcement actions because they fear that the increased costs of complying with new MSW regulations could lead to increased illegal disposal. **Vigorous enforcement and imposition of stiff penalties are necessary to provide a strong disincentive for improper management.** The ability of citizens to sue the Federal Government for lack of enforcement (RCRA Sec. 7002) also is a potentially important mechanism to ensure Federal implementation of existing regulations.

Improving the Flow of Information

The success of any national effort to adopt a waste prevention and materials management policy and manage MSW effectively will depend heavily on the quality and dissemination of key information. "Information" is broadly conceived to include not only knowledge and data needed by decisionmakers about the generation of MSW and management of materials, but also adequate education and research efforts.[17]

Option 1: Information Clearinghouse

Legal authority to create an information clearinghouse already exists in RCRA (Sec. 8003), yet one has never been established. Although EPA has plans to establish one (57), Congress could specify a timeframe for doing this and address the functions of the clearinghouse. Alternative approaches also are available, for example, establishing a quasi-

---

[16]See box 1-B, as well as RCRA Sec. 4005(c).

[17]Many of the institutional structures needed to collect and disseminate information, sponsor research, and encourage education are the same for both prevention and materials management (particularly recycling), which suggests that programs might be most efficient if they address both elements together.

governmental organization based on a cooperative agreement among government, business, and the public. Such an organization could perform several functions, perhaps more efficiently and flexibly than a government clearinghouse. Regardless of the form chosen for the clearinghouse, the centralization of MSW information programs could help reduce the duplication of effort now occurring as more and more communities reconsider MSW collection and attempt to control increasing management costs.

To aid MSW prevention efforts, the clearinghouse could offer technical and economic data on labeling, MSW generation, sources of toxic substances in MSW, trends in products and packaging, and actions that individuals can take to reduce MSW generation. This information could help consumers and public interest groups identify ways to change their purchasing decisions, and it could help industrial producers, especially smaller companies with limited technical resources, make use of techniques developed by others. For example, information about certain kinds of product design changes and chemical substitutions might be transferred across products and industries, assuming the information is not proprietary. Information on other environmental implications of product purchases (e.g., effects of solvents used in cleansers on ozone formation) also could be made available through a clearinghouse.

With respect to recycling, a clearinghouse could provide information and assistance on: 1) specifications regarding secondary materials quality and methods for ensuring quality control; 2) secondary materials prices and production; 3) technical developments that minimize costs and improve the quality of secondary materials; and 4) collection programs for secondary materials. It also could provide guidance to consumers about recycling different materials, as well as assistance to businesses (e.g., by providing information about recycling networks). Much of this information could be provided by the Department of Commerce under existing RCRA authorities and existing programs.

The clearinghouse also could provide performance, design, and economic information for incineration and landfilling. In addition, a clearinghouse could develop procedures to evaluate the costs and effectiveness of different management programs. For example, a computer model that helps communi-

ties assess the comparative costs of various management scenarios (e.g., see ch. 2) could be housed and accessed through the clearinghouse.

One key function of a clearinghouse would be to disseminate this information. Moreover, a clearinghouse could foster its collection and compilation, and it could identify and address important information gaps. External activities, such as conferences and workshops, could support these efforts. Special institutes could be established to gather information on specific materials for which information currently is not collected. "Peer matching" programs, similar to those sponsored by EPA in the past, could help communities identify other communities with facilities or programs similar to those which it might be considering.

Option 2: Education

The Federal Government also has opportunities to improve education about MSW prevention and materials management. This could involve not only an information clearinghouse, but also educational materials such as pamphlets, grade-school curricula, and public service announcements. To sustain new efforts in these areas, it is critical that the Nation's children—the next generation of consumers—be well-informed about the entire MSW system and the environmental implications of how the Nation uses natural resources.

The links between the extraction of virgin resources and the mounds of waste that are discarded daily, as well as other related environmental problems, must be made more apparent to the next generation than they are to most Americans today. Both manufacturers and consumers need to know how their decisions about products affect MSW generation and management, and what opportunities exist for making changes that lead to MSW prevention or increased recycling. States and localities with established recycling programs usually cite the importance of education—particularly at the grade school level—in the success of their efforts (ch. 8).

Congress could encourage Federal MSW educational efforts through a number of specific options. For instance, EPA and the Departments of Commerce and Education could sponsor conferences with industry and local and State officials to develop educational materials, and undertake educational campaigns of their own. Congress also could provide funding for educational grants and programs.

The Federal Government also could promote using household hazardous waste collection programs to educate citizens about alternatives to toxic products. Public concern over the proper management of household hazardous wastes (e.g., discarded solvents, paints, batteries, and cleansers) is evident, and special collection and management programs for them are increasing throughout the country (ch. 8). Although such programs may be expensive and their significance in terms of risk reduction is not known, they are useful tools for educating the public and manufacturers.

Public service advertising could also be used to educate people about MSW issues. One nongovernmental example is a joint campaign by the Environmental Defense Fund (EDF) and The Advertising Council to promote recycling (13). The campaign uses TV, radio, newspaper, and magazine advertisements.

Option 3: Increase Federal Research

Another option available to Congress is to increase Federal research funding on MSW issues for agencies such as EPA, National Institute of Standards and Technology, Forest Products Laboratory, Bureau of Mines, and the Department of Energy. EPA, for example, listed specific topics that merit additional research in its *Agenda for Action* (57) and is compiling a detailed list of research and development projects as part of a Municipal Innovative Technology Evaluation Program (19).

Funding for Federal MSW research should address at least three areas: 1) developing evaluation methodologies to assess the effectiveness of prevention and management programs; 2) exploring innovative methods and technologies for MSW prevention (e.g., developing substitutes for toxic substances, designing products to be more durable or to generate fewer residuals); and 3) exploring innovative methods and technologies to improve MSW management (e.g., new uses for secondary materials, enhanced degradation of MSW in landfills, improved testing procedures and processing techniques for residues from waste management) (see chs. 5, 6, and 7).

IF YOU'RE NOT RECYCLING YOU'RE THROWING IT ALL AWAY.

Please write the Environmental Defense Fund at: 257 Park Ave. South, NY, NY 10010 for a free brochure. EDF Ad Council

Photo credit: Office of Technology Assessment

Advertising could be a powerful tool for motivating consumers to recycle or purchase products that cause fewer environmental problems. Manufacturers could use ads to promote their products that are more recyclable or durable, use more secondary materials, or contain fewer toxic substances.

Funding

An important concern when considering any new Federal policy or program is how such activities will be funded. In general, new or independent sources of funding are desirable, rather than expecting new programs to compete with existing ones for scarce budget dollars. Federal revenues would be necessary to fund many of the Federal activities that Congress could require for MSW prevention and materials management and that are discussed in this chapter.

Funding for planning and implementing MSW prevention and management programs, of course, needs to be developed by all levels of government. Some funding mechanisms used at the State level could be applied at the national level as well, perhaps more effectively. Other funding options might be more appropriate or feasible for State and local governments, or for any level of government, to apply.

Federal options for raising revenues are available. These options include fees on packaging and/or other products, user or ''waste-end'' fees, and a national income tax. Such fees, in addition to raising funds for MSW programs, possibly could help internalize the costs of waste generation and management, if they are set at high enough levels. For example, high fees might create an incentive for manufacturers to consider the impact of the products on the wastestream when they are designing new products.

Fees of any sort are likely to be discriminatory, since it is cumbersome to apply fees on all parts of the wastestream equally. They also can be difficult to administer, given the number of entities potentially subject to the fees (e.g., manufacturers, retailers, distributors, consumers). Some types of fees may be better able to overcome these obstacles than others.

Option 1: Product Fees

One option is to impose a fee either on the virgin materials used in packaging and containers or on the packages and containers themselves. Proposals have been introduced in several States, for example, to impose a tax on packaging and containers, with the level of the tax varying based on whether a product is recyclable and/or made of recycled materials (ch. 8). The product fee concept also could be applied to products that are more toxic or less durable. In addition, requiring products to be labeled accordingly would help consumers make purchasing decisions based on these considerations. The advantage of this approach is that the fee also might affect decisions regarding product design and manufacturing.[18] In addition, this fee could generate significant revenues for prevention and recycling activities, although it is not clear whether a decrease in MSW generation or an increase in recycling would occur as a result.

Because packaging and containers are estimated to account for only about 30 percent of the wastestream by weight, this is a selective or discriminatory measure. However, a fee based on a specific subset of products can be justified as consistent with the goals of prevention and materials recovery. It can be argued that packaging and containers are a significant, visible, and problematic portion of the wastestream and therefore warrant such discriminatory measures. A more equitable proposal is a fee on *all* products that become MSW. However, this approach would be more cumbersome to administer

because of the large number of products and manufacturers involved.

Option 2: User or Waste-End Fee

In contrast to these "front-end" approaches, a user or "waste-end" fee could be charged on a weight or volume basis when MSW is sent to management facilities. Some communities and States already administer such fees for particular facilities or for "problem wastes" (e.g., tires and batteries), and they use the fees to fund research and special management programs (ch. 8).

If a waste-end fee was applied to all MSW sent to management facilities, and consumers were billed directly (at household and commercial establishments) by the waste haulers to recover the fees, it could create an incentive for consumers to consider the quantity, durability, and even toxicity of products. In turn, changes in consumer decisions could pressure manufacturers to address the potential for MSW prevention when products are designed and manufactured. Moreover, if the administering government wished to promote one management method over others, it could alter the fees as necessary. It is not known how large user fees would have to be to accomplish these goals. Furthermore, given that the amount needed to promote a particular method is likely to vary locally, such an approach is likely to be most feasible at the local level.

Concerns have been raised that user fees could lead to illegal disposal by consumers or haulers. However, some evidence exists that consumers will respond to increased waste disposal charges by changing their purchasing decisions and, for example, recycling more MSW (39). A key to making user fees effective is to make them part of a comprehensive approach that includes available alternatives (e.g., ways to reduce generation or to recycle) and adequate information about the rationale for the fees.

Option 3: National Income Tax

Another possible option would be to establish a special income tax paid by all citizens. Although an income tax may not be politically feasible, even at a low rate it could raise significant revenues. For example, over $300 million would be raised annu-

---

[18]The specific rate per ton for this or any similar fee could be based on the level of funding needed to support various activities. OTA makes no judgment in this report on what funding level would be needed.

ally if the rate charged was $1 per person for an individual or family with an adjusted gross income of less than $25,000 and $2 per person for higher incomes. This option is equitable because every person produces garbage. Distributing these tax revenues to various MSW programs also could be justified by potential future reductions in management costs to the public and an improved environment. Moreover, this system would be administratively simple to implement. While it could be referred to as a waste generation fee, rather than a tax, one disadvantage is that it could be viewed as setting an unwanted precedent for establishing taxes linked to specific issues.

Specific MSW Program Options

Waste Prevention

Reducing the amount or toxicity of MSW is a *preventive* action, and thus it has a fundamentally different function from waste management.[19] Reducing MSW generation and toxicity offers many potential benefits—fewer environmental problems with waste management, lower waste management costs, increased conservation and efficient use of resources (including materials, energy, and land associated with waste generation and management), and increased public confidence in government MSW policies and in industry.

Several obstacles have precluded substantive waste prevention efforts to date. Some of these are cultural or economic (i.e., market-driven). For example, one deterrent is that manufacturers have little incentive to consider the problems or costs of MSW disposal when they design and make a product because most products do not become waste until long after leaving a factory.[20] Similarly, individual consumers currently have little economic incentive to consider the implications of their purchasing and consumption patterns.[21]

Another consideration is that reducing MSW generation is inconsistent with America's demand for convenience and disposable products and, for that matter, for all types of products (box 1-A). Containers and packaging, which are mentioned frequently as potential targets for waste prevention efforts, are a large and visible part of MSW, but they serve many functions (e.g., sanitation, theft prevention, public safety, weight reduction, customer appeal) that must be considered.

The likelihood that production and consumption patterns will change hinges on behavioral and cultural attitudes, as well as economic considerations, and thus it is difficult to estimate whether and when prevention, particularly in terms of quantity, might have a significant effect on MSW. Also, since there is no standardized way of defining and measuring prevention, it can be difficult to know when it has occurred.

Prevention and recycling efforts can sometimes work at cross purposes. For example, multi-component "barrier" plastic bottles (i.e., bottles made of several layers and types of plastics) are now being used for products such as ketchup and syrup. Although this design reduces the weight of waste generated, glass bottles can be more readily recycled. The new plastic bottles are complex mixtures and can only be recycled into items such as lumber substitutes, and few facilities exist to do such recycling.

Another constraint is that State and local officials, the traditional decisionmakers for MSW management, can do little to influence manufacturing decisions or consumer buying patterns. Most products are marketed in more than one State, and officials cannot easily mandate changes in products that flow in interstate commerce. In addition, manufacturers that market products in more than one State can face severe difficulties if they have to meet varying State and local requirements on products and packaging.

---

[19]The precedent for prevention efforts exists with hazardous wastes (48,50,52). Although MSW probably is not as great an overall threat to human health and the environment, the Nation has an opportunity to shift its thinking toward a more preventive mode for MSW as well.

[20]This is different from the situation with industrial wastes, especially hazardous wastes, produced at a manufacturing plant itself. In that case, the waste comes directly from production processes and disposal costs can be linked directly to the processes. Products and materials only become MSW, however, after they have been used for some purpose.

[21]This is in part because waste management costs often are paid either through municipal taxes that cover many services or by institutions and businesses, not by individuals. Even if costs rise, there is no assurance that they will reach a sufficiently high level to cause changes in consumption patterns.

Strong Federal actions, however, might overcome the various obstacles to MSW prevention, change general perceptions about its feasibility, and ensure that attention is not focused solely on developing management capacity. Possible options for Federal efforts can be grouped into four categories:

- establish goals for quantity and toxicity reduction, and give prevention high priority within EPA and other Federal agencies;
- provide economic incentives (e.g., grants, awards, procurement);
- improve information flow to the public and manufacturers (e.g., labeling, waste audits, research, clearinghouse); and
- ban specific products or substances.

In addition, other critical activities include educating manufacturers and consumers about prevention possibilities (see ''Improving the Flow of Information'' above) and deciding whether to use product fees to promote prevention (see ''Product Fees'' above).

Option 1: Develop National Goals and Assure Them High Priority

Option 1A: Goals to Reduce Quantity of MSW

Congress could set incremental goals to reduce the quantity of MSW generated and thus help focus attention on the potential offered by prevention. One reasonable goal would be to attempt to offset estimated future increases in MSW generation. For example, because MSW generation is increasing by about 1 percent annually (box 1-A), an initial prevention goal might be 1 percent per year.[22] Such a goal symbolizes a long-term commitment, yet it should not prove disruptive to the economy or consumers. If this could be achieved, the volume of MSW generated would remain constant and local officials would have to manage the same amount of MSW as they do now. A more ambitious goal could be set to lower the actual amount of MSW generated.

Setting any goal raises several problems, however.[23] First, how would quantity reduction be measured on a national basis? Given the range of uncertainty in estimates about MSW generation (ch. 3), any change on the order of a few percent would be overwhelmed by estimating errors, and it would not be clear whether a real change had occurred.[24] Second, even if quantity reduction (and associated savings in waste management costs) could be measured, it would still be difficult to resolve all potential trade-offs, particularly to quantify other potential benefits (e.g., using less materials and energy) and costs (e.g., effects on GNP and convenience) offered by prevention and to assess the performance and effects of new or alternative products. Quantity reduction also has to be evaluated in terms of its effects on MSW toxicity; for example, using cadmium-coated bolts to reduce corrosion might make bolts more durable and reduce waste, but it also can increase potential toxicity when the products are discarded in MSW.

Option 1B: Goals to Reduce Toxicity of MSW

If toxic substances in MSW that pose risks to the public and the environment could be identified and then eliminated from products and materials that become MSW, then recycling, incineration, and landfilling facilities would be safer and conceivably easier to site and operate.[25] This might even abate the need for quantity reduction. In addition, manufacturers might lower their own costs by reducing their use of toxic chemicals in production. Examples reviewed by OTA demonstrate that reducing the amount of toxic substances in some products is technically feasible and is actually occurring, at least on a limited basis (ch. 4).

Many toxic elements serve important functions in products (e.g., cadmium as a heat stabilizer in some plastics). However, it is sometimes possible to identify more benign substitutes (e.g., to replace metal-based inks or synthetic organic pesticides) that are not prohibitively expensive. Identifying

---

[22]This figure is an example of a **goal**, not an indication of how much prevention is possible.

[23]These problems also are associated with setting goals for any management method (e.g., see ''Recycling'' below).

[24]The same might be true for the estimate that per-capita generation is increasing by about 1 percent annually, because it is based on a model of how materials flow through society (ch. 3). In both cases, standardized methods have not been developed for measuring changes based on *actual* generation and collection.

[25]It is important to note, however, that some environmental problems associated with MSW management have little to do with toxic substances in products. For example, methane emissions and acidic leachate are both generated from the natural decomposition of organic materials in MSW (e.g., yard wastes, paper). In addition, small industrial and commercial generators of hazardous wastes can legally dispose of them along with ordinary MSW.

targets for toxicity reduction efforts involves distinguishing substances of concern, particular products containing the substances, and likely reductions in toxicity. Thousands of products become MSW, however, and it is difficult to trace the lifecycle—from design to discard—of substances or their potential substitutes in these products. In many cases, proprietary considerations constrain public evaluations of substitute substances (e.g., a substitute for mercury and cadmium in household batteries). Requiring industry to conduct waste audits might help alleviate these problems.[26]

As an initial goal, Congress could require EPA to identify those metals and organic chemicals likely to contribute significantly to the risks associated with MSW management. EPA could then be required to study a given number of those substances each year.[27] For each substance, EPA could evaluate product sources, technical feasibility of elimination or of substitution with benign substances, effects on potential risks, economic and social costs to industries and consumers, and incentives and/or regulatory initiatives likely to be effective in achieving reduction. This would be similar to EPA's current efforts on lead and cadmium (16,57).

Option 1C: Assure High Priority for MSW Prevention in Federal Agencies

Federal efforts to promote prevention are most likely to succeed if they have high visibility and support, particularly at EPA. Congress could direct EPA to give high priority to MSW prevention efforts. For example, Congress already is considering establishing a high-level EPA office for waste minimization.[28] This office could devote some resources to MSW prevention efforts (e.g., providing grants and awards, establishing an information clearinghouse, analyzing effects of new regulations on the potential for prevention). These efforts are unlikely to entail major costs to the Federal Government. Furthermore, authorizing such spending by EPA would send a signal about the seriousness of Federal efforts.

Photo credit: Office of Technology Assessment

Some products can be redesigned to contain fewer or none of the substances that pose risks when the products are discarded as MSW. Manufacturers have reduced the level of mercury in these household batteries by using other substances, but evaluating how much toxicity reduction has been achieved is difficult because information about the substitutes is proprietary.

Congress also could require all Federal agencies to establish an "MSW prevention officer" position. The responsibilities of this position could include promoting prevention, reviewing agency activities with respect to impacts on MSW generation, and coordinating efforts with EPA. The position could also be given similar responsibilities with respect to procurement and recycling, although this might draw some attention and resources away from prevention efforts.

Option 2: Provide Economic and Other Incentives

Option 2A: Grant Fund

Congress could provide direct economic assistance to projects designed to promote MSW prevention. For example, it could establish a *grant fund*, financed by one of the funding mechanisms dis-

---

[26]Waste audits, conducted during the design of a product, identify potential byproducts and impacts of production and use of the product on the waste stream and the environment.

[27]It has proven difficult for EPA to identify toxic substances in a systematic way for regulation. Alternative approaches that would shift the burden of proof to manufacturers could be considered. For example, manufacturers could be required to conduct waste audits and evaluate the effect of using a given substance on human health and the environment.

[28]EPA established an Office of Pollution Prevention, but the primary focus of the office has been on hazardous wastes; in addition, it does not have agency-wide visibility.

cussed above. A grant program could be administered by EPA, an interagency task force, or a national commission. Whatever group administers such a program, it could select projects, review project performance, provide public accountability of the results, disseminate results, and prepare an annual report to Congress.

Activities that might be eligible for grants could include: 1) industrial research and development projects; 2) capital investments to modify manufacturing plants to produce products that create less MSW or have fewer toxic substances; 3) outreach programs to educate consumers about their role in MSW generation and prevention; 4) research projects on removing institutional and social obstacles to prevention; and 5) innovative ideas for use by nonmanufacturing businesses (e.g., retailers, service providers, advertising or marketing companies).

Option 2B: High-Visibility Awards

To focus national attention on MSW prevention and provide incentives for its practice, Congress could authorize annual awards for noteworthy prevention accomplishments. These could be Presidential awards, similar to the Malcolm Baldridge National Quality Awards (Public Law 100-107) established by Congress to motivate American industries to increase their competitiveness through improved product quality. Alternatively, an awards program could be developed and administered by EPA, the Department of Commerce, or a national commission. The range of possible recipients is broad: manufacturers, individual researchers, non-profit and public interest groups, marketing companies, and government agencies.

Option 2C: Federal Procurement

Federal procurement programs exist to purchase products made from some secondary materials, allowing prices that are slightly higher than those for products made from virgin materials (ch. 5). These programs could be extended to products that generate less MSW or are less toxic, such as water-based inks. Congress could explicitly require Federal agencies not to discriminate against such products (except where they are not available or do not meet critical technical specifications) and authorize a 5-to-10 percent price preference for such products,

a level similar to those in State procurement programs for recycled goods.

The major benefits of such a program would be to: 1) strengthen the leadership role of the Federal Government; and 2) provide an initial market for these products, which could help reduce financial risks faced by manufacturers if they attempt to change product design or composition, or risks faced by service providers trying to change some aspect of how they do business. As with any procurement programs, two important drawbacks exist: defining exactly what products qualify for preferential treatment, and inducing Federal agencies to actually make such purchases.

Option 3: Improve Information Flow

Option 3A: Develop Labeling With Prevention Information

Labels often are used to convey key information or ideas about products and influence purchase decisions (e.g., "no cholesterol" and "no caffeine" labels on many food products). One option is to authorize the use of a special logo on products that are considered to benefit the environment or help resolve waste management problems. In West Germany, for example, the Federal Environmental Agency has given "Environmental Angel" awards to companies for such products (figure 1-5). The angel logo can then be used by the companies to market the product. Canada is instituting a special label for products that are recycled, recyclable, biodegradable, energy conserving, or free of ozone-depleting substances (11), and similar systems are being considered in Norway and Japan (62). Similarly, labeling on "reduced waste" products could be used in the United States by manufacturers to gain advantages in the marketplace, by retailers to implement marketing efforts, by procurement offices to determine product preferences, and by consumers to guide purchasing decisions.

Another idea is to use the ratio between the amount of MSW ultimately generated and the amount of useful product (53). Other ratios conceivably could be developed to address toxicity, durability, repairability, and reuse. The information could be coded by color, symbol, or numerical ranking, as long as the system was easily understood. However, the information needed to make these judgments (e.g., volume, durability, toxicity, or repairability and reusability) is complex and often unavailable.

Congress has several options to address the labeling issue. One approach might be to mandate establishment of design institutes or product review boards, or direct Federal agencies (e.g., EPA, Consumer Products Safety Commission, National Institute of Standards and Technology) to begin developing technically sound methods to rate products on MSW-related criteria.

Alternatively, a commission or advisory panel could be appointed to study and make recommendations regarding labeling programs. To ensure that the recommendations are turned into actions, Congress could give the commission a blue-ribbon status and require the EPA Administrator and Secretary of Commerce to review and implement the recommendations, unless they could demonstrate sufficient reason for not doing so. The commission could assess standardized ways of defining and measuring prevention, types of labels, criteria for labels, categories of products to target, how to determine success (in terms of actual toxicity or quantity reduction), past labeling efforts, educational opportunities, social and economic costs of labeling and prevention, and how to address imported products (e.g., legal or trade agreement limitations to labeling requirements on imports; whether data on toxicity could be required).

Option 3B: Data on MSW Generation

Federal prevention efforts will need accurate and up-to-date information on many aspects of MSW, including the quantity or toxicity of specific products; the impacts of new products and social trends on MSW generation; and the generation of MSW by different sectors (i.e., residential, commercial, institutional). This type of information would be useful for MSW management programs, as well. Congress could direct EPA to establish an ongoing program to conduct specific studies on MSW generation and potential prevention targets; for example, these studies could address:

- the quantity and toxicity of MSW generated by residents and commercial and institutional establishments, especially in terms of different products;

Figure 1-5—The "Environmental Angel" Logo

SOURCE: Deutsches Institut für Gütesicherung und Kennzeichnung, "Verzeichnis der Produkte und Zeichenanwender sowie der jeweiligen Produktanforderungen" (Bonn: June 1988).

- the effects of educational efforts (e.g., measuring how consumers change their habits when prevention goals are clearly articulated);
- future changes in MSW generation patterns at the community level to gain an understanding of how prevention might help local MSW management; and
- targets for prevention efforts, in terms of both quantity and toxicity, and the potential costs and benefits of such efforts.

Industry also could provide important information, particularly about toxic substances. Industries could be called on to perform waste audits or draw up nonbinding plans that identify potentially toxic substances in products, explore the feasibility of reducing these substances, and estimate the costs involved.

Option 4: Banning Specific Products and Substances

A more prescriptive approach to MSW prevention would be to ban products and substances that are considered undesirable.[29] Fast food packaging, some

---

[29]The use of taxes or deposits to help improve the **management** of such products and substances is discussed in "Recycling."

Photo credit: Office of Technology Assessment

Several communities and States have passed legislation that would ban the use of some plastic materials, such as the polystyrene used in these plates and cups, or require the use of biodegradable materials.

plastic products (e.g., grocery bags, foam polystyrene cups), and packaging in general are lightning rods for public attention and certain types have already been banned in some communities. These bans have strong symbolic value, and the threat of a ban can motivate private sector action to change the composition of particular products (e.g., chlorofluorocarbons in polystyrene foam containers).

Bans generally focus on a small portion of MSW. One study found that paper and plastic fast food packaging currently comprises about 0.3 percent by volume of the material excavated at several landfills; disposable diapers (which are part plastic and part paper) comprise about 1.5 percent (37,38). Even so, this still could be useful in achieving any incremental goal for quantity reduction. However, it often is not clear whether the replacements for banned products are better in terms of reducing quantity or toxicity or of using fewer natural resources during manufacturing (chs. 4 and 5).

Bans or regulations on using specific substances in products that become MSW may have more merit if substitutes can be found that reduce toxicity. Congress could require EPA to identify additional substances of concern and assess the effects of

banning or regulating these substances pursuant to its existing authority under the Toxic Substances Control Act (TSCA).

Recycling

The current level of MSW recycling in the United States is low, about 10 percent. Although it is difficult to say how much recycling is possible, most people agree that recycling can be increased. Substituting recycled or "secondary" materials for virgin materials conserves natural resources. It sometimes results in varying amounts of energy savings, depending on the product and material involved (ch. 5).

From a national perspective, recycling is attractive and deserves precedence over incineration and landfilling because it can contribute to national goals such as energy and materials conservation. From a local perspective, recycling is attractive because of its potential to divert at least some materials from landfills or incinerators, which helps conserve available capacity; it also can reduce waste management costs and reduce risks to human health and the environment in some cases.

The materials management aspect of the MSW policy suggested in this report provides a framework for considering these benefits and recognizing the material resources contained in MSW. OTA has identified certain constraints to the collection, processing, and manufacturing of secondary materials that could be reduced by government intervention (see, for example, box 1-E and ch. 5). Many State and local governments and businesses already are addressing some of these limitations. Many of these efforts have been successful, particularly those related to collection (chs. 5 and 9), but the actual rate of increase in recycling at the national level has not been determined.

EPA is promoting an initial national recycling and prevention goal of 25 percent by the year 1992. Some cities already appear to be recycling more than this (ch. 8), and proponents suggest that much higher rates are possible (5,23).[30] It is safe to say that more

---

[30]A recent report identified 15 communities, both large and small, that recycled more than 25 percent of their waste (23). However, while it is likely that these communities are recycling large amounts of their MSW, the estimates in many cases include **more** than MSW (e.g., construction debris, wood chips), as defined here. For example, Islip, New York (the city infamous for the Mobro garbage barge), is estimated to have a recovery rate of 32 percent. When construction debris is deleted, the estimate drops to 25 percent. This points out, once again, the problems involved in defining MSW and in calculating and comparing overall recycling rates.

Box 1-E—General Market Factors

Recycling—despite its promise as an important element in an MSW prevention and management strategy—has two important caveats that policymakers should consider. First, policymakers should be aware of the distinction between supply- and demand-limited materials. Second, they should be aware that market prices for secondary materials can fluctuate dramatically.

In addressing the first issue, Federal activities should be flexible to distinguish between materials that are not being recycled at a high level because they are either *supply-limited* (i.e., are not collected in sufficient amounts or are too highly contaminated for current manufacturing processes) or *demand-limited* (i.e., buyers are relatively scarce even though supplies may be available). This distinction matters from a Federal perspective because some options may be ineffective if applied indiscriminately to all types of materials. The distinction generally is not as important to the private sector because from that perspective the market sets the prices required to bring forth needed supplies. The market does not assure that all sources of supply are being tapped, however. In this case, for example, a valuable source of supply of raw materials exists in MSW, but the potential supplier (i.e., waste generator) is not always aware of the value of those materials.

These distinctions also are time-dependent. Markets are constantly in flux, and a material now in short supply could be in oversupply at a later date. Materials in MSW considered as supply-limited in 1989 include old corrugated containers, office papers, single-resin plastics, glass, tin cans, and aluminum. Demand-limited materials include old newspapers, mixed papers, mixed plastics, used oil, tires, compost, and ferrous scrap other than tin cans.

Second, the 1988-89 market environment has some materials priced at or near their peak levels. Given the history of fluctuation in most materials markets (ch. 5), recycling decisions should not be made only on the basis of current prices. Of course, markets will always exist for most materials. The question is: where will contractions in the system occur when demand declines? The existing private infrastructure has substantially increased collection rates for many materials (e.g., aluminum, glass, and paper). However, increased municipal collection of MSW provides a supply of materials that is not sensitive to demand. In some cases, these materials will be made available even at negative prices because municipalities can afford to pay manufacturers to take collected materials as long as the fee is less than disposal would cost. As a result, private sector suppliers are likely to be less competitive and to constitute "marginal" supply sources during times of declining demand to a wider extent than ever before. Efforts to manipulate markets, therefore, must consider potential effects on employment and tax revenue generated by private sector suppliers.

---

efforts are necessary to reach that goal nationally. Although such a goal is a useful target, it does not appear to be based on a quantitative evaluation of market potential. The actual amount that recycling can be increased on a national level is not easily predicted, nor is such a prediction particularly worthwhile given the dynamic nature of materials markets.

Translating any specific national goal for recycling into action requires a close look at recycling rates for each material component of MSW. Rather than setting percentage targets for the amount of material that should be recycled, it may be more realistic to set targets for *progress* (e.g., surpassing historical rates of increase in recycling of a given material). Target rates of progress could be set for each material based on economic conditions and relevant technical factors; box 1-F indicates, on a qualitative basis, where market expansion appears particularly promising.

Regardless of the manner in which targets are set, **it is important that flexibility be maintained to allow recycling programs to be designed for local conditions.** In general, markets for secondary materials fluctuate considerably over time, often rapidly (ch. 5). **The ability to sustain marketing of collected materials at high levels cannot always be assured. The dynamic nature of markets is a key factor affecting the reliability of recycling as an MSW management alternative.**

This conclusion has important implications. If many communities around the country decide at roughly the same time to collect secondary materials and market them to reprocessors and manufacturers, prices for those materials may drop and some

Box 1-F—Markets for Recycled Materials

About 10 percent of MSW was recycled in 1986 (15). Although this figure may seem small, it masks considerable activity in the recycling arena. In fact, higher recycling rates have been reported for particular materials (figure 1-6). For most materials, many opportunities exist to increase materials recovery from MSW, both in the short and longer terms. The state of the economy, both nationally and globally, will play a large role in determining whether these opportunities will be realized.

Recycling is the management alternative that traditionally goes the farthest beyond the Federal Government's purview. Carefully tailored policy options may help stimulate these markets, but blanket policies that address all materials equally may be ineffective and, even worse, wasteful.

Aluminum constitutes only 1 percent of MSW, but it has a recycling rate of at least 25 percent. Aluminum cans are recycled at a 55 percent rate. The technology and economic incentives exist to enable a significant increase in this recovery rate. The major barrier is the inadequacy of the collection process.

Paper and paperboard, comprising 41 percent of total discards, are recovered from MSW at a rate of at least 22 percent. Some short-term opportunities exist to increase this rate, particularly for tissue, newsprint, and linerboard, but technical and capacity barriers may delay more dramatic increases.

Glass, mostly containers, accounts for about 8 percent of MSW and is recovered at a rate of at least 10 percent. The glass industry is actively expanding processing capacity for post-consumer glass (known as cullet), which in many cases can reduce the cost of producing glass containers. Technically, when colors are separated, 100 percent cullet can be used in making new containers, considerably more than the current industry average of 25 percent (which includes industrial scrap).

Iron and steel account for about 7 percent of MSW and are recovered at a rate of at least 4 percent. Some potential exists for increased recycling of steel cans, which account for about one-third of ferrous scrap. Recent increases in detinning capacity will improve the recycling rate for "tin" food cans, and major steel mills are gearing up to increase consumption of bimetal (steel and aluminum) beverage cans. Recovery of other ferrous scrap is not likely to expand significantly, because supply from other sources is abundant and growth in demand is limited.

Plastics, which make up about 7 percent by weight of MSW, have the lowest recovery rate among MSW components—only about 1 percent. Recycling of post-consumer plastics is in its infancy, with most efforts focused on two resins (PET and HDPE). However, considerable market potential exists for increased recycling of these and other resins. The plastics industry also is making efforts to develop recycling collection/processing systems.

Yard and food waste is an important part—about one-fourth—of MSW, but only negligible amounts of this material are recycled. However, composting has been receiving considerable attention over the past year, and a number of localities are considering it as an alternative to incineration or landfilling of these materials. Marketability will be determined largely by the quality of compost.

Figure 1-6—MSW Recycling Rates: Franklin v. Industry Estimates

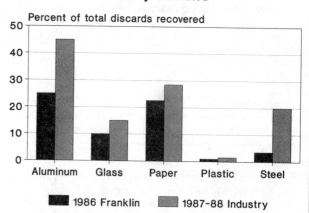

NOTE: Industry estimate for paper includes pre-consumer scrap; industry estimate for steel includes higher total for white goods plus ferrous scrap recovered at incinerators.

SOURCE: American Paper Institute, *1987 Annual Statistical Summary, Waste Paper Utilization* (New York, NY: June 1988); K. Copperthite, U.S. Department of Commerce, personal communication, 1989; Franklin Associates, Ltd., *Characterization of Municipal Solid Waste in the United States, 1960 to 2000 (Update 1988)*, final report, prepared for the U.S. Environmental Protection Agency (Prairie Village, KS: March 1988); B. Meyer, Aluminum Association, personal communication, 1989; K. Smalberg, Steel Can Recycling Institute, personal communication, 1989; Society of the Plastics Industry, personal communication, 1988.

communities may be unable to market the materials they collect. In these cases, communities may have to pay an additional cost to landfill or incinerate the materials, pay reprocessors or manufacturers to take the materials, or store the materials temporarily.

Within this context, opportunities for government intervention to stimulate recycling exist in the following areas:

- information and education (e.g., clearinghouses, technical assistance, advertising, awards);
- research and development (e.g., grants, loans);
- development of standardized definitions, testing procedures, and labeling systems;
- development of health and environmental regulations for recycling facilities;
- market development (e.g., procurement programs, direct subsidies to industries to use secondary materials, local economic development, export markets);
- fees and pricing policies (e.g., changing prices and subsidies for other management methods; product charges); and
- regulatory actions (e.g., requiring secondary materials recovery, banning materials from landfills, national deposit legislation).

Although some of these actions may be most appropriately addressed by a particular level of government, many can be addressed at all levels—Federal, State, and local. Specific options within each of these areas are discussed below.

Option 1: Increase Information and Education

Information is critical to increase the ability of consumers and businesses to make decisions regarding recycling and recycled products. Currently, the Federal Government (through the Departments of Commerce, Interior, and Agriculture) publishes detailed information regarding production, consumption, and prices on many virgin materials, including aluminum, steel, and wood products. However, similar information for many secondary materials is difficult to obtain, particularly historical information.

Option 1A: Improve Collection and Dissemination of Information

Congress could require Federal agencies (including the Department of Commerce, under existing

RCRA authorities) to increase the collection and analysis of data on consumption, production, and prices of materials recoverable from MSW. These data are available from industries in most cases. This option, then, would only entail expanding the coverage of current data series and would not require new programs, although it might require additional funding. The information could be published in monthly and annual reports, which could be disseminated through a clearinghouse. Interagency working groups could be formed to identify new information needs and delegate data collection responsibilities.

Option 1B: Increase Education

Educational programs can raise environmental consciousness and help consumers identify materials that can be reclaimed from their trash cans, as well as increase awareness of how materials are used in society. Programs aimed at elementary schools can provide long-term benefits by instilling the ideas of materials and energy conservation in young people. Education is primarily a local and State function, but the Federal Government could assist in several ways. For example, Congress could direct EPA to renew public outreach programs or specify that some portion of any grants to States be given to communities for education programs. Education also can be achieved through information provided on product labels.

Option 1C: Awards for Product Design and Labeling

Another information incentive would be to give awards or grants for innovative product design (e.g., designing existing and new products to be recyclable, as advocated by some public interest and environmental groups), new recycling technologies, and labeling systems. EPA or the Department of Commerce could develop guidelines on how to evaluate products for awards and projects for grants.

Option 2: Research and Development

Many industries, including paper, glass, aluminum, steel, and, more recently, plastics, undertake research to enhance reprocessing capabilities, yet technologies still do not exist to adequately reprocess some materials, such as non-color-sorted glass (ch. 5). Technological limits also inhibit some secondary materials manufacturing processes (e.g., waste paper de-inking), and could benefit from additional research. Although some improvements are occurring (e.g., for recycling of polystyrene), technical refinements and capacity expansion take time and money. Furthermore, information developed by industry is often proprietary, thereby limiting the spread of innovation. Private industry rarely researches product design with recycling as a criterion, although this also is changing. For example, the Society of Packaging and Handling Engineers is preparing a list of simple criteria to help packaging manufacturers consider environmental effects when they make decisions about materials and containers for products (43).

Government-sponsored research on improvements in reprocessing and manufacturing, as well as design for recycling, could help quicken the pace of technological innovation in this area. In the past, the Department of Commerce, the National Forest Products Lab, and the Bureau of Mines have conducted research on secondary materials. For example, the National Forest Products Lab is testing new methods to remove contaminants from waste paper.

Congress could encourage new research and development by providing incentives such as tax exempt bonds, low-interest loans, loan guarantees, research grants, and tax credits and exemptions. Low-interest loans and loan guarantees have several advantages: they do not require an immediate Federal revenue source and they are relatively easy to administer. Research grants require additional expenditures, but they are a traditional means of stimulating new research. Congress, for example, could establish research grant programs at EPA or the National Science Foundation. Some grants could be given to public institutions, particularly where the proprietary nature of industrial research limits expansion of recycling capacity. Or, perhaps, joint ventures between national laboratories and industry could be sponsored.

In contrast, tax credits and exemptions can result in lost Federal revenues and, more important, generally have not been proven to be effective (chs. 5 and 8). Most Federal tax credits employed in the past have been too small (10 to 15 percent) and State tax credits affect too small of a base (because State

tax rates are relatively low) to have a significant financial impact on business decisionmaking.

Option 3: *Standardized Definitions, Labeling, and Avoided Cost Calculations*

The absence of a standardized language for recycling and recycled products hinders communication and understanding among consumers, reprocessors, manufacturers, and communities. The Federal Government has opportunities to clarify several of these hindrances by providing leadership in the areas of definitions and testing procedures, labeling, and avoided cost calculations.

Option 3A: *Standardize Definitions and Testing Procedures*

Standardized definitions and reporting methods for determining ''recycled content'' and ''recyclability,'' along with standardized procedures to test the performance of secondary materials, would help consumers and manufacturers make decisions about secondary products and materials. Congress could instruct EPA or the National Institute of Standards and Technology to develop standardized definitions and procedures, or to use industry standards such as those being established by the American Society of Testing Materials or the National Recycling Coalition (e.g., ref. 14). In either case, the information could be disseminated through an information clearinghouse.

Option 3B: *Standardize Guidelines for Labeling*

Standardized labeling guidelines could be developed to provide information about recyclability and materials content on product labels. Standardized labeling could help transfer meaningful, consistent information to consumers and, in conjunction with education programs, enhance the recognition of recycled and recyclable products. Currently, most products are not labeled to denote secondary materials content or recyclability, although the Society of the Plastics Industry has established a voluntary labeling program to identify the specific resins from which plastic containers are made. Some manufacturers are using the recyclability issue as a marketing tool; standardization could help ensure that consumers receive accurate information. Labels also could be used to denote non-recyclability.

Congress could require EPA or other Federal agencies to begin developing guidelines for standardized labeling of different products. Because the development of any labeling program is likely to be extremely complicated, as discussed above for prevention, Congress could commission an in-depth study of the entire labeling concept and consider legislative initiatives after receiving the report. To ensure that U.S. industries are not unfairly disadvantaged, Congress could extend labeling requirements to imported products.

Option 3C: Standardize Avoided Cost Calculations

The collection of secondary materials can be encouraged by providing collectors with a portion of the net savings (if any) that result from *not* incurring the cost of incineration or landfilling. This savings is known as "avoided cost."[31] When the collector is a community, the community retains the savings because its overall disposal costs are lowered, which provides an incentive for recycling. The main problem with implementing the avoided cost concept widely is the absence of an accepted calculation procedure, which makes it hard to evaluate competing claims about the costs of different waste management scenarios.

Several methods to calculate avoided costs have been suggested (4,8,34). Congress could direct EPA to develop a standardized procedure to ensure that appropriate "avoided costs" were used by all. The calculation could include parameters such as current landfill costs, trash collection and transfer costs, environmental costs of collection and disposal, the opportunity cost associated with tying up land as a landfill, and the discounted capital cost of developing a new landfill (i.e., when recycling occurs and conserves landfill capacity, a savings arises as the cash outlay required to construct a new landfill is pushed further out into the future). The avoided cost has to be compared with costs for collecting and processing secondary materials, all of which will change as market conditions vary.

Option 4: Regulations for Recycling Facilities

Manufacturing processes that use secondary materials generate various residuals such as air emissions, wastewater discharges, and solid waste sludges (ch. 5). Many of these processes are regulated to some extent. For some, however, such as facilities that process commingled recyclables, specific regulations and acceptable practices have not been developed. At the same time, other regulatory activities, particularly those concerning certain hazardous wastes, have disrupted the recycling system. Both of these issues are appropriate for consideration at the Federal level.

Option 4A: Ensure Adequate Regulation of Recycling Facilities

Air emissions, solid wastes, and other residues from recycling facilities (including ones for composting) should be regulated to ensure that they do not threaten human health and the environment, just as other management facilities or manufacturing processes are regulated. Congress could require EPA to ensure that regulations (i.e., standards for design, operation, and residuals management; permitting and reporting procedures) extend to all recycling facilities, including those that initially process secondary materials. Such regulations would be an important component of a comprehensive Federal MSW policy, and OTA's suggested management approach is based on the assumption that all management methods are designed to ensure adequate protection for human health and the environment. Failure to ensure adequate regulation for recycling facilities could create expensive problems in the future and increase the level of uncertainty regarding the potential for recycling.

Option 4B: Resolve Conflicts With Hazardous Waste Regulations

Regulations regarding the management of hazardous substances (e.g., lead in batteries and PCBs in washing machines, refrigerators, and other appliances) have caused some recyclers to stop accepting these products because of fears about liability and because of increased costs of complying with the regulations (ch. 5). In some cases, this leads to improper disposal of the products. This illustrates the need for careful consideration of the effects of hazardous waste and other regulations on recycling. Congress could direct EPA to clarify current regula-

---

[31]The use of an avoided cost calculation involves the explicit comparison of the economic value of materials and energy with the cost of land disposal; these cost comparisons will change over time.

tions regarding the recycling of products known to contain hazardous materials, and to identify other products that might cause similar problems in the future (e.g., sodium azide in automobile air bags). EPA could begin developing guidelines for the proper handling of these kinds of products before any regulations take effect, to avoid disruptions in the recycling chain. EPA also could analyze the effect of developing regulations to restrict the use of certain materials in the manufacture of products when they pose similar problems.

Option 5: Market Development

Obviously, it serves no purpose to collect materials for which there is little or no demand (e.g., mixed plastics and mixed paper). Successful government intervention in commodity markets is difficult because of the many complex factors affecting supply and demand. Nevertheless, Several options are available to the Federal Government to help directly develop markets: expanded procurement, direct subsidies, economic development initiatives, and building export markets. (Options 6 and 7 discuss additional ways that the Federal Government can affect markets.)

Option 5A: Procurement Programs

One of the most direct government approach to create new and expanded markets is to buy recycled products. This could be significant, because local, State, and Federal Governments purchase about 20 percent of the goods and services produced in the U.S. economy. In 1976, Congress directed EPA to develop guidelines for procurement of recycled materials (Sec. 6002 of RCRA), but EPA did not issue any final guidelines until 1988. Guidelines now exist for the procurement of some goods produced with secondary materials (fly ash in cement and concrete, paper products, retread tires, re-refined oil, and building insulation that uses secondary materials) (ch. 8). These products are made from demand-limited materials, with the exception of recycled printing and writing paper, which is probably the most visible recycled product purchased by the government.

Congress could direct Federal agencies to increase their procurement programs for recycled products, particularly of additional demand-limited materials (e.g., old newspaper, mixed waste paper,

compost). The difficulties in expanding such programs, however, include developing guidelines about what constitutes recycled products, ensuring that agencies purchase the products, and minimizing the number of specifications for the same product that a manufacturer has to meet. In addition, the extent to which procurement can stimulate increased recycling is unclear (ch. 8), although its educational effect usually is considered positive.

Additional provisions could allow private manufacturers to petition Federal agencies to purchase a product made from secondary materials instead of products made from virgin materials, and to require such substitutions unless the recycled products do not meet specifications (25).

Option 5B: Direct Subsidies

Congress also could provide direct subsidies to manufacturers to increase their use of secondary materials. For example, EPA or the Department of Commerce (or a State using Federal grant money) could provide a direct subsidy such as a loan guarantee to a newspaper publisher to construct a newsprint mill that uses old newspapers. This type of subsidy has one major advantage—it can be targeted at specific problem materials in specific locales. It directly attacks the problem of insufficient demand (in this example, by assuring the construction of a facility that will need old newspaper), while at the same time guaranteeing a ready final market (e.g., a newspaper printed on recycled newsprint). However, competitors who made investments without the benefit of a Federal grant might consider such a subsidy inequitable.

Option 5C: Economic Development

Efforts to build markets for recycled materials can provide economic development opportunities for State and local governments. Although the Federal Government has reduced its involvement in local economic development activities, this option remains important from the perspective of many communities. By coupling local economic development with secondary materials processing facilities, the community retains more control over the market than if the materials were consumed outside of the area. In addition, the community benefits directly because the increase in processing and manufacturing activity stimulates employment, tax revenues, and economic growth. Numerous mechanisms are available to States to promote business development, including low interest loans, loan guarantees, government equity partnerships, and direct grants (20,22).

Option 5D: Building Export Markets

Demand for secondary materials also could be increased by developing foreign markets. Current government programs that promote exports in general could be modified to address exports of secondary materials. For example, the Department of Commerce manages the Export Trading Company Act of 1982 (Public Law 97-290), which allows companies to operate as joint ventures and market larger quantities of products abroad without being subject to antitrust restrictions. Congress could direct the Department of Commerce to apply the provisions of this act to assist exporters of secondary materials. The Department also could be directed to identify foreign markets for recycled materials as part of its data-gathering responsibilities.

Although export markets are important outlets for many secondary materials from the United States, they are less stable than domestic markets. In addition, foreign manufacturers gain the benefit of U.S. citizens' and communities' efforts to separate and upgrade the quality of these materials. They also realize the value added when they manufacture new products. Often, foreign products made from low-cost secondary materials present stiff competition for U.S. producers.

Option 6: Fees and Pricing Policies

Fees or changes in current pricing policies could be imposed on different parts of the MSW generation and management system to stimulate recycling. These include fees to stimulate rates of progress in increasing recycling, disposal fees to change the costs of other management methods, and product charges.

Option 6A: Rate of Progress Fees on Manufacturers

If Congress were to set target goals to increase recycling of individual materials, it could encourage compliance by imposing a fee on those manufacturers or industries which fail to make adequate progress (e.g., achieve a certain percentage of

recycled material in a product) by a specified date. A similar fee mechanism has been employed by the State of Florida in its new recycling legislation (ch. 8). Although cumbersome to administer, this approach would be likely to increase demand for secondary materials.

Option 6B: Increasing the Cost of Alternatives

If Congress or the States required that a user fee be assessed for using landfills and incinerators, the increased costs to haulers (who probably would be paying the fee) most likely would be passed on to their customers (who generate the waste). If the fee was large enough, it should make materials recovery more attractive economically. Several States have instituted successful disposal fees for waste delivered to landfills, including New Jersey and Illinois. However, as mentioned earlier there are problems with such a system. Briefly, it would be difficult to determine the size of the fee to account for regional variation and to administer the fee on a national level. Another application of this option at the local level might be to impose a higher pick-up fee if consumers fail to participate in curbside separation for recycling (ch. 5).

Another way to indirectly influence waste management is to remove existing subsidies that promote or require the use of virgin materials. Substantial Federal tax incentives encourage the use of virgin materials, despite strenuous attempts to remove them from the tax code during the 1986 tax revision. For example, one remaining incentive is the mineral depletion allowance, which allows mineral producers to deduct from 5 to 22 percent of the value of minerals produced when they compute their taxable income from a mineral property.

Whether this option would be effective is uncertain. Data from the 1970s, indicate that removing the incentives may not significantly affect secondary materials markets (ch. 5). It would be useful to review the effects of virgin materials subsidies under current economic conditions to determine whether the conclusions of the earlier analyses still hold. Thus, Congress could direct the Departments of Commerce, Interior, Transportation, and Agriculture to analyze the effects of eliminating virgin materials subsidies on the recovery of secondary materials and on the virgin materials industries themselves, including effects on international competitiveness. From this, a more definitive conclusion about the benefits and costs of such subsidies could be drawn.

The effect of the Public Utility Regulatory Policies Act (PURPA) on the development of waste-to-energy facilities and on recycling also could be considered. PURPA provides for the guaranteed purchase of electricity generated by small, non-utility generators (including, but not limited to, waste-to-energy facilities), at a rate equal to the cost of a utility itself generating that electricity (47). That rate, called avoided cost, is determined by each State. Some people consider this to be a form of subsidizing waste-to-energy facilities. Removing this provision, however, will not necessarily result in less incineration and a subsequent increase in recycling. Waste-to-energy facilities could continue to sell electricity at going rates, sell steam instead, or raise tipping fees to cover losses in revenues.[32] Removing the provision also could harm other co-generators, which might pose problems if the Nation's energy picture changes for the worse. The Federal Energy Regulatory Commission is already considering restricting the definition of avoided cost to remove the difference between the going electricity rate and the rate paid to small generators, which would render the issue moot (ch. 6).

Option 6C: Product Charges

Products can be designed to be more easily recycled, a concept termed "design for recyclability." Congress could place a tax on difficult-to-recycle products to provide an incentive for such design.[33] Such a tax, which should be levied on the manufacturer for optimal effect, would have to be large enough to influence product design decisions. The size of the tax required to induce a manufacturer to redesign products will differ for different products. This concept also could be used to promote "design for reduction."

Option 7: Require Secondary Materials Recovery and Reprocessing

The Federal Government could more aggressively promote secondary materials recovery and reprocessing by the following methods: 1) requiring deposits on recyclable or problematic products; 2) requiring that post-consumer secondary materials be used to the extent technically feasible in place of virgin materials; 3) requiring communities to establish separation programs; 4) banning products that are difficult or impossible to recycle; 5) banning certain materials from landfills or incinerators (also see "Incineration" and "Landfills" below); and 6) acting as a buyer of last resort and creating a national stockpile of secondary materials.

These options could be used to increase recycling, but all would likely entail costs to other sectors of the economy. Thus, mandatory recycling approaches such as these should be undertaken only with a clear understanding of their social and economic costs. For example, mandating that secondary materials be used in manufacturing (e.g., of newsprint, as mandated in Connecticut and proposed in other States), regardless of their costs relative to virgin materials, would increase markets for secondary materials but disrupt markets for virgin materials. The costs to the virgin materials industries thus should be considered before implementing such a policy. In addition, to ensure that the competitiveness of U.S. industries is not harmed, imported products would have to be subject to similar provisions.

Of all these options, only deposit systems have received much scrutiny. For this reason, deposit legislation is discussed here to illustrate the complexities associated with adopting such options.

Deposit Legislation—Proposals for a mandatory deposit system for beverage containers appear before Congress annually, and they are designed to address a variety of issues including litter control and energy conservation (46).[34] National deposit legislation recently has been proposed in Congress as a means to increase the recycling and reuse rates

---

[32]A tipping fee is the price paid by a waste transporter to have the waste managed at a particular facility.

[33]Some proposals also would ban certain products. With respect to plastics, for example, one purpose of the bans is to encourage manufacturers to use plastics that can be recycled or will degrade and to use other recyclable materials, or to use plastics that can be incinerated without forming hazardous compounds. It is not clear, however, that substitute materials necessarily will be more compatible with recycling.

[34]Deposits could also be applied to other types of materials in MSW, for example, car batteries and tires (ch. 8). These deposits could be incorporated into the price of a new car, as well as into the cost of replacement batteries and tires. Furthermore, deposits could be used to develop recy

of beverage containers. The nine States which have deposit legislation (figure 1-7), however, adopted it primarily because of concerns over litter control (ch. 8). In general, beverage container deposit systems capture between 70 and 90 percent of the targeted containers and appear particularly effective in reducing litter (3,17). Data reported by several States with deposit systems indicate that total roadside litter decreased between 15 and 50 percent, and beverage container litter decreased by as much as 80 percent (18,41).

The impact on the MSW stream, however, is less certain, and its calculation is problematic. Critics of mandatory deposit legislation contend that it has a relatively small impact on MSW disposal problems, because beverage containers are a small, albeit highly visible, portion of the MSW stream.[35] New York State estimates that since adoption of its Returnable Beverage Container Law, 5 percent by weight and 8 percent by volume of MSW has been diverted toward recycling (18,32). Curbside programs to collect recyclables can cover a broader portion of MSW and thus have the potential to achieve greater diversion of materials from landfills.[36] In the past, deposit legislation may have stimulated the development of processing facilities and recycling markets, but curbside and other types of recycling programs also have this potential.

One major concern about deposit systems has been the potential to increase costs to consumers, retailers, the beverage industry, and the government. The extent of such increases is disputed (27,36,40). It appears overall, however, that both the benefits and costs of deposit systems are considerable and not out of proportion to each other (31,36,41). Studies generally indicate a net gain of jobs and some energy and resource savings, but the rate of price increases for beverages in nonrefillable containers is above normal inflation. Costs for changing over to a system for returnable/refillable containers might be high for the beverage industry, but if the necessary transportation and processing infrastruc-

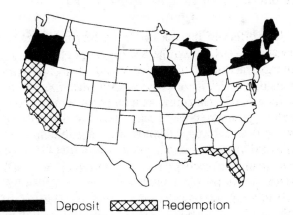

Figure 1-7—States With Deposit or Redemption Systems

■■■■ Deposit   ⊠⊠⊠⊠ Redemption

SOURCE: Office of Technology Assessment, 1989.

ture were developed they could be at least partially recovered within a few years (31,41). Deposit systems also can internalize the disposal cost of beverage products, as can curbside collection programs.

In some States with deposit legislation, such as New York, Massachusetts, and Connecticut, curbside collection programs also are being adopted. California and Florida have adopted modified versions of mandatory deposit or redemption legislation. In 1987, California enacted a redemption law for beverage containers that mandates the establishment of ''convenience'' buy-back centers for recycling (ch. 8). Yet the financial stability of the convenience centers, administrative burdens associated with implementing the program, and other difficulties are creating concern over the viability of this approach.

In 1988, Florida adopted a deposit-fee system that affects all types of containers, not just beverage containers. As of October 1, 1992, a disposal fee of 1 cent will be levied on any container sold at retail which is not recycled at a 50 percent rate in Florida.

---

[35] Beverage containers overall constitute 6 to 11 percent of MSW on a national basis (ch. 3). Most deposit legislation covers a smaller portion of MSW, approximately 5 percent, because some types of containers are not included (e.g., for wine, liquor, and milk).

[36] It is not clear whether existing recycling programs are negatively affected in States which adopt a deposit or redemption law (e.g., California), or whether the adoption of mandatory recycling in States which already have deposit laws (e.g., New York) is detrimental to overall effectiveness of waste management. One recent study concluded, based on an analysis of Vermont and New York, that comprehensive municipal recycling programs are more efficient and cost-effective if beverage containers are included in them and participation rates are high (17) (also see ch. 2). However, the distribution of costs would shift from the private to the public sector.

The fee will increase to 2 cents if the 50 percent target is not met by October 1, 1995. The inclusive scope of materials covered by the Florida law is generally viewed positively, but it is too soon to judge how easily this program will be implemented.

Proponents of mandatory deposit systems argue that statewide or nationwide consistency is desirable, that the costs of disposal are internalized on the industry and consumers (rather than to all taxpayers), and that deposits could be used for a variety of purposes (e.g., particularly difficult-to-dispose-of items). States are independently devising programs to encourage recovery of materials from MSW, including deposit, redemption, and/or mandatory recycling programs, as appears most appropriate for their particular circumstances. In this light and in the interest of maintaining flexibility at the Federal level with respect to recycling strategies, it is not clear whether it is desirable at this time for Congress to adopt national deposit legislation or any other single approach to encourage materials recovery and recycling.

Incineration

The role of incineration is one of the most contentious issues in MSW management. Public opposition to incineration has grown dramatically in many communities because of concerns about the presence of undesired metals and organic chemicals in emissions and in the ash residues. In addition, incinerators often are expensive for municipalities, and the potential for stricter regulations on air emissions and ash disposal will increase both the financial risk and cost of new incinerators. These factors have caused some cities to postpone or cancel plans for incinerators (chs. 2 and 6).

At the same time, however, incineration is attractive because it treats MSW (e.g., destroys pathogens), can be adapted to recover energy, and greatly decreases the amount of material that must be landfilled. Also, newer facilities that use up-to-date operating procedures and pollution control technologies are capable of emitting much lower concentrations of pollutants into the atmosphere than are older facilities (ch. 6). This abatement of air pollutants, however, puts more pollutants in the remaining ash;

as a result, some environmental groups contend that certain forms of ash should be managed as hazardous wastes.[37]

A national policy based on prevention and materials management would promote opportunities to reduce the concentrations of pollutants in emissions and ash. If the strategies outlined in this report were implemented, products in MSW would ideally be composed of fewer toxic substances, and noncombustible materials such as glass or metals would be separated for recycling and/or landfilling and would not enter furnaces. Yard wastes would also be separated for composting, which would alleviate problems with moisture control and nitrogen oxide emissions at incinerators. Communities could then use incineration and energy recovery to manage some of the non-recyclable portions of MSW, and possibly to manage combustible materials collected for recycling when markets for those materials are depressed.

The use of incineration may increase during the next few decades, but to what extent is very unclear. Over 160 MSW incinerators (including about 120 waste-to-energy facilities) now combust about 10 to 15 percent (by weight) of the MSW generated in the United States (ch. 6); about one-fourth of this remains as ash that must be managed in other ways (primarily disposed of at landfills). About 45 facilities were under construction as of spring 1989, and plans to build additional facilities have been negotiated in some communities. If all of these are actually built, the portion of MSW that would be managed at incinerators is estimated to increase to about 25 percent by the end of the century (including the remaining ash) (ch. 6).

Nevertheless, it is not clear how much new incinerator capacity will actually be developed. There is some indication that the rate at which plans for increased incineration capacity are being canceled is greater than the rate at which new capacity is actually being developed (ch. 6). In addition, the costs of future facilities will depend on what pollution controls and operating procedures are required by permitting authorities. Some States have issued specific regulations for incinerator emissions and ash, but these regulations vary widely (ch. 6). A

---

[37]Technical uncertainties about ash (e.g., whether it is worse than non-incinerated waste, how much it contributes to leachate problems) cannot be resolved easily with current information, yet decisions can be made about managing ash that do not require final resolution of the uncertainties.

few Federal regulations apply to emissions (e.g., for particulate matter; in addition, "New Source Review" and "Prevention of Significant Deterioration" evaluations are conducted by the States under the provisions of the Clean Air Act), but MSW incinerators generally are not subject to Federal regulation. EPA is scheduled to propose regulations concerning emissions in late 1989, but it will not propose guidelines or regulations for ash management until Congress clarifies whether or not ash should be managed as a hazardous waste.

Thus, considerable uncertainty exists about what will be required in the future. There is a general consensus that Federal regulations should be finalized as soon as possible to help reduce this uncertainty. This would provide: 1) a consistent national guideline for the development of new facilities; 2) greater assurance to the public that the risks associated with incinerators are being properly controlled; and 3) a rationale for local and State officials to require particular designs and pollution controls. There is, however, debate about how emissions and particularly ash should be regulated. Two additional issues related to incineration are capacity and siting (see "Ensuring Capacity" above) and the relationship between incineration and recycling (ch. 2).

Option 1: Clarify Ash Management

The first issue that needs to be resolved is whether the "household waste exclusion" applies to ash. This refers to a provision in the 1984 Hazardous and Solid Waste Act amendments (Sec. 3001(i)), in which waste-to-energy facilities that burn MSW were exempted from regulation as hazardous waste treatment facilities. However, Congress did not clarify whether the ash from these facilities also was exempt from regulation as a hazardous waste. As a result, confusion exists over whether this ash should be managed as a hazardous waste if it fails a standard toxicity test known as the Extraction Procedure, or EP, test. EPA has stated that it will not propose guidelines for ash management until Congress clarifies this issue (ch. 6).

A second issue to be addressed is the lack of guidance on the design and operating standards that Subtitle D facilities (i.e., facilities for managing

Photo credit: Office of Technology Assessment

MSW incineration decreases the amount of material that must be landfilled and in most cases is coupled with energy recovery. Although incineration capacity has increased during the last decade, siting new incinerators is often controversial because of public concerns about risks associated with emissions and ash and the effects of incineration on recycling.

nonhazardous wastes) should meet for managing ash if and when ash is considered nonhazardous.

Option 1A: Clarify the Household Waste Exclusion

Congress should clarify the "household waste exclusion." If Congress decides that the exclusion *does* apply, then managing ash of any type as a hazardous waste under Subtitle C would be out of the question.[38] If the exclusion *does not* apply, then

---

[38]The two basic types of ash are **fly** ash, which consists of the small particles that become entrained in gases leaving the furnace, and **bottom** ash, which is the uncombusted or partly combusted residue that accumulates on the bottom of the furnace. When fly and bottom ash are mixed together, the mixture is called **combined** ash. In this report, use of the word "ash" without one of these three qualifying terms refers to any type of ash.

EPA or Congress needs to specify those conditions under which ash should be managed as a hazardous waste. Congress, for example, could decide whether to *list* fly ash as hazardous, or to use toxicity *testing* as the basis for deciding whether ash should be managed as hazardous.

Listing—Congress could direct EPA to list fly ash as a hazardous waste, because fly ash samples generally fail the EP test. This would eliminate the need for testing. The costs of managing fly ash as a hazardous waste will be more than current costs, although by how much is uncertain. Another uncertainty is whether there is any difference in potential human health risks associated with managing fly ash in a Subtitle C hazardous waste facility, as opposed to a double-lined Subtitle D facility, or even as opposed to managing combined ash in a single-lined Subtitle D monofill.[39]

Testing—Alternatively, periodic testing could be required and any ash that fails the EP test (or an equivalent) would then be managed as a hazardous waste. This would raise several problems, however. First, there is considerable controversy about the utility of the EP test (ch. 6), and it is not clear whether an acceptable alternative test can be developed. Second, EPA's proposal to lower the maximum contaminant level (MCL) for lead in drinking water (53 *Federal Register* 31516, Aug. 18, 1988) could lower the corresponding limits for lead in EP tests, which in turn means that more ash would test as hazardous.

Option 1B: Decide How to Manage Ash Under Subtitle D

Little guidance exists on the design and operating standards that Subtitle D facilities should meet for ash management. EPA's proposed Subtitle D criteria do not address ash management in detail, and EPA has not indicated whether, and especially when, it might develop specific regulations for ash. Most States have not addressed this issue. As a result, Congress could decide how ash should be managed, in particular whether the standards to be met should depend on the type of ash involved or on the results

of toxicity testing. Whether to allow co-disposal of ash with MSW must also be decided.

Specify Facility Standards According to Ash Type—One approach to ash management is to specify different design and operating standards for facilities that handle different types of ash. This would avoid problems associated with managing ash based on test results and provide an easy basis for management decisions. There are many possible design and operating specifications. For example, fly ash might be managed in a monofill with double-liners and double leachate detection/collection systems. This would provide about the same control over fly ash as would management in hazardous waste facilities, but whether it would lower costs in comparison with those at hazardous waste facilities is unclear. Treated ash or combined ash might be managed in a monofill with a single liner and single leachate/collection system.[40] In addition, standards could be developed for situations in which treated ash could be used (e.g., in construction materials). The primary drawback of this approach is its lack of flexibility in cases where characteristics of the ash (e.g., variability in leaching potential) or the facility itself (e.g., great distance from groundwater) might make the specified controls unnecessary.

Specify Facility Standards Based on Test Results—Alternatively, toxicity test results could be used to indicate the type of facility necessary to manage the type of ash. For example, any ash that failed the test might be managed at facilities with double liners and double leachate detection/collection systems. Untreated ash that passed the test might be managed at facilities with single liners and leachate systems. Treated ash that passed the test might be co-disposed with MSW. Conditions under which exclusions were acceptable (e.g., certain site characteristics) also could be determined. This approach would manage ash on an environmental basis (i.e., its potential to leach metals into groundwater). The related problems are the same as those noted above—unreliable tests, the effect of changes in MCLs, and the extra expense of frequent testing. In addition, facility operators will face the uncertainty

---

[39]These facilities differ in the degree to which they provide control over leachate. Facilities with single liners, for example, generally are considered to provide less control than facilities with double liners.

[40]After ash is collected from the grate or from air pollution controls, it usually is left untreated (i.e., not subjected to any additional special treatment). It can be treated, however, with chemical or thermal processes to make it safer to dispose of or reuse (ch. 6).

of not knowing what type of management will be required, even though they often need or want to know what will happen to the ash before a facility is built.

Should Co-Disposal With MSW Be Allowed?— EPA's proposed Subtitle D regulations would not prohibit co-disposal of untreated ash and MSW. The chances of mobilizing metals from untreated ash will almost always be greater in co-disposal situations than in monofill situations, although whether this will always lead to levels of regulatory concern is unknown (ch. 6). As a result, it makes sense to keep *untreated* ash and MSW separate. Whether co-disposal with treated ash should be allowed is uncertain. Treatment technologies appear promising (ch. 6), but additional research on long-term performance is required. Congress could require EPA to sponsor more research regarding treatment and address this issue in ash management regulations.

Option 2: Clarify the Regulation of Emissions

Although emissions are less controversial than ash management, the only Federal regulations that apply to emissions from MSW incinerators are those that apply to all sources of emissions (e.g., for particulate matter and mercury). Specific performance standards for new MSW incinerators and guidelines for existing incinerators are scheduled to be proposed by EPA in November 1989, but they would not become effective until 1991. Congress could give additional direction to EPA by specifying: 1) whether to base standards on the best available control technologies or on risks; and 2) when, and to what level, to require retrofitting of older facilities.

Option 2A: Choose Standards Based on BACT or on Risks

EPA is regulating new facilities on the basis of guidelines that require the use of best available control technologies (BACT) to control emissions in the interim before it promulgates final emissions regulations. Currently accepted BACT (e.g., scrubbers, particulate controls such as baghouses or electrostatic precipitators, automatic combustion controls) can enhance the performance of new incinerators and provide much greater control than did previous technologies (ch. 6). It also allows some flexibility in deciding which combination of

technologies to use. Congress could allow EPA to continue on this course, either by not addressing this issue or by statutorily defining the use of BACT.

A recent recommendation by EPA Region 10 regarding a permit for a new incinerator in Spokane, Washington, could have significant implications for the definition of BACT (58). The recommendation, made in response to opposition from several citizen groups, would include pre-combustion requirements for source separation and recycling as part of the BACT provisions in the permit. This would mark the first time such a linkage between recycling and incineration was made in a permit. The local solid waste agency opposed including these provisions in the permit itself, contending that receipt of construction funding from the State already is linked to development of a recycling program, and that the agency already plans to develop a drop-off and curbside recycling program with a 45 percent recycling goal (12). This situation is a good example of both the opportunities and difficulties of implementing the materials management concept at the local level. Although the recommendation was denied in this case, EPA has indicated that provisions for source separation and recycling are likely to become a routine part of future permits for new incinerators.

Whether BACT is sufficient to meet public concerns about potential risks, however, probably will vary from area to area. Some people would like standards to be based on risk, to provide more stringent protection than current BACT. Requiring EPA to develop risk-based standards might be a better way to help build public confidence and aid in the siting process. On the other hand, a strictly risk-based approach has several disadvantages, including: whether adequate technologies are available to achieve the desired protection, the additional costs of using such technologies, and the uncertainties inherent in risk assessment methodologies and results (ch. 2). The risk-based approach also could lead to fewer controls, depending on circumstances.

Another alternative is to promulgate regulations that require BACT, but that also allow additional, risk-based controls in specific situations. This approach would be similar to that of the Federal water pollution control program, which uses standards based on best available technologies and, where indicated by risk-based toxicity testing, additional controls (51). It also implies that minimum, as opposed to uniform, regulations would be needed. No matter what form emissions regulations take, they probably will bring higher prices to the municipal users of such facilities. This can be considered as one way of internalizing waste management costs.

A related issue is whether standards should be minimum or uniform. Minimum standards allow States to impose additional and possibly more stringent limitations, which provides the States with the flexibility to respond to specific conditions within their jurisdictions. Uniform standards would mean that the same standards and testing procedures apply to all situations. This would simplify the regulatory process and reduce the number of different tests that companies have to perform to satisfy different State testing requirements. However, it means that States would not have the power to impose additional limitations if they felt Federal standards were not sufficient to protect public health. It is likely that EPA will use the minimum standards approach in its regulatory proposals.

Congress also could require that EPA develop guidelines for training incinerator operators to help ensure greater efficiency and safety. EPA could base these guidelines in part on the efforts of the American Society of Mechanical Engineers (ASME), which is developing a certification program for some incinerator operators. ASME is not developing a training program, however (ch. 6). Congress also could direct EPA to increase its research on the technical and economic feasibility of new emissions control systems and improved monitoring methods (e.g., of continuous emissions).

Option 2B: Establish Policies Regarding Existing Incinerators

With respect to retrofitting existing incinerators, Congress could decide whether all old facilities should be required to retrofit, no matter what the cost, or whether some or all should be exempted under certain conditions. If one objective is to reduce potential risks to human health and the environment, old facilities should be required to eventually meet

the same or similar standards as new facilities. In some cases, improvements can be achieved with relatively small changes in operating procedures (e.g., computerizing controls, increasing operator training) (ch. 6). In other cases, however, retrofitting will involve adding pollution controls (e.g., scrubbers, baghouses). This can be expensive and could lead to some facilities closing, which might reduce risks but would also affect available waste management capacity. One of the many factors that could be considered is the appropriate age of existing plants for which to require retrofitting. Retrofitting may be important, for example, for facilities that have been operating for 5 or more years but that do not meet current BACT standards and are scheduled to continue operating for at least an additional 5 years. For facilities nearing the end of their projected lifetime, retrofitting may not be worthwhile. Another factor could be size, with larger facilities located near larger population centers being evaluated first.

Congress could consider innovative means to finance the retrofitting of existing facilities. For example, the Massachusetts Solid Waste Act requires each facility operator to set aside 3 percent of all tipping fee revenues into a dedicated fund that will be used to meet future State pollution control requirements (28). Congress could adopt this approach for existing, and perhaps new, incinerators by requiring that a similar provision be included in permit renewals and in new permits.

Landfills

Landfills will always be needed to manage the residues from recycling and incineration, as well as for the noncombustible, nonrecyclable portion of the wastestream. Indeed, a continued high percentage of all MSW could be landfilled if the Nation were willing to site or expand more landfills, pay the costs of transporting MSW to these landfills, pay for pollution controls, and accept some unavoidable risks. Some new landfills are being sited, and permitted capacity at existing landfills has been expanded in some cases (ch. 7).[41] In some localities, landfills will remain the primary management method, especially where recycling and/or incineration capacities cannot be developed economically, or

---

[41]Landfills must have permits to operate legally; some facilities may have additional space that is not permitted, but such space is not considered to be available capacity.

where landfills can be located away from aquifers (e.g., in some arid areas).

Overall, the current decline in permitted landfill capacity seems likely to continue. **Increased landfill capacity cannot be relied on as a nationwide solution to MSW problems, given current attitudes about siting and desires to move toward prevention and other forms of management**.

Implementing a prevention and materials management policy could reduce some associated risks and prolong the life of some landfills. For example, much of the MSW in landfills consists of paper and paper products, yard and food wastes, and plastics (ch. 3).[42] Thus, separating and composting yard waste could divert a large portion of MSW from landfills and reduce some potential leachate problems (ch. 7). Moreover, new landfills that use BACT (e.g., synthetic liners, leachate collection systems) and proper siting procedures can be managed much more safely than could past landfills.

The issues raised by landfilling thus are similar to those for incineration. Two of these issues, the Federal role in resolving siting problems and developing capacity, were discussed above. The primary issue discussed here is how to ensure that new and existing facilities provide adequate public health and environmental protection. Most States have some guidelines or standards for MSW landfills, in some cases based on criteria developed by EPA in 1979, and many older, substandard landfills have closed instead of being upgraded to meet these standards. EPA is revising recently proposed regulations for the design, operation, and location of Subtitle D landfills. Congress could provide additional direction to EPA, particularly guidance on whether the regulations should use a risk-based or design-based approach and whether they should apply to facilities that close before the standards become effective. Congress also could clarify the issue of municipal liability for corrective action.

Option 1: Give Additional Direction to EPA's Regulatory Effort

Option 1A: Specify How Landfills Should Be Regulated

The regulations currently proposed by EPA do not require the use of BACT. Instead, they would allow States to regulate each aquifer with a different risk-based standard, so long as the associated cancer risk fell below a specified range. Depending on the risk level chosen for a given site, some new landfills might be built without liners or leachate collection systems. This flexibility may be desirable, but the range of allowable risks is wide (between one additional cancer death per 10,000 people and one per 10 million people), and EPA provided little guidance on which design features would meet particular risk-based standards. These and other problems with the proposed regulations are discussed in chapter 7.

Congress could endorse this risk-based approach, or it could direct EPA to specify uniform design criteria based on BACT, and thus provide clearer direction to communities and States about how new landfills should be built. The major problem with a design-based approach is its lack of flexibility, particularly for sites located in arid areas, far from an aquifer, or in special geological areas. This problem could be addressed, however. For instance, site-specific variances from uniform criteria could be allowed, assuming that the alternative provides a similar level of protection. Alternatively, EPA could specify different design features for use in different situations, although this might prove to be a formidable task given the variability in site characteristics. Whatever final form the regulations take, the costs of developing and operating new landfills will be higher in the future.

Option 1B: Extend Corrective Action and Closure Requirements

Some MSW landfills have been associated with environmental problems (e.g., groundwater contamination; ch. 7), and it is possible that more will cause problems in the future. EPA's proposed regulations include corrective action, closure, post closure, and financial assurance requirements to help remedy

---

[42]These materials represent about two-thirds by weight of the waste in landfills. The average total volume cannot be determined because data are lacking on the composition by volume of MSW entering landfills.

future problems. Existing landfills that close within 18 months after the regulations are promulgated, however, would not be subject to the corrective action requirements unless State regulations require otherwise (ch. 7). As a result, the rate at which substandard facilities close is likely to increase because they could avoid potentially expensive closure and corrective action procedures. Congress could address this issue by directing EPA to consider making all existing landfills subject to the requirements at the time the regulations are promulgated. While this would impose substantial costs on some landfill operators, it would provide for the orderly closing of substandard facilities and avoid some of the problems discussed in Option 2 below.

Option 2: Clarify Municipal Liability Provisions

The Comprehensive Environmental Response, Compensation, and Liability Act (CERCLA, commonly known as Superfund) currently can be used for remedial actions at landfills, and indeed 20 percent of the sites on the National Priorities List (NPL) are municipal landfills.[43] Although local governments do not relish the idea of having their landfill on the NPL, Superfund does provide two advantages to municipalities—a source of funding for cleanup, and the sharing of liabilities for cleanup and corrective action among industrial waste generators, transporters, and local owners and operators.

In proposed amendments to CERCLA, however, EPA suggested deferring the listing of additional municipal landfills on the NPL after corrective action requirements under Subtitle D of RCRA are issued (53 *Federal Register* 51394, Dec. 21, 1988). This deferral policy would apply only to currently active landfills, not to previously closed ones. It would require that active landfills meet financial responsibility requirements for cleanup to assure some funding for remediation efforts that do not fall under Superfund.

One important consequence of this proposed policy, however, is that it would make local landfill owners and operators liable for corrective action and cleanup costs, instead of sharing liability with waste generators and haulers.[44] This policy is supported by representatives of industrial waste generators, who contend that MSW alone can generate toxic leachate and that corrective action at municipal landfills should be handled under a separate program (60).

The disadvantage to municipalities is that the costs of identifying, ranking, and cleaning up Superfund-type sites are high (49,55), and few municipalities are likely to be able to bear such costs. Moreover, most municipalities have either expected to share liabilities with waste generators and transporters or been unaware of their liabilities under Superfund. The position of organizations representing municipalities (e.g., National League of Cities, Governmental Refuse Collection and Disposal Association) is that Superfund should continue to be used for corrective action and cleanup of municipal landfills (45).

Congress could allow EPA to continue developing the deferred listing policy, in conjunction with development of corrective action requirements under proposed Subtitle D criteria. If Superfund is not used for cleanup of additional municipal landfills, one possibility for easing the financial burden on municipalities is for States to place a tax on tipping fees at all landfills. Revenues could be placed into trust funds to support corrective action programs. This approach is being tried in some States (e.g., Massachusetts).

Alternatively, Congress could direct EPA to revise the proposed amendments, specifically to continue including municipal landfills in Superfund and to develop procedures for allocating liability among municipalities and industries. Another alternative is to allow States to petition EPA to defer individual sites. In this approach, site-specific conditions would be considered and the deferred site would be handled under other programs. The position of the municipal representatives on this approach is that, if it is adopted, States should be required to obtain the concurrence of the local government owner and operator when a municipal site is considered for deferral.

A longer term approach to avoiding such problems is to keep certain materials out of landfills. For

---

[43]The NPL is the list of sites designated by EPA for cleanup action under the auspices of the Superfund program.

[44]At least initially, this would be true. In theory, however, the costs could later be recovered through legal action against waste generators, but some argue that in practice this would be unlikely (45).

example, localities could be encouraged to remove and compost yard wastes, which would reduce the probability that leachate will cause problems. Some States have banned the disposal of such materials in MSW landfills if composting facilities are available. The disposal of industrial wastes and small quantity generator hazardous wastes at MSW landfills also could be phased out as other management capacity for these wastes is developed. In the interim, landfill operators could be required to meet stricter standards and provide better records if they accept such wastes.

CONCLUDING REMARKS

One of the difficulties in developing a coherent MSW policy is that trash touches virtually all the threads of our social fabric. Products and packaging, yard waste—all eventually become part of the MSW stream. The system that produces MSW is so complex and dynamic that no single option is guaranteed in and of itself to solve MSW problems. In fact, it is not clear that there is a single given combination of options that is best.

What is clear, however, is that unless we develop a more comprehensive approach, the Nation will continue to have problems with capacity, siting, and costs for MSW management. Many of the options described in this report have been suggested before. They have not been acted on, however, and problems have worsened.

We can choose to continue facing piles of trash, or we can turn in a new direction. By implementing a policy that considers MSW in the context of materials use, a policy based on the concepts of waste prevention and materials management, we have a chance to solve the problems associated with MSW.

CHAPTER 1 REFERENCES

1. American Paper Institute, *1987 Annual Statistical Summary, Waste Paper Utilization* (New York, NY: June 1988).
2. Ayers, R.U., and Kneese, A.V., "Production, Consumption, and Externalities," *American Economic Review,* June 1969 (available from Resources for the Future, reprint #76).
3. Belasen, A.T., *The New York State Returnable Beverage Container Law—Economic Effects, Industry Adaptations, and Guidelines for Improved Envi-*

4. Berkman, M.P., and Dunbar, F.C., "The Underpricing of Landfills," paper presented at Third Annual Conference on Solid Waste Management and Materials Policy (New York, NY: Feb. 13, 1987).
5. Center for the Biology of Natural Systems, *Development and Pilot Test of an Intensive Municipal Solid Waste Recycling System for the Town of East Hampton,* report submitted to New York State Energy Research and Development Authority (Flushing, NY: 1988).
6. Clean Japan Center, "Waste Volume on the Rise and Measures Against It," *Clean Japan* 14:6-10, February 1989.
7. Copperthite, K., U.S. Department of Commerce, personal communication, 1989.
8. Crew, M.A., and Kleindorfer, P.R., "Landfill Tipping Fees Should Be Much Higher," *Waste Age,* pp. 131-134, February 1988.
9. Deutsches Institut fur Gutesicherung und Kennzeichnung, "Verzeichnis der Produkte und Zeichenanwender sowie der jeweiligen Produktanforderungen" (Bonn: June 1988).
10. Dunbar, F.C., and Berkman, M.P., "Sanitary Landfills Are Too Cheap!" *Waste Age,* pp. 91-99, May 1987.
11. Environment, "Environmentally Friendly Products," *Environment* 31(2):23, 1989.
12. Environment Reporter, "EPA Region X Calls for Recycling as Possible Incinerator Permit Condition," *Environment Reporter* 19(49):2565-2566, Apr. 7, 1989.
13. Environmental Defense Fund, "National Advertising Campaign on Recycling Launched by the Environmental Defense Fund & the Advertising Council," news release (New York, NY: Sept. 15, 1988).
14. Ferrand, T., "Memorandum, Proposed NRC Standard Definitions" (Absecon, NJ: Ferrand Associates, Nov. 16, 1988).
15. Franklin Associates, Ltd., *Characterization of Municipal Solid Waste in the United States, 1960 to 2000* (Update 1988), final report, prepared for the U.S. Environmental Protection Agency (Prairie Village, KS: March 1988).
16. Franklin Associates, Ltd., *Characterization of Products Containing Lead and Cadmium in Municipal Solid Waste in the United States, 1970 to 2000, Executive Summary and Chapter 1,* final report prepared for U.S. EPA, Municipal Solid Waste Program (Prairie Village, KS: January 1989).
17. Franklin Associates, Ltd., *The Role of Beverage Containers in Recycling and Solid Waste Manage-*

ronmental Policy, Rockefeller Institute Working Paper No. 31 (Albany, NY: State University of New York, spring 1988).

ment, A Perspective for the 1990s, final report prepared for Anheuser-Busch Companies, Inc. (Prairie Village, KS: April 1989).

18. Golub, N.M., Strachan, J.R., Berle, P.A.A., et al., *Final Report of the Temporary State Commission on Returnable Beverage Containers* (Albany, NY: Mar. 27, 1985).

19. Greenblott, J., Technical Resources, Inc., personal communication, September 1988.

20. Hemphill, T., "Financing Options: The Next Phase of Market Development," *Recycling Today* 26(12):58-66, December 1988.

21. Institute for Local Self-Reliance (ILSR), "National Recycling Research Agenda Project," Final Report to National Science Foundation (Washington, DC: 1980).

22. Institute for Local Self-Reliance (ILSR), *Financing Mechanisms to Promote Recycling at the State and Local Level* (Washington, DC: 1985).

23. Institute for Local Self-Reliance (ILSR), *Beyond 25 Percent: Materials Recovery Comes of Age* (Washington, DC: 1989).

24. Kneese, A.V., and Bower, B.T., *Environmental Quality and Residuals Management* (Baltimore, MD: Johns Hopkins University Press, 1979).

25. Kovacs, W.L., "The Coming Era of Conservation and Industrial Utilization of Recyclable Materials," *Ecology Law Quarterly* 15:537-625, 1988.

26. Kovacs, W.L., and Anderson, A.A., "States As Market Participants in Solid Waste Disposal Services—Fair Competition or the Destruction of the Private Sector?" *Environmental Law* 18:779-816, 1988.

27. Lesser, W., and Madhavan, A., "Economic Impacts of a National Deposit Law: Cost Estimates and Policy Questions," *Journ. Consumer Affairs* 21(1):122-140, summer 1987.

28. Massachusetts Department of Environmental Quality Engineering, "Q&A, Questions & Answers on the Solid Waste Act of 1987," Division of Solid Waste Management (Boston, MA: January 1988).

29. McCarthy, J., Congressional Research Service, personal communication, February 1989.

30. Meyer, B., Aluminum Association, personal communication, 1989.

31. Moore, W.K., and Scott, D.L., "Beverage Container Deposit Laws: A Survey of the Issues and Results," *Journ. Consumer Affairs* 17(1):57-80, summer 1983.

32. New York State Department of Environmental Conservation, Division of Solid Waste, *New York State Solid Waste Management Plan, 1987-88 Update* (Albany, NY: March 1988).

33. Obermeier, T., Federal Republic of Germany, personal communication, March 1989

34. Oregon Department of Environmental Quality, "An Evaluation of the True Costs of Sanitary Landfills for the Disposal of Municipal Solid Waste in the Portland Metropolitan Area," prepared by ECO Northwest, April 1986.

35. Page, T., *Conservation and Economic Efficiency, An Approach to Materials Policy* (Baltimore, MD: Johns Hopkins University Press, 1977).

36. Porter, R.C., "Michigan's Experience With Mandatory Deposits on Beverage Containers," *Land Economics* 59(2):177-194, May 1983.

37. Rathje, W.L., Hughes, W.W., Archer, G., and Wilson, D.C., "Source Reduction and Landfill Myths," paper presented at ASTSWMO National Solid Waste Forum on Integrated Municipal Waste Management (Lake Buena Vista, FL: July 17-20, 1988).

38. Rathje, W.L., University of Arizona, personal communication, Feb. 1989.

39. Riggle, D., "Only Pay For What You Throw Away," *BioCycle* 30(2):39-41, February 1989.

40. Rose, D., "National Beverage Container Deposit Legislation: A Cost-Benefit Analysis," *J. Environmental Systems* 12(1):71-84, 1982-83.

41. Rozett, J.M., "Resolving the "Bottle Bill" Controversy: The Role of Policy Analysis in Decision Making," Rockefeller Institute of Government, New York Case Studies in Public Management No. 14 (Albany, NY: State University of New York, November 1984).

42. Smallburg, K., Steel Can Recycling Institute, personal communication, 1989.

43. Society of Packaging and Handling Engineers, "Memorandum Re: SPHE Recycling and Disposal Guidelines for Packaging Professionals" (Reston, VA: July 11, 1988).

44. Society of the Plastics Industry, personal communication, 1988.

45. Steinzor, R.I., "Comments of the National League of Cities and the Governmental Refuse Collection and Disposal Association on EPA's Proposed Revisions to the Superfund National Contingency Plan" (Washington, DC: Spiegel & McDiarmid, Mar. 23, 1989).

46. U.S. Congress, Office of Technology Assessment, *Materials and Energy From Municipal Waste,* OTA-M-93 (Springfield, VA: National Technical Information Service, July 1979).

47. U.S. Congress, Office of Technology Assessment, *Industrial and Commercial Cogeneration,* OTA-E-192 (Springfield, VA: National Technical Information Service, February 1983).

48. U.S. Congress, Office of Technology Assessment, *Technologies and Management Strategies for Hazardous Waste Control,* OTA-M-196 (Springfield,

VA: National Technical Information Service, March 1983).

49. U.S. Congress, Office of Technology Assessment, *Superfund Strategy*, OTA-ITE- 252 (Springfield, VA: National Technical Information Service, April 1985).

50. U.S. Congress, Office of Technology Assessment, *Serious Reduction of Hazardous Waste*, OTA-ITE-317 (Springfield, VA: National Technical Information Service, September 1986).

51. U.S. Congress, Office of Technology Assessment, Wastes in Marine Environments, OTA-O-334 (Washington, DC: U.S. Government Printing Office, April 1987).

52. U.S. Congress, Office of Technology Assessment, *From Pollution to Prevention: A Progress Report on Waste Reduction*, OTA-ITE-347 (Washington, DC: U.S. Government Printing Office, June 1987).

53. U.S. Congress, Office of Technology Assessment, "Workshop on MSW Reduction" (Washington, DC: July 14-15, 1988).

54. U.S. Congress, Office of Technology Assessment, *Issues in Medical Waste Management—Background Paper*, OTA-BP-O-49 (Washington, DC: October 1988).

55. U.S. Congress, Office of Technology Assessment, *Assessing Contractor Use in Superfund—Background Paper*, OTA-BP-ITE-51 (Washington, DC: U.S. Government Printing Office, January 1989).

56. U.S. Environmental Protection Agency, *Report to Congress, Solid Waste Disposal in the United States, Volume II*, Office of Solid Waste and Emergency Response, EPA/530-SW-88-011B (Washington, DC: October 1988).

57. U.S. Environmental Protection Agency, *The Solid Waste Dilemma, An Agenda for Action*, Report of the Municipal Solid Waste Task Force, Office of Solid Waste (Washington, DC: February 1989).

58. U.S. Environmental Protection Agency, 'Spokane Regional Waste to Energy Project PSD Appeal No. 88-12 (Spokane, Washington)," Memorandum from G. O'Neal, Air and Toxics Division, to R.L. McCallum, Chief Judicial Officer, EPA Region X (Seattle, WA: 1989).

59. Water Pollution Control Federation, "Waste Minimization and Waste Reduction," *Journ. Water Poll. Control Fed.* 61(2):184, 1989.

60. Webster, I., "Municipal Solid Waste Landfills: Toxic Chemical Releases and the Role of Industrial Wastes in Those Releases," unpublished manuscript (Los Angeles, CA: Unocal Corp., 1988).

61. World Commission on Environment and Development, *Our Common Future* (New York, NY: Oxford University Press, 1987).

62. Worldwatch Institute, "Environmental Seal of Approval," *WorldWatch* 2(3):6- 7, May/June 1989.

Chapter 2

The MSW System in Transition

CONTENTS

Boxes

Figures

Tables

The MSW System in Transition

INTRODUCTION

The United States is a land of abundant natural resources. Although the limitations of this great wealth are becoming apparent—declining energy resources, polluted air and water, rising land costs, signs of industrial decline—societal attitudes regarding the use of this wealth have not yet adjusted. Our social and economic philosophies in many ways still emphasize "consumerism," tending to divert attention away from the idea of resource conservation. We have a high per-capita waste generation rate, and that rate seems to be increasing (ch. 3).

There is no easy answer to the question of why our society has become such a prodigious waste producer, nor is there an easy way to reverse this trend. Some elements that contribute to the overall trend are obvious: for instance, factors such as a product's appearance and convenience are more important to today's consumers than where it came from and what will happen when it is discarded. Other elements are less visible, however. As our standard of living has increased and a smaller share of the population is engaged in the physical production of goods, people have become less aware of how materials are obtained and transformed into usable products.

Whether the tendency toward increased waste is an inherent characteristic of U.S. consumers or whether it is the result of manufacturers' advertising is unclear. It is true, however, that in the past product designers and manufacturers have not been burdened with the responsibility for the ultimate fate of their products, that is, what happens to the products after they are used. Neither have the majority of consumers been concerned with the ultimate disposal of their waste.

Heightened concerns about our industrial prowess, our deteriorating environment, and what some claim to be an apparent lack of concern for the future are forcing us to reexamine our values. The problems emerging with MSW reflect this convergence of concerns: can U.S. industry respond adequately to help us generate less MSW; can we devise better materials use and waste management strategies; and are we willing to work today to ensure that future generations are not forced to pay a high price for our carelessness?

This chapter briefly examines societal, institutional, and industrial influences that have shaped the present MSW situation. Understanding the evolution of the problem and the dynamics of the "system" that manages our MSW can help illuminate likely targets for change. The chapter begins with a discussion of the interrelationships among production decisions, consumption patterns, waste generation, and MSW management. The evolution of the public and private waste management infrastructure also is described. Two key issues affecting the entire MSW system—the risks and the costs associated with different management methods—are also examined.

MSW GENERATION AND MANAGEMENT AS PART OF A "SYSTEM"

The nature and quantity of MSW that we generate, and how we manage it, are determined by a multitude of decisions made at all levels of the socioeconomic system. Linkages among different stages in the lifecycle of MSW—product design, manufacture, distribution, use, and discard—often are unclear and may even be invisible. Each of these linkages represents a leverage point for changing decisions and thus the MSW status quo. But people's awareness of the MSW system, and their role in it, is growing, especially in parts of the country where waste disposal costs have increased and disposal capacity has declined. For example, the intense public opposition to the siting of MSW management facilities has prompted some citizens to question their own consumption patterns and waste disposal practices.

Product Design and Manufacture: The Beginning of the MSW Lifecycle

The design of products has enormous influence on MSW management. For example, products that contain potentially toxic substances, for whatever functional reasons, have led to concerns about human health and environmental risks associated with landfilling, incineration, and recycling (see "Risks Associated With Management Methods" below).

Product design is very dynamic. Manufacturers continually change products for reasons that include increased marketability and safety and decreased costs of production and materials. This has led to many changes that ultimately effect MSW management—e.g., the shift in packaging and containers to using lighter materials such as plastics and paper in place of glass and metal (chs. 3 and 4).

In general, however, the entire production end of the MSW lifecycle has not received much attention as a focus for solving MSW problems, at least until recently. Design and production changes are rarely undertaken in response to concerns about MSW management. Although manufacturers have incentives to reduce the costs and liabilities associated with their industrial wastes, they have little incentive to worry about disposal costs for their final products (ch. 1). This, in turn, means that changes in product design can have unintentional, negative effects on MSW management—e.g., the use of multi-material packaging can make such packaging more difficult to recycle.

Now, however, there is growing awareness of the link between the design and production of consumer products and MSW management problems. In a few instances, issues related to MSW management have manifested themselves at the product design stage (e.g., degradable plastic bags, mercury-free household batteries). There is a growing movement advocating "design for recycling," i.e., designing products to be recyclable or to use more recycled materials. This concept could be extended to include "design for reduction," a call for products designed to be less toxic or more durable, or to use fewer materials. These changes all could have positive effects on MSW management (chs. 1 and 4).

The Federal Government, State governments, industries, and consumer groups are all wrestling with how to promote these types of changes. State governments in the Northeast, for example, have created a waste reduction task force to work with industry on ways to reduce MSW toxicity and quantity (ch. 8). Working with the Conservation Foundation, EPA sponsored a dialog beginning in 1988 on MSW reduction, with representatives from government, industry, academia, and public interest groups (ch. 8). Continued and increased interest in how to address product design will be a critical factor in the future success of MSW reduction and recycling efforts. OTA discusses policy options related to these issues in chapter 1.

Changes in the Public and Private Waste Management Infrastructure

The Evolution of Waste Management Practices

In the past, waste management meant simply getting rid of the trash. Often, this was done for a low cost by a local, privately owned waste disposal company, the municipality, or sometimes by residents at a local dump. Government attention to waste was minimal, even at the local level. Municipal government involvement in waste management consisted, at the most, of owning collection vehicles and the landfill. No consideration was given to how much waste was generated or to its characteristics. No one really cared what ended up at the landfill or where it came from.[1]

Most recovery of materials for recycling occurred at no cost to residents because it was done by local private scrap collectors or by volunteer groups as a fund-raising activity. The volume of materials collected was dependent on the price for the materials in the marketplace. When prices fell, collection declined and when prices increased, collection increased. Waste collection and disposal costs were generally not affected, however.

Some additional materials recovery occurred outside the purview of the municipal budget at drop-off or buy-back centers operated by charity

---

[1]Experiences of local governments with MSW management, including the myriad of problems that have faced local officials, are discussed in ch. 8.

groups or environmental organizations.[2] These centers became particularly popular during the 1970s, when social awareness of resource conservation and environmental protection was high. However, neither these centers nor the traditional scrap industry were viewed as part of the waste management system.

At the same time, litter reduction efforts also increased, and several States passed beverage container deposit legislation (ch. 8). The costs of these programs were borne principally by the beverage industry, the consumer, and the retail sector. Studies indicate that this type of legislation reduced beverage container litter by as much as 80 percent (9,12). In general, however, the legislation was not oriented toward waste management, and the reduction in the amount of MSW sent to incinerators or landfills was less than 5 percent.[3]

By the mid-1970s, the recovery of materials and energy from MSW as a waste management alternative was entering its infancy, especially in terms of government policy. Technologies for recovering energy and materials from mixed waste were unproven, and many municipalities were wary of the financial, social, and political risks involved. Many private firms, however, viewed energy and materials recovery as promising business opportunities and rushed to offer related products and services. Firms expanding into these activities included those involved in pollution control, petrochemicals and oil, aerospace, solid waste collection and disposal, containers and packaging, engineering and construction consulting, and machinery and equipment manufacturers (2). In other words, there was no shortage of willing entrants into the emerging, but yet unknown, materials and energy recovery segments of the waste management field.

Since that time, energy recovery and, more recently, materials recovery have proven to be a boon to the waste management business. Numerous technologies have been developed to recover materials from mixed MSW, to sort commingled recyclables, or to process recyclables separated by waste generators (i.e., by households, offices, etc.). Al-

Photo credit: Office of Technology Assessment

Consumers can often take separated materials such as used aluminum beverage cans to a "buy-back" center that pays for the materials and then further processes them for market.

though these types of activities were once viewed as being oriented toward commodities—designed to profit strictly from the marketing of materials—they are now also viewed as a waste management service. In some instances, municipally owned materials recovery facilities compete with private recyclers, further spurring the private sector to view recovery of materials from waste as a business opportunity.

Many of these changes in the structure of the waste management industry occurred over several generations. Box 2-A describes these types of changes for one California community.

The Current Status of the Waste Management Industry

By 1988, analysts were projecting waste management industry-wide revenues of $18 billion over the years 1988 through 1995 from waste-to-energy incinerators alone (19). The materials recovery

---

[2]A drop-off center can be a permanent site or a mobile trailer accepting one or more materials. These centers are often operated by nonprofit groups or by communities. A buy-back center has a similar arrangement, except that cash is exchanged for the material. Aluminum recycling centers, often operated by aluminum companies, are the most prevalent form of buy-back operation.

[3]Metal, glass, and plastic beverage containers covered under these programs normally make up about 5 percent of the waste stream.

Box 2-A—*Generations of MSW and Materials Management*

Adaptation and innovation—in collection, management methods, and financing—have proven to be key ingredients in the evolution of MSW management in Marin County, California. One of the driving forces behind the county's ambitious recycling program is Joseph J. Garbarino. For Garbarino, MSW management is more than a business, it's a family tradition. Marin Sanitary Service, a waste collection and hauling company that is over 40 years old, is owned by Garbarino and three partners. Garbarino's father, John, an Italian immigrant, was a garbageman and his daughters, Susan and Patricia, work in the business. Garbarino notes that many people in the Bay area garbage business had uncles, fathers, and grandfathers who hauled garbage there earlier in the century.

The latest advance in the business is a recycling processing facility, the Marin Resource Recovery Center in San Rafael, that is generations removed from earlier methods of collection and management. Earlier in the century, scavenging (an "old name for recycling," according to Garbarino) was a normal part of garbage collection and scrap dealers played an integral role in managing discarded materials; in the early 1920s, garbagemen in the Bay area even formed the Scavengers' Protection Association to avoid competing too strenuously among themselves. A team of men would set out collecting burlap garbage sacks, with one man sorting the discards on a horse-pulled wagon or later on a flatbed truck. Anything that could not be reused was disposed of in San Francisco Bay, apparently helping to build Treasure Island. As the consequences of this disposal method became better understood, techniques began to change. "Sanitary landfills" became the favored MSW management tool; the San Quentin Disposal Site operated from 1958 to 1987, and Marin Sanitary Service began disposing MSW in the Redwood Landfill in 1948.

At about this same time, compaction collection trucks were introduced in Marin County. The advent of these "packer" trucks in the late 1950s was a significant reason that many garbage collectors stopped recovering materials for several decades. In the late 1970s, after some of the initial recycling enthusiasm of the early 1970s (which had spawned and seen the demise of numerous community recycling programs) had settled, Marin Sanitary Service became re-involved in the business of recycling. Garbarino helped develop Marin Recycling, a pioneering residential curbside collection program owned by three companies, with initial funding from the California Waste Management Board. In 1980, Marin Recycling bought its first recycling collection trucks. Given recent trends, Garbarino predicts that one day the county will have more recycling collection trucks than packer trucks.

For Garbarino, the orientation toward recycling is practical and wise business. He argued early for curbside collection of recyclables because it would prolong the life of local landfills and give area trash haulers additional business opportunities. Today, Garbarino stresses the importance of managing waste in ways that are environmentally sound as well as profitable, and he supports increased waste reduction and recycling efforts.

Since 1980, the curbside program has collected cans, bottles, and paper—initially about 1,000 tons per year, currently 22,500 tons per year. The facility also accepts a similar amount of source-separated materials from nearby cities. An innovative recycling surcharge conceived by Garbarino was adopted by the 16 participating communities to subsidize the program. It helped the program survive a recession shortly after it began and the surcharge is still in place today, 8 years later. Marin Recycling now services about 168,000 of the 225,000 residents in the county. In 1987, Marin Sanitary Service opened the Marin Resource Recovery Center, housed on an 18-acre site in San Rafael, to process recyclables. The center receives about 5,000 to 6,000 tons of materials a month, mostly from the commercial sector, and recovers about 1,500 tons a month (other residues and trash loads are sent to a landfill). The $9.5 million center was financed for Marin Sanitary Service by a local bank. It receives materials from private haulers who are charged a tipping fee and from the commercial collection program. The center also buys baled cardboard from grocers and re-bales it for export. In addition, a collection of pigs, rabbits and other farm animals consume some of the food waste from local restaurants and grocers.

Garbarino plans to expand the apartment complex component of the residential curbside program and may build a refuse-derived fuel facility in an effort to meet Marin County's 50 percent recycling goal. Today, Marin Recycling and the Resource Recovery Center collect and divert between 20 to 30 percent of source-separated materials from residences and businesses for recycling. Over the years, Garbarino has worked closely with the communities and their local and State public officials. Undoubtedly, this cooperation will be important to the future evolution of Marin County's MSW and materials management approach.

SOURCE: J.J. Garbarino, personal communication, March 1988; P. Garbarino, personal communication, August 1989.

segment of the industry also is likely to experience substantial growth in the next few years. Such projections for growth have prompted Wall Street analysts to proclaim the waste management industry "recession proof."

The six largest public U.S. waste management companies in fiscal 1987 reported annual revenues of $5 billion from solid and hazardous waste services. In many instances, these large companies were formed by consolidation and vertical integration, and many are becoming international concerns. For example:

- Western Waste, the fifth largest waste management firm (in terms of 1987 revenues), purchased the routes and other assets of 10 waste hauling companies in fiscal 1987;
- Browning-Ferris Industries, the Nation's second largest waste management firm, acquired more than 100 solid waste-related businesses; and
- Attwoods PLC, a British company, acquired 12 small Florida waste hauling companies, a medium-sized waste management company in Maryland, and several other waste-related enterprises to make it the fourth largest waste management firm in the United States.

A hint of future trends in waste management can be gleaned from the pages of these companies' annual reports. All plan continued acquisitions of related businesses to increase capacity for waste treatment and disposal. The industry also is responding to the growing desire in many municipalities to reduce the quantities of waste going to incinerators and landfills (20). For example, a number of companies involved primarily in the waste-to-energy industry have become increasingly involved in materials recovery, both as a means of improving combustion and of keeping up with the changing needs expressed by local governments.

Changing Roles for the Public and the Private Sector

"Grassroots" recyclers have enjoyed revitalized interest, as the public takes a more active role in exploring solutions to MSW problems. Statewide recycling associations formed in the late 1970s have flourished and are helping to educate the citizenry about the benefits of materials recovery. The Na-

Photo credit: Office of Technology Assessment

In the late 1950s, most communities began using "packer" trucks to collect and compact mixed MSW and then transport it to landfills.

tional Recycling Coalition, with members representing local private recyclers as well as State government officials, has helped increase awareness and facilitate information flow from the local level to the national level. State officials have initiated regional recycling associations, such as the North East Recycling Coalition and the Great Lakes Recycling Coalition, to pursue a variety of cooperative efforts designed to enhance recycling in member States. Such pursuits include cooperative purchasing of products made from recycled materials and development of standards and definitions to become part of a common recycling language. Along with these efforts, many nonprofit recycling centers increased their participation in the MSW system, undertaking community outreach activities and expanding the types of materials they handle.

The trend toward increasing materials recovery by the public sector as a means of managing MSW has caused some stress on parts of the existing private infrastructure, however. Traditional scrap dealers, who in the past worked primarily with industrial customers, now must compete with increasing supplies of materials from the residential waste stream. These dealers were once able to act as a sort of "safety valve," turning the materials supply on and off in response to demand. Their ability to perform this function is changing, however, because the recovery of materials by municipal governments is increasing. Municipal materials recovery is motivated not by price but by avoidance of ever-increasing disposal costs. Therefore, declining commodity prices, which would normally trigger a reduction in supply, can be overshadowed by the need to avoid disposal costs in municipal recycling programs. The existence of a supplier that is not sensitive to prices will put additional pressure on those that are solely motivated by profit.[4] The full effects of these changing waste management trends on the private recycling sector will only be fully realized when recession occurs and materials markets, and prices, shrink.

Some municipalities have attempted to enlist the private scrap sector into the MSW management system. In some cities, existing buy-back and drop-off centers have been included in the overall MSW management plan, either alone or as supplements to curbside recycling programs. In Philadelphia, Pennsylvania, an existing nonprofit buy-back center was used in a pilot recycling program as a materials recovery facility to sort commingled recyclables.

The ownership of MSW management facilities is another factor in transition. Although the trend is toward increased activities to be included in MSW management systems, the operation and sometimes ownership of these activities is often private. As the system becomes more complex and market oriented, municipalities (especially the smaller ones) may be reluctant to assume the primary responsibility for operating a complex business. The large waste management companies that have emerged are sophisticated in the technical aspects of MSW management and financially capable of accepting some of the associated business risks. At the municipal level, the prospect of contracting out increasingly complicated waste management services has become particularly attractive. In some larger metropolitan areas, however, governments may view private scrap dealers as unnecessary intermediaries robbing the public sector of needed revenue.

The private financial sector also has become more involved in MSW management activities. The proliferation of multi-million dollar municipal waste-to-energy facilities in municipalities with limited budgets necessitated the creation of sophisticated financing schemes, and Wall Street brokerage houses have developed a substantial business in creating financing packages for such facilities. In fact, the involvement of large investment houses in the waste-to-energy industry may even have helped reduce the skepticism that many municipal officials had toward this technology. Because the capital requirements for materials recovery facilities are much lower than for incinerators, making financing easier, similar financial sector involvement in recycling may be limited.

As the MSW management infrastructure has evolved, there has been an increasing awareness of the risks associated with management activities and concern over the increased costs associated with improved management methods. The risks and costs associated with MSW practices are two major factors decisionmakers must weigh when devising suitable MSW strategies for their communities.

RISKS ASSOCIATED WITH MSW MANAGEMENT METHODS

Public opposition to the siting of MSW management facilities in part stems from concerns about the potential health and environmental risks associated with these facilities. Potential risks are posed, for example, by:

- emissions and ash from incinerators;
- emissions and leachate from landfills; and
- emissions, effluent, and sludge residues from recycling (including processing and manufacturing facilities).

Some of these are created when the organic portion of MSW (e.g., yard wastes, paper, and plastics) is processed, burned, or decomposed. Others stem from the metals and organic chemicals contained in products discarded in MSW—in "house-

---

[4]An analogous situation existed in the world copper market, which consists of industrial country suppliers, who are primarily profit-motivated, and of developing country suppliers, who are motivated more by a desire to maintain employment and generate foreign exchange. As copper prices fell during the 1982 recession, developing country suppliers refused to cut back on supply, and in some instances even increased supply to maintain earnings in the face of lower prices. The result was that prices were pushed down even further, to the point where they had been during the Great Depression, a much lower drop than that which occurred in the overall level of economic activity. The price depression experienced by the world copper industry was not matched by that for other industries.

hold hazardous wastes'' (e.g., solvents, paints, batteries, and cleansers) and other products (e.g., metal additives in plastics). Non-MSW (e.g., industrial non-hazardous solid waste) discarded at landfills also contributes metals and organic chemicals (chs. 3 and 7). After being discarded, these substances can pose potential risks in any MSW management activity—landfilling, incineration, or recycling (chs. 5, 6, and 7).[5] The extent to which any of one of these products or substances contribute to overall risks from MSW management is not clear.

Various public interest and private industry groups have attempted to promote one management method over the other on the basis of comparative risk. However, little effort has been made, even at the Federal level, to **quantitatively** assess the comparative risks posed by **different** MSW management methods. It is beyond the capabilities of current risk assessment efforts to compare risks among management alternatives (e.g., of potential risks associated with landfilling, incineration, or recycling), although comparisons of options within a type of management alternative are possible (e.g., a comparison of landfill designs). OTA has found no quantitative evidence to support a definitive comparison of human health and environmental risks associated with recycling, incineration, and landfilling.

Quantitative estimation and comparison of the relative risks associated with different management methods is difficult, in part because of problems inherent in risk assessment methodologies and in part because of data deficiencies. For example, it is clear that some potential environmental risks are associated with all MSW management methods because all processing, treatment, or disposal methods result in some type of waste byproduct. Many proponents of recycling contend that it poses fewer risks than alternative MSW management methods. However, given current data, it is not possible to quantitatively determine whether recycling produces more or less pollutants, or poses greater or fewer risks, per ton of material processed than do incineration or landfilling.[6] To compare the overall

potential risks quantitatively, an in-depth analysis would have to assess the location of all facilities, all waste products from manufacturing and management facilities, exposure pathways and dosages, and potentially affected populations. Obviously, this would be an extremely expensive and time-consuming task.

Some qualitative comparisons can still be attempted, however. Many secondary materials can be recycled several times before their ultimate disposal (and some, such as glass and aluminum, can be recycled indefinitely), thus decreasing the use of virgin materials. Since recycling a product avoids the production of pollutants from both manufacturing a new product and landfilling or incinerating the old product, recycling materials several times would seem to produce less pollutants on an overall basis than would incineration or landfilling.

A second question that can be addressed concerns the relative risks **within** a given method. Most risk assessments have focused on the relative risks within a single management method. Given these risk assessment methodologies and available data, it is possible to make comparisons within a particular method and indicate which pollutants are of greatest concern for those methods. The relative reductions in risk that might be achieved by retrofitting older facilities or designing new facilities with different controls can also be estimated.

For example, pollutants of concern in incinerator emissions include organic chemicals such as dioxins and metals such as mercury. Human exposure to these substances may be greater through food chain pathways than through inhalation pathways (ch. 6). However, there is considerable debate about the extent of exposure and subsequent risks associated with these pollutants and these pathways. Nevertheless, it is clear that the risks associated with new, well-operated incinerators (e.g., with a scrubber/fabric filter system and computerized combustion) are substantially lower, in some cases orders of magnitude lower, than those associated with old facilities. Moreover, the risks associated with emis-

---

[5]Defining exactly what is toxic is an enormous task beyond the scope of this report. OTA discusses these issues here on the assumption that when substances are identified as posing risks, then attempts should be made to get them out of the waste stream.

[6]A comparison can be made, though, between manufacturing processes using secondary materials (i.e., those recovered from the waste stream) and those using virgin materials. In many instances, using secondary materials to produce a given product produces less pollutants and saves energy in comparison with extracting virgin materials and subsequently manufacturing the same product (ch. 5).

sions from new incinerators appear to be within the range of risks allowed under regulations for other activities (e.g., drinking water standards). One consequence of better emissions controls, however, is that the resulting ash residues have higher concentrations of some substances. In particular, there is considerable controversy about the metals contained in the ash and the extent to which they might leach into groundwater (ch. 6).

Similar environmental problems can be associated with recycling, particularly the actual processing of collected secondary materials, and with landfilling. But as was the case with incinerators, newer recycling and landfill facilities offer greatly improved performance over older facilities. Composite liners, groundwater monitoring, and gas collection systems, for example, make today's landfills safer than in the past.

Many older facilities will continue to operate for several decades, thus national-scale analyses of the overall risks from MSW management cannot be made on the basis of newer facilities alone. The relative risks among available management options for particular communities could vary greatly depending on local conditions, raising serious questions about whether a national-scale analysis would be worth the cost. Most decisionmakers agree that standards for different management methods should be developed to ensure adequate protection for human health and the environment. The prevention and materials management approach to MSW suggested by OTA is predicated on the assumption that all facilities comply with these standards.

COSTS OF MSW MANAGEMENT

Increased concern about risk coupled with the increased complexity in MSW management combine to increase its overall cost. Although MSW management in the past typically played a small part in municipal budgets, costs are increasing more rapidly than many other budget items. As a result, municipal governments across the Nation are focusing more attention on the costs of managing MSW and seeking ways to improve the efficiency of the system.

As local officials plan for future MSW management, a key question they face is which management method or combination of methods is most economical for their community. Varying social, economic, and demographic conditions will make different approaches best for different communities. This is already evident in the multiplicity and variety of MSW management systems now operating throughout the country. In communities where disposal capacity problems have not surfaced, little attention is generally paid to the costs of trash collection and disposal. Often, these items are not broken out separately in the municipal budget and may be combined with items such as street cleaning. It is not uncommon to find that the municipal government official responsible for solid waste disposal knows little about the costs and characteristics of solid waste in the community.

To collect information on a variety of cities and counties across the Nation, OTA conducted a limited survey on the costs of MSW management. In addition, a cost estimation model was constructed for OTA by Energy Systems Research Group (ESRG) of Boston to examine the sensitivity of system costs to various relevant factors (box 2-B). This information provides the basis for the discussion in this section.

Solid Waste Management Costs in Perspective

Although MSW management costs are increasing, they represent a relatively small portion of most municipal budgets and an even smaller portion of the average family's budget. Among the 41 cities and counties responding to OTA's survey, the MSW budget ranged from 0.1 to 19.2 percent of the total municipal budget, but averaged only about 5 percent. Based on the data, annual MSW expenditures per person ranged from $6 to $130, averaging about $60. Thus the average family covered in the survey typically spends less than 1 percent of its income on MSW management.[7] Data from the Bureau of the Census (16) also indicate that MSW has not been a major budget item for cities and counties. For the majority of communities for which information is reported to the Bureau, the portion of the municipal

---

[7]The median family income in the United States in 1987 was $31,000 as estimated by the U.S. Bureau of the Census (17).

Box 2-B—OTA Survey and Computer Model of MSW Management Costs

To gather information about the costs of waste management practices around the United States, OTA surveyed 44 cities and counties (see table 2-1). Each prospective respondent was contacted by phone and by mail, and 93 percent completed the survey. The survey was not designed to represent a statistically significant sample of nationwide waste management practices. Rather, the survey was an attempt to increase awareness about the variation among municipalities in the level of attention to MSW management, the distribution in costs, and the problems encountered.

Those surveyed were chosen to provide geographic and demographic diversity and to encompass a range of MSW management strategies, from landfill only, to waste-to-energy incineration and landfill, to intensive recycling. Ownership of landfills and incinerators was relatively evenly divided between public and private, with counties tending toward more public ownership of facilities than cities. Among the cities, 52 percent of the landfills and 33 percent of the incinerators were publicly owned. By comparison, counties owned 70 percent of the landfills and 80 percent of the incinerators that they used. Residential trash collection was undertaken by municipal crews in 31 communities, by contractors in 16, and solely by residents or private haulers in 5.

Of the 41 cities and counties responding to the survey, 11 reported having no residential recycling program of any type. Of those with recycling programs, 19 reported curbside recycling programs (5 of which were mandatory), 26 had drop-off programs, and 18 had buy-back programs. Only 5 communities reported having some type of private curbside program, while 19 of the drop-off and all but one of the buy-back programs were privately operated. Composting programs were reported in 19 of the communities surveyed, and 13 of the communities had household hazardous waste programs. Fourteen of the respondents used some type of avoided cost calculation to justify their recycling program.

In addition to the survey, OTA contracted with Energy Systems Research Group, Inc., to develop a computer model to help understand the costs of MSW management alternatives. Because accounting methods differ widely and hundreds of factors have a bearing on system costs, cost data available from different public and private sources are not easily comparable. The model calculates the costs of various management methods under a variety of different demographic and economic situations. The model is not designed to determine the ''optimal'' system configuration. Its results thus depend on local or site-specific details. OTA, therefore, has not used the model to provide generic comparisons of the costs of different management methods. Instead, the model is used to show the effects of changing key parameters on system costs. All costs are reported in 1988 dollars unless otherwise noted.

The base case for all analyses with this model includes the following conditions:

- a municipality with a population of 500,000,
- 75 percent of the population lives in single-family housing,
- residential waste generation is 2.4 pounds/person,
- commercial waste generation is 1.2 pounds/person,
- commercial collection is paid for by the commercial generators, and
- all facilities are designed to accommodate commercial waste.

In the model, the landfill is assumed to be state-of-the-art, with leachate and methane collection systems, liner systems, and monitoring wells. Land costs are relatively low, $1,500 per acre, and transport distance from collection point to the landfill averages 15 miles. The cost includes closure and post closure expenses.

The incinerator included in the model's calculations uses advanced pollution controls (i.e., wet scrubber and baghouse filter) and generates electricity, which is sold at a rate of $0.06 per kWh. Ash is disposed of in a monofill with a double composite liner system and a leachate collection system. The incinerator produces ash equal to 23 percent by weight of the waste burned. Residential wastes not sent to the incinerator include major appliances, tree stumps, and tires; these wastes are sent to the MSW landfill.

Table 2-1—List of Cities and Counties Surveyed

West:
Seattle, WA
King County, WA
Yakima, WA
Marion County, OR
Portland, OR
San Francisco, CA
Davis, CA
San Jose, CA
Los Angeles, CA

Rocky Mountain/Southwest:
Denver, CO
Boulder, CO
Livingston (Park County), MT
Pocatello (Bannock County, ID
Albuquerque, NM
Phoenix, AZ
Prescott, AZ
Austin, TX
San Antonio, TX
Tulsa, OK

Midwest/Central:
Minneapolis, MN
Chicago, IL
Carbondale, IL
Kalamazoo, MI
Springfield, MO
Waukesha County, WI
Cincinnati, OH

Southeast:
Tampa (Hillsborough County), FL
St. Petersburg (Pinellas County), FL
Fairfax County, VA
Shreveport, LA
Charlotte (Mecklinburg County), NC
Chattanooga, TN
Atlanta (Gwinnett County), GA

Northeast:
Philadelphia, PA
Newark (Essex County), NJ
Cape May County, NJ
Boston, MA
Marblehead, MA
Somerville, MA
Hamburg, NY
New York, NY
Delaware Solid Waste Authority, DE
Montgomery County, MD
Peterborough, NH

budget allocated to MSW appears to be less than 10 percent of the total.[8]

It is not surprising, therefore, that this budget item has received little attention in the past. In fact, only about half of the communities responding to OTA's survey charged fees directly related to trash disposal costs; the rest paid the collection and disposal bill out of general revenues, bond funds, grants, or some combination of these, somewhat obscuring MSW costs within the budget. The level of detail in the survey responses indicated that the various components of MSW costs generally are not well-defined or accounted for. This was particularly true of recycling programs. Of the 19 respondents who reported having curbside residential recycling programs, only 8 had cost information on the program and 11 had an estimate of the amount of materials collected. Only six communities were able to report a separate quantity of commercial waste recovered, although it is likely that commercial materials recovery occurs everywhere. Ten of the respondents incinerated a portion of their waste, but only half of those were able to report on the capital and operating costs associated with that option. (All reported a tipping fee, however.) Other analysts seeking detailed MSW cost information from local governments have noted similar difficulties (1,6,13,15).

Although it is not possible to draw broad conclusions from a small survey, the responses indicated that definitions and calculation methods are a problem, particularly for recycling. With few exceptions, most of the communities were not aware of the

[8]The Bureau of the Census reports data on State and local government expenditures in the "Government Finances" series (16). Solid waste expenditures are reported as "sanitation other than sewerage." Average expenditures as reported in this source (1986, latest available) are actually less than 3 percent of total expenditures.

amounts of materials being recovered from the MSW stream or the costs associated with that recovery. As recycling programs become more elaborate, and more commonplace, it is likely that communities will become more aware of their costs and effectiveness. Such an awareness is essential for the efficient operation of a recycling program as well as a MSW management system.

Results from the ESRG model indicate that a variety of factors can have a significant impact on the overall costs of MSW management. For each MSW management method, factors were chosen for sensitivity tests based on the generally accepted knowledge about the important cost factors. Although an exhaustive sensitivity analysis was not performed for each MSW management method, OTA attempted to analyze those factors that most often come into question when discussing costs. For example, OTA examined the sensitivity of landfill costs to pollution controls and transportation distances and of recycling costs to the efficiency of the collection process and the prices obtained for the materials collected. Figure 2-1 shows the variation in estimated costs for different MSW management scenarios. Table 2-2 describes each major scenario tested. As shown in the figure, if existing landfill costs are relatively low (scenarios 1-1b) then system costs will increase when additional MSW management alternatives are added. Under the model's assumptions, waste-to-energy incineration (scenarios 2 and 2a) increases costs by a larger percentage than recycling programs (scenarios 3-3d and 4-4c). However, when landfill costs are extremely high (scenario 6), the addition of alternative management methods (in this case, recycling and composting) can reduce overall system costs by avoiding the costs of landfilling (scenario 6a).

This model, while of course used here in hypothetical scenarios that are not applicable to any particular community, highlights the importance of close attention to every cost element of the MSW management system. The more complex the system, the more important it becomes to carefully monitor each cost component. Increased complexity brings increased costs. Improved cost accounting methods

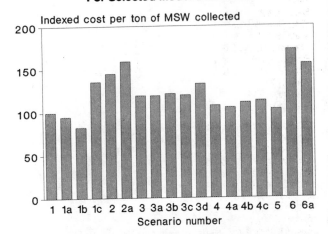

Figure 2-1—Comparison of MSW Management Costs For Selected Model Scenarios

Indexed cost per ton of MSW collected

Scenario number

NOTE: The cost of scenario 1 is set equal to 100, and then the costs of all other scenarios are compared with scenario 1. For example, the cost of scenario 2 is approximately 45 percent greater than the cost of scenario 1. See Table 2-1 for scenario descriptions.

SOURCE: Office of Technology Assessment, 1989.

and practices can help all municipalities control the expected further rise in MSW management costs.

Landfills: The Indispensable Option

Survey Results

Landfills were relied on exclusively by 13 of the survey's respondents.[9] Per-capita solid waste management costs were relatively low for these respondents, ranging from $6 to $44 and averaging about $25. On a per ton basis, solid waste management costs were below $70 for these communities, and landfill disposal costs accounted for 12 percent or less of the total.

Fifteen communities provided capital or operating cost information on landfills. Operating costs ranged from less than $3 to about $40 per ton, with 13 of the 15 respondents reporting costs of $12 or less; capital costs were not reported on a comparable basis. The highest operating costs were for a landfill with state-of-the-art technology, including a triple liner system, leachate collection systems, and monitoring wells.

---

[9]This figure includes those respondents who reported that materials recovery occurred, but who did not know the exact amount. Some of these communities have recycling programs, but it was assumed that because they are not aware of the amounts recycled, then recycling is not considered a part of their MSW management strategy and no costs are incurred.

Table 2-2—Description of Model Scenarios for MSW Management Cost Comparisons

Scenario	Collection	Incineration	Recycling	Composting	Transfer	Landfilling
1	Mixed waste in 31 cu. yd. packer trucks 75% single family 25% multi-family					Land cost = $1,500/acre. Includes composite liner, leachate collection, monitoring wells, methane collection, methane price = $3/1,000 cu.ft.
1a	Same as 1 except: 50% single family 50% multi-family					Same as 1
1b	Same as 1					Landfill has no pollution controls, no methane recovery
1c	Same as 1				Transfer with 50-mi. shipping distance. Shipping cost = 20 cents/ton mile	Same as 1
2	Same as 1	1,100 TPD capacity site-erected mass burn (cost $122 million). 100% of energy used to generate electricity. Electricity price = 6 cents/kWh. Ash disposed in monofill with double composite liners, leachate collection, monitoring wells				Materials landfilled include discarded appliances, stumps, tires
2a	Same as 1	Same as 2 except electricity price = 3 cents/kWh			Same as 1	Same as 2
3	Mixed waste same as 1. Recyclables collected in 15 cu.yd. capacity compartmentalized vehicles. Residential diversion rate = 4.5%		Curbside separation; Recyclables placed pre-sorted at curb in stackable containers. Materials in single family collection: ONP, glass, Al. Multi-family collection: ONP. Processing facility densifies and bales materials for market			Same as 1
3a	Same as 3 except Residential diversion rate = 6.8%. Participation and capture rates = commingled program		Same as 3			Same as 1
3b	Same as 3 except Residential Diversion Rate = 6.4%. Participation and capture increase by 10 percentage points		Same as 3			Same as 1

3c	Same as 3 except for deposit on glass, Al, and plastic beverage containers that removes them from waste stream. Waste generated is reduced by 6%	Same as 3		Same as 1
3d	Same as 3 except number of stops per hour for collection of recyclables is cut in half	Same as 3		Same as 1
4	Mixed waste same as 1. Recyclables collected in 20 cu. yd. closed body recycling vehicle. Residential diversion rate = 8.0%	Comingled recyclables placed in single 0.06 cu. yd. container at curb. Materials in single family collection: ONP, glass, Al, Fe. Multi-family: ONP, glass, Al, Fe. Processing facility separates, cleans, densifies, and bales materials for market		Same as 1
4a	Same as 4 except participation and capture increase by 10 percentage points. Residential diversion rate = 10.9%	Same as 4		Same as 1
4b	Same as 4 except for deposit on Al, glass, and plastic beverage containers that removes them from waste stream. Waste generated reduced by 6%	Same as 4		Same as 1
4c	Same as 4 except number of stops per hour for collection of recyclables is cut in half	Same as 4		Same as 1
5	Mixed waste same as 1. Yard waste collected separately in same collection vehicle. Residential diversion rate = 9.3%		Leaves and other yard waste placed in paper bags at curb 20 weeks per year. Composting done at 2 10-acre sites. Compost sold for $3/cu. yd.	Same as 1
6	Same as 1	Same as 4	Same as 1c	Land cost = $5,000/acre. Double capital costs and most operating costs
6a	Mixed waste same as 1. Recyclables same as 4 except participation and capture = 90%. Yard waste same as 5. Residential diversion rate = 33.0%	Same as 4	Same as 1c	Same as 6

KEY: TPD = tons per day; kWh = kilowatt hour; Residential diversion rate = percentage of residential waste diverted from landfill by recycling or composting; ONP = old newspaper; Al = aluminum; Fe = iron and steel.

SOURCE: Office of Technology Assessment, 1989.

Model Results

To understand how different factors affect landfill costs, OTA used the ESRG model. Model results are for a hypothetical scenario only and should not be interpreted as applying to any particular community's situation. Costs can vary considerably, depending on site-specific conditions. As noted above, OTA's intent is to indicate the types of factors that are likely to have the greatest bearing on costs, not to predict actual costs in real situations. For this analysis, OTA examined the effects of collection efficiency, transportation distances, and pollution controls on landfilling costs.

For a landfill-only scenario (scenario 1), the model calculated a total cost to the municipality for MSW collection and disposal of $58 per ton, $18 of which is accounted for by landfill disposal costs.[10] By comparison, if the landfill used by the municipality had no pollution controls, total cost would have been $48 per ton, with only $8 attributed to landfill disposal (scenario 1b). In scenario 1, therefore, pollution controls add about $10 to the cost per ton of waste disposed. The $8 estimated for landfill disposal with no pollution controls is consistent with the landfill operating costs reported in OTA's survey, most of which were less than $12.

It is interesting to note that the addition of a transfer station (where MSW is transferred from packer trucks to larger trucks or rail cars for long hauls) to the hypothetical municipality, with a subsequent 50-mile transport distance to a landfill, increased total MSW costs to $78 per ton, with $20 per ton added for the transfer and long haul (scenario 1c). Thus the model indicates that the need for transfer and long haul adds more to the landfilling cost than pollution controls. In the real world, these transfer and transportation costs may even be greater in some situations. For example, one community in OTA's survey reported an expected combined transfer and disposal cost of $44 per ton to support a new transfer, transport, and landfill system (not including collection) to be developed to dispose of waste 140 miles away (7).

Collection costs, the other main component of OTA's model scenario, are primarily dependent on truck and operator efficiency. Ignoring problems caused by congestion and one-way streets common in high population density areas, the model indicates that collection can take place more efficiently in those areas. For example, by changing the hypothetical municipality from 75 to 50 percent single-family housing, overall residential collection costs were reduced by about $3 per ton (scenario 1b). By comparison, a 50-percent increase in stops per hour, which could be realized with higher density housing, reduced average residential collection costs by $8 per ton. The model also estimated that a similar cost saving ($7 per ton) will result if the amount of trash picked up per stop is increased by 50 percent.

Incineration and Landfilling

Survey Results

Incinerators were used by 12 (30 percent) of the survey respondents to dispose of anywhere from 6 to 90 percent of their waste; detailed information was provided for only 10 of these sites. In communities with operating incinerators, per-capita MSW management expenditures ranged from $21 to $82, and averaged $46. Total MSW management costs per ton, available for only 4 of the 12 municipalities, ranged from $77 to $230 per ton. The share of these total costs attributed to incinerator operation ranged from 17 to 55 percent.

Capital and operating cost information on incinerators was available for 6 of the 12 communities. Operating costs ranged from $18 to $50 per ton, and capital costs ranged from $3 million for a 72-ton-per-day (TPD) modular incinerator to $80 million for a 1,200-TPD mass burn incinerator. The average tipping fee for the five operating incinerators for which that information was reported was $31. Two of the incinerators increased tipping fees by about $10 per ton after the survey was completed. One increase was in response to lower-than-expected revenues from the sale of steam generated at the plant.

In addition to these existing incinerators, four respondents are in the process of building new incinerators, all of which are expected to be operational by 1991. Two reported expected tipping fees

---

[10]This estimate is consistent with other recent landfill cost estimates. For example, one study (3) estimated total landfill costs for a state-of-the-art landfill at $11.25 per ton in 1986 dollars. This study also estimated that landfill development cost $4.23 per ton in 1975 and will cost $18.30 per ton in 1990.

in the $75 to $80 range in the first year; no information was available for the other two.

In general, the capital costs reported in OTA's survey were within the range of published data. The 1986-87 Resource Recovery Yearbook (4) reported adjusted capital costs (in 1986 dollars) of advanced-planned and existing incinerators ranging from $250,000 to $429 million, and averaging $58 million. Capital costs of modular plants were reported as below $10 million (1986 dollars). Average operating and maintenance costs were reported in the Yearbook as $22 per ton, which is within the range of OTA's survey results.

In OTA's survey, only six of the communities using incinerators reported on revenues from energy generation; the two newest incinerators generated electricity, and four others generated steam. Revenues from the sale of this energy averaged about $10 per ton of waste incinerated per day.

The amount of ash generated from these incineration facilities ranged from 11 to 31 percent by weight of the MSW burned, and averaged 20 percent. Ash disposal costs were reported for only three incinerators and varied widely (i.e., $4.50, $28, and $49 per ton).

Of 12 communities using incinerators, 9 reported materials recovery from some type of recycling program (including 2 recovering metals from incinerator ash). Five recovered less than 5 percent from the waste stream, three recovered between 10 and 20 percent, and one recovered 34 percent.

Model Results

The cost of building and operating an incinerator are dependent on the same factors affecting the cost of any large industrial facility—materials, engineering, labor, and financing. One of the most attractive and different features of modern incinerators, however, is that they can recover and sell energy. Although a multitude of factors can affect the costs of incineration, the revenues from electricity sales are often considered one of the most important factors in the viability of an incinerator operation. This analysis of incinerator costs therefore focuses on changes in electricity revenues.

Using the assumptions described in box 2-B, the model calculated the costs for a site-erected mass burn incinerator, an ash monofill, and an MSW landfill. In this hypothetical scenario (scenario 2), 13,000 tons of residential waste are sent to the MSW landfill, compared with 214,000 tons in the landfill only scenario. The use of the incinerator reduced the amount of waste landfilled by 74 percent (even accounting for the ash landfilled) and increased system costs by 45 percent.

Given these assumptions, the model calculated a total MSW system cost of $83 per ton of residential waste collected. The capital cost of the incinerator was $121.8 million (with a capacity of 1,100 TPD), and net operating costs (including debt service, ash disposal, and accounting for electricity revenues) amounted to $45 per ton of waste burned. Electricity revenues amounted to $10 million annually.[11] On a percentage basis, collection costs accounted for 48 percent of total MSW system costs, incineration accounted for 51 percent, and MSW landfilling accounted for 1 percent.

To determine the sensitivity of system costs to electricity revenues, the electricity rate received by the incinerator in the model scenario was cut by half, to $0.03 per kWh (scenario 2a). The model estimated that electricity revenues were reduced to $5 million annually, and net operating costs for the incinerator increased from $45 to $61 per ton of waste burned. The drop in electricity revenues caused a substantial increase in the estimated cost of incineration per ton of residential waste collected, which jumped from $43 to $58 and thus accounted for 63 percent of total system costs. Total system costs estimated for this scenario increased to $92 per ton of residential waste collected, compared with costs of $83 per ton under the original incineration scenario.

As mentioned above, construction costs for new waste-to-energy facilities have been reported to reach $400 million or more for large facilities (3,000 TPD). Research undertaken for the model indicates that significant economies of scale do not exist for these facilities—the capital and operating cost per ton is relatively constant over a range of capacities. This has also been reported by other investigators (5). However, running a plant below its operating

---

[11] This estimated revenue was significantly higher than the energy revenues reported in the survey on a per ton of waste burned per day basis (i.e., $25 per ton per day compared with $10 per ton per day).

capacity could increase per ton costs substantially because the fixed costs that must be covered, regardless of throughput, are a large proportion of total costs. The costs presented here only represent a reasonable hypothetical plant; financing mechanisms, as well as local economic conditions, might produce significantly different costs.

Materials Recovery: The Moving Target

The characteristics of existing community recycling programs are as varied as the communities themselves. Thus it is difficult to generalize about the elements of a successful recycling program. The success of a recycling program, more aptly called a materials recovery program, can be as dependent on geography and demographics as it is on choosing the right collection equipment.

Early experience with intensive community recycling programs shows that the education and income level of the population can be positively related to participation rates (11). This finding is supported by pilot programs in a low-income community in Illinois (14) and in several areas in Rhode Island (8). OTA's survey did not collect demographic information, and it therefore has not verified these conclusions regarding the effects of education or income on recycling programs.

Other factors also have an impact on the success of recycling programs. Convenience and consistency are both crucial to maintain high citizen participation; therefore, weekly curbside recyclable pickup on the same day as trash pickup is likely to result in higher materials recovery than monthly pickup on a separate day or a drop-off program (10). The number of separations required of the resident can also affect recovery rates. Fewer separations require less space at the residence for storage and can reduce collection time for pick-up crews, a crucial factor in the recycling cost equation. In addition, how commercial establishments and high-density apartment buildings are handled greatly affect a program's overall success.

The commitment of governments to recycling also affects the recycling rate; mandatory recycling programs achieve better recovery rates than voluntary, although exceptions do exist (10). Similarly, municipally provided recycling bins and good public outreach programs both can have positive effects on recovery rates (14).

Survey Results

Respondents to OTA's survey reported a variety of recycling programs; however, 6 of the 41 specifically reported that no materials were reclaimed from their MSW and 11 reported having no formal recycling program. Of the remaining 24 communities, 5 had mandatory curbside recycling and 15 had voluntary curbside programs. Another 4 cities planned to start voluntary programs in the near future. Drop-off programs were reported in 26 communities, and buy-back programs were reported in 18. In addition, 19 communities had white goods recycling programs, 19 had composting programs, 13 had household hazardous waste collection programs, 10 had tire collection programs, 13 had some type of battery collection program, and 21 had waste oil programs. At least one-third of these programs were privately operated, which is no doubt one of the major reasons that information is sparse on the amounts of materials collected.

Only about 10 communities were able to report information on materials collected and revenues obtained from the sale of recyclables. The materials collected and number of programs in which they are included were as follows:

Aluminum	10
Glass	10
Newspaper	9
Steel	8
Corrugated	4
Office paper	3
Mixed paper	3
PET	3

Revenues for materials showed surprising variation. For example, 1988 aluminum revenues varied from $12 per ton for aluminum commingled with glass (paid by intermediate processor), to $1,075 per ton for aluminum collected in a curbside separation program, to $1,300 per ton for aluminum sold by a drop-off center, to a projected $1,340 per ton for aluminum collected in a commingled program and processed in an intermediate processing facility. Flint glass revenues for drop-off programs varied from $20 to $60 per ton.

Consumers sometimes can leave separated materials at igloos or other containers placed in conspicuous areas by the community or firm running a recycling program. These drop-off programs do not pay consumers for the materials, unlike buy-back programs.

For the curbside recycling programs, reported operating costs minus materials revenues varied from $26 to $110 per ton, and averaged $62 per ton. Interestingly, both the least expensive and the most expensive of these programs was a voluntary commingled collection program. Trash collection and disposal costs for those communities with curbside recycling programs ranged from $44 to $220 per ton, and averaged $98 per ton. Per-capita MSW expenditures for these communities averaged $42.

Information on other types of recycling programs was sparse. One drop-off center reported operating costs, net of revenues, at $32 per ton for 1986. One buy-back center reported operating costs after revenues of about $25 per ton. In many instances, the costs reported were only rough calculations because detailed statistics are often not kept. Sometimes the processing of recyclables is contracted out, and the contracting community does not require the processor to provide detailed reports on materials sold and revenues generated. Also, definitions of what is to be included in the recycling cost calculation vary by community. As a result, these reported costs must be viewed with caution. They are provided to indicate the range of variation that can be encountered in communities with different recycling scenarios.

Model Results

OTA's model can provide some insight into the specific cost components of a recycling program. In terms of economics, the success of recycling programs depends primarily on the efficiency of the collection process, the level of participation by residents, and the prices obtained for the materials collected. Using the ESRG model, each of these elements can be examined separately to determine its effects on recycling costs.

Collection efficiency depends on the number of set-outs (i.e., MSW pick-up sites) that can be served per hour and how often the collection truck must return to the unloading area. Factors determining set-outs served per hour include truck design, number in crew, housing density, traffic congestion, and road conditions. Factors affecting the frequency of return trips include family size, waste generation rate, recovery rate, and the mix of recyclable materials.

Curbside Collection of Separated and Commingled Materials—The first general scenario for recycling used in the model was a curbside separation program serving the community outlined in box 2-B. The materials included in the single-family housing program were newspapers, glass containers, and aluminum containers. Newspapers also were collected in multi-family housing areas. The materials collected in the program were assumed to be processed to a limited extent at a central facility sized to process commercial recyclables as well. However, the municipality in the scenario did not pay for collection and processing of the commercial recyclables. All MSW not recovered for recycling was sent to a landfill for disposal.

The model calculated costs on a systems cost basis—all per-ton costs were figured on total residential MSW collected. Because the community in this example paid for collection, processing, and landfilling, it is appropriate to spread all the costs over the total amount of waste that must be managed. In this example, the community collected 214,314 tons of MSW, of which 9,691 tons were recovered for recycling (4.5 percent of residential waste collected) (scenario 3). Using the accounting method described above, the model estimated that the total MSW management cost per ton of material collected amounted to $68.81, of which trash collection accounted for 58 percent, landfilling for 25 percent, recyclables collection for 16 percent, and recyclable processing for 1 percent. An additional scenario was created in which participation and capture rates for the materials collected were set to equal those assumed for a curbside commingled program (i.e., they are somewhat higher). The amount of recyclables collected in this version was 14,638 tons (scenario 3a). The model estimated that total system costs in this scenario were reduced slightly to $68.69 per ton of material collected, with the major savings resulting from the increased diversion of material from the landfill and the lower total landfilling cost.

Another scenario was created to model a curbside commingled recycling program (scenario 4). This program was assumed to have higher participation and capture rates than the original curbside separation scenario, because fewer separations are required; materials prices were assumed to be the same. Materials collected from both single and multi-family households included newspaper, glass, aluminum, and ferrous containers, which were assumed to be processed in a materials recovery facility. In this scenario the community also collected a total of 214,314 tons of MSW, but 17,236 tons were recovered for recycling (8 percent of residential waste collected). The total MSW management cost for this scenario was estimated by the model to be $61.82 per ton, of which trash collection accounted for 62 percent, landfilling for 28 percent, recyclables collection for 9 percent, and recyclable processing for 1 percent. The increased recycling efficiencies in this scenario compared with the curbside separation scenario are realized by more productive collection of recyclables—more material is collected per stop, with no decrease in pickups per hour. Overall system costs for recyclables collection in this scenario were estimated at about half those for the model's curbside separation recycling scenario.

One important component of the total cost of any collection system, according to the model, is the time required for a fully loaded vehicle to unload and return to the collection route. For example, increasing the distance the commingled collection vehicle traveled to drop off recyclables from 5 to 10 miles increased recyclables collection costs by an estimated 2 percent. Much more important, however, is the number of pickups that the collection vehicle is able to make in a fixed time period (21). Reducing recyclables pickups per hour by one half (while holding the amount of recyclables picked up per household) increased overall system recyclables collection costs by an estimated 57 percent for the hypothetical commingled program (scenario 4c) and by 71 percent for the curbside separation program (scenario 3d).

According to the model, participation and capture rates also affect the efficiency of a recycling program. Increasing participation and capture rates by 10 percentage points resulted in a 21 percent decrease in collection costs per ton of recyclables collected for the curbside separation program (scenario 3b) and in a 25 percent decrease for the commingled program (scenario 4a). Again, the increased productivity of the collection vehicle was responsible for the cost savings.

The revenues obtained from the sale of the recyclables are also an important factor in recycling program costs. Using the model's basic scenarios, revenues from residential recyclables amounted to $591,000 for the curbside separation program and to

$1,047,000 for the commingled program. When materials prices in the model were cut in half, revenues also declined by half. For the curbside recycling processing facility, this caused an increase in net processing costs from $14.67 per ton of recyclables processed to $45.16 per ton. For the commingled recycling materials recovery facility, net processing costs increased from $8.10 per ton of recyclables processed to $38.47 per ton. In terms of total system costs, the effect was less, but still significant. Total system costs per ton of waste collected increased by 2 percent ($1.38) in the curbside program and by 4 percent ($2.44) in the commingled program. Total system costs were more affected in the commingled program mainly because larger amounts of materials were processed. In general, the model indicates that the proportional effect of decreased prices on system costs will increase as the amount of material recycled increases.

Beverage Container Deposits and Residential Recycling—One often-asked question is, how will beverage container deposit systems affect the economics of municipal recycling programs? To analyze this question, a scenario was created to simulate the effects of requiring a deposit on all glass, aluminum, and plastic beverage containers, assuming that this resulted in the capture of 80 percent of those containers. Given the waste composition assumed in the model, an estimated 40 percent of all the glass containers, 60 percent of all aluminum containers, and 40 percent of all plastic containers were recovered in the deposit system and were not available for curbside recycling or trash collection. The scenario changes the waste stream because deposit items do not enter it and thus the waste stream was only 94 percent as large as in the original scenario. This change had effects on both curbside and commingled recycling programs.

Because deposit systems reduce the amount of materials collected for recycling, the cost efficiency of municipal recycling programs is diminished. The collection cost per ton of recyclables collected in the model's curbside separation program increased by 23 percent when a deposit system was operating (scenario 3c). The net cost of materials processing increased by more than 200 percent with the deposit system as a result of both decreased efficiency of equipment use and decreased revenues. For the

commingled recycling program, the collection cost per ton of recyclables collected increased by 13 percent and the net cost per ton for materials processing increased by more than 400 percent with the deposit system (scenario 4b). On a system cost basis the deposit system increased overall costs per ton by 0.3 percent for the curbside separation recycling scenario and by 3 percent for the commingled recycling scenario.

One of the most important factors affecting these costs is aluminum revenues. Because aluminum revenues are potentially the biggest profit earner for most processing facilities because of their high value per ton, including aluminum beverage containers in the deposit system sharply reduces the revenues of those facilities. In its beverage container redemption system, California has dealt with this problem by allowing the processing facilities to receive the redemption value for the containers they collect to augment their revenues. In addition, their system includes a processing fee that must be paid by the manufacturer of the product to ensure that recycling can be carried out economically (ch. 8).

The overall effect of a deposit system on the costs of MSW management is to reduce total costs (but not necessarily per-ton costs) to the public sector because less waste is generated that must be managed by the municipality. The costs of managing the used beverage container portion of the waste stream is transferred to the consumer, the retailer, and the beverage industry. (In the California example, the State government incurs some costs in administering the program.) OTA did not attempt to determine what those costs are and how they compare with the costs to the municipality of managing used beverage container wastes.

Separate Collection and Composting of Yard Waste—Composting is another MSW management method that has received increased attention and has been included with many recycling programs. The composting scenario analyzed by the model included the collection of residential leaves, grass clippings, and small brush (scenario 5). This scenario assumed that the waste was set out in paper bags and picked up by trash collection vehicles on a separate route; the compost facility was assumed to be centrally located and to sell the compost for $3 per cubic yard; the participation rates for the program were set at 70 percent for leaves and 50 percent for grass and brush; and capture rates were 80 percent for both. Using these assumptions, the model estimated that the yard waste composting program collected 19,855 tons each year, about 9 percent of the residential waste stream.

The total cost per ton of residential waste collected for this configuration was $59.27, about 2 percent more than the total cost per ton for the landfill only scenario. Collection was a major factor in the costs of the composting program. For the paper bag composting program, collection cost about $40 per ton of yard waste collected and processing cost only about $4.50 per ton of yard waste collected. On a system cost basis, the composting program amounted to only about 7 percent of the total cost per ton of waste collected. According to the model, composting programs will have a similar effect on a system that includes a recycling program.

Recycling and Composting in a Community With High Landfill Costs—Different scenarios must be compared carefully because many assumptions must be made to run the model. Changing these assumptions can result in very different cost configurations. OTA attempted to choose realistic assumptions but they were not necessarily representative of the entire range of possibilities. Many communities, of course, will differ from these assumptions. One clear difference may be landfill costs because the model used relatively low landfill costs in its base scenarios.

To examine the effects of high landfill costs, OTA created another scenario that increased land costs from $1,500 to $5,000 per acre, substantially increased most capital and operating costs, and added a transfer station with a 50-mile haul to the landfill (scenario 6). This scenario increased total system costs to $99 per ton of waste collected for a MSW management system with a transfer station and landfill only, compared with the original landfill only scenario cost of $58 per ton. The landfill and transfer costs amounted to about 60 percent of total system costs in this high cost scenario.

In another run of the model, the high landfill cost scenario was modified to add a commingled recycling program and yard waste composting in addi-

tion to the transfer station and landfill (scenario 6a). This scenario made very optimistic assumptions about the success of the recycling and composting programs. Participation and capture rates equaled 90 percent for both, resulting in 33 percent of the waste stream being diverted from the transfer station and landfill. Avoiding this costly part of the MSW management system for this large a portion of the waste stream decreased total system costs to $90 per ton of waste collected.

CHAPTER 2 REFERENCES

1. Bishop, R., Willard Bishop Consulting, Ltd., personal communication, 1989.
2. Ganotis, C.G., and Hopper, R.E., "The Resource Recovery Industry," *Environmental Science and Technology*, 10(5):425-429, May 1976.
3. Glebs, R.T., "Landfill Costs Continue To Rise," *Waste Age*, pp. 84-93, March 1988.
4. Government Advisory Associates, Inc., *1986-87 Resource Recovery Yearbook* (New York, NY: 1987).
5. Institute For Local Self Reliance, *Garbage Disposal Economics: A Statistical Snapshot* (Washington, DC: 1987).
6. Institute For Local Self Reliance, *Costs of Recycling Programs* (Washington, D.C.: April 1989).
7. Johnson, B., "Portland: First In the West To Send Waste Long Distance," *World Wastes* 31(10):21-26, October 1988.
8. Keller, J., "Curbside Recycling in RI Communities," Presentation at Rutgers University, Nov. 17,1988, revised Dec. 27, 1988.
9. New York State Commission on Returnable Containers, *Final Report of the Temporary State Commission on Returnable Beverage Containers* (Albany, NY: Mar. 27, 1985).
10. Peters, A., and Grogen, P., "Community Recycling: What Is Working Best?" *BioCycle* 29(5):32-36, May/June 1988.
11. Pieters, G.G.M., and Verhallen, T.M.M., "Participation in Source Separation Projects: Design Characteristics and Perceived Costs and Benefits," *Resources and Conservation* 12:95-111, 1986.
12. Rozett, J.M., "Resolving the "Bottle Bill" Controversy: The Role of Policy Analysis in Decision Making," *New York Case Studies in Public Management*, no. 14, November 1984.
13. Schall, J., Energy Systems Research Group, Inc., personal communication, 1989.
14. Snow, D., and Johnson, C.A., "Trends in Collecting Recyclables," *Waste Alternatives—Recycling*, pp. 40-48, June 1988.

15. Snow, D. "Trends In Collecting Recyclables," *Waste Reduction and Recycling*, pp. 58-65, Summer 1989.

16. U.S. Department of Commerce, Bureau of the Census, *Government Finances in 1985-86*, Government Finances GF-86, No. 5 (Washington, DC: November 1987).

17. U.S. Department of Commerce, Bureau of the Census, *Statistical Abstract of the United States, 1988*, 108th ed. (Washington, DC: U.S. Government Printing Office, December 1987).

18. U.S. Environmental Protection Agency, *Multimaterial Source Separation in Marblehead and Somerville, Massachusetts*, SW-822 (Washington, DC: December 1979).

19. Waste-to-Energy Report, "Wall Street Sees Waste-To-Energy Market Likely To Grow Even In Recession," *Waste-To-Energy Report*, pp. 1-2, Jan. 27, 1988.

20. Waste-to-Energy Report, "Project Growth Seen Slowing, Operating Services Continuing to Expand," *Waste-to-Energy Report*, pp. 1-2, Mar. 9, 1988.

21. Willard Bishop Consulting, Ltd., *Efficiency Guidelines For Curbside Recycling Programs* (Barrington, IL: February 1989).

Generation and Composition of MSW

CONTENTS

Boxes

Figures

Tables

Generation and Composition of MSW

INTRODUCTION

The rate at which the Nation creates municipal solid waste (MSW; see box 3-A) is increasing because our total population is growing, as is the average amount that each person throws away. It is important to have adequate information about MSW generation if we are to make wise decisions about future waste management. In addition, knowing what products and materials comprise MSW and evaluating trends in their use can guide efforts to reduce MSW generation and toxicity.

To help understand MSW generation and composition, the Environmental Protection Agency (EPA) commissioned Franklin Associates to develop and periodically update a model providing a general picture of the quantities and composition of MSW generated each year, and how different products (including but not limited to packaging) contribute to the waste stream. Although the EPA/Franklin model is not without limitations, it is the only available major source of national-scale MSW information.

The national scale of the model presents some problems, however. Community officials who must make decisions about how to manage MSW need data on local conditions and generation. Indeed, recognizing that the generation and composition of MSW varies greatly among communities, EPA and Franklin Associates repeatedly caution against using the model's national estimates for State and local planning.

This chapter discusses the EPA/Franklin model's estimates of national MSW generation rates. It then examines estimates of the average amount of MSW generated in different communities as a way to illustrate variability among communities. The local per-capita rates are compared with some State and National estimates to indicate the problems that can arise in estimating these rates at any level. Information on the relative weights and volumes of different materials and products in MSW also is reviewed. Finally, information on the types of chemical substances in MSW is reviewed briefly.

MSW GENERATION ESTIMATES

National Estimates From the EPA/Franklin Model

The best national estimates of MSW generation are derived from the EPA/Franklin model. This model was first developed in the early 1970s and it is periodically updated (10). Box 3-B includes a brief description of the model and some of its limitations.

According to the model, 158 million tons of MSW were generated in 1986; by the year 2000, MSW generation will reach 193 million tons, an increase of 22 percent in 14 years (10).[1] For comparison, at least 250 million tons of hazardous waste are generated annually, and the amount of nonhazardous industrial solid wastes is even greater. The model may underestimate total MSW generation somewhat, however, because some local data suggests that per-capita generation rates may be greater than those estimated by the model (see "Per-Capita Generation Rates" below).

The model's conclusion that MSW generation has grown and will continue to grow is significant. There are two primary reasons for this growth—increases in total population and increases in the average amount of MSW generated

---

[1]These numbers refer to the weight of "gross" discards, that is, the total amount generated. The model's estimates of past and future generation have been revised periodically. For example, in 1979 the model estimated that MSW discards for 1977 were 136 million tons, while in 1986 the model estimated that discards for 1977 were 122 million tons (8). Adjustments are to be expected with any model as its assumptions and data inputs are refined over time. In this model, for example, adjustments have been made for food and yard wastes, based on additional field sampling data, and to correct for moisture loss in sampling these wastes (12). More recent estimates, however, are generally presented with fewer qualifiers (such as a range of estimates).

per person (the per-capita rate). Population growth appears to be the more important factor. From 1970 to 1986, the U.S. population increased by 18 percent while MSW as estimated by the model increased by about 25 percent. This suggests that about 70 percent of the growth in total generation is attributable to population growth and about 30 percent is the result of increased per-capita generation.

Per-Capita Generation Rates

Any community planning to develop MSW management capacity (whether for recycling, landfilling, or incineration) must know what types and quantities of MSW it is producing, both currently and in the future. Projections to determine management capacity needs often are calculated on the basis of the average amount of MSW generated by each person (i.e., per-capita rates). However, as the following discussion shows, standardized sampling methods need to be developed so that communities can make reasonable estimates.

Estimates of Per-Capita Rates

OTA obtained sample information on MSW generation rates from 28 cities and 9 counties (table 3-1).[2] This table should *not* be used to rank cities and counties in terms of MSW generation because of problems with the comparability and consistency of the data. For example, communities gather data on different portions of MSW. Some communities probably included items such as construction and demolition debris, even though asked not to do so; others were not sure what portions of MSW were included in their data.

Furthermore, the estimates presented in any given study can differ from other investigators' estimates for the same area. Some variability in per-capita MSW estimates is to be expected. Some of the variability stems from actual local and/or seasonal differences in waste streams, or from demographic and socioeconomic factors. However, variation also can be attributed to different definitions and sampling methods (23, 29). One study in Brevard County, Florida, attempted to evaluate definition differences (21). According to county records, the total per-capita generation rate for all waste materi-

---

Box 3-A—Defining MSW

MSW is defined here as post-consumer solid wastes generated at residences (e.g., single-family units and apartment buildings), commercial establishments (e.g., offices, retail shops, restaurants), and institutions (e.g., hospitals, schools, government offices). These wastes may be categorized as either materials or products:

- *Materials*
  —paper, yard waste, food waste, glass, ferrous and non-ferrous metals, plastics, textiles, rubber, wood, management residues (e.g., incinerator ash, some recycling residues).
- *Products*
  —durable goods (e.g., appliances, furniture, tires);
  —nondurable goods (e.g., magazines, tissue paper, clothing, motor oil, small plastic products, batteries, household cleansers);
  —containers (e.g., cans, bottles, boxes) and packaging/wrapping (e.g., made of paper, paperboard, plastic, glass, metals, ceramics, wood).

Defining MSW is not always straightforward, as different people will often include different materials and products. These ''gray areas'' can add confusion to MSW debates. As defined here, for example, MSW does not include automobile bodies, demolition and construction debris, municipal wastewater or drinking water sludges, and ash from industrial boilers. Some municipalities are responsible for managing these items, and some of the materials are discarded into MSW landfills. As a result, some observers may consider the first two items in particular (i.e., auto bodies and construction debris) to be components of MSW. These differences must be recognized when data from different reports are compared, especially with respect to waste generation and recycling rates.

In addition, industries generate nonhazardous process waste and ''small quantity generators'' produce hazardous wastes that often are discarded in landfills along with MSW (ch. 7). Although OTA does not consider these wastes to be MSW per se, their management in this manner can pose potential risks for human health and the environment (e.g., groundwater and surface water contamination) and cause problems for MSW managers.

---

[2]This sample is not random. Cities and counties were selected to represent large and small communities from all regions of the country (see chapter 2 for more details).

Box 3-B: The EPA/Franklin Model

The EPA/Franklin model uses a "materials flow" methodology to estimate MSW generation—it traces the flow of materials from production, through consumption, and on to disposal. The model begins with information about the historical production and consumption of materials and products (e.g., using data from the Department of Commerce and trade associations). These data are converted to waste generation estimates using assumptions about losses of materials in manufacturing, lifetimes of materials and products, recycling rates, and effects of imports and exports. Values are adjusted for products destroyed in use (e.g., cigarette paper) or diverted from the waste stream for long periods (e.g., library books). For materials like food and yard waste, values are based on sampling data from a range of sources.

Because the model relies on this "materials flow" approach, it generally does not use data measured at the points of generation (i.e., households, offices, stores) or management (i.e., landfills, incinerators, recycling facilities). Thus, the model does not predict how much the residential, commercial, and institutional sectors contribute to MSW, nor whether the generated waste actually ends up in recycling facilities, incinerators, or landfills.

What Does the Model Include and Exclude?

Some components of MSW are not included in the model, such as liquids, some packaging, and some nondurable items. According to the model's developers, these components might add 5 percent to the total estimates (12).

Liquids—One missing category identified by EPA and Franklin is liquids, including things such as inks, motor oil, paints, toiletries, and medicines. For the personal care products, the model only accounts for empty containers, and assumes that all contents are consumed or vaporized or that residuals are deposited into sewer systems. Motor oils are not included because about 60 percent of discarded motor oil is assumed to be recycled, leaving only about 660,000 tons ending up in landfills or incinerators (8, 9). For printing inks, about 825,000 tons were produced in 1987, of which perhaps 50 percent end up in MSW (26).[1] Including both inks and motor oil in the model would increase MSW by about 1 percent. Taken separately, this number is small, but it does indicate that the combination of several unaccounted-for waste categories could raise the estimated MSW rate by several percentage points. In addition, these types of products are often considered to contribute potentially toxic substances to MSW.

Packaging—Most packaging on imported goods is not accounted for, although the model does account for glass containers (e.g., for wine and liquor). One packaging company official estimates that the amount of imported packaging (e.g., glass, corrugated boxes, and other materials) amounts to about 2.5 million tons per year (2).

Miscellaneous Nondurables—This category includes disposable products such as diapers, foam cups, home-use bags and wrap, and trash bags. The amount discarded in 1986 was estimated to be about 2.8 million tons per year (10). Recent data suggest this estimate may be low. For example, diapers alone make up about 1 percent by weight of the material excavated from several landfills, equivalent to about 1.5 million tons per year.

Imported and Exported Products—This category needs additional study (13) because several imported and exported products are not accounted for:

- major appliances—only the estimates for microwave ovens account for imports and exports, because only this type of product had a relatively large portion of imports (i.e., net imports exceeding 5 percent of domestic shipments before 1984) (13); increases in imports of other appliances will not be reflected in MSW estimates for some time, since these products have lifetimes of up to 20 years;
- containers—only imports/exports of empty glass containers and glass bottles containing alcoholic beverages are counted; no adjustments are made for steel containers or aluminum containers and packaging;
- miscellaneous durable and nondurable goods;
- subassembled items—imported items for which final assembly occurs in U.S. plants (e.g., in the electronics industry), and exported parts for assembly abroad with the final product being reimported (e.g., the apparel industry), are not included; and
- goods and packaging carried by international travelers—the net difference between goods and packaging carried in by U.S. residents who travel abroad (12 million in 1986) (38) and goods carried out by visitors from other countries is not included.

[1]Although some ink used on products would end up as MSW, some weight loss due to evaporation of solvent-based inks is expected. In addition, waste ink used by printers would end up in cleaning solvents (most of which would be disposed of into sewer systems) or cleaning rags (which would be sent to commercial laundries).

als delivered to landfills was estimated to be 8.5 pounds per day. However, only 3.9 pounds per day was considered to be MSW as defined by the EPA/Franklin model. In this case, then, potential discrepancies among different estimates are caused primarily by the use of different definitions.

Even given these problems, the data in table 3-1 still are useful to illustrate that per-capita MSW generation varies widely among different cities and communities, in this survey between about 2 and 9 pounds per day. The data also can be compared—taking into account all the previously expressed caveats—with national estimates of per-capita generation. For instance, the average per-capita residential MSW generation in table 3-1 is 2.6 pounds, while the average per-capita generation for all MSW (i.e., residential, commercial, and institutional waste) is 4.5 pounds. In contrast, the EPA/Franklin model estimates that each person in the United States generated 3.6 pounds of MSW per day in 1986 and will generate 3.9 pounds per day in 2000. After accounting for recycling, the EPA/Franklin model estimated that the per-capita rate for the remaining discards was 3.2 pounds per day in 1986 and would be about 3.5 pounds per day in 2000 (10).

Problems in defining and differentiating MSW also appear in data collected at the State level. For example, OTA compiled MSW estimates available from 15 States that include over one-half of the U.S. population and calculated a per-capita rate of over 6 pounds per day. However, the utility of these data is questionable because State records generally do not differentiate between MSW and other commonly landfilled wastes (e.g., demolition and construction waste) (12).

Thus, the definition of MSW is an important issue to consider when evaluating estimates of local MSW generation. If decisionmakers need information on all the types of solid wastes that might need management (e.g., including construction and demolition debris), then the more encompassing per-capita estimates may be valid. On the other hand, if what is needed is information specifically about MSW as defined in this report, then these estimates are less useful than information about the generation of specific components of MSW (e.g., paper, plastics,

and yard wastes). Information about individual components can be quite useful to communities trying to implement a strategy based on materials management (ch. 1). In either case, much more information is needed about the amounts and ultimate deposition of MSW and of materials such as construction and demolition debris.

The essential problem is that there is no standardized definition of what constitutes MSW, as well as no standardized methodology for collecting data on its generation (19). Each State and locality defines MSW differently and thus collects different statistics. If the data include wastes such as construction and demolition debris, they are difficult for planners to use. Because there is no standard way of classifying materials, many studies include categories such as "not elsewhere classified" or "other."

Another problem with available MSW data is that few studies have estimated the relative portions of MSW contributed by the residential, commercial, and institutional sectors. Yet this information has important implications for local MSW management. For example, curbside separation programs may be best suited for areas with a high proportion of single-family dwellings. Some studies include only residential wastes, while others include some or all of an area's commercial, institutional, and industrial wastes (table 3-1). Based on data in table 3-1 (and given the definitional problems), the **residential** MSW in the sampled localities ranged between 26 percent and 76 percent of total MSW, with an average of 48 percent.

In addition, some local studies have not fully accounted for potential changes in the per-capita rate and have made future projections solely on the basis of expected population growth. In one study, for example, the per-capita rate was held constant, and recycling (including composting) and modular incinerators were assumed to be flexible enough to handle any growth in per-capita rates that might occur (33). In another study, the per-capita rate was estimated to grow by 0.34 percent per year to 2000 and then was held constant beyond 2000, with no explanation as to why the rate should be constant after that time (17).

Table 3-1—Selected Examples of MSW Generation Rates in U.S. Cities and Counties[a]

City/county	Amount of MSW (× 1,000 tons)	Type[b]	Percentage residential[c]	Per-capita rate (pounds per day)
Albuquerque, NM.	310	all	46	4.3
Austin, TX.	178	?		2.1
Bannock County, ID.	65	all	50	5.5
Boston, MA.	550	all	45	5.0
Charlotte, NC.	225	R,C		3.3
Chattanooga, TN.	286	all	58	9.4
Chicago, IL.	2,200	R	50	4.0
Cincinnati, OH.	213	R		3.2
Denver, CO.	275-500[d]	all		3.1-5.7
Fairfax County, VA.	1,039	?		7.5
Gwinnett County, GA.	386	all	76	6.7
Hamburg, NY	4	all		2.1
Hillsborough County, FL.	535	all	38	3.7
King County, WA.	1,300	all		5.1
Los Angeles, CA.	1,432	R		2.4
Marblehead, MA.	19	all		4.6
Marion County, OR.	216	?		5.7
Minneapolis, MN.	160	R		2.5
Newark, NJ.	325	R,C		5.4
New York, NY.	7,500	?		5.8
Park County, MT.	12	all		7.3
Peterborough, NH.	3	all		3.3
Philadelphia, PA.	1,700	all	51	5.8
Phoenix, AZ.	1,200	all		7.0
Pinellas County, FL	1,160	?		7.5
Portland, OR.	335	R		3.9
Prescott, AZ.	52	?		5.7
San Antonio, TX.	880	?		4.9
San Francisco, CA.	967[d]	all		7.2
San Jose, CA.	635	all		4.8
Seattle, WA.	687	all	36	7.7
Shreveport, LA.	307	all	26	7.8
Somerville, MA.	36	all		2.2
Springfield, MO.	200	all		7.8
Tulsa, OK.	240	R,C		3.6
Waukesha County, WI.	296	all	45	5.5
Yakima, WA.	17	R		1.9

[a]These data are from a survey of local solid waste management officials conducted by OTA from November 1988 to March 1989. Respondents were asked not to include construction/demolition debris, but some were unable to provide differentiated data.
[b]R = residential; C = commercial; I = institutional.
[c]For localities collecting all types of MSW and differentiating among residential, commercial, and institutional MSW.
[d]Includes both city and county.

SOURCE: Office of Technology Assessment, 1989, after K. Cox, *Background Data on Municipal Solid Waste: Generation, Composition, Costs, Management Facilities, State Activities* (Takoma Park, MD: 1989)

How Fast Is the Per-Capita Rate Changing?

Although the national per-capita estimates are imperfect, they still provide useful approximations of how fast average per-capita generation rates are changing. Thus, acknowledging that the EPA/Franklin model may somewhat underestimate total MSW generation, it is estimated that for the years 1970 to 1986 the per-capita MSW generation rate has increased 0.7 percent annually (10).[3]

Factors Affecting Per-Capita Generation

Reasons for the increasing per-capita rate are not clear, because many factors can affect per-capita generation in a given area. These include socioeconomic status, household size, demands for convenience, and degree of urbanization. As the following discussion indicates, this area clearly warrants additional research.

[3]Comparable data from earlier years are not available.

Socioeconomic Status—The effect of socioeconomic status on MSW generation is uncertain. A mid-1970s study in Texas found that income and urbanization were correlated with per-capita generation rates (34). Another study based on data from the 1970s reported that lower income households produced more residential wastes per capita than higher income households, although not for certain components such as newspapers and yard wastes (30).

One clear trend is that people in the United States have become more affluent, on average. One indicator is that disposable personal income, expressed in constant 1982 dollars, grew from $8,134 to $10,947 per person between 1970 and 1986 (38). This implies that we are buying more products of **all** types, which probably has at least some effect on MSW generation.

Household Size—Based on some limited studies, smaller households appear to produce more MSW per household member (28), and smaller households are becoming more common (38). From 1960 to 1986, the number of persons per household declined from 3.3 to 2.7 persons. This is partly because the portion of single people (i.e., never-married, widowed, or divorced adults) in the population increased from 28 percent in 1970 to 37 percent in 1986; during the same period, the number of single parents increased from almost 9 million to almost 13 million. These trends, in turn, contributed to an increase in the number of households from 63 million in 1970 to 88 million in 1986 (38).

Demand for Convenience—One common assumption is that demand for convenience has increased as the number of single-person households and the proportion of women in the work force have increased, and that this has led to a proliferation in packaging and single-use products. However, this may not be true. The proportion of packaging in MSW actually has been declining, at least by weight (see ''Product Categories'' below). Single-use products are very common, but whether they have a significant impact on increasing per-capita rates is unclear. However, convenience as a substitute for time has certainly led to an increase in single-serving food products. Packaging for this type of product tends to be more wasteful than for goods with multiple servings (ch. 4).

Degree of Urbanization—The majority of the U.S. population lives in urban areas; the proportion increased from 64 percent in 1950 to 74 percent in 1980 (38). However, rural areas may have lower per-capita generation rates, at least for some MSW components. For example, one study of MSW composition in a rural county concluded that the paper fraction was lower than expected because newspapers were published weekly instead of daily and because used paper tended to be consumed as fuel (27).

Comparison With Other Countries

In general, citizens in the United States often are considered to be more wasteful than citizens in other industrialized countries. However, the magnitude of any real differences is uncertain, as are the reasons for any such differences.

Most of the data on MSW generation in other countries suffer from the same problems as U.S. data, particularly differences in what types of wastes are included in the estimates. In addition, in the United States, post-consumer materials that are recycled are generally included in the definition of MSW. In contrast, Japan and many European countries (e.g., Sweden, Germany, Switzerland, Norway, and Spain) define MSW as including only those materials sent to waste treatment or disposal facilities (18). This definition excludes materials recovered for reuse, under the premise that these materials are resources and not wastes.

Data collection and record-keeping also vary widely among countries. In Japan, for example, almost all municipalities weigh MSW to the gram at landfills and incinerators; furthermore, data on the amounts of combustible and noncombustible materials are collected by each municipality and published annually by the national government (18). This type of effort is rarely practiced in the United States. National governmental agencies rarely aggregate the data that do exist. In most countries (including the United States), information on recycling is generally collected only for specific materials, by the industries that rely on those materials.

Nevertheless, some data from countries that tend to have better record-keeping are presented in table 3-2. Based on data from the early to mid-1980s, for example, citizens in Sweden generated an estimated

**Table 3-2—Estimated MSW Generation Per Capita
in Different Countries
(pounds per person per day)**

Country	Gross discards[a]	Net discards[a]	Year
United States	3.6	3.2	1986
West Germany	—	2.6	1984/85
Sweden	—	2.4	early to mid-1980s
Switzerland	—	2.2	—
Japan	—	3.0	1987

[a]Gross discards refer to total MSW generation; net discards refer to MSW remaining after recycling but prior to energy recovery.

SOURCES: Franklin Associates, Ltd., *Characterization of Municipal Solid Waste in the United States, 1960 to 2000 (Update 1988),* report prepared for U.S. EPA, Office of Solid Waste and Emergency Response (Prairie Village, KS: 1988; G. Goosmann, "Municipal Solid Waste Management in the Federal Republic of Germany," pp. 118-126 in *A Selection of Recent Publications (Vol. 2),* Federal Environmental Agency, Federal Republic of Germany (Berlin: 1988); A.J. Hershkowitz, *International Experiences in Solid Waste Management,* contract prepared for U.S. Congress, Office of Technology Assessment (Elmsford, NY: Municipal Recycling Associates, Inc., 1988; Clean Japan Center, "Waste Volume on the Rise and Measures Against It," *Clean Japan* 14:6-10, February 1989.

2.4 pounds of MSW per person per day after recycling. Japan appears to have had a similar rate at that time (18), but recent data indicate that the per-capita rate after recycling rose to 3.0 pounds per day in 1987 (5). This is close to the EPA/Franklin estimate for the United States of 3.2 pounds per day after recycling. Another study reported that several nations (e.g., Australia, Bulgaria, Canada, Hungary, New Zealand, Republic of Korea) have generation rates similar to the U.S. rate, at least based on data from the United Nations, the Organisation for Economic Cooperation and Development, and national sources (47); however, OTA considers comparisons based on these data to be tenuous because of differences in definitions and data collection techniques. No studies have been conducted to critically analyze the relationships between per-capita generation rates in different countries and per-capita income, land availability, social attitudes, or other factors.

MATERIAL AND PRODUCT COMPOSITION

Most MSW data are collected in terms of weight of materials (e.g., tons of glass), not in terms of volume or toxicity. Weight data are useful for some decisions; for example, prices for secondary materials are usually based on weight. On the other hand, weight data do not necessarily provide the information needed to assess the feasibility of waste reduction, particularly to help identify appropriate targets for government action. The volume of materials that enter the MSW stream often is a more useful measure for decisionmakers, particularly when assessing collection capabilities and landfill capacity.

Estimated MSW Proportions By Weight

Materials

Studies around the country show similar trends in the proportions of some materials in MSW. For example, data compiled by OTA from nine studies and another compilation of data from 40 studies (table 3-3) indicate that the largest categories of materials in MSW by weight are paper and yard wastes. However, there is substantial variation within the studies. In the nine studies, the proportion (by weight) of yard waste ranged from 0 to 39 percent, while paper ranged from 30 to 46 percent. Data from the 40 studies show similar trends, although the ranges were somewhat higher for paper (36 to 55 percent). These data also are similar to estimates from the EPA/Franklin model.

Some of the wide variation in the estimates can be attributed to differences in sampling and definitions. Other possible causes of variability include location, socioeconomic conditions, and seasonality. The effects of seasonality, for example, are most visible in the amount of yard waste produced, particularly in the Northeast and other temperate zones. The greatest amounts of yard waste in these areas are generated in the fall or spring, and the least in winter (ch. 5). Seasonal tourism and the presence of nonresident university populations also influence the seasonal composition of MSW.

The EPA/Franklin model estimates the weights of different materials in MSW (table 3-4). These estimates must be interpreted carefully (box 3-B), but they do indicate that the proportions of materials and products present in the MSW stream after recycling have changed over time. Paper and plastics, in particular, have been increasing rapidly.

Even after recycling, paper and paperboard products comprise the largest category of materials in

Table 3-3—A Comparison of Estimated Percentages of Different MSW Components, by Weight

Material	9 studies		40 studies	
	Mean	Range	Mean	Range
Total paper	38.8	29.9-45.9	46.7	36.5-54.7
Newspaper	6.3	4.3-8.1		
Corrugated	7.9	4.7-13.1		
Mixed	21.9	19.6-25.2		
Magazines	0.7	0.7		
Total metal	4.9	1.5-9.4	8.5	4.0-14.7
Aluminum cans	0.9	0.8-1.0		
Miscellaneous aluminum	0.7	0.2-1.6		
Other non-ferrous	1.0	0.0-3.4		
Total glass	7.8	3.6-12.9	8.4	6.0-13.7
Glass containers	6.4	6.1-6.6		
Total plastic	8.8	5.3-12.6	5.3[c]	2.0-9.0[c]
Plastic film	3.1	3.1		
Plastic containers	0.9	0.7-1.0		
Yard waste	18.2	0.0-39.7	9.5	0.4-25.0
Food waste	14.7	1.3-28.8	7.8	0.9-18.2
Wood	2.6	0.7-8.2	2.6	0.5-7.0
Textiles	3.4	1.1-6.2	3.3	0.7-5.0
Rubber	0.4	0.0-1.0	—[c]	—[c]
Diapers	—	—	1.5	0.5-2.9
"Not elsewhere classified"	9.2	3.8-16.6	—	0.5-10.0

[a]Compiled from 9 local studies that did not have more than 10 percent (on average) of MSW in the "Not elsewhere classified" category (6).
[b]Compiled from 40 local studies (20); whether these studies were selected on the basis of the same criteria (i.e., less than 10 percent in the "Not elsewhere classified" category) as the 9 local studies is unknown.
[c]Plastic, rubber, and leather were compiled together.

SOURCE: Office of Technology Assessment, 1989, after K. Cox, *Background Data on Municipal Solid Waste: Generation, Composition, Costs, Management Facilities, State Activities* (Takoma Park, MD: 1989); R.N. Kinman and D.K. Nutini, "Household Hazardous Waste in the Sanitary Landfill," *Chemical TIMES & TRENDS* 11:23-29 and 39-40, 1988.

Table 3-4—EPA/Franklin Model Estimates, by Percent by Weight, of Materials and Products in MSW[a]

	After materials recovery			Before materials recovery
	1970	1986	2000	1986
Materials:				
Paper and paperboard	32.4	35.6	39.1	41.0
Glass	11.1	8.4	7.1	8.2
Metals	12.0	8.9	8.5	8.7
Plastics	2.7	7.3	9.2	6.5
Rubber and leather	2.7	2.8	2.3	2.5
Textiles	1.8	2.0	2.0	1.8
Wood	3.6	4.1	3.6	3.7
Food wastes	11.4	8.9	7.3	7.9
Yard wastes	20.6	20.1	19.0	17.9
Miscellaneous inorganics	1.7	1.8	1.9	1.6
Products:				
Durable goods	12.4	13.6	13.6	
Nondurable goods	19.0	25.1	28.1	
Containers and packaging	34.9	30.3	30.0	
Other wastes (food, yard, miscellaneous inorganics)	33.6	30.8	28.1	

[a]In all cases, estimates are for percentages **before** energy recovery during incineration; materials recovery refers to recycling of secondary materials.

SOURCE: Franklin Associates, Ltd., *Characterization of Municipal Solid Waste in the United States, 1960-2000*, report prepared for U.S. Environmental Protection Agency, Office of Solid Waste and Emergency Response (Prairie Village, KS: 1988).

MSW (36 percent). The second largest category by weight is yard and food wastes, which represent over one-fourth of MSW, although this proportion has declined steadily. Plastics comprise a small but rapidly growing category, with an expected increase to 9 percent by 2000. Glass, non-ferrous metals, rubber, textiles, leather, and wood have changed little over time, while ferrous metals have declined somewhat. Among recycled materials, paper and paperboard represented over 86 percent of the total amount recycled in 1986; glass and metals represented 6.5 and 5.9 percent, respectively (10).[4]

Product Categories

The EPA/Franklin model also provides estimates of the proportions of different *product* categories, again after recycling (table 3-4). In 1986, durables (e.g., furniture, tires, appliances) were estimated to make up about 14 percent of MSW, nondurables (e.g., newspapers, tissue paper, clothing) about 25 percent, and containers and packaging, the largest category, about 30 percent (which represents a slight decline from estimates for earlier years). According to these data, the nondurables category has grown the fastest, and it will continue to grow through 2000, although at a slower rate. The percentages of durable products and of containers and packaging are expected to remain about the same through the year 2000.

These major categories also are broken into smaller subdivisions (9, 10). Among *containers and packaging*, for example, beverage containers made up between 6 and 11 percent of MSW by weight in 1986, with glass containers being the largest component. These data were analyzed to estimate the percent change of a product in MSW for a given period. Product categories expected to increase by more than 10 percent through 2000 include:

- furniture and furnishings,
- books and magazines,
- office papers and commercial printing papers,
- beer and soft drink cans,
- aluminum foil and closures,
- corrugated boxes, and
- plastic containers and other plastic packaging.

Photo credit: Office of Technology Assessment

The second largest category by weight of materials in MSW is yard waste (including leaves, grass clippings, weeds, and prunings). Properly controlled composting of the wastes yields high-quality compost. Separating yard wastes from other MSW helps reduce leachate generation at landfills and nitrogen oxide formation at incinerators.

For example, beer and soft drink aluminum cans are expected to increase by 14 percent from 1990 to 1995, while all aluminum is expected to increase by 18 percent. Additional information on product trends, including containers and packaging, is discussed in chapter 4.

Technological changes have caused some change in the nature of MSW. For example, the portion of office and commercial printing papers (e.g., computer printouts, high-speed copier products, direct mail advertising) in MSW increased from an estimated 3.4 percent in the 1970 to an estimated 6.1 percent in 1984 (9). Plastic containers and packaging and disposable packaging associated with micro-

---

[4]Other data tend to confirm these trends. One study reported data based on over 2000 samples of **residential** MSW collected from Tucson households between 1978 and 1988 (44). Plastics increased from 5 percent to 10 percent by weight, presumably reflecting the increasing use of plastics in place of glass and metal containers. Paper increased from 30 percent to 35 percent, possibly reflecting increases in direct mail advertising and home computer output.

Photo credit: W. Johnson

Corrugated cardboard comprises about 7 percent of MSW by weight. About 40 percent of the waste paper exported from the United States is old corrugated cardboard, in high demand because of its strong softwood fibers.

Photo credit: Office of Technology Assessment

Newspapers comprise the largest single item excavated from landfills. About 23 percent of the newsprint manufactured in the United States is made from waste paper, almost all of which is old newspapers (ONP). Supplies of ONP have increased because more communities now collect it, but by late 1988 some communities were paying waste paper dealers to take collected ONP.

wave frozen foods also have increased (43). In some cases, these have replaced other previously used materials, so the net change is difficult to assess. Within the containers and packaging category, for example, heavier materials such as glass and steel have been declining, in part because they are being replaced by lighter materials such as aluminum and plastics. The use of multi-material packaging (e.g., multiple layers of plastics, foil, paper; metal caps; and paper or foil labels) also appears to be increasing. This type of packaging tends to be lighter than previous packaging, but it also is harder to recycle.

Landfill Excavation Data by Volume and Weight

Information from landfill excavation studies being conducted by "The Garbage Project" at the University of Arizona (29, 35) is significant because it includes data on both the volume and weight of materials, and some of the data illustrate changes in the waste stream during the last 20 years. The data must be interpreted carefully, however. The studies have only been conducted at a few landfills to date. Moreover, the data only refer to the volume and weight of materials present when the landfills were excavated, not to the amounts that originally entered the landfill or that might have been recycled or incinerated instead.

Figure 3-1 presents volume data for different materials excavated from studied landfills. According to the investigators, the major variability in these measurements is within different sections of landfills, not between landfills, regardless of the type of climate (28). This is because the major source of moisture in the studied landfills has been the garbage itself, not rainwater or groundwater.

Paper and paper products have increased steadily and now comprise approximately 55 percent by

Figure 3-1—Average Volume (by percent) of Materials Excavated From Landfills

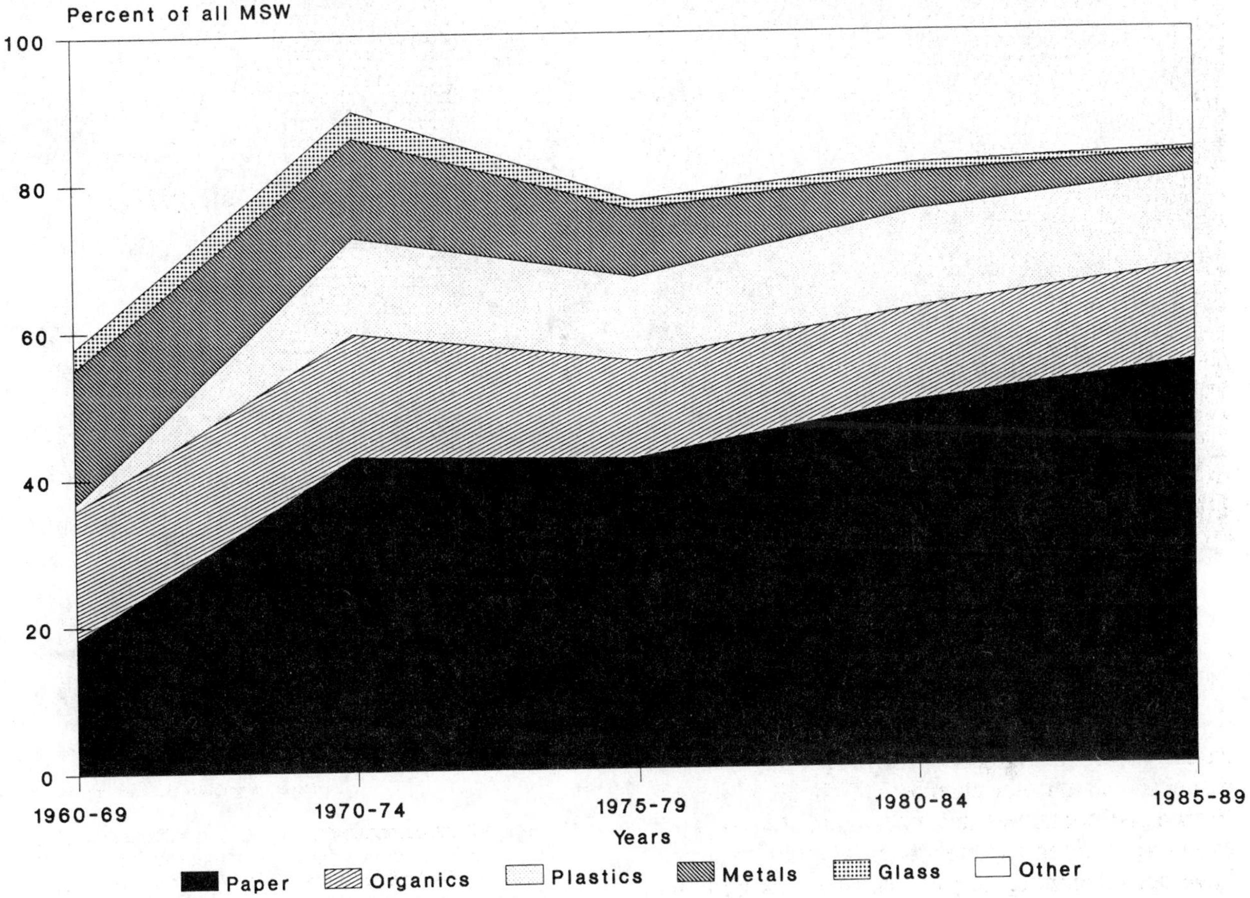

Percent of all MSW

SOURCE: W.L. Rathje, University of Arizona, personal communication, February 1989.

volume (and almost one-half by weight) of the materials excavated (figure 3-1). While the volume of plastics increased in the early 1970s, it has remained essentially unchanged since the early 1970s, hovering around 12 to 13 percent. By weight, plastics comprise about 7 percent of landfilled MSW, thus indicating that they take up more volume than weight measurements alone might suggest. Not surprisingly, denser materials such as glass, rocks, and ferrous metals comprised a smaller percentage by volume than by weight.[5] During the last 20 years, the volume of glass has declined to less than 1 percent. The volume of metals has declined from 18

percent in the 1960s to about 3 percent today; the decline is probably due to use of lighter metals, increased recycling of aluminum beverage cans, and replacement of some metals by plastics. Overall, the weight of MSW may be increasing more slowly than is its volume because of these types of changes (10).

Paper used for packaging has increased steadily to comprise 19 percent of landfilled MSW, and paper used in nonpackaging (e.g., computer paper, printing and writing paper other than newsprint and glossy magazines) has risen to 13 percent (figure 3-2). Newsprint has risen recently to about 18 percent by both volume and weight, and it comprises the largest

[5]The density of some MSW components also is affected by many factors between the points of generation and disposal, including exposure to weather and variation in levels of compaction during handling and transportation.

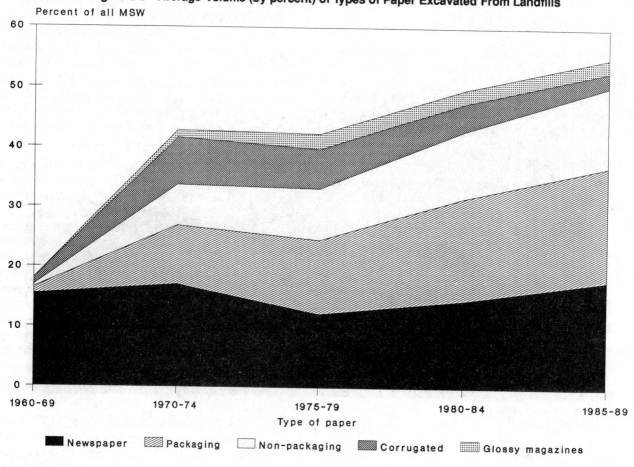

Figure 3-2—Average Volume (by percent) of Types of Paper Excavated From Landfills

Percent of all MSW

Type of paper

Newspaper | Packaging | Non-packaging | Corrugated | Glossy magazines

SOURCE: W.L. Rathje, University of Arizona, personal communication, February 1989.

single-item product in the landfills. In contrast, corrugated cardboard has declined from a peak of 6 percent in the early 1970s to less than 3 percent today.

These landfill excavation studies have generated interesting information about several components of MSW that have drawn public and media attention: plastics, fast-food packaging, and disposable diapers. Aside from finding that the volume of plastics has remained constant since the 1960s, the investigators also found, on the basis of limited sampling, that most plastic beverage containers compress under the pressure of overlying materials. This is different than glass bottles, of which more than half are found intact (28). Although the overall volume of plastics

has remained constant, the relative amounts of film and rigid plastic products have fluctuated, without any discernible trend.

Fast-food packaging comprised only 0.3 percent, by both weight and volume, of the excavated material. Diapers were less than 1.0 percent by volume and by weight, on average. In contrast, a different study indicated that single-use disposable diapers make up 3.5 to 4.5 percent by weight of all MSW generated at residences and up to 2 percent of all MSW (22).[6] This difference may not be surprising, since the materials in the landfill excavations generally represented a combination of residential, commercial, and institutional MSW.

[6]About 18 billion single-use diapers were purchased in the United States in 1988 (22). About two-thirds of a disposable diaper is made of cellulose, a component of wood (and paper) that is degradable under proper conditions; the remainder is mostly plastic (e.g., polyester or polypropylene liners, polyethylene backsheets or outer layers).

CHEMICAL COMPOSITION

Basic Chemical Composition

MSW consists mostly of water, various elements (e.g., carbon, hydrogen, oxygen, chlorine, and nitrogen), and incombustible materials (e.g., glass, metals, ceramics, minerals, clay, and dirt) (16). In addition, various trace metals and organic chemicals can be present, but little aggregated information exists on their concentrations in MSW prior to recycling, incineration, or landfilling.

One chemical of particular concern is chlorine because it can be involved in the formation of dioxins and other chlorinated organics, as well as hydrogen chloride, during incineration (ch. 6). The major sources of chlorine in MSW appear to be paper and plastics. In Baltimore County, Maryland, for example, paper was estimated to contribute 56 percent of the total chlorine in the combustible portion of MSW; in Brooklyn, New York, plastics contributed an estimated 52 percent (4).

Chlorine is used directly to make certain products, such as PVC plastics and insulation and textiles. Chlorine is also used to bleach pulp for papermaking. In the pulping process, chemicals remove roughly three-fourths of the lignin (which makes up about half of wood), and bleaching removes the rest. Elemental chlorine (as a gas) has been the preferred bleaching chemical because it is cheaper, effective in dissolving lignin while maintaining the strength of the pulp, and can achieve higher-brightness paper than alternative bleaches. The alternatives, which include hypochlorite, chlorine dioxide, peroxide, and oxygen, generally are less efficient and more expensive than chlorine gas.

Combustibility

Some components of MSW are combustible—organic materials such as paper, plastics, textiles, rubber, and wood. The organic fraction of MSW was estimated to be about 81 percent by weight in 1986 (10). It appears to be growing slowly, primarily because the portions of paper and plastics in MSW also are growing.

One measure of MSW that is related to combustibility is "higher heating value" (HHV), or the number of Btu of energy that could be produced per unit of MSW. In general, MSW can generate from 4,500 to 6,000 Btu per pound. The average Btu value of MSW may be increasing because both plastic and especially paper, which have increased over the last 10 years, have high Btu values (figure 3-3). Paper wastes comprise a large portion of MSW and thus contribute much of its average total HHV. Food and yard wastes both have low Btu values, while inorganic materials such as metals and glass have no Btu value.

However, MSW is not homogeneous, either in its Btu values or its composition, between different locations or even over short periods at the same location. For example, combustibility can vary drastically because the portion of yard wastes can more than double during certain seasons. Yard wastes have high moisture content and low Btu values, so the overall HHV of the MSW decreases during summer and fall, when large amounts of yard waste are generated. Moisture content is also important because it affects the stability of the combustion process (16) and combustion efficiency during "cold starts" of an incinerator (ch. 6). In addition, evaporating moisture during the initial stages of combustion requires the use of energy and thereby affects operating costs.

Removing particular materials from MSW prior to incineration (e.g., through source separation) can affect combustibility.[7] For example, removing yard wastes and inorganic recyclables such as glass and metals can reduce moisture and increase average HHV. In contrast, removing paper and plastics lowers HHV and increases moisture content. The net effect will depend on exactly what is removed.

Degradation

Some of the materials (e.g., paper and yard wastes) in MSW decompose or degrade, while others do not. In general, the rate of decomposition depends on local landfill conditions, such as temperature, moisture, oxygen levels, and pH (ch. 7). In theory, a large portion of MSW should eventually decompose because it tends to have a high level of degradable carbon. For example, one study estimated that degradable carbon comprised 34 to 59 percent of MSW (24). Another study estimated that

---

[7]The potential trade-offs between recycling and incineration of different materials are also discussed in chapters 1 and 6.

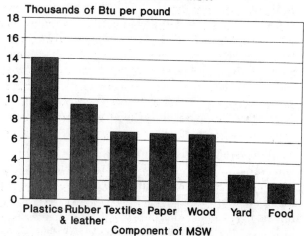

Figure 3-3—Relative Btu Values per Pound for Materials in MSW

SOURCE: Franklin Associates, Ltd., *Waste Paper, The Future of a Resource 1980-2000*, prepared for the Solid Waste Council of the Paper Industry (Prairie Village, KS: December 1982).

paper products and textiles were composed of about 40 percent degradable carbon, while yard and food wastes were composed of less than 20 percent carbon (3).

The landfill excavation study, however, has revealed some interesting insights about decomposition. In these landfills, paper products in particular, but also food wastes, have not degraded rapidly; in fact, it appears that degradation in general may be slow (29). For example, newspapers that were still readable after years of burial were found in all of the studied landfills. Paper and food waste excavated from part of one landfill were in the same condition as similar materials buried 5 to 10 years earlier in another part of the landfill.

Toxic Substances and Household Hazardous Waste

When MSW is landfilled, incinerated, or recycled, some of the composite metals and organic chemicals have the potential to harm public health and the environment (chs. 5, 6, 7). These are often called toxic or potentially harmful substances, although their potential effects on health and the environment depend on rates of exposure and dosage, sensitivity of exposed individuals, and other factors.

Toxic Substances in MSW

Many potentially harmful metals and organic chemicals are components of products and packaging that are used at residences and offices and then discarded as MSW. Available data focus on three metals—mercury, lead, and cadmium. For example, mercury is a component of most household batteries, as well as fluorescent light bulbs, thermometers, and mirrors. Sources of lead include solder in steel cans and electronic components, automobile batteries, paint pigments, ceramic glazes and inks, and plastics. About two-thirds of all lead in MSW (after recycling) is estimated to be from automobile batteries (11). Cadmium is found in metal coatings and platings; rechargeable household batteries; pigments in plastics, paints, and inks; and as a heat stabilizer in plastics. Nickel/cadmium batteries are the largest source, accounting for an estimated 52 percent after recycling, and plastics contribute about 28 percent.

The **noncombustible** portion of MSW is estimated to contain 98 percent of the lead and 64 percent of the cadmium (11). This suggests that separating noncombustible materials from MSW that is to be incinerated would be likely to reduce the amounts of these metals in emissions and ash (see ch. 6). Furthermore, because plastics account for an estimated 71 percent of the lead and 88 percent of the cadmium in the remaining **combustible** portion of MSW, efforts to manufacture plastic products without these metals also might help reduce amounts of these metals in emissions and ash. The toxicity issue is discussed in more detail in chapter 4.

Household Hazardous Wastes

Household hazardous wastes (HHW) are discarded products that contain potentially toxic substances, but that tend to be stored at residences for relatively long periods of time before being discarded.[8] Although there is no standardized definition of what products and materials comprise HHW, they generally include common household items such as cleaning products, automobile products, home maintenance products (e.g., paint, paint thinner, stain,

---

[8]The term ''household hazardous wastes'' is not used here in the legal sense of being a hazardous waste as defined in RCRA, although some of the substances in such wastes may be classified as hazardous in RCRA (see ch 8).

varnish, glue), personal care products, and yard maintenance products (e.g., pesticides, insecticides, herbicides). In most cases these items are not hazardous while in storage, or during use if properly handled, but they may release potentially toxic substances after they have been discarded.

More than 100 substances that are listed as RCRA hazardous wastes are present in household products (table 3-5). The substances include metals (e.g., mercury, lead, silver) and organic chemicals (e.g., trichloroethylene, benzene, toluene, parathion).

Several studies have looked at the amounts of HHW generated. In two communities, Marin County, California, and New Orleans, Louisiana, HHW from single-family dwellings was sorted and weighed (42). Between 0.35 and 0.40 percent of the total MSW was considered hazardous, and each household threw away an average of 50 to 60 grams of HHW each week.[9] Other studies in Albuquerque, New Mexico, and the Puget Sound area in Washington reached similar conclusions: in general HHW comprises less than 1 percent of MSW (25, 41). Data from Los Angeles County, California, Portland, Oregon, and several localities in Michigan indicated that the quantities of actual constituents of concern were even lower, less than 0.2 percent (20). This has led some analysts to conclude that placing HHW in landfills is not a problem (20). However, the extent to which HHW contributes to environmental problems at landfills is unclear. Given the total quantity of MSW generated each year, even the apparently low proportion of 0.2 percent would mean that about 300,000 tons of potentially toxic substances in HHW are discarded each year.[10] Yet, when spread among thousands of facilities, the potential impacts should be lessened.

Data from residences in several areas (Tucson and Phoenix, Arizona; Marin County, California; and New Orleans, Louisiana) have been compiled to indicate which HHW products were most commonly discarded; the data include containers but exclude automobile batteries (45). The largest category was household maintenance products, making up 37 percent by weight. Household batteries contributed 19 percent, cosmetics 12 percent, household cleaners 12 percent, automobile maintenance products 11 percent, and yard maintenance products 4 percent. About 80 percent of the automobile products was motor oil. Socioeconomic status appears to affect the types of HHW generated. Households in higher-income neighborhoods discarded more pesticides and yard products than did lower-income neighborhoods; cleaning materials were more common in middle-income neighborhoods; and automobile maintenance products were more common in lower-income neighborhoods (31, 45).

One study at a California landfill indicates similar trends (20). Two thousand fifty-six containers of HHW (whether empty or with residue) received at the landfill were sorted and counted. Of the six categories of containers, 40 percent had household and cleaning products; 30 percent automotive products; 16 percent personal products; 8 percent paint and related products; 3 percent insecticides, pesticides, and herbicides; and 4 percent were other products considered hazardous.

The effects of a one-day collection program for HHW in Marin County on subsequent generation of HHW raise an intriguing dilemma (31). Two months after the collection day was held, the amount of HHW in the normal MSW pickup was twice as high as it was before the collection day. This suggests that the educational effect of the collection day was short-lived or, as seems more likely, that people did not want to keep HHW around after they learned about it. If the latter proves true, regular collection days would be needed to keep HHW out of the normal MSW collection system. Chapter 8 discusses HHW programs in more detail.

Other Sources of Toxic Substances

Household products and materials in landfills and incinerators are not the only sources of potentially harmful chemicals in MSW. Under RCRA, businesses that generate less than 100 kilograms of hazardous wastes per month are allowed to deposit them in solid waste landfills (including municipal landfills) or have them burned in MSW incinerators (36, 37). These businesses are known as ''very small

---

[9]These data refer to the weight of that portion of the waste that contains the hazardous ingredients, not including contaminated containers or other contaminated articles such as paint brushes and oil-soaked rags. Thus, they probably underestimate total amounts.

[10]Many hazardous household products also are emptied into sewer systems (40). When household cleaners are used, for instance, the product is washed down the drain and ends up in municipal sewage treatment plants.

Table 3-5—Examples of Hazardous Ingredients in Common Household Commodities[a]

Ingredient	Types of products found in
Acetic acid	household cleaners (starch powder), adhesives (microfilm)
Acetone	adhesives (film, microfilm, model, fishing rod, shoe, plastics, fabric, china solvent, canvas), pet maintenance (soaps), cosmetics (nail polish)
Acrotein	pet maintenance
Acrylic acid	adhesives
Aldicarb	pet maintenance
Aldrin	pet maintenance
Aniline	cosmetics (perfume), stain (wood)
Arsenic (III) oxide	paint (non-latex anti-algae)
Arsenic (V) oxide	paint (non-latex anti-algae)
Arsenic acid	pet maintenance
Aziridine	pet maintenance
Benzene	household cleaners (spot remover, degreaser, destainer, oven cleaner), stain, varnish, adhesives, cosmetics (nail polish remover)
Butyl alcohol	engine treatment (degreaser)
Cadmium	household batteries, paints, photographic chemicals
Carbon tetrachloride	household cleaners (degreaser, destainer)
Chloral (hydrate)	cosmetics (hair treatment)
Chlordane	pet maintenance (flea powders)
Chlorinated phenols	paint (latex)
Chlorobenzene	household cleaners (degreaser, destainer)
Chloroform	household cleaners (lipstick spot remover), pet maintenance (mange drug)
Chromium	paint (wood preservative), photographic chemicals
Creosote	pet maintenance (repellant)
Cresol	household cleaners (disinfectant), engine treatment (degreaser)
Cresylic acid	engine treatment (degreaser)
Cyclohexane	adhesives
DDD	pet maintenance (dips)
DDT	pet maintenance
Dibutyl phthalate	paint (non-latex plasticizer), adhesives (builder's, model, vinyl wood glue, thermoplastic, china water emulsion, china solvent), cosmetics (nail polish)
m-Dichlorobenzene	household cleaners (disinfectant)
o-Dichlorobenzene	household cleaners (disinfectant, toilet bowl cleaner)
p-Dichlorobenzene	household cleaners (disinfectant, toilet bowl cleaner, air sanitizer, air deodorant)
1,2-Dichloroethane	household cleaners (rugs, upholstery, tar remover)
1,2-Dichloroethylene	household cleaners (rugs, upholstery), polish (shoe)
2,4-Dichlorophenoxyacetic acid (2,4-D)	pet maintenance, insect repellants
1,2-Dichloropropane	household cleaners (tar remover, wax, wax remover)
1,3-Dichloropropylene	household cleaners (wax)
Dieldrin	pet maintenance
Diethyl phthalate	paint (non-latex plasticizer), adhesives (fabric, metal), polish (metal)
Dimethoate	pet maintenance
Dinoseb	pet maintenance
1,4-Dioxane	adhesives (film)
Disulfoton	pet maintenance
Endosulfan	pet maintenance
Endrin	pet maintenance
Ethanol	household cleaners (dish detergent, disinfectant)
Ethyl acetate	household cleaners (spot remover, degreaser/destainer), paint (lacquer thinners), adhesives (film, leather, fabric, china, model glue), cosmetics (nail enamel)
Ethyl ether	engine treatment (degreaser)
Ethylene dibromide	engine treatment (fuel additives)
Ethylene dichloride	household cleaners (carpet cleaner/deodorizer), engine treatment (degreaser, fuel additives), adhesives (film)
Ethylene oxide (condensate)	household cleaners (disinfectant)
Ethylidene dichloride	adhesives
Formaldehyde	household cleaners (starch, disinfectant, air sanitizer), polishes (shoe, plastic), adhesives (gum arabic, library paste, waterproof glue)
Heptachlor	pet maintenance
Hexachlorobenzene	household cleaners (disinfectant)
Hexachloroethane	insect repellants
Hexachlorophene	cosmetics (cleansing creams, conditioning cream, face mask)
Lead	stain/varnish, automobile batteries, paint

Table 3-5—Examples of Hazardous Ingredients in Common Household Commodities[a]—Continued

Ingredient	Types of products found in
Lead acetate	cosmetics (hair coloring)
Lindane	pet maintenance (soaps, sprays, dips)
Mercury	household cleaners (disinfectant), paint (non-latex anti-algae, latex), household batteries
Mercury fulminate	household cleaners (disinfectant)
Methanol (methyl alcohol)	engine treatment (degreaser, antifreeze/coolant), adhesives (film), household cleaners (rust and ink remover), (degreaser), stain/varnish, cosmetics (nail polish)
Methoxychlor	household cleaners (air sanitizer), pet maintenance (powders, dips, soaps, sprays)
Methylene chloride	household cleaners (air sanitizer, oven cleaner, tar remover), engine treatment (degreaser), paint (anti-corrosion non-latex), stain/varnish, adhesives (air filter, film)
Methy ethyl ketone	household cleaners (degreaser), adhesives (film, microfilm, fishing rod, china (butanone) solvent), cosmetics (nail polish)
Methyl isobutyl acetone	adhesives (china solvent, microfilm)
Methyl methacrylate	cosmetics (nail polish), adhesives (dental plate)
Methyl parathion	pet maintenance
Naphthalene	household cleaners (glass cleaner, carpet cleaner/deodorizer, air sanitizer, air deodorant)
Naphthalene, 2-chloro	household cleaners (glass cleaner)
1,4-Naphthalenedione	household cleaners (glass cleaner)
1,4-Naphthaquinone	household cleaners (glass cleaner)
1-Naphthylamine	household cleaners (glass cleaner)
2-Naphthylamine	household cleaners (glass cleaner)
2,7-Naphthalenedisulfonic acid	household cleaners (glass cleaner)
Nitrobenzene	polish (shoe)
Parathion	pet maintenance
Pentachlorophenol	household cleaners (starch), pet maintenance, adhesives (dental plate), paint (wood preservative)
Phenols	adhesives (gum arabic, dextrin, flexible glue), household cleaners (pine oil, disinfectant), paint
Phenyl mercuric acetate	polishes (shoe), household cleaners (starch, disinfectant)
Phorate	pet maintenance
Phosphoric acid	household cleaners (spot remover, glass cleaner, disinfectant, degreaser), polish (auto)
Phthalates	adhesives (microfilm), polish (metal)
Propane	paint (latex)
Resorcinol	cosmetics (hair coloring and tonics)
Selenium	photographic chemicals
Silver	household batteries, photographic chemicals
Silvex	pet maintenance
Sodium o-phenylphenate	adhesives (library paste)
Sulfuric acid	household cleaners (toilet bowl cleaner)
Sulfuric acid, thallium salt	polishes (metal)
Tetraethyl lead	engine treatment (fuel additives)
Toluene	household cleaners (spot remover, degreaser), lubricating oil (all-purpose, brake/clutch/hydraulic fluid, motor oil), paint (latex, lacquer thinners), adhesives (microfilm, plastic, leather, fabric, rubber), cosmetics (nail polish)
Toxaphene	pet maintenance (dips), insect repellants
1,1,1-Trichloroethane	polishes (general, shoe), adhesives (contact cement), household cleaner (oven cleaner, rugs, upholstery)
1,1,2-Trichloroethane	polishes (shoe)
1,1,2-Trichloroethylene	engine treatment (fuel additive), household cleaners (degreaser/destainer, carpet cleaner/deodorizer, rugs, upholstery)
2,4,5-Trichlorophenoxyacetic acid (2,4,5-T)	pet maintenance
Trichloromonofluoromethane	household cleaners (air sanitizer)
Warfarin	pet maintenance
Xylene	transmission fluid, engine treatment (degreaser), paint (latex, non-latex, lacquer thinners), adhesives (microfilm, fabric), cosmetics (nail polish)

[a]Determination as hazardous based on 40 *Code of Federal Regulations* 261.
SOURCES: Based on U.S. Environmental Protection Agency, *Sources of Toxic Compounds in Household Wastewater*, EPA 600/2-80-128 (Cincinnati, OH: August 1980) (39); D.C. Wilson and W.L. Rathje, University of Arizona, The Garbage Project, personal communication, March 1989 (compilation of data from refs. 15, 32, and 35).

quantity generators'' and include vehicle maintenance shops (which handle lead-acid car batteries
and used motor oil), drycleaners, pesticide application services, and others (10,37). One study estimated that there are about 450,000 very small
quantity generators in the country and that they
generate about 197,000 tons of hazardous waste
annually (1). How much of this waste is sent to
MSW landfills and incinerators is unknown. Even if
all of it is discarded at MSW landfills, it would
represent much less than 1 percent of all landfilled
waste; however, it does contain toxic substances,
and about one-fourth of all MSW landfills accept
such wastes (ch. 7).

In addition, some nonhazardous industrial wastes
are discarded in MSW landfills (ch. 7). Although
most nonhazardous wastes currently are managed
"on-site," pressure to send them to off-site landfills
may increase in the future if regulations guiding
on-site management become more stringent.

It also is important to note that some of the
materials in MSW are not always handled by MSW
management methods. For example, liquid cleansers
may be washed down the drain and into the
municipal sewage treatment system (40). Pesticides
(e.g., from spraying lawns) can be carried by rain
into storm drains, which generally discharge into
surface waters. Pesticides also can be dumped on the
ground or into sewers, or stored at home.

RESEARCH NEEDS

Although this chapter is filled with statistics, the
data base available about MSW is actually quite
limited and quite uncertain. There is general consensus that total MSW generation in the United States
is increasing. But translating this broad conclusion
into guidance for local decisionmakers is difficult.
Communities need better information about local
conditions and better ways to collect that information. The States and the Federal Government could
benefit, too, from better information as they work to
develop wise MSW policies.

Additional research is needed on many topics
related to MSW generation. The Federal Government, for example, could sponsor or conduct
research on many of these topics, including:

- standardized definitions of MSW;

- standardized data collection and reporting
  methods;
- why and how MSW generation and composition vary among communities and in relation
  to demographic and socioeconomic factors;
- amounts and composition of MSW produced
  by residential, commercial, and institutional
  sectors;
- amounts of other nonhazardous wastes sent to
  MSW management facilities (including, but
  not limited to, construction and demolition
  debris);
- the relationship between weight and volume;
- degradation rates in landfills; and
- compilations of existing generation and composition studies.

CHAPTER 3 REFERENCES

1. Abt Associates Inc., "National Small Quantity Hazardous Waste Generator Survey, Final Report,"
   prepared for U.S. Environmental Protection Agency,
   Office of Solid Waste (Cambridge, MA: February
   1985).
2. Alexander, J., James River Corp., personal communication, February 1989.
3. Bingemer, H., and Crutzen, P., "The Production of
   Methane from Solid Wastes," *J. Geophysical Research* 92 (D2): 2181-2187, February 1987.
4. Churney, K.L., Ledrod, A.E. Jr., Bruce, S.S., and
   Domalski, E.S., *The Chlorine Content of Municipal
   Solid Waste from Baltimore County, MD and
   Brooklyn, NY,* National Bureau of Standards report
   NBSIR 85-3213 (Gaithersburg, MD: October 1985).
5. Clean Japan Center, "Waste Volume on the Rise and
   Measures Against It," *Clean Japan* 14:6-10, Febru-
   ary 1989.
6. Cox, K., *Background Data on Municipal Solid
   Waste: Generation, Composition, Costs, Manage-
   ment Facilities, State Activities,* contract prepared for
   U.S. Congress, Office of Technology Assessment
   (Takoma Park, MD: 1989).
7. Franklin Associates, Ltd., *Waste Paper, The Future
   of a Resource 1980-2000,* prepared for the Solid
   Waste Council of the Paper Industry (Prairie Village,
   KS: December 1982).
8. Franklin Associates, Ltd., *Characterization of Municipal Solid Waste in the United States, 1960-2000,*
   Working Papers (Prairie Village, KS: July 11, 1986).
9. Franklin Associates, Ltd., *Characterization of Municipal Solid Waste in the United States, 1960-2000,*
   report prepared for U.S. EPA, NTIS No. PB87-
   178323 (Prairie Village, KS: July 25, 1986).

10. Franklin Associates, Ltd., *Characterization of Municipal Solid Waste in the United States, 1960 to 2000 (Update 1988),* report prepared for U.S. EPA, Office of Solid Waste and Emergency Response (Prairie Village, KS: Mar. 30, 1988).

11. Franklin Associates, Ltd., *Characterization of Products Containing Lead and Cadmium in Municipal Solid Waste in the United States, 1970 to 2000, Executive Summary and Chapter 1,* final report prepared for U.S. EPA, Municipal Solid Waste Program (Prairie Village, KS: January 1989).

12. Franklin, M., Franklin Associates, Ltd., personal communication, Feb. 15, 1989.

13. Franklin, M., Franklin Associates, Ltd., personal communication, Apr. 17, 1989.

14. Goosmann, G., "Municipal Solid Waste Management in the Federal Republic of Germany," pp. 118-126 in *A Selection of Recent Publications* (Vol. 2), Federal Environmental Agency, Federal Republic of Germany (Berlin: 1988).

15. Gosselin, R.E., Smith, R.P., et al., *Clinical Toxicology of Commercial Products* (Baltimore, MD: Williams & Wilkins: 1984).

16. Hasselriis, F., "What's in Our Garbage?" *Waste Alternatives/Waste-to-Energy* 1(2): 74-77, September 1988.

17. HDR Engineering, Inc., "Lake County Solid Waste Management Plan," prepared for Lake County Joint Action Solid Waste Planning Agency, Lake County, Illinois (Omaha, NB: February 1988).

18. Hershkowitz, A.J., *International Experiences in Solid Waste Management,* contract prepared for U.S. Congress, Office of Technology Assessment (Elmsford, NY: Municipal Recycling Associates, Inc., October 1988).

19. Kahn, Z.K., and Sable, E., "Planning a Program to Determine Physical and Chemical Characteristics of Municipal Solid Waste," *Resource Recovery/Cogeneration World* 1:15-18, 1988.

20. Kinman, R.N., and Nutini, D.L., "Household Hazardous Waste in the Sanitary Landfill," *Chemical TIMES & TRENDS* 11:23-29 and 39-40, July 1988.

21. Korzun, E.A., Stephens, N.T., and Heck, H.H., "The Impact of Increased Recycle Rates on Markets for Recycled Paper, Plastic, Metals, Glass, and Rubber in Florida" (Melbourne, FL: Florida Institute of Technology, no date).

22. Lehrburger, C., *Diapers in the Waste Stream, A Review of Waste Management and Public Policy Issues* (Sheffield, MA: December 1988).

23. McCamic, F.W., "Waste Composition Studies: Literature Review and Protocol," prepared for Massachusetts Department of Environmental Management, Bureau of Solid Waste Disposal (Ferrand and Scheinberg Associates, October 1985).

24. Miller, W.C., "Integrating Energy and Materials Recovery in Solid Waste Management Plans: The Importance of Waste Composition Studies," pp. 1-12 in *Proceedings of the 1987 Conference on Solid Waste Management and Materials Policy, Session 4, Vol. 4, Waste Composition Studies,* Feb. 11-14, 1987 (Albany: 1987).

25. Morse, L., "Data," pp. 104-107 in *Summary of the Third National Conference on Household Hazardous Waste Management,* Nov. 2-4, 1988 (Boston, MA: Dana Duxbury & Associates, Inc., February 1989).

26. National Association of Printing Ink Manufacturers, Inc., letter to OTA, Sept. 8, 1988.

27. Northwest Regional Planning Commission, *Burnett County Waste Reduction/Recycling Study* (Wisconsin: 1987).

28. Rathje, W.L., University of Arizona, personal communication, February 1989.

29. Rathje, W.L., Hughes, W.W., Archer, G., and Wilson, D.C., "Source Reduction and Landfill Myths," paper presented at *ASTSWMO National Solid Waste Forum on Integrated Municipal Waste Management* (Lake Buena Vista, FL: July 17-20,1988).

30. Rathje, W.L., and Thompson, B., *The Milwaukee Garbage Project* (Washington, DC: Solid Waste Council of the Paper Industry, 1981).

31. Rathje, W.L., and Wilson, D.C., "Archaeological Techniques Applied to Characterization of Household Discards and Their Potential for Contamination of Ground Water," paper presented at *Third International Symposium on Industrial Resource Management* (New York: Feb. 11-14, 1987).

32. SCS Engineers, *A Survey of Household Hazardous Wastes and Related Collection Programs,* report to U.S. Environmental Protection Agency, Office of Solid Waste, Special Wastes Branch (Reston, VA: 1986).

33. Strand Associates, Inc., "Sauk County Solid Waste Reduction and Recycling Study" (Madison, WI: February 1988).

34. Texas Department of Health, *Solid Waste Management Plan for Texas, 1980-1986, Volume 1—Municipal Solid Waste* (Austin, TX: 1981).

35. The Garbage Project, "The Mullins Dig, An Archaeological Excavation of Three Modern Landfills," working outline (Tucson: University of Arizona, Bureau of Applied Research in Anthropology, 1987).

36. U.S. Congress, Office of Technology Assessment, *Technologies and Management Strategies for Hazardous Waste Control,* OTA-M-196 (Washington, DC: U.S. Government Printing Office, March 1983).

37. U.S. Congress, Office of Technology Assessment, *Wastes in Marine Environments,* OTA-O-334 (Washington, DC: U.S. Government Printing Office, April 1987).

38. U.S. Department of Commerce, Bureau of the Census, *Statistical Abstract of the United States, 1988,* 108th edition (Washington, DC: U.S. Government Printing Office, December 1987).

39. U.S. Environmental Protection Agency, *Sources of Toxic Compounds in Household Wastewater,* EPA 600/2-80-128 (Cincinnati, OH: August 1980).

40. U.S. Environmental Protection Agency, *Report to Congress on the Discharge of Wastes to Publicly Owned Treatment Works,* Office of Water Regulations and Standards, EPA 530/SW-86-004 (Washington, DC: February 1986).

41. U.S. Environmental Protection Agency, *A Survey of Household Hazardous Wastes and Related Collection Programs,* EPA/530-SW-86-038 (Washington, DC: October 1986).

42. U.S. Environmental Protection Agency, *Characterization of Household Hazardous Waste from Marin County, California, and New Orleans, Louisiana,* Environmental Systems Monitoring Laboratory (Las Vegas, NV: August 1987).

43. U.S. Environmental Protection Agency, *The Solid Waste Dilemma, An Agenda for Action,* EPA/530-SW-89-019 (Washington, DC: February 1989).

44. Wilson, D.C., "Ancient Trash, Modern Solid Wastes: An Archaeologist's Perspective on Reuse, Recycling, Waste, and Landfill Degradation," paper presented at *National Solid Waste Management Symposium* (Prescott, AZ: Apr. 10, 1989).

45. Wilson, D.C., and Rathje, W.L., "Quantities and Composition of Household Hazardous Wastes: Report on a Multi-Community, Multi-Disciplinary Project," paper presented at *U.S. EPA Conference on Household Hazardous Waste Management* (Boston, MA: Nov. 2-4, 1988).

46. Wilson, D.C., and Rathje, W.L., University of Arizona, The Garbage Project, personal communication, April 1989.

47. World Resources Institute, *World Resources 1988-89* (New York, NY: Basic Books, Inc., 1988).

Chapter 4

MSW Prevention

CONTENTS

OVERVIEW

The Nation's current concerns about MSW arise from the increased visibility of several related problems: declining landfill capacity, overuse of virgin materials, and the presence of toxic substances in discarded products. One strategy to cope with these problems is to promote "MSW prevention." OTA defines MSW prevention as activities that reduce the toxicity or quantity of discarded products **before** the products are purchased, used, and discarded.[1] Prevention should not be confused with waste management, which occurs **after** MSW is generated (ch. 1). Box 4-A discusses differences between prevention, recycling, and degradability.

There are two basic routes to MSW prevention— manufacturers can change the design of products and the way they are packaged, and consumers can alter purchasing decisions about existing products and the way they use and discard products (figure 4-1).

Two distinct characteristics of MSW need to be kept in sharp focus—toxicity and quantity (figure 4-1). To product manufacturers, reducing toxicity means eliminating or finding benign substitutes for substances that pose risks when they ultimately are discarded as MSW. Reducing quantity means changing the design of a product so that less MSW is generated when the product or its residuals are discarded.[2] From a consumer's perspective, both toxicity and quantity reduction involve deciding to buy products that reflect such changes. Quantity reduction also includes backyard composting of yard wastes (i.e., within a household's property lines), since this eliminates materials that otherwise would be managed by the commercial or public sectors. Reduction also can include reusing an item without changing its form, structure, or function.

The motivation for promoting MSW prevention is strong and simple. The public is increasingly sensitive about potential human health and environmental risks associated with all MSW management methods. Reducing toxicity would make all management methods safer and help restore public confidence in waste management policies and programs. For example, reducing the amounts and types of organic chemicals in materials sent to landfills would mean less air pollution (e.g., from volatile organic chemicals) and less toxic leachate.

Reducing the quantity of discarded materials would mean that the useful life of existing and future waste management facilities could be extended and new replacement capacity could be developed at a slower rate. Currently, however, the amount of MSW generated in the United States increases by about 1 percent each year, a rate of increase that is expected to continue through at least the year 2000 (ch. 3). Overall population growth accounts for about two-thirds of the increase, but the average amount that each person generates (i.e., the per-capita rate) also has increased over the years. At the same time, available capacity for properly managing MSW is declining (chs. 1 and 7).

As reviewed in this chapter, some reductions in MSW toxicity and quantity already have occurred, and many more possibilities exist. With respect to toxic substances, the link between management problems and product design is clear, and manufacturers and EPA need to make stronger efforts to identify and reduce such substances. Identifying these substances and their major sources is not easy, however, especially given difficulties in estimating potential risks (chs. 5, 6, and 7), the thousands of products that are currently in commerce, and the functional purposes of the substances. Nevertheless, when such substances and sources are identified, then the feasibility and costs of developing products

---

[1]EPA uses the term "source reduction" (12, 91).

[2]Throughout this report, OTA's use of the term "products" includes packaging as well. The term "packaging" generally is used only when that subset of products is the focus of discussion.

Box 4-A—Prevention, Recycling, and Degradability

New products can be designed to make MSW management easier. Just as toxicity and quantity can be considered when new products are designed, so can properties such as recyclability and degradability. If products are recyclable or degradable, less MSW might need to be sent to landfills or incinerators. Yet neither reduces the toxicity or quantity of MSW **before** it is generated. For this reason, OTA does not include recyclability and degradability as part of MSW prevention, a view shared by some other observers (e.g., 38). Instead, these two aspects of MSW are considered part of waste management.

Recycling, for example, occurs when an item is valued for its material content and the material is used to manufacture new items. However, recycling does not reduce MSW generation rates because it involves the separation, collection, and processing of materials **after** they are discarded. Although recycling is not a preventive measure, the link between the production/design portion of the MSW "system" and the ability to increase recycling is still important. As OTA pointed out in chapter 1, one key aspect of a materials management policy is to coordinate product manufacturing with the needs of management methods, in this case by designing products to be recyclable.

Similarly, degradable products do not decrease generation rates, although they can help reduce the visual problems and wildlife injuries associated with plastic litter (ch. 5). Degradable products generally are discarded into the MSW management system, where they end up in landfills. They may or may not degrade depending on the product and conditions at the landfill (chs. 5 and 7). Degradable products might even increase MSW generation rates in some cases. For example, some degradable plastic bags may require more polyethylene to have the same strength as non-degradable bags.

development of non-toxic alternatives is needed (12).

It is difficult to target products for quantity reduction efforts. Many people assume that demands for convenience have caused the proliferation of packaging and single-use products, but this is only partly true. In many cases, the relative proportion of packaging in MSW actually has decreased, at least by weight.[3] Moreover, packaging performs critical functions such as decreasing food spoilage and preventing pilferage or tampering. Even the use of plastics, which is criticized by many people, may contribute to reduction in some cases (box 4-B). In addition, measuring quantity reduction is difficult because there are no standard methods for determining how much is generated (ch. 3).

Even so, there are some obvious opportunities to reduce the quantity of MSW. These include reducing some packaging (e.g., multi-material packaging, which makes recycling difficult), some uses of paper (e.g., in direct mail advertising, oversized newspapers), and single-use products (e.g., diapers). In addition, yard wastes make up a large portion of MSW in many areas (ch. 3) and efforts to increase backyard composting could be important.

The major problem associated with MSW prevention is that MSW generation itself is a social phenomenon tied to social customs and personal preferences and lifestyles. Reducing the quantity of MSW generated will require changes in the attitudes of most Americans. This can only occur if producers and consumers assume joint responsibility for MSW generation, and it will involve changes in manufacturing design practices and in consumer purchasing decisions.

These changes would likely have positive and negative economic and social effects. As noted above, the potential benefits are attractive. Reducing toxicity would make MSW management safer and could have economic benefits associated with a decrease in cleanup costs of future hazardous waste sites. Reduced MSW quantity could lower the rate at which landfills are reaching capacity and possibly the rate at which costs for consumers and communi-

without the substances can be evaluated. Additional research is needed, however, to develop potential MSW prevention strategies. For example, independent testing of the toxic content of materials and

---

[3]The estimated **weight** of all containers and packaging in MSW declined from 35 percent in 1970 to 30 percent in 1986; while more packaging may be entering the MSW stream, lighter materials such as plastics and paper have been replacing heavier materials such as glass and metals (ch. 3). Little information is available on the **volume** of packaging. Based on limited data from excavations at landfills (ch. 3), the volume of plastics stayed relatively constant during the last 15 years, the volume of paper packaging increased slightly, and the volume of glass and metal decreased.

Figure 4-1—Routes to MSW Prevention

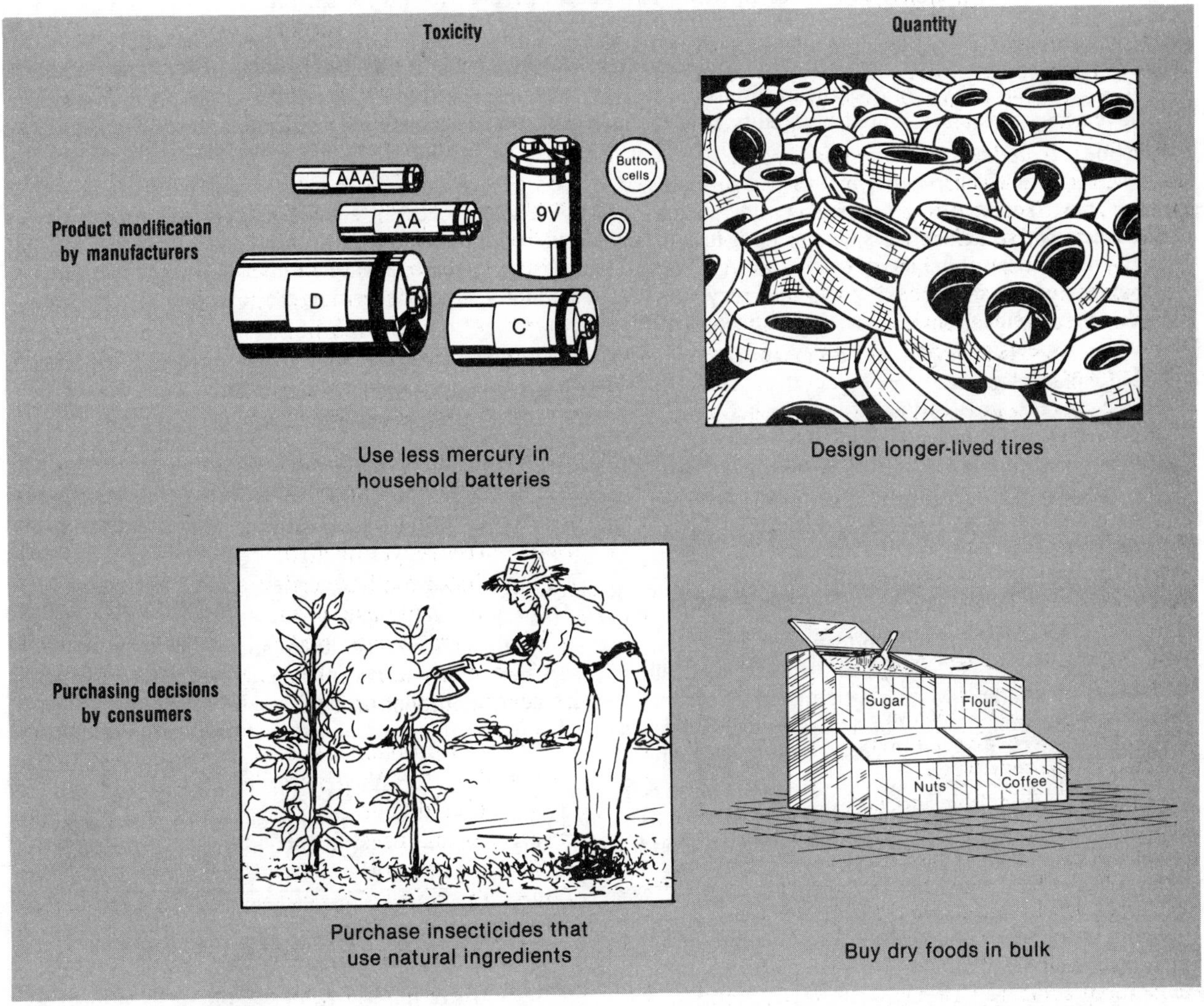
Toxicity
Quantity
Product modification by manufacturers
AAA
AA
9V
Button cells
D
C
Use less mercury in household batteries
Design longer-lived tires
Purchasing decisions by consumers
Sugar
Flour
Nuts
Coffee
Purchase insecticides that use natural ingredients
Buy dry foods in bulk

SOURCE: Office of Technology Assessment, 1989

ties are rising. Negative effects are possible, however, and they are likely to be unevenly distributed throughout society. For example, quantity reduction could affect employment, tax revenues, and the gross national product in unpredictable ways because about 70 percent of MSW consists of manufactured goods. Quantity reduction also could have negative economic impacts on some recyclers, although whether such effects would be enough to significantly affect recycling operations is unknown. For example, a change in battery components could affect recycling systems whose intent is to collect and sell specific metals.

Given these obstacles, it is uncertain just how much MSW prevention, particularly in terms of reducing quantity, will be achieved in the long-run. However, it is a certainty that little will be accomplished if the Nation maintains its current MSW practices. Although manufacturers have an economic incentive to reduce production and materials costs, they have little incentive to consider the ultimate costs for disposal of their products. Unless products or materials are available that perform well and have costs comparable to existing materials, manufacturers are unlikely to adopt alternatives in the absence of incentives (12). Similarly, there is

---

Box 4-B—Does Shifting to Plastics Mean MSW Prevention?

Many people are concerned about the growing use of plastic materials and their long-term effect on the environment, public health, and supplies of nonrenewable resources. These concerns may be caused more by the visibility of their use rather than the materials themselves. With respect to MSW, issues of concern about plastics include non-recyclability, non-degradability, contributions to dioxin emissions from incinerators, and use of landfill capacity.

Questions about plastics in MSW are not easily resolved. For example, virtually all types of plastics are recyclable from a technical perspective, although the capacity for such processing and the markets for products may be limited. Degradable plastics are appealing to many people and would provide benefits to certain sectors of society (e.g., corn growers if the use of cornstarch in biodegradable plastics increases), but there are unanswered questions about their effects on the environment and recycling (ch. 5). Similarly, issues concerning the contribution of plastics to dioxin emissions cannot be answered unequivocally (ch. 6).

Even so, switching to plastic materials can result in MSW quantity reduction, at least in terms of **weight**, because plastics generally are lighter than the materials they replace. For example, reduction could occur when thin plastic "shrink-wrap" films replace thicker corrugated cardboard or when plastic beverage bottles replace metal or glass bottles. Conversely, reduction would not occur when single-use plastic products replace reusable products, or when plastic added to existing products increases the weight or volume per unit of a product.

Whether these types of changes would decrease the **volume** of MSW depends on the specific case. In addition, if the plastic product is not easily recyclable, then the amount of MSW diverted from landfills or incinerators may not decrease.

Plastics and MSW prevention also must be considered in the context of toxicity. Different additives (e.g., metals or organic chemicals) are incorporated into polymer matrices during the production of plastic resins and others are added during the fabrication of plastic products (ch. 5). In fact, the variability of additives is what allows these materials to be tailored to different applications. There are unanswered questions, however, about what happens to additives when plastic materials are recycled, incinerated, and landfilled. To assess the potential for toxicity reduction, it would be necessary to evaluate each individual plastic material, its additives, and its potential health and environmental effects during MSW management.

On a broader scale, however, the use of plastics may not contribute to overall reductions in waste generation by society, primarily because their manufacture is associated with the generation of large quantities of hazardous waste (e.g., chlorinated benzenes, carbon tetrachloride, methylene chloride, trichloroethylene).

---

little incentive for consumers to consider MSW prevention.

The potential benefits of both toxicity and quantity reduction suggest that a concerted effort to promote prevention is worth starting today. There is a limit to what local and State governments can do to provide such incentives (chs. 1 and 8). The Federal Government, however, can provide strong leadership, actions, and positive incentives for MSW prevention efforts. Without Federal involvement, success is unlikely. This chapter discusses issues associated with MSW toxicity and quantity reduction, examples of successful changes, and some of the opportunities that different consumers can attempt. Current Federal and State activities related to MSW prevention are discussed in chapter 8, and policy options are discussed in chapter 1.

TOXICITY REDUCTION

Toxicity reduction refers to changing the design of products prior to manufacturing so they contain fewer or none of the substances that pose risks when those products become part of the MSW management stream. Toxicity reduction also can occur when products with toxic substances last longer. However, lowering the toxicity of a product by half would not be considered toxicity reduction if the change means that the product's lifetime is also cut in half.

Reducing the toxicity of MSW is an approach that emerged out of policies regarding industrial hazardous waste reduction (75, 77). The dynamics for MSW prevention efforts are different, however, primarily because the generator of a **product** with a toxic component is **not** responsible for its disposal, which is the opposite of the case for most generators of industrial hazardous waste. In principle, reducing the toxicity of MSW can decrease MSW management costs and exposure problems at all points in the lifecycle of a product, from point of manufacture to point of ultimate disposal or management. If the substances in MSW that pose the greatest risks to humans could be identified and removed from or substantially reduced in products, then those items would be safer.

What and Where Are Toxic Substances?

To identify substances and products for toxicity reduction efforts, information is needed about the types and amounts of toxic substances in MSW, which products contain significant quantities of them, and potential for exposure and toxic dosage during MSW management. With this information, specific substances and products could be targeted for initial reduction efforts.

Some toxic substances are known to pose human health and environmental problems (e.g., lead and benzene), and some can degrade machines and equipment. However, the state of our knowledge about potentially toxic substances in MSW is uncertain. Little is known about the distribution of toxic substances in various products, what exposures during or after MSW management are sufficient to cause problems, and what relative risks these substances pose when different MSW management systems are used.

An initial way to screen the universe of substances is to use existing regulatory lists. In addition, two general sources of information can be used to link particular toxic substances with products: 1) analyses of materials "flow," usually done for other purposes, that inventory substances from their origins to their end use; and 2) local household hazardous waste collection programs around the country, which collect discarded products containing hazardous substances.

Existing Regulatory Lists

Existing regulatory lists of toxic substances provide an initial basis of information about the extent of toxic substances. Several lists exist in environ-

mental laws or regulations. For example, the Comprehensive Environmental Response, Compensation, and Liability Act (CERCLA) defines hazardous substances; the Resource Conservation and Recovery Act (RCRA) defines hazardous wastes; the Clean Water Act defines priority toxic pollutants; and the Clean Air Act defines hazardous air pollutants.[4]

This information has limitations. For example, many suspect chemicals are likely to exist that are not listed. In addition, hundreds of new chemicals are introduced into production and commerce by industry each year.

Obviously, it is impossible to analyze at one time the potential harm of hundreds of chemicals, nor could the Federal Government implement any toxicity reduction program that encompassed all substances at once. The lists simply provide a guide to potential and sometimes actual toxicity. **The Federal Government needs to determine where its efforts in promoting the reduction of toxics in MSW should be concentrated**. EPA reached the same conclusion (91).

Materials Flow Inventories

Complete studies of how a given substance is used and flows through society are limited. With respect to MSW, most of the available information deals with metals.

Data on Metals—Three heavy metals that are generally recognized as toxic to humans are cadmium, lead, and mercury. These are used in many products (92):

- cadmium—metal coatings and platings for white goods; rechargeable household batteries; electronics and fasteners; color pigments for plastics, paints, printing inks; heat stabilizers in plastics;
- lead—rustproofing paints; wire and cable insulation, for electrical stability; bottle caps; contact base of incandescent light bulbs; and
- mercury—fluorescent lights, batteries, power control switches for lights and thermostats, mildew-proofing paints.

---

[4]The words toxic and hazardous are not used here in their legal or regulatory technical sense. Instead they are used to refer to materials that are harmful when people are exposed to them in sufficient concentrations.

Photo credit: Office of Technology Assessment

Lead is used in many products, including lead-acid automobile batteries, consumer electronics, paints and inks, some food packaging, and light bulbs. Most lead-acid batteries are recycled, but these batteries still account for about 65 percent of the lead present in MSW after recycling.

Table 4-1—U.S. Consumption and Demand for Lead, Cadmium, and Mercury

End use	Tons	Percent
Mercury demand by end use, 1983:		
Electrical	1,024	55
Caustic soda and chlorine	306	16
Paints	230	12
Instruments	94	5
Dental supplies	61	3
Other	153	8
Cadmium demand by end use, 1983:		
Coating and plating	1,410	34
Batteries	1,120	27
Pigments	660	16
Plastic stabilizers	620	15
Other	330	8
Lead consumption by class of product, 1986:		
Storage batteries	940,899	76
Metal products	160,949	13
Other oxides	76,619	6
Gasoline additives	31,452	3
Other	29,663	2

SOURCES; U.S. Department of the Interior, Bureau of Mines, *Mineral Facts and Problems 1985 Edition,* Bulletin 675 (Washington, DC: 1985); U.S. Department of the Interior, Bureau of Mines, *Minerals Yearbook* (Washington, DC: 1986).

They also can be found in trace quantities in some products. For example, printing inks classified as non-lead-based can still contain lead in trace concentrations below 600 ppm.

The Bureau of Mines estimated how these metals are distributed among all end uses (table 4-1). In 1983, most cadmium (34 percent) was used in coating and plating; the second largest use was batteries (27 percent in 1983), which are expected to top the list in the year 2000. Cadmium use in plastics as a pigment and sometimes as a stabilizer is expected to grow to third place in 2000. Mercury end uses in 1983 were primarily electrical (55 percent).

One materials flow analysis on lead and cadmium specifically analyzes metals in MSW (29). Lead-acid batteries (primarily from automobiles) accounted for 65 percent of the lead after recycling, while consumer electronics (e.g., TVs, radios, and VCRs) accounted for 27 percent (figure 4-2). Nickel/cadmium household batteries are the largest source of cadmium, accounting for an estimated 52 percent, while plastics contribute 28 percent. Along with the Bureau of Mines data, this information indicates that automobile batteries are the major source of lead in

MSW, while household batteries are major sources of mercury and cadmium, and plastics are major sources of lead and cadmium, as well. One European study found that household batteries contributed the highest fraction of mercury, cadmium, zinc, and manganese in urban waste (55).

Little analysis of the contents of packaging has been conducted, but most of the materials used in packaging (i.e., paper, plastics, steel, glass) may be sources of toxic substances, particularly metals (28). Sources of lead in packaging include solder in steel cans, paint pigments, ceramic glazes and inks, and plastics. Sources of cadmium include the coating and plating on metals and pigments in some plastics. There also are many other additives in plastics (ch. 5).

Data on Organic Chemicals—Synthetic organic chemicals are used intentionally in many common consumer products—e.g., toluene in inks, formaldehyde in particle board and glues, chlorobenzene in cleaners, and methylene chloride in spray propellants (92) (also see ch. 3). The production of these chemicals has proliferated since the 1940s because of technological changes in invention and mass production. Relatively little information is available,

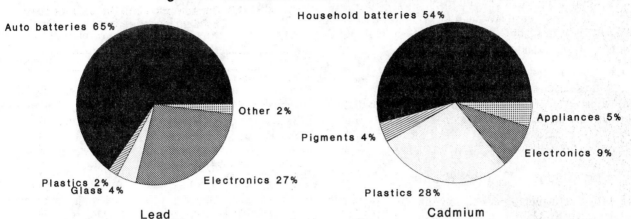

Figure 4-2—Distribution of Lead and Cadmium in Products

Lead:
- Auto batteries 65%
- Other 2%
- Electronics 27%
- Glass 4%
- Plastics 2%

Cadmium:
- Household batteries 54%
- Appliances 5%
- Electronics 9%
- Plastics 28%
- Pigments 4%

SOURCE: Franklin Associates, Ltd., *Characterization of Products Containing Lead and Cadmium in Municipal Solid Waste in the United States, 1970 to 2000, Executive Summary and Chapter 1*, Final report prepared for the U.S. Environmental Protection Agency, Municipal Solid Waste Program (Prairie Village, KS: January 1989).

however, on the end uses of organic chemicals in different products.

Determining which products are major sources of particular organic chemicals will involve substantial research. Other questions about organic chemicals need to be considered. Should chemicals used as "active" and "inert" ingredients in pesticides be counted?[5] How should the chemical form of the substance, exposure, and dosage be accounted for? In addition, obtaining information on particular ingredients can sometimes be difficult because of proprietary considerations. Still, existing regulatory lists at least provide some insight into usage of these chemicals.

Household Hazardous Waste Lists

EPA defines "household hazardous waste" as products discarded from residences which contain substances already regulated under RCRA as an industrial hazardous waste (89).[6] Over 100 substances classified as hazardous under RCRA are found in common household products (ch. 3). Although the list in chapter 3 is not comprehensive, it indicates the wide range of products that contain

hazardous substances.[7] EPA also has compiled similar lists (89). One list covers household hazardous wastes; a second lists "household items that may be hazardous." EPA cautioned that not every commercial product of the general types listed contains the specific component.

Lists of these products also have been compiled by local or State organizations for use by consumers. Their formats vary widely. Most lists include categories such as automotive products (e.g., oils, batteries); cleaners (e.g., detergents, drain and oven cleaners); paints and polishes; pesticides and insecticides; and miscellaneous. One list gives each category a toxicity rating (39). Its rating system may be too simple because of the wide range of products and product compositions in each category, but it does provide consumers with some information about relative toxicity. Another example is a "Household Hazardous Waste Wheel" (19). This educational tool lists 36 types of products in four categories (house, auto, pesticides, and paint products) and identifies hazardous ingredients and their properties, management methods, and alternative products.

[5]Inert ingredients are inactive chemicals that facilitate the effects of active ingredients. They include solvents such as water, baits for attracting pests, dust carriers such as clay or talc, fillers, wetting and spreading agents, propellants, and emulsifiers (10). EPA groups them into four lists, the first of which, for example, contains 57 of the most toxic inerts currently used in products.

[6]However, no Federal regulations exist for household hazardous wastes.

[7]The list does not include many pesticides, and it is restricted to hazardous wastes as defined by RCRA.

Some European lists of household hazardous waste contain items rarely found on U.S. lists. In West Germany, for instance, the product groups defined as household hazardous waste include fluorescent tubes and medicines (34).

Chapter 3 includes some data on the frequency at which these products (excluding automobile batteries) appear in residential MSW. For example, household maintenance and cleaner products are estimated to make up almost half of the household hazardous wastes discarded from residences.

Examples of Toxicity Reduction

Product reformulation is an ongoing process in industry, occurring continually for safety and market reasons. Various examples show that industry can use its creativity to develop new alternatives and reap spin-off rewards without loss of competitive position or jobs. For example, the use of chlorofluorocarbons (CFCs) as propellants in most aerosols was banned by EPA and the Food and Drug Administration in 1978 (22). Initially, the void was filled by hydrocarbons, which already were used in about half of the aerosol market and in pump sprays. The change also resulted in expanded commercial development of new products, new ways of applying materials, and new technology. More recently, plastics manufacturers are moving to eliminate the use of CFCs in the foam polystyrene used in fast-food packaging (ch. 5).

Investments in research and development on the reformulation of products is expensive and time-consuming, however. For example, according to the vice president of research and development at one company, approval of one pesticide for home use can sometimes take 10 to 15 years and cost $10 million (22).

In addition, many manufacturers argue that their products are unsafe only when they are mishandled and improperly discarded. For example, the Chemical Specialties Manufacturers Association argues that chemical specialty products, which often are included on household hazardous waste, are formulated to maximize their safety during use and minimize potential environmental effects (9).[8] To promote proper use of these products, the Association is supporting a program called "Disposal: Do It Right," run by the Household Products Disposal Council. This group distributes information about the safety of chemical products and how to properly use and dispose of them.

Some manufacturers have made changes in the composition of products that ultimately become MSW. Some cases involve substances whose toxicity, given sufficient exposure and dosage, is undisputed, such as lead, mercury, and cadmium. For example, lead in exterior house paints has been replaced with titanium and zinc pigments (85) and the use of lead soldering in food cans has declined from 90 percent of such cans in 1979 to about 20 percent in 1986 (84). Box 4-C highlights another example, where Polaroid eliminated mercury in camera batteries by redesigning the battery.[9] Two other examples—efforts to reduce the use of lead in printing inks and the use of mercury in household batteries in general—are discussed below.

Organic chemicals also can be the targets of toxicity reduction efforts. For example, perchloroethane has been replaced with a water-based solvent in Dow's Spray 'n Wash product (7). Another example—Safer, Inc., which produces nontoxic garden insecticide products—is highlighted in box 4-D.

Often these types of substances are the focus of attention from environmental and public health interest groups, or potential targets of government regulations or bans. The household battery industry's voluntary program to reduce mercury, for example, is at least in part a response to questioning and concerns expressed by environmentalists and public health interest groups (60). In other cases, changes have been made more quietly.

Lead-Based Inks

Printing inks traditionally have contained lead. During the last 10 to 15 years, however, manufacturers and users of these inks have reduced the use of lead in response to customer pressure, concerns about employee health, technological changes, and concerns about industrial wastes. For example,

---

[8]Members of the Association manufacture, for example, detergents, disinfectants, deodorants, hair spray, waxes and polishes, roach killers, garden pesticides, and automotive products.

[9]OTA's highlighting of particular brand-name products does not in any way imply endorsement of those products.

Box 4-C—Polaroid's Mercury-Free Battery For Film Cassette

Household batteries are one of the most common contributors of mercury in MSW, and the popularity of cameras using small ''button'' batteries has increased the potential for MSW problems from this source. The Polaroid Corp. has conducted extensive research to reduce the mercury content of its camera batteries. Special to the Polaroid case, however, is the fact that the battery providing power to run the camera's electronics, optics, and film transport is built into the film cassette itself. Thus, each time an empty film cassette is discarded, a battery is discarded as well. The system uses a carbon/zinc battery.

Part of Polaroid's motivation in developing reduced-mercury batteries was market-generated. Polaroid already had decided to reduce mercury in its products when, in 1986, the Swiss government issued regulatory requirements on household batteries. The requirements set limits on allowable concentrations of metals in various household batteries and required labels on batteries exceeding the limits to warn consumers to dispose of them separately because of concerns about the emission of metals from MSW incinerators. Although Switzerland accounted for only 1 percent of the company's market, the Swiss regulations are typical of guidelines being developed in other countries.

In early 1987, Polaroid was producing some batteries with 50 percent less mercury and by fall of that year all Polaroid batteries met this goal; mercury levels were reduced from 0.18 to 0.09 percent by weight. Other adjustments were still necessary, however, to meet the Swiss standard (i.e., combined weight of cadmium and mercury in carbon/zinc batteries not to exceed 0.025 percent). In April 1988, mercury was eliminated from all new Polaroid batteries and in 1989 new Polaroid film cassettes sold throughout the world will contain mercury-free batteries.

Polaroid's complete conversion to mercury-free batteries took about 2 years; the cost of the research, development, and conversion reached several hundred thousand dollars. The relatively short time involved is somewhat misleading, however. Years of previous research set the stage for the conversion. Some side benefits were generated as well; for example, the new battery eliminated some of the costs previously needed to protect workers from mercury, reduced some waste treatment costs, and enhanced the potential to recycle battery components. These cost savings are expected to offset development costs in about 3 years.

SOURCE: H. Fatkin, Health, Safety & Environmental Affairs, Polaroid Corp., personal communication, August 1988 and February 1989.

---

printers of corrugated and kraft paper have reduced the use of lead pigments and shifted to water-based inks to eliminate the generation of hazardous wastes from the cleaning of press equipment and to comply with air emissions regulations for volatile organic chemicals (12). Companies such as Procter & Gamble have eliminated the use of metal-based inks for printing on packaging.

According to the National Association of Printing Ink Manufacturers (NAPIM), pigments with heavy metals such as lead are not widely used in printing ink today (47). In the mid-1970s, the American Newspaper Publishers Association (ANPA) prohibited the use of lead pigments in ANPA-approved newspaper inks and developed a logo to identify acceptable inks.[10] According to ANPA, most newspapers in the United States request inks carrying this logo (13, 47).

Lead is the dominant heavy metal used in chrome yellow and molybdate orange pigments; about 60 percent of the weight of these pigments is lead. NAPIM estimated that these two pigments comprised only 0.4 percent (3,300 tons) of all the printing ink produced in the United States in 1987. According to NAPIM, cadmium-based pigments are used only in inks where extreme chemical resistance is required (e.g., labels on acid bottles). NAPIM also contends that use of lead-based orange and yellow inks can be further reduced by using organic pigment substitutes, when exact color matches, opacity, and/or light fastness are not required properties in the printed product.

Household Batteries

Household batteries use several metals in their electrode systems (table 4-2), of which mercury and cadmium are of greatest concern. Data from the

---

[10]''Non-lead based'' inks still can legally contain lead in concentrations below 600 ppm, however.

Box 4-D—Safer, Inc., Alternatives to Petrochemically Based Pesticides

In the mid-1970s, two scientists in Canada began studying the use of naturally occurring fatty acids in killing specific insect pests. In 1978, these scientists formed Safer, Inc., a privately held company that is a developer and marketer of pesticides and plant-care products.

According to the company, its fatty-acid based pesticides products are specific to the targeted pest, degrade rapidly, and are 8 to 93 times safer (in terms of toxicity) than some commonly used petrochemically based pesticides. As such, they would be likely to have fewer of the disadvantages associated with the petrochemically based pesticides—indiscriminate effects on pests as well as beneficial insects (e.g., pollinating honeybees), birds, and pets; other environmental hazards such as water pollution; health hazards posed to persons applying the chemicals; and the development of pest strains resistant to the chemicals. However, they may take longer to achieve their desired effects than do the petrochemical pesticides. In addition, they are too expensive to be used commercially; the homeowner market is the largest market for Safer's products at this time.

Like the petrochemically based pesticides, Safer's pesticides are subject to EPA regulations under the Federal Insecticide, Fungicide, and Rodenticide Act. Because of the nature of the products, however, Safer's pesticides usually must undergo only the first of three levels of required testing; occasionally, a product will be reformulated if it is found to cause unacceptable skin irritation.

In addition to its these pesticides, Safer is exploring microbiological and biotechnological approaches to pest control. The company expects demand for these types of products to increase for at least three reasons: growing consumer awareness of the hazards associated with the use of petrochemicals, increased regulation of the pesticides, and initiatives such as California's voter-approved Proposition 65, which requires manufacturers to prove that substances used in products are not toxic. Safer is trying to develop markets with landscape companies, nurseries, and other commercial outlets, as well as in agricultural operations.

SOURCE: M. Goldberg, Safer, Inc., personal communication, August 1988.

National Electrical Manufacturers Association (NEMA) show that mercury use in household batteries is declining (figure 4-3), despite an overall increase in the number of batteries produced.[11] In 1983, 753 tons of mercury were used in U.S. production of household batteries, of which 49 tons were used in mercuric oxide button cells. This represented about 40 percent of all end uses of mercury (table 4-1).[12] NEMA estimates that in 1989, 168 tons of mercury will be used, a decline of 78 percent from 1983, with about 31 tons to be used in button cells.[13]

Thus, depending on the total amount of mercury used in the United States in 1989, household batteries might account for less than 20 percent of total consumption, although they still could be the major source of mercury in MSW. In addition, if the concentration of mercury per battery reaches some lower limit and overall battery sales continue to rise,

then the total contribution of mercury could begin to rise again. This might be tempered by a shift toward rechargeable cadmium/nickel batteries and lithium batteries, but cadmium and lithium pose problems of their own (e.g., lithium is reactive with water).

Household batteries are changing in other ways. The service life of alkaline batteries has increased by up to 30 percent in recent years (48). Alkaline batteries have longer service lifetimes than do carbon/zinc batteries, and consequently their market share continues to increase while that of carbon/zinc batteries continues to decrease.

Changes in consumer electronic products also have had a large effect because they require more batteries and longer service lifetimes, as well as batteries of reduced dimensions. This has increased

---

[11]Mercury historically has been a component of batteries that use zinc as the negative electrode material. It reduces the tendency of zinc to react with other battery components. Information on recycling household batteries, including Japanese and European experiences, is discussed in ch. 5.

[12]In comparison, natural sources of mercury may be greater. The World Health Organization (96), for example, estimated in the mid-1970s that about 30,000 metric tons of mercury were deposited annually in rain. Of course, those amounts were dispersed over the entire global surface.

[13]Mercuric oxide button batteries are being replaced slowly by newer systems such as zinc/air batteries.

Table 4-2—Electrode Systems of Common Household Batteries

Battery type	Electrode system
Carbon/zinc	Zinc, manganese dioxide, and either zinc chloride or ammonium chloride
Alkaline/manganese	Zinc, potassium hydroxide, and manganese dioxide
Mercuric oxide	Zinc, potassium hydroxide, and mercury oxide
Silver oxide	Silver oxide and either potassium hydroxide or sodium dioxide and zinc
Zinc/air	Zinc, potassium hydroxide, and oxygen
Nickel/cadmium	Cadmium hydroxide, potash lye, and nickel hydroxide
Lithium	Lithium and one of manganese dioxide, carbon monoflouride, bismuth trioxide, thionyl chloride, or sulfur dioxide

SOURCE: Organization for Economic Cooperation and Development, *Fate of Small Quantities of Hazardous Waste*, Environmental Monographs No. 6 (Paris: August 1986).

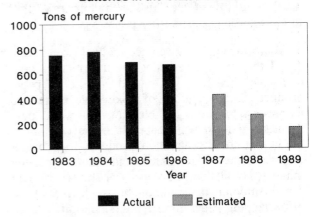

Figure 4-3—Trends in Use of Mercury in Household Batteries in the United States

SOURCE: National Electrical Manufacturers Association, personal communication, February 1989.

batteries and longer service lifetimes, as well as batteries of reduced dimensions. This has increased the use of rechargeable batteries, which cost more and require a recharger but which can be used hundreds of times (44). Rechargeable batteries are most often used as built-in components in appliances. Currently, most are nickel/cadmium batteries, and NEMA estimates that 75 to 80 percent of the nickel/cadmium batteries used by consumers are built into and sealed inside of appliances. This means, however, that when these products are discarded, most of the cadmium in the batteries is also discarded.[14] Rechargeable lithium batteries are not expected to begin displacing nickel/cadmium batteries for several more years. Another development is the potential commercialization of plastic casings on household batteries (44).

As batteries change, the evaluation of whether or not toxicity reduction is occurring has to be assessed on the basis of the toxicity of the substitute materials. Lithium batteries do not contain cadmium, mercury, or lead, but lithium compounds are reactive with water and they can affect the nervous system. Zinc/air batteries contain mercury, but in smaller amounts than the mercuric oxide ones they replace. Information about substitute materials for mercury is proprietary, however, and this makes evaluations of toxicity reduction difficult.

Consumer Purchasing Decisions

Consumers have the option to make purchasing choices about products on the basis of toxicity. Not surprisingly, public opinion favors the opportunity to purchase products that pose fewer potential risks when discarded. In a 1987 survey conducted in Massachusetts, 95 percent of the respondents wanted manufacturers to develop substitute nonhazardous products (71). Over three-fourths (77 percent) preferred this to redesigning the original product to have a lower concentration of the toxic substance in question.

Making wise purchasing decisions, however, is not easy. For instance, many household cleaners are considered to be potential household hazardous wastes, but a glance at cleaners in any store will confuse even knowledgeable consumers. Some products contain no information about their contents. Some have cautions about proper use of the product and warn against direct contact, implying toxicity. Other products contain a long list of chemicals that to most consumers is "chemical mumbo jumbo."

Lists of household hazardous wastes are one source of information about alternative products. Consumers armed with these types of lists can make better decisions about the products they bring into their homes than they can by relying on current

---

[14]NEMA estimates that collection programs for cadmium batteries that are not sealed inside appliances would account for less than 5 percent of all cadmium consumed in the United States (48).

labeling information. **Developing effective methods to convey toxicity information on product labels would be of great use to consumers willing to change their purchasing patterns.**

Another example of a choice available to consumers, if they were given adequate information, concerns bleached (i.e., white) and unbleached paper products. Small quantities of dioxin have been found in wastewater from the bleaching of wood pulp necessary to make white paper. Informed consumers might opt to buy common products (e.g., paper plates, coffee filters, tissue, and sanitary papers) made from unbleached paper, regardless of their brownish color, if they knew this fact. In Sweden, gift wrapping paper, coffee filters, and other products made from unbleached paperboard are now available. However, this trend is occurring at least in part because unbleached board is stronger and cheaper than bleached paper and often is not a visible component of packaging.

QUANTITY REDUCTION

In essence, reducing the quantity of the Nation's MSW involves changing the nature of many common products, including packaging. It can occur, for example, if the lifetime of a product is held constant while its weight or volume is reduced, or if weight or volume are held constant while the lifetime is increased.[15] In addition to products, materials such as yard wastes can also be the focus of prevention efforts (i.e., through composting in residential backyards).

Discussions about quantity reduction often focus on packaging, which makes up about 30 percent of all MSW by weight. OTA believes, however, that attempts to reduce MSW should consider **all** components in the MSW stream, rather than only packaging. For example, paper and paperboard products make up over one-third of MSW by weight, and much of this is not packaging. Yard wastes comprise another 20 percent or so on average, and more so in certain areas or at certain times of the year (chs. 3 and 5). In fact, given the changes in social attitudes and behavior that are required, it seems likely that quantity reduction will best be achieved through

many small cumulative changes in product design and consumer behavior. This approach is more likely to have greater impact than focusing only on packaging because no one product or industry group is singled out for undue attention.

Measuring changes in MSW generation will be difficult, given current definitions and methodologies (chs. 1 and 3). Small changes in generation rates are likely to be masked by sampling errors and natural fluctuations. In addition, it is not always obvious what constitutes quantity reduction.

The information needed to make decisions about which products to target for reduction efforts is complex. Useful information would include:

- types, composition, and amounts of products being produced;
- how consumption of products is changing over time;
- why certain products are purchased and who buys them;
- feasible alternatives to current products;
- consumer behavior after products are purchased;
- disposal costs relative to product durability and toxicity; and
- full costs of disposable and reusable products.

Obtaining such complex data is difficult. Cost estimates must account for use of energy and materials, labor, waste management, and equipment. And these must be considered over the entire lifecycle of a product, from virgin material extraction or secondary material recovery, through processing, manufacturing, and use for final products.

Deciding What Products and Materials to Target

If the Federal Government develops policies to emphasize MSW quantity reduction, it will have to decide how to measure reduction and which products and materials to target. This section discusses: 1) difficulties in measuring quantity reduction; 2) national estimates regarding products in MSW; and 3) factors influencing producer and consumer decisions.

---

[15]In addition, the effect of such changes on the toxicity of the products must be considered.

Measuring Quantity Reduction

One critical question is how to measure a reduction in quantity. Small changes in MSW generation are difficult to detect because of problems stemming from the different definitions and sampling methodologies used in studies of MSW generation (ch. 3). Any sampling methodology, no matter how standardized, also is subject to sampling error, and this source of variability can sometimes overwhelm detection of real changes.

A related problem concerns measuring MSW by weight versus volume. Most MSW analyses, including the EPA/Franklin model (ch. 3), are based on weight, yet MSW volumes may change independent of weight. The use of lighter but higher volume materials appears to be increasing, for example, in the case of plastics replacing glass containers. Volume data are more important than weight data for some MSW management decisions (e.g., for estimating landfill capacity) and thus are important for quantity reduction efforts. However, comprehensive data on the volumes of products and materials simply are not available.

The degree to which materials can be compacted also complicates the interpretation of data about MSW quantity. The volume of MSW depends at least in part on its compactability and the degree to which it is actually compacted. As noted in chapter 3, there is some evidence that plastic bottles are more readily compacted in landfills than are glass bottles. The design of collection vehicles also is usually based on volume capacities, but vehicles using public roadways can be limited by their total tonnage.

Another factor to consider is whether reducing a product's residuals that become MSW causes any change in the overall amount of waste generated in its production. For instance, improvements in packaging have decreased food spoilage and thus decreased food wastes, but it is possible that the production of the packaging itself causes an increase in industrial waste generation.

No matter what type of strategy is pursued, there obviously are many factors to consider. Some

criteria to help target products for quantity reduction might include (94):

- the amount and scarcity of feedstock materials and energy required for manufacture;
- the volume of a product and its manufacturing byproducts that will have to be discarded;
- the difficulty and environmental impact of disposing of a product and its manufacturing byproducts;
- the useful life, reusability, or recyclability of a product; and
- the availability of alternatives.

These are reasonable criteria, yet their very nature indicates just how difficult it is to evaluate the potential for quantity reduction.

National Estimates About Products in MSW

The EPA/Franklin model (ch. 3) estimates the portions by weight of different categories of products in MSW. It indicates that the largest component of MSW is, has been, and will continue to be packaging and containers (table 4-3). By 1986 packaging and containers had leveled out at 30 percent of all MSW, where it is projected to remain to 2000. The second largest category typically has been nondurables, and this is the only major category whose relative proportion is estimated to be growing. The relative proportion of food wastes is estimated to be declining.[16]

In terms of absolute weight, all major categories except food waste are expected to grow (table 4-4). The model also includes information about various subcategories of products. For example, subcategories of MSW that are expected to increase by more than 10 percent by the year 2000 include furniture and furnishings, books and magazines, office papers and commercial printing papers, beer and soft drink cans, aluminum foil and closures, corrugated boxes, plastic containers, and other plastic packaging (ch. 3). Beer and soft drink aluminum cans are expected to increase 14 percent from 1990 to 1995, while all aluminum was expected to increase 18 percent in the same period.

Several caveats must be noted, however. First, because the data are in terms of weight, the

---

[16]Food wastes could be decreasing because of increased use of sink garbage disposals, better packaging, or increased consumption of pre-prepared meals are resulting in less spoilage.

Table 4-3—Estimated Proportion of Products and Other Materials in MSW, By Decade and Including 1986, After Materials Recovery

Category	Percentage (by weight)					
	1960	1970	1980	1986	1990	2000
Durables[a]	11.1	12.4	13.8	13.6	13.6	13.6
Nondurables[b]	18.5	19.0	22.1	25.1	25.8	28.1
Containers & packaging	29.4	34.9	32.6	30.3	30.5	30.3
Food wastes	14.9	11.4	9.2	8.9	8.4	8.9
Yard wastes	24.5	20.6	20.5	20.1	19.8	20.1
Miscellaneous inorganics	1.6	1.7	1.7	1.8	1.9	1.8

[a]**Durables** include major appliances, furniture, tires, and miscellaneous items such as sporting equipment, hobby supplies, toys, jewelry, consumer electronics, and watches.

[b]**Nondurables** include paper products such as newspapers, books and magazines, office paper and commercial printing, tissue, towels, plates and cups, plus clothing and footwear.

SOURCE: Franklin Associates, Ltd., *Characterization of Municipal Solid Waste in the United States, 1960 to 2000 (Update 1988),* report prepared for the U.S. Environmental Protection Agency, Office of Solid Waste and Emergency Response (Prairie Village, KS: Mar. 30, 1988).

proportions can be biased toward categories with materials that tend to be heavier. This may give greater emphasis to the durables and packaging categories. For instance, paper comprises the largest materials group within the nondurables category, but it is lighter than materials such as glass and metals. Also, the EPA/Franklin model has some acknowledged limitations that could affect these estimates (ch. 3).

Another problem is that national estimates cannot account for variations in the composition of products in local MSW. Local studies show wide variations in the portions of **materials** in MSW (ch. 3) because of differences in both local conditions and sampling methods. However, few studies examine **products** at a local or State level.

Factors That Affect Consumer and Producer Choices

Many factors can affect the decisions made by producers and consumers, and often they can act as constraints on MSW prevention. Several factors that appear to influence MSW per-capita generation rates—household size, degree of urbanization, socio-economic status, and demand for convenience—were discussed in chapter 3. Some additional factors that influence MSW generation rates are discussed here. Although these factors all can influence per-capita generation to some degree, it is not clear how they interact.

Information Availability—Consumers rarely are provided with information that allows them to make product purchasing decisions based on the idea of reducing the toxicity or quantity of products discarded in MSW. Instead, and not unreasonably, they make choices based on product quality, convenience, attractiveness, and price. Consumers could be encouraged to include MSW prevention in their decisionmaking in the same way that other changes (e.g., in diet) are encouraged—primarily by education, information, and example. This is one rationale for some of the options discussed in chapter 1, such as an information clearinghouse and labeling programs. This assumes, however, that alternatives do exist and that consumers have knowledge about these alternatives.

Product Cost Factors—Several factors influence product cost and also inhibit quantity reduction. For example, products that last longer because of higher quality manufacturing often have higher purchase prices. However, these products may not always be affordable to all consumers. Thus some consumers, out of necessity, choose cheaper, less durable products. Another example involves buying food products in large containers or in bulk, which can result in less packaging per product. Some consumers cannot afford to buy larger amounts due to low cash flow, lack of storage space at home, or the need to reach shopping areas by foot or bus.

Purchase price is not always a guide to longer lifetimes, however, and consumers often lack the information needed to compare lifecycle costs with purchase costs. For instance, most battery manufacturers offer several grades of batteries, but they do not give the consumer enough information to know

**Table 4-4—Estimated Percent Change in the Total Weight of Products and
Other Materials in MSW, By Decade**

Category	Percent change in total weight, by decade			
	1960-70	1970-80	1980-90	1990-2000
Durables	34	14	14	14
Nondurables	27	19	35	25
Containers & packaging	41	5	13	15
Food wastes	5	-7	5	-2
Yard wastes	2	3	11	9
Miscellaneous inorganics	21	14	22	16

SOURCE: Franklin Associates, Ltd., *Characterization of Municipal Solid Waste in the United States, 1960 to 2000 (Update 1988)*, report prepared for the U.S. Environmental Protection Agency, Office of Solid Waste and Emergency Response (Prairie Village, KS: Mar. 30, 1988).

whether a $2 battery will last more than twice as long as a $1 battery.

Another factor is the cost of repair versus replacement. Replacement costs today tend to be less than repair costs. This may result from the difference between lower foreign labor costs for production and higher domestic labor costs for repairs, or the difference between automated production costs and manual repair costs. Whatever the reasons, it encourages consumers to throw items away and replace them rather than get them repaired.

Advertising—Whether consumers make decisions about products because they are influenced by advertising, or whether advertising is geared to respond to consumer demands is arguable; both occur to some extent. Some researchers studying packaging characterize consumer demand for convenience as being very strong (69). At the same time, however, consumers also demand products that are safe, functional, and aesthetically appealing. Moreover, consumer boycotts demonstrate that moral values can be attached to certain products regardless of their marketing methods.

Of greater significance, however, is that advertising has rarely, if ever, used reduction of MSW toxicity or quantity as a selling point, even though over $50 billion are now spent on national advertising each year (82). Some producers told OTA that industry does not promote its good actions because the public regards such advertising as self-serving, or that consumers do not care and thus such advertising does not help to sell products (79). However, some advertising of this sort has occurred, for example, chemical manufacturers' slogans for better living based on better chemistry.

Overall Consumption Patterns—Disposable personal income in the United States grew from $716 billion in 1970 to $3.02 trillion in 1986, while personal savings as a percent of this income declined from 8 to 4 percent in 1986 (82). This means that we now are spending more of our income on goods and services.

One outcome of increased consumption is that households today tend to have multiple sets of some consumer products. Since 1975, for instance, the average number of television sets has increased by 20 percent, to almost 2 per household (82). Increased ownership of goods can increase MSW generation when this kind of consumption encourages other purchases (e.g., records and tapes) that generate packaging waste. In addition, changing fads and technological advances can increase MSW by encouraging the replacement of goods that are still usable but "out of style." For example, the anticipated introduction of high-definition TV in the 1990s may render current TV sets obsolete or at least more likely to be discarded.

Historical data also show that since the 1950s personal consumption expenditures have shifted among durables, nondurables, and services (figure 4-4). The shift toward services may be moving some MSW generation from households to institutions and also may be increasing certain kinds of wastes. For instance, Americans spent 55 percent more for meals and beverages purchased outside the home in 1986 than in 1980, and franchise restaurants grew from 33,000 in 1970 to an estimated 86,000 in 1987 (82). This results not only in the shifting of some food waste generation from households to restaurants, but also in the perception that packaging wastes and litter have increased.

Figure 4-4—Shifts in Personal Consumption

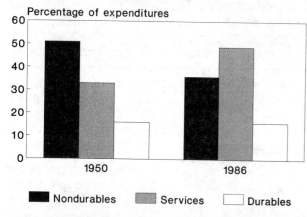

SOURCE: U.S. Department of Commerce, Bureau of the Census, *Statistical Abstract of the United States, 1978,* 99th annual edition (Washington, DC: U.S. Government Printing Office, September 1978); U.S. Department of Commerce, Bureau of the Census, *Statistical Abstract of the United States, 1988,* 108th edition (Washington, DC: U.S. Government Printing Office, December 1987).

Product Trends

Examining trends in the production and consumption of different categories of products can help identify potential targets for efforts to reduce MSW generation. This section discusses trends in the following categories: packaging, "single-use" products, reusable products, mail and telephone books, and miscellaneous technological changes.

Packaging

Packaging refers to materials used to prepare finished goods for shipment, distribution, storage, merchandising, and end use (41). In 1986, an estimated $55 billion was spent on packaging—about 4 percent of the value of all finished goods made in the United States (41). Slightly more than half of these expenditures are on packaging for food and beverages.

Functions of Packaging—Packaging consists of all kinds of containers (e.g., boxes, jars, cans, bottles, and bags) and packing materials made from a variety of materials (e.g., paper, plastic, glass, and metal).[17] Packaging is used for multiple purposes (12, 69), including:

- protection during shipping and shelf-life;
- protection to prevent tampering;
- prevention of food spoilage;
- compliance with government regulations;
- provision of information;
- protection of consumers against toxic contents;
- attractiveness and merchandisability; and
- provision of convenience.

For example, one recent trend has been toward self-service shopping, accompanied by an increase in mass merchandising and a decrease in the number of sales people (e.g., modern home centers have replaced many traditional hardware stores). This has contributed to increased pilferage in retail stores and, consequently, to an increase in protective packaging for thousands of products. Shoplifting, for example, accounts for 27 percent of theft losses in supermarkets (employee theft accounts for 53 percent) (26). Even a small amount of pilferage may represent a large portion of a company's profit margin.[18] The functions of packaging are often interrelated. For example, the use of plastic wrap and bags helps decrease food spoilage, which reduces the generation of food waste from households (12), and these materials make it easier to display the products and information about the contents.

Defining Excessive Packaging—One major complaint heard about packaging today is that it is "excessive." However, what one person views as excessive may be considered necessary by another person. Defining excessive is particularly difficult because packaging serves so many functions simultaneously.

The "blister pack" (i.e., packaging made of semi-rigid clear plastic that encases small products) illustrates this difficulty. This form of packaging offers several advantages: it allows small items to be sold in self-service displays, thereby reducing the need for employee service, and it helps avoid pilferage. The package also provides space for information about the product. Although most of the marketing and convenience value accrues to the

---

[17]The packaging industry characterizes packaging into three basic groups (54)—primary (i.e., a package such as a bottle, can, or box that is in direct contact with the product), secondary (i.e., packaging such as a six-pack that unites several primary packages), and tertiary (i.e., packaging that serves to transport products from manufacturers to retailers).

[18]OTA attempted to quantify total retail losses resulting from pilferage but was unable to do so.

retail store, cost savings from reduced pilferage can be passed on to consumers. However, the common perception is that this type of packaging is wasteful because once removed it is discarded.

Indeed, how quickly packaging enters the MSW stream is one criterion for evaluating packaging. For example, packaging that serves only to transport a product must be removed in order to use it. In some cases, this packaging can be recycled; for example, the recycling rate for corrugated cardboard used in packaging is relatively high (ch. 5). In other cases, as with the blister packs, the packaging ends up in landfills or incinerators.

Industries generally respond to charges of excessive packaging by stating that profit factors already drive them to design minimal packaging. It is true that the amount of materials used in packaging has been reduced in some instances. However, this argument is not valid for all products. For example, the higher profits obtained from cosmetics, fragrances, and luxury goods can justify packaging that is more than minimal. As an example of an extreme, one cosmetic product includes a cellophane wrap, a cardboard box, a corrugated sheet to protect the mirror, and a plastic container (62).

In the 1970s, EPA suggested that the communication and convenience functions of packaging could be better targets for eliminating excessive packaging than would be the protection function (87). Recent analyses by academic researchers agree, but they also note that reducing convenience could create enormous consumer outcry (69).

This suggests that prevention efforts might be served best not by having the Federal Government define excessive packaging, but instead by having it concentrate on getting MSW-related criteria incorporated into decisions about packaging design. For example, the government could provide incentives for manufacturers to consider packaging reduction in their designs; the government also could periodically evaluate packaging from an MSW prevention perspective. In addition, industry efforts to develop such criteria could be encouraged. These and other policy options are discussed in chapter 1.

Data on Packaging and Containers—Table 4-5 presents data from the EPA/Franklin model about packaging and containers. Paper packaging is the largest subcategory, comprising over one-half of all packaging and almost 20 percent of all MSW by weight. Together, corrugated boxes and glass containers make up almost 60 percent of all packaging. Packaging made of plastics, a target of many community bans, amounts to about 4 percent by weight of all MSW, although its share may be increasing.[19]

Before targeting any of these subcategories for reduction, various trade-offs need to be considered. For example, eliminating all plastic packaging apparently would reduce MSW generation by 4 percent by weight. However, in reality the replacement materials are likely to be heavier and thus could actually increase MSW, at least in terms of weight. The use of lighter-weight materials such as plastics and paper has brought cost savings to manufacturers and retailers, and it has decreased concerns about breakage of glass bottles. Other concerns (e.g., litter, recyclability), however, again illustrate the trade-offs that need to be balanced.

Eliminating plastic packaging might even increase the volume of MSW. For example, corrugated cardboard boxes, which make up 67 percent of paper packaging and 12 percent of all MSW by weight, are being replaced in part by shrink-wrap film in combination with a cardboard or rigid plastic tray, in consumer products such as baby food jars and canned food (72, 73). The newer packaging makes it easier to display products. It also takes up less volume when discarded and thus can lower disposal costs. One study estimated that the use of multi-material flexible packages in place of metal cans and glass bottles can bring savings in the costs of transporting filled and empty containers, even though the replacement material is more expensive to produce (72). A West German study estimated that replacing plastic with other materials would increase the weight of packaging by a factor of 4, volume by a factor of 2.5, and use of energy during production by a factor of 2 (31).

One packaging change that can negatively affect both MSW generation and recycling, however, is the

---

[19]For example, discards from households in Tucson, Arizona, exhibited an increase in the weight of plastic from about 5 percent in 1978 to 10 percent in 1988 (95). The increase was attributed to the replacement of glass and metals in packaging by plastics.

Table 4-5—Estimated Weights and Percentages of Different Containers and Packaging in Gross Discards of MSW, by Material, in 1986

	Amount in thousands of tons	Percent of material category	Percent of containers and packaging	Percent of gross discards
Glass:				
Beer & soft drink bottles	5,543	47.0		3.5
Wine & liquor bottles	2,135	18.1		1.4
Food & other bottles/jars	4,128	35.0		2.6
Subtotal	11,806		22.1	7.5
Steel:				
Beer & soft drink cans	118	4.2		0.1
Food cans	1,777	62.7		1.1
Other nonfood cans	747	26.4		0.5
Barrels, drums, pails	91	3.2		0.1
Other steel packaging	101	3.6		0.1
Subtotal	2,834		5.3	1.8
Aluminium:				
Beer & soft drink cans	1,317	78.8		0.8
Other cans	50	3.0		0.0
Aluminum foil	302	18.1		0.2
Closures	3	0.2		0.0
Subtotal	1,672		3.1	1.1
Paper & paperboard:				
Corrugated boxes	19,444	66.9		12.3
Other paperboard	5,440	18.7		3.4
Paper packaging	4,163	14.3		2.6
Subtotal	29,047		54.5	18.4
Plastics:				
Containers	2,871	50.0		1.8
Other packaging	2,798	48.7		1.8
Other miscellaneous	73	1.3		0.0
Subtotal	5,742		10.8	3.6
Miscellaneous other:				
Wood	2,101			1.3
Rubber/leather	13			0.0
Textiles	103			0.1
Subtotal	2,217		4.2	1.4
Total	53,318			33.8

SOURCE: Franklin Associates, Ltd., *Characterization of Municipal Solid Waste in the United States, 1960 to 2000 (Update 1988)*, report prepared for the U.S. Environmental Protection Agency, Office of Solid Waste and Emergency Response (Prairie Village, KS: Mar. 30, 1988).

trend toward wrapping products (by both manufacturers and retailers) in multiple layers of packaging or making containers with multiple materials (12). When this causes the size of the package or the complexity of the design to increase, subsequent MSW generation can increase (although by how much is unknown) or, in the case of multi-material products, recycling can become more difficult.

Beverage Containers.—The use of materials in beverage containers has changed dramatically during the past 20 years. In particular, the use of plastic in containers is increasing. This trend is difficult to quantify on a national basis; the EPA/Franklin model does not estimate the amounts of paper or plastics used specifically for beverage containers, although it does do so for glass, steel, and aluminum.

Based on data from the model (table 4-5), the total weight of beverage containers is estimated to be between 5.8 and 11.0 percent, with an amount nearer the lower figure more likely. Glass bottles for beer, wine, and soft drinks account for 3.5 percent; steel cans for beer and soft drinks account for 0.1 percent; and aluminum cans for beer and soft drinks account for 0.8 percent. The amount of paper (e.g., for milk cartons) could be as high as 3.4 percent but probably is lower (because the category "other paperboard" contains nonbeverage containers), while the amount of plastic could be as high as 1.8 percent.

In some cases, lighter-weight materials may not be used because they do not impart the proper image. For example, plastic is sometimes viewed as a low value material, while glass is considered by some customers to impart a quality or premium image (83). Glass and ceramic jars dominate in the imported and gourmet foods markets and for some cosmetic products.

Food Packaging—It is difficult to estimate how food packaging is changing over time. Data from the EPA/Franklin model suggest that food packaging comprises 10 percent or more of MSW by weight. According to the model, steel food cans and glass food jars for nonliquid products make up another 3.7 percent (table 4-5). In addition, about 12 percent of all MSW is corrugated cardboard, and one representative of the packaging industry estimated that up to one-half of this—or 6 percent of MSW—might be used for food packaging (1). The amount of other paperboard and plastic used in food packaging cannot be estimated.

Some visible changes in food packaging have occurred. Consumers are buying more "ready to eat" foods and "fast-food" meals.[20] Changes in packaging have made such foods convenient to purchase, prepare, and eat, as well as last longer. The use of plastic packaging is increasing, and many consumers prefer plastic containers for a variety of foods (20). These changes have increased the amount of packaging entering the MSW stream, but at the same time packaging manufacturers have reduced the amount of material used in other packages.

The phenomenal growth in the use of microwave ovens is having a striking effect on food preparation and packaging design. In 1986, almost 21 million microwave ovens were imported or produced in the United States, twice the amount than in 1983 (82). One survey indicated that 83 percent of all respondents had microwave ovens (20). Microwaveable products often tend to use "container cooking" packaging: they include a cooking/serving dish and several layers of plastic and paper wrapping to preserve the contents, improve the effectiveness of the microwave as a heat source, make the product table-ready, and eliminate the need for dishwashing.

Photo credit: Office of Technology Assessment

Foam polystyrene made with chlorofluorocarbons (CFCs) as blowing agents has been of concern because CFCs contribute to global warming. Most fast-food packaging made of foam polystyrene, such as this clamshell, no longer contains CFCs. However, fast-food packaging is a lightning rod for public attention and certain types have been banned in some communities.

Reducing this type of packaging is a challenge, but it would be possible. For example, MSW would be reduced if a dish was not included with every purchase or if the functions of the wrappers were restricted to protection. Durable cooking ware also could be designed so that microwaveable food could be packaged in simple pouches, ready to be placed in reusable ware for cooking.

Shipping Packaging—Packaging used in shipping is undergoing changes that reduce the weight of the materials used. This reduction is related to the development and use of new materials and designs that decrease transportation and waste management costs to manufacturers, wholesalers, and retailers (72). For example:

- General Motors introduced reusable, collapsible or stackable boxes to replace expendable corrugated boxes for parts delivery from its suppliers;

- Nordyne ships mobile home air-conditioner and furnace units that are shrink-wrapped with plastic onto pallets, with corners, tops, and bottoms protected by corrugated cardboard; and

---

[20]This also could be shifting some generation of food waste from residences to the industrial and commercial facilities that prepare such foods.

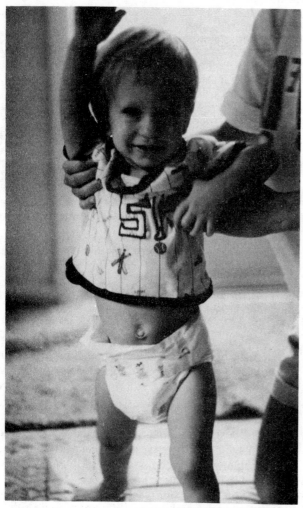

Infants wearing single-use, disposable diapers are a common sight. Consumers like these diapers because of their convenience and buy more than 18 billion every year. The total cost of using a diaper service for the cotton equivalent of disposable diapers appears to be less than the cost of buying and disposing of the disposable diapers.

- Gerber has adopted a distribution package for glass jars that includes shrink wrap and a corrugated tray but does not require corrugated partitions between the bottles.

Changes in the design of containers can eliminate the need for some shipping packaging. For example, interlocking plastic bottles have been introduced to reduce packaging costs for the beverage industry. This eliminates the need for cartons, overwraps, and plastic straps, although trays may still be needed to support the weight of multiple containers (25).

"Single-Use" Products

Products that are used once and discarded have become ingrained in our society, replacing similar products with longer lifetimes. They are often called "disposable" or "throwaway" products, but because all products and packages are ultimately disposable, OTA generally calls these "single-use" products. They include some diapers, plastic and paper plates and cups, single-use razors, plastic utensils, and many other products, even some cameras and flashlights. One product that has received particular attention is polystyrene foam cups (ch. 8). (See box 4-E.)

One appeal of single-use products is convenience—they help people save personal time and help retailers save labor costs. For example, a paper or plastic plate, cup, or utensil does not have to be washed and stored; a single-use camera does not require time to replace film. Another appeal is purchase price. Often they can be purchased for a fraction of the initial cost of the alternative reusable product. For example, a new single-use baby bib designed for newborn babies to 18-month-old babies sells in packages of one dozen for less than $2 (52).

Single-use products make a substantial contribution to the U.S. economy. For example, sales of single-use razors are around $100 million per year (3), and sales of single-use diapers are around $4 billion (43).

The one single-use product that makes the largest identifiable contribution to MSW generation is the single-use (disposable) diaper. Consumers buy more than 18 billion disposable diapers every year, and these make up about 2 percent of all MSW and perhaps 4 percent of all residential MSW (43) (ch. 3). The annual lifecycle cost of all single-use diapers, including landfilling costs, have been estimated to be about $3.9 billion (43).

In contrast, a diaper service can reuse a cotton diaper about 150 times, resulting in fewer diapers being sent to landfills and in fecal material being sent for treatment at municipal sewage treatment plants. The costs of washing (including electricity, labor, profit, and waste water processing) the cotton

---

Box 4-E—Foam Polystyrene Packaging

Public concern about foam polystyrene (PS) packaging (e.g., fast-food containers and meat trays) originated over the use of chlorofluorocarbons (CFCs) as blowing agents and the impacts of CFCs on ozone depletion and global warming. New concerns about the volume of PS packaging in landfills have increased the visibility of this issue. As a result, PS packaging has been the target of legislative bans in several States and localities (ch. 8).

The actual use of CFCs in foam products is relatively small and foam PS accounts for only 2 to 3 percent of the use of CFCs. The use of CFC-11 and CFC-12 ended voluntarily in 1988 for most foam PS packaging associated with food products. Some foam PS products, such as most molded foam cups, do not use CFCs as the blowing agent; these typically use other hydrocarbons such as pentane. More significant uses of CFCs are in refrigeration, air-conditioning, and polyurethane production.

Similarly, PS comprises a small percentage of all plastics produced and those that are discarded in MSW. By weight, plastics contribute a relatively small portion of MSW, around 7 percent. About 2 million tons of PS (both rigid and foam) were consumed in the United States in 1987 (68)—about 10 percent of all plastics used and about 15 percent of the plastics used in packaging and in consumer and institutional markets (ch. 5). Half of this was used in durable products including appliances, building and construction, toys, and housewares. Packaging and single-use disposable products comprised the other half.

The foam PS portion in packaging and single-use products has attracted considerable recent attention. About 230,000 tons of foam PS are used in single-use products such as cups, plates, and clamshells. Almost 30 billion hot drink foam cups are used and discarded each year, but their overall weight amounts to less than 100,000 tons (1). About 220,000 tons of foam are used for packaging such as trays (for meats, poultry, and fish), molded cups, and loose packaging fill. Given these low numbers, it is not surprising that data from landfill excavations show the total amount of fast-food packaging (both paper and plastics) in landfills to be very small, about 0.25 percent by both weight and volume (59).

Nevertheless, the actual and proposed bans on foam PS have demonstrated how industry can respond relatively quickly to change to alternative production materials and begin establishing pilot recycling programs. For example, industry has responded to the CFC concern by substituting other blowing agents. By the end of 1988, CFC-12 was no longer used in most foam PS food packaging, including foam cups, sandwich cartons, trays, and carry-out containers; it was replaced with hydrochlorofluorocarbon-22, which has 5 percent of the ozone-depletion potential of CFC-12. Manufacturers of egg cartons and meat trays are working to phase out the use of CFC-12 by the end of 1989. However, some substitutes for CFC blowing agents create their own problems for recycling. At least one company had to eliminate the recycling of foam PS industrial scrap because the new hydrocarbon blowing agents (pentane, butane, and propane) were flammable and the recycler could not afford to modify its equipment with appropriate safety features.

---

equivalent of 18 billion disposable diapers might be about $2.3 billion.[21]

These estimates, however, do not account for differences in external costs (i.e., pollution) from the initial extraction, transportation, or manufacturing of raw materials into either disposable or cotton diapers. They also do not account for differences in how a baby's skin responds (e.g., fewer rashes occur with the single-use diapers) or for the appeal of convenience. In addition, newer highly absorbent single-use diapers require fewer changes than older versions; if this reduced the number of changes by one-half, then the overall costs of single-use and

cotton diapers would be about the same. Even then, however, more single-use diapers would end up in landfills, while washable diapers could still be reused (and their fecal content sent into the sewer system for appropriate treatment).

Longer-Lived and Repairable Products— Changes in product durability or lifetime usually are caused by intentional decisions about product design. For example, single-use products usually are less durable and have shorter lifetimes. In addition, many single-use products are designed with no intention of repair because the cost of purchasing a replacement is less than the cost of repair. Examples include

---

[21]Lehrburger (43) calculated a cost of $227.8 million, but OTA's calculations indicate an error by a factor of 10.

small consumer electronic products (e.g., hand calculators), home and beauty care appliances, and disposable cameras. Many of these products cost less than $20. Another example is plastic throwaway telephones; one company was reported to be selling this item at the rate of 8,000 units per month in 1987 (35).

Manufacturers in the United States are attempting to improve their competitiveness in international markets. Two associated concepts have the potential to reduce MSW generation, although waste prevention is not an intentional consequence. First, quality manufacturing can result in products that last longer. One U.S. company that promotes a strategy based on increased product lifetimes and, consequently, less MSW generation is the Maytag Corp., whose image is based on making long-lived appliances. Second, improved design can also bring less waste and increased industrial competitiveness (6). For example, steel-belted tires last longer than their predecessors, so the generation of waste tires might be lowered.

Increases in durability, however, do not always reduce MSW generation. For example, longer-lived tires are subject to more stress over their lifetime simply because they are longer-lived. Tire manufacturers addressed this partly by increasing their use of new synthetic and natural rubbers, which in turn led to a decline in the recycling of rubber from old tires (57). In addition, steel-belted tires are more difficult to recycle than are rubber tires.

One way to encourage manufacturers to consider MSW issues when they design products would be to offer awards to stimulate higher quality manufacturing. This is done already in some areas. For example, the Department of Commerce awarded the first Malcolm Baldridge National Quality Awards in 1988.[22] Although reducing waste is not one of the seven criteria for the award, increased quality can bring increased product durability and reduced waste. Motorola, Inc., a 1988 award winner, has a quality goal of ''zero defects in everything we do,'' including product performance.

Reusable Products

Systematic reuse of products such as refillable beverage bottles could effect MSW generation, but it is a practice that is disappearing as single-use products gain in popularity. It is instructive to consider the benefits and costs of returning to reuse systems.

Beverage Bottles—Many people recall the days when it was common practice to have residential delivery of milk and when most soda and beer bottles were refillable. Both systems required that empty bottles be returned for washing and refilling, which helped avoid replacement costs for discarded bottles and also helped (even if unintentionally) internalize the costs of waste management.

In the late 1940s, almost all beer and soft drinks were sold in refillable bottles, but during the 1950s the share of nonrefillable bottles and metal cans increased (57). Data from the soft drink industry show that by 1986 only 14 percent of the volume of soft drinks was packaged in refillable glass bottles, with the balance packaged in one-way glass, plastic, and cans (49). On a volume basis, refillable glass packaging declined by 8 percent between 1985 and 1986; on a unit basis, it declined by 6 percent.

These changes affect the overall weight of bottles that enter the MSW stream because while refillable bottles tend to be heavier than single-use bottles, they also last much longer. By 1966, for example, even though the total weights of shipments of refillable and single-use soft drink bottles were about the same, the **number** of shorter-lived, nonrefillable bottles was greater than refillables.

Most refillable beverage systems in the United States have disappeared, including those in States with beverage container deposits, which are designed to stimulate recycling.[23] The remaining systems are concentrated in the Midwest, where about 25 percent of the volume of soft drinks sold is packaged in refillable bottles, and in the South, where refillables are almost 12 percent of the market (49). This compares with 2 to 6 percent in other areas of the United States. Refillable bottling systems have declined primarily because of changes in the beverage industry infrastructure and the cost of

---

[22]The awards are the result of an 1987 amendment to the Stevenson-Wydler Technology Innovation Act of 1980.

[23]See ch. 8 for discussion of mandatory beverage deposit and recycling systems.

refillable systems. Returned bottles have to be cleaned and the resulting wastewater has to be disposed of properly. In addition, glass bottles are heavy and costly to transport back to the bottling facilities.

Whether a return to refillable systems is economically feasible is unclear. The cost factors mentioned above suggest that switching to refillables might increase the cost of beverages. A return to such a system also would be difficult because the infrastructure for it no longer exists, and the capital investments required for refillable systems are greater than those required for new one-way systems (1). In addition, curbside collection, which is being used in many communities to collect recyclable containers, probably would not work as a return mechanism for refillable glass or plastic bottles given the rough handling they are likely to receive; refillable glass cannot be chipped and plastic cannot be punctured.

On the other hand, the use of refillable bottles could lower the costs that the public sector must pay to manage increasing numbers of soft drink and beer containers, particularly if energy savings are realized by such systems or if refillable bottles decrease MSW generation. For example, some reduction by weight in MSW generation would occur if bottles were reused instead of discarded. However, current refillable bottles are usually glass, which weighs more than single-use containers made of aluminum or plastic. Thus, the refillable bottles would have to be refilled several times to obtain an equivalent savings of weight. With respect to the total energy requirements associated with using different bottles, the breakeven point between aluminum cans and refillable glass bottles has been estimated to range from 4 to 26 trips (1,46).

The importance of transportation costs in MSW management (ch. 2) suggests that one way to reduce costs would be to develop a lightweight refillable plastic beverage bottle. Refillable plastic bottles are being tested by Coca-Cola in West Germany. Preliminary testing shows many technical obstacles that must be overcome, including the fact that the bottles become brittle and shrink slightly after repeated washing. Coca-Cola expects to overcome these problems, however (16). In addition, sophisticated chemical detection equipment is used to test the bottles after they are washed to avoid the threat of contamination.

Refillable Bottle Systems in Europe—Refillable bottle beverage systems are still common in some European countries. In Denmark, for example, one directive requires that beer and carbonated soft drinks be sold in refillable bottles (4, 37). A deposit is collected on the sale of beverages to encourage returns, and the number of different bottles has been limited to simplify the return systems. An estimated 99 percent of the bottles are returned (4). This law has been viewed as an anti-free trade action within the European Community. In September 1988, however, the European Community court ruled that the law was justified because it was based on environmental concerns.

In West Germany, the government has been trying for years to reverse the decline of refillable beverage bottles. The government enacted the Waste Avoidance and Waste Management Act of 1986, which requires the environment minister to negotiate with industries to set voluntary measures regarding products (ch. 8). Negotiations between the government and the beverage industry led to the development of a deposit system, and the market for single-use bottles is expected to decline as a result.

Conditions favoring refillable bottle systems in Denmark and West Germany, however, are not necessarily present in United States. For example, transportation of refillable bottles probably is less costly in Europe. Denmark has only 2 breweries, but it is small and has a dense population. West Germany has hundreds of local breweries and extensive local distribution. In the United States, in contrast, the largest brewer has only 11 breweries for the entire country.

Other Reuse Systems—In the United States, vestiges of reuse systems remain for products other than beverage bottles. Diaper services and nonprofit organizations that recycle used goods and clothes (e.g., Goodwill and shops that sell worn garments on consignment) are examples. Another example is bottled water delivery services that use refillable bottles. In the past bottled water services were associated mainly with offices, but residential use in the United States has doubled since 1980 (15). Growth in bottled water use in homes is mainly because of public concerns about the quality of

Photo credit: Office of Technology Assessment

Over 10 billion mail-order catalogs were mailed to consumers in 1987, most of which are discarded in MSW. Products purchased through the mail tend to arrive with more packaging than products purchased at retail stores.

public, piped water supplies. In contrast to buying small single-use bottles of water at retail stores, a home delivery system does not generate MSW because the bottles are refillable, can save money, and can be more convenient, although it does require storage space.

Mail and Telephone Books

Direct mail advertising includes items such as solicitations for contributions, mail order catalogs, and offerings of sweepstake contests. This is a category of paper products that tend to have short lifetimes. Commonly referred to as ''junk mail,'' much of it is third class mail. The total weight of third class mail in 1986 was 3.3 million tons; it is the fastest growing segment of mail, having doubled on a pounds-per-capita basis between 1980 and 1986 (82). Assuming that most third class mail is discarded, it would represent about 1.5 percent of MSW.

Increased use of catalogs is one factor contributing to the growth in third class mail. The number of catalogs mailed doubled between 1980 and 1987; over 10 billion catalogs were mailed in 1987 (17).

This can affect MSW in two ways: 1) unwanted and out-of-date catalogs are discarded, and 2) merchandise ordered through catalogs tends to arrive with more packaging than does merchandise purchased from retail stores, although some packaging is reused by consumers. The 10 billion catalogs could weigh between 1 and 2.5 million tons, which would make up about 1 percent of MSW.[24]

Mailing lists are at the heart of direct mail advertising and marketing. These lists are generated by postal zip codes and are based on assumptions about numbers of residences per building. Thus single households often receive multiple versions of the same mailing. In many cases, lists are rented to other companies, although one survey reported that 55 percent of all adults disapproved of this practice (70).

Another change in the mail is that some magazines now arrive wrapped in polyethylene film, or polybags.[25] In some instances, the film has replaced heavier paper wrappers, and this results in less MSW generation by weight. However, when it replaces only a mailing label adhered to the magazine itself, then MSW generation will increase, although the increase may only be on the order of 0.01 percent.[26] Polybags also could affect MSW generation because they allow loose sheets of advertising to be enclosed. The increased use of polybags has been enhanced by changes in costs. Cost savings include faster stuffing of magazines and loose advertising sheets by machine and lower costs for materials, as well as savings in postage costs for periodicals that switch from paper to plastic wrap.

Telephone books are another growing source of MSW. Many residences now get several telephone books from different companies competing for customers. Out-of-date books tend to be discarded when a new book arrives, and most probably end up in landfills (59). About 83 million households have telephone service (82). If each household discards one 3-pound telephone book per year, then 120,000 tons, or 0.1 percent of MSW, would be generated annually. This is a conservative estimate because

---

[24] The weight calculation is based on an assumption that catalogs weigh 4 to 8 ounces each, which is conservative for some catalogs. The 1 percent figure would be included in the 1.5 percent figure for third-class mail cited above.

[25] Polybags also are used to protect and extend the shelf life of other products, such as bread and toilet paper.

[26] One manufacturer of plastic sheeting for polybags estimates that 6,000 to 24,000 tons of plastic per year are used in manufacturing polybags (61). This is about 0.004 to 0.015 percent of MSW, but not all is used for magazines.

some households discard more than one book and because it does not include telephone books from commercial establishments.

Miscellaneous Technological Changes

Technological changes can influence MSW generation rates, sometimes inadvertently. In addition to the microwave oven (see "Food Packaging"), one recent example is the computer, which has increased the use of paper. It originally was thought that the widespread adoption of computers would create a "paperless" society. However, OTA reported in 1983 that office copiers and computers have provided high-volume markets for paper use (74), and at least one other report has attributed increases in MSW generation to increased use of paper for computers and similar products (95).

Some technological changes that appear to reduce MSW generation in fact simply divert wastes to a different waste stream. For example, the use of household garbage disposals has increased during the past few decades, so less food waste may be entering MSW. However, this does not change food waste generation; it instead diverts food wastes into the sewer system.

Examples of MSW Quantity Reduction

Some firms have made product and packaging changes that happen to result in MSW quantity reduction. In general, these changes have not occurred because of MSW disposal problems, but rather in response to traditional economic forces such as improving product quality, reducing production costs, reducing costs of compliance with environmental and safety regulations, and appealing to consumer preferences. Industries have responded to public concern over MSW issues by funding recycling projects and research (ch. 5), but not by directing funding toward MSW prevention efforts.

MSW quantity reduction should be an opportunity for innovative thinking by industries, however. For example, it could lead to the development of new materials, new products, and new concepts in packaging. This, in turn, could bring millions of dollars of savings to industry (72, 73).

Changes that can decrease MSW generation can take many guises—reducing the size of products (i.e., "downsizing"), increasing product lifetimes,

putting more product into the same kind of package, putting the same amount of product into less packaging (i.e., "lightweighting"), and using both less product and less packaging. Various examples show that quantity reduction is technically and economically possible, regardless of the motivation behind the change:

• Some manufacturers offer concentrated versions of products (e.g., frozen juices, concentrated pesticides, and concentrated soaps). Box 4-F describes one such product successfully marketed by Procter & Gamble in West Germany but not in the United States (figure 4-5).
• Packaging changes initiated by Procter & Gamble (27) include:
  —Pampers and Luvs diapers and diaper packages changed so that net total amount of materials in product and package was 50 percent less than preceding design;
  —Jif peanut butter and Scope mouthwash packages changed from glass to PET, reducing weight of packaging by 80 and 90 percent, respectively;
  —Tide with Bleach eliminates need for separate purchase of bleach.
• Half-gallon ice cream cartons hold the same quantity, but their weight has been reduced by about 30 percent by changing the materials used (1).
• Shrink and stretch wrap plastic materials are replacing higher volume corrugated paper in many applications.
• General Electric changed the tub of a dishwasher from enameled steel to engineered plastic, which enable the warranty on the dishwater to be increased because the tub was more durable.
• A new blow-molding tool for plastic (HDPE) milk bottles reduces their weight 10 percent while increasing strength (58).
• A heat-set technology makes it possible to use PET containers for liquids that must be hot-filled. The new technology allowed a juice company to switch from glass to plastic bottles, resulting in a 25 percent reduction in weight. The change was made to appeal to consumers' desire for lighter weight and safer bottles and to affect long-term cost savings in bottling and shipping.

Box 4-F—Procter & Gamble Concentrated Laundry Product

In the Federal Republic of Germany, Procter & Gamble introduced a concentrated form of a fabric softener. This was marketed in addition to its existing, ready-to-use product, which was packaged in a 4-liter reusable plastic bottle. The concentrated product, sold in a flexible pouch, is used by cutting open the pouch, pouring the contents into the empty 4-liter bottle, and filling the bottle with water. The concentrated form requires about 85 percent less packaging.

The company promoted the product by emphasizing it as an initiative to reduce packaging material and waste. In addition, promotional materials pointed out that lower storage and transport costs meant that retail stores would benefit from the lower cost of the concentrate (about 60 percent less). The information also pointed out that stores could display more product in the same amount of shelf space (10 pouches in the same space as three bottles).

The company targeted its products to consumers by promoting the trouble-saving aspects of the concentrate, whose package takes up much less space and is therefore more easily discarded than the ready-to-use product. TV commercials dramatically illustrated the differences in volume of waste between the bulky plastic bottle and a rolled-up flexible pouch. The consumer campaign also had a logo—a person pouring the concentrate into the bottle—and an accompanying slogan encouraging the consumer to ''take part, to refill instead of throw away.''

The reductions in waste generation associated with the flexible pouches might, however, be offset by increases in the amount of packaging needed to protect the product during shipping. In fact, however, the pouches have not required any additional protection and they are shipped in corrugated boxes just as the plastic bottles.

Procter & Gamble tested and marketed a similar product in the United States. Unlike the German product, this product was a concentrate sold in a plastic bottle; it was formulated to be used in smaller quantities than the undiluted product rather than being poured into another container and diluted.

This concentrated product was not as successful as was hoped, although is still being sold in the United States today. The product was called a ''triple concentrate,'' and some people in the company speculate that consumers did not understand the term. Some also speculate that the failure of one concentrate in the United States and the success of another in West Germany may be in part attributed to a greater awareness of waste disposal problems among German consumers.

SOURCE: E. Fox, Procter & Gamble, personal communication, February 1989.

- A West German technology for making narrowneck beer and soft drink bottles is reported to reduce their weight by 12 to 17 percent, which would reduce materials costs; however, use of the technology would require major capital expenditures for new machinery (67).

- Neutrogena has made a single-bar shampoo soap since about 1960; while this product requires some packaging, it avoids the use of larger containers. It differs from liquid shampoos in that it is made from soaps rather than detergents, leaves a residue when used in hard water, and is marketed primarily for men (50).

- Plastic bags bought by McDonald's to ship products to its stores are designed to be reused as garbage bags.

- Erol's, a large video rental and sales chain, trains its sales people to reuse the distinctive plastic bags that tapes are carried in and to ask customers to return tapes in the bags, in the process saving about $1 million and over 25 million bags annually (21).

PREVENTION OPPORTUNITIES FOR CONSUMERS

Consumers can play a powerful role in MSW prevention through their purchasing decisions, which can ultimately shape demand for products and influence product design. However, little information exists to guide consumers or offer incentives to exercise that power—even motivated consumers are limited in such circumstances. Even so, consumers have some opportunities to reduce waste by making different purchasing choices and by reusing products and packaging in their homes and places of business.

Figure 4-5—Advertising Used in West Germany for Procter & Gamble's Concentrated Fabric Softener

Eine gemeinsame Initiative zur Entlastung der Umwelt.

Lenor NACHFÜLL-PACKUNG

Die Lenor Nachfüll-packung ist eine Initiative zur drastischen Verringe-rung von Packmaterial und dem damit verbun-denen Abfallvolumen.

Die Nachfüllpackung ent-hält ein 1:4 Konzentrat, das vom Verbraucher in eine leere 4 ltr. Weichspü-lerflasche gefüllt und mit 3 ltr. Wasser zu 4 ltr. gebrauchsfertigem Pro-dukt aufgefüllt wird. Dies führt gegenüber der 4 ltr. Weichspülerflasche zu:

85 % weniger Verpackungs-material

85 % weniger Abfallvolumen

This ad emphasizes the product's value in reducing packaging waste and as the fact that it takes up less storage space in households.
SOURCE: E. Fox, Corporate Packaging Development, Procter & Gamble, personal communication, February 1989.

Individual Consumers

Some States and public interest groups issue bulletins or brochures listing possible actions that individual consumers can take to be more responsible in their MSW generation (e.g., 56, 65). Household hazardous waste programs also provide such information.

Some of the ways in which individual consumers can influence MSW generation include:

- buying items that are reusable instead of disposable,
- selecting product brands that are durable or repairable,
- buying in bulk or large sizes,
- buying lighter versions of products,
- avoiding containers made of mixed materials,
- composting yard and food wastes in residential backyards,
- buying fresh rather than pre-packaged fruits and vegetables,
- donating usable but unwanted materials to friends or charities,
- buying products that contain fewer potentially toxic substances,
- reusing product containers and purchasing beverages in refillable bottles, and
- using home delivery of water instead of purchasing bottled water.

Some of these topics have been discussed in this chapter. This section discusses one idea for providing information to consumers (the ratio of product content to packaging) and several activities that consumers can undertake to reduce MSW generation (buying in bulk, reusing product containers, composting in backyards, and reducing waste from telephone books and mail).

Ratio of Product Content to Packaging

One type of information that can help guide consumers is the ratio of product content to packaging. OTA has calculated, for illustrative purposes, the ratio of product content to packaging for a number of consumer products (table 4-6). Because products usually have information about net weight (i.e., weight of the contents), the contribution of packaging can only be obtained by weighing the total item and subtracting the net weight.[27] As the numerical value of the Content/Packaging (C/P) ratio increases, more content is purchased. As the C/P ratio approaches 1, the consumer is buying as much content as package. A C/P ratio of less than one means that more packaging than product content is bought.

However, this evaluation method does not always work. A package of 10 Twinnings teabags, for instance, is less wasteful than a box of 25 bags. The small set of bags has only a polypropylene wrapper, while the larger version also has a box. In addition, the functions of the contents also need to be considered; with laundry detergents, for example, the number of washing loads that can be accomplished with a given ratio may be more important than actual weight.

One way to extend this idea is to include the unit price (cost per ounce) in the calculations. Based on the data in table 4-6, the unit cost of many items decreases as less packaging is used. Thus, stores that make unit costs available may also be providing a guide for less wasteful buying. However, there is a critical limitation to this pricing concept. Unit prices are often related to product quality and brand name (e.g., over-the-counter medicines), so that products with the same C/P ratio could have very different unit prices.

The trend toward single-serving packages offers two important benefits, reduced food spoilage for individuals who do not consume multiple servings, and convenience. However, food packaged in single servings not only has less product per package, but the packages often are wrapped twice or are combined into packs of three or four (similar to beer six-packs) to encourage multiple purchases. For example, one package of three single cartons of orange juice with straws is wrapped in polypropylene or plastic wrap. It has 18 ounces of product per ounce of packaging (table 4-6); in contrast, frozen concentrate has a ratio of 53 to 1, and a single multiple-serving carton has a ratio of 28 to 1. Buying concentrated products thus can result in less packaging per unit of product.

---

[27]This simple calculation is only possible for solid weights. For fluid ounces, the total item must be weighed and the empty packaging weighed because the conversion from fluid ounces to ounces can vary depending on the density of the liquid.

Table 4-6—Relationships Between Contents and Packaging of Selected Products

Product	Weight (ounces)			Content/ package ratio	Percent packaging		Total cost per ounce
	Contents	Total	Package		of contents	of total	
Minute Maid Orange Juice							
Pack of 3	28.1	29.75	1.61	17.5	5.7	5.4	0.04
Frozen concentrate	53.3	54.3	1	53.3	1.9	1.8	
Carton	70.75	73.25	2.5	28.3	3.5	3.4	0.03
Fresh juice				0.7			
Chicken-of-the-Sea Tuna							
Pack of 3	9.75	13.5	3.75	2.6	38.5	27.8	0.26
Bumble Bee can	6.5	8	1.5	4.3	23.1	18.8	
Safeway can	6.5	8.25	1.75	3.7	26.9	21.2	
Del Monte green beans							
Microwave Ready Vegetable Classic	11.5	13.75	2.25	5.1	19.6	16.4	0.11
Can	16	18.5	2.5	6.4	15.6	13.5	0.04
Can	8	10	2	4.0	25.0	20.0	0.06
Fresh	16	16.1	0.1	160.0	0.6	0.6	
Del Monte yogurt cup							
Pack of 4	19	21.75	2.75	6.9	14.5	12.6	0.10
Del Monte pudding cup							
Pack of 4	20	22.5	2.5	8.0	12.5	11.1	0.08
Jello Instant Pudding & Pie Filling	4	4.5	0.25	16.0	6.3	5.6	
with 2 cups milk	20.2	21.05	0.85	23.8	4.2	4.0	
Mueller's Old Fashioned Egg Noodles							
Box	12	14	2	6.0	16.7	14.3	0.09
Cello bag	16	16.5	0.5	32.0	3.1	3.0	0.09
Lipton Tea							
Loose in box	8	9.25	1.25	6.4	15.6	13.5	
Bags in box (12)	3	4.25	1.25	2.4	41.7	29.4	
Twinnings Tea Bags (English breakfast)							
Bags/box (25)	1.8	3.25	1.45	1.2	80.6	44.6	
Bags/cello (10)	0.66	1	0.34	1.9	51.5	34.0	
Tide Laundry Detergent							
Box	42	44	4	10.5	9.5	9.1	0.09
Box	17	19.75	2.75	6.2	16.2	13.9	
Mennen Deodorant							
Speed Stick	2.25	4	1.75	1.3	77.8	43.8	1.33
Lady Speed Dry	1.5	3.75	2.25	0.7	150.0	60.0	1.73
Milk 2%							
Carton - 1/2 gal.	69	71.5	2.5	27.6	3.6	3.5	

NOTE: Limitations include few data on liquid-containing packages or shipping packages.

SOURCE: Office of Technology Assessment, 1989.

However, this example points out another limitation of the C/P ratio. In particular, it does not account for shifting the production of waste to elsewhere. For example, rinds and pulp are discarded during production of orange juice. More oranges are used in making one ounce of frozen concentrate than one ounce of normal-strength juice. Thus, the amount of food waste discarded during production of the concentrate might be greater than the amount of packaging associated with the normal-strength juice.

Buying in Bulk

Buying dry, unwrapped products in bulk instead of buying prepackaged items is another way to reduce packaging, especially if consumers use their own reusable containers. This approach has been popular at food cooperatives, which represent a very small percentage of total food purchases, but the availability of bulk products in regular supermarkets has increased in recent years. For wet foods, however, buying in bulk is less practical because of concerns about spoilage.

Reusing Product Containers

Consumers can control packaging that is added at the cashier or check-out stand. For example, consumers can request that their groceries not be double-bagged and that frozen foods not be placed in individual plastic bags. They can consolidate purchases in department stores into one large bag rather than several smaller ones. Consumers also can find second uses for bags (e.g., using grocery bags as garbage liner bags, or carrying empty bags with them when they go shopping).

Backyard Composting

In some areas of the country, the largest fraction of MSW is yard wastes (chs. 3 and 5). **Reduction** of yard wastes only can occur by household action—i.e., backyard composting and mulching—as opposed to **recycling** in municipal and private composting operations. Industry has no operational role in backyard composting, but it does market compost products that facilitate home yard waste reduction, such as small shredders and chippers, lawnmower attachments, materials for compost bins, and pitchforks.

Backyard composting does not necessarily add major chores to standard yard and garden upkeep because the materials have to be dealt with in some way; however, it does require space and proper maintenance. Many brochures and periodicals from State and local organizations provide details on how backyard composting can be done cheaply and effectively (e.g., 45, 66). In the State of Washington, a nonprofit organization trains ''master composters'' and promotes home composting, and Seattle has a grant to distribute home composting bins and educate citizens about how to compost in their backyards (8). Given the amount of yard wastes in MSW, backyard composting may be one of the most effective ways for consumers to change their MSW generation rates.

Mail and Telephone Books

One way to reduce the growth in mail order catalogs is for individual consumers to remove their names from mailing lists (e.g., by contacting the Direct Marketing Association). In West Germany, it is illegal to deliver anonymous (i.e., not individually addressed) advertising mail if a household places a sticker on its mailbox or door saying that such mail is not wanted (34). Another way is to replace catalogs with electronic systems, such as TV shopping (24) and computerized telephone solicitors that are already in place but have not yet captured a large share of direct mail markets.

Electronic systems offer a way to reduce the use of telephone books. The French telephone company offers subscribers free use of a mini-computer terminal, the ''Minitel,'' as an alternative to a printed telephone book, as well as to provide other electronic services. Use of the Minitel for the latter purposes incurs a charge, while the telephone listings do not. The decrease in telephone books, however, might be offset initially by packaging waste from computers and from cable hook-ups.

Offices, Institutions, and Retailers

Changes in technology and in office practices have changed the nature of MSW generated at offices, institutions, and retail stores.[28] Photocopying machines largely have replaced carbon paper and

---

[28]OTA's separate background paper on medical wastes concluded that the amount of hospital waste generated per bed may have increased significantly within the last decade (80). Part of this suspected increase is caused by an observed—but unquantified—increase in the single-use items used in hospitals and other medical facilities.

their use of paper represents a growth area for paper manufacturers. Inked fabric typewriter ribbons have been replaced by plastic ribbons that only cycle once. Computer and typewriter printer ribbons, however, are being replaced by chemical toners, which may help reduce office waste, especially because some can be recharged. Some toners, however, may contain toxic substances.

Waste prevention efforts undertaken by offices, commercial establishments, and other institutions have a potentially wider effect than simply reducing their own waste generation (and, in some cases, the costs of waste disposal). In particular, prevention efforts in these establishments can help to educate employees so they practice waste prevention in their own homes. State and public interest groups are beginning to seek ways to help offices and institutions practice MSW prevention (42, 62). For example, offices and institutions could evaluate actions such as:

- more precise inventorying and ordering of materials;
- reusing materials (e.g., file folders, paper clips) within an office or business;
- adopting new technologies that use raw materials more efficiently;
- negotiating with suppliers to provide goods in more practical packaging;
- evaluating waste generation to determine where changes might be made;
- using more durable and repairable equipment;
- negotiating good service contracts;
- dual-sided copying;
- converting the blank side of paper to scratch paper;
- using electronic mail instead of paper memos;
- reduced mailing and distribution lists; and
- using reusable items for food service.

The use of electronic mail, for example, is now extending beyond internal office use. The Electronic Data Interchange Association has estimated that about 3,500 companies use electronic interchanges for external communication to some extent and that 10,500 will do so by 1991 (5). The driving force is to cut costs, but paper reduction and the loss of clerical jobs may be additional results.

Many possibilities also are applicable to retailers. The Rhode Island Solid Waste Management Corp.

(62) cites several MSW reduction actions that have already been taken, for example, by some restaurants. In one, a pub converted some of its beer sales from single-use bottles to draft or to returnable bottles. Waste disposal savings were estimated to pay for the system in 4 years.

Public restaurants also could evaluate the possibility of converting paper and plastic single-service items to reusable ones. Restaurants benefit from single-service ware when they save on labor costs, water use, detergents, space, and investments in dishwashing equipment. However, at least part of the internal saving is converted into a cost for society, which must pay the burden of mounting waste problems. Fast-food restaurants, especially ones with take-out foods, might suffer some loss of consumer satisfaction, however, as well as an increase in operating costs. Thus, the benefits of a change to reduced MSW generation will depend not only on cost trade-offs but also on the willingness of consumers to change their eating habits.

Retail shops also generate waste in the form of the paper and plastics used to protect goods in transport. Once the products are received, this material becomes waste unless it offers some potential for reuse onsite. Reuse and recycling is common for corrugated cardboard. That opportunity, however, may not be available for other materials unless the shipping material has been designed with reuse in mind, and small retailers do not have the ability to affect that design. Large retailers, however, can pressure design changes in some cases.

Retail shops can control some of the packaging materials (e.g., wrapping papers, boxes, and shopping bags) that are added to consumer purchases. Often two or three layers of packaging are added, sometimes only so that an advertising logo can be displayed, even when the product is already well-protected and easily carried.

U.S. grocery stores typically include the cost of bags with the cost of groceries. According to Safeway, its 166 stores in the Baltimore-to-Richmond corridor use almost 4 million bags per week (three times as many plastic as paper), for a cost of about $110,000 (11). The use of plastic bags results in waste prevention (because they occupy about 1/6 the space, especially during storage, that paper bags occupy) and cost savings to the corporation (because paper bags cost about 4 cents each, compared with 2 cents each for plastic bags). However, plastic bags may bring other MSW problems related to their durability (chs. 3 and 5). One way to encourage a reduction in the number of bags used would be to charge customers for the bags. Some European stores charge customers extra for shopping bags; in Denmark, the cost varies depending on whether the bag is plastic (about 10 cents) or paper (about 20 cents). One store in Massachusetts charges its customers 3 cents per bag and encourages customers to bring their own bags. This has resulted in a 40-percent reduction in bag consumption (64).

CHAPTER 4 REFERENCES

1. Alexander, J.H., James River Corp., personal communication, Feb. 15, 1989.
2. Allen, D., Preventive Environmental Protection Project, National Toxics Prevention Fund, personal communication, Feb. 21, 1989.
3. BIC Corp., *Annual Report, 1987,* Mar. 30, 1988.
4. Biles, S., "A Review of Municipal and Hazardous Waste Management Practices and Facilities in Seven European Countries," working paper prepared for German Marshall Fund of the United States (Portland, OR: February 1987).
5. Brown, W., "Electronic Pulses Replacing Paper in Workplace," *The Washington Post,* p. F1, Sept. 2, 1988.
6. Business Week, "Smart Design, Quality is the New Style," *Business Week,* pp. 102-113, Apr. 11, 1988.
7. Catlett, R., Dow Consumer Products, Inc., personal communication at Office of Technology Assessment Workshop on MSW Reduction (Washington, DC: July 14-15, 1988).
8. Chapman, C., Washington Department of Ecology, personal communication, Feb. 16, 1989.
9. Chemical Specialties Manufacturers Association, "Letter from R. Engel, President, to Office of Technology Assessment," May 26, 1988.
10. Chemical Times and Trends, "Going Places With Inerts," *Chemical TIMES & TRENDS* 11(2):42-44, April 1988.
11. Cockrell, A., Safeway, personal communication, Aug. 3, 1988.
12. Conservation Foundation, "EPA Municipal Solid Waste Source Reduction: Design for Disposal Policy Dialogue, Meeting Summary" (Washington, DC: Aug. 31, 1988).
13. Cunningham, W., American Newspaper Publishers Association, personal communication, Sept. 9, 1988.
14. Dawson, C., "Safe Products Through Cooperation," *Chemical TIMES & TRENDS* 11(1):35-37, January 1988.
15. Deer Park Spring Water, Inc., "The Bottled Water Explosion: A Source Book and Guide" (Lodi, NJ: undated).
16. Dichting, D., Coca-Cola Co., personal communication, Feb. 8, 1989.
17. Direct Marketing Association, "News & Information," press release (New York, NY: undated).
18. Environmental Council of Rhode Island, "Solid Waste Management Policy" (Providence, RI: September 1986).
19. Environmental Hazards Management Institute, "Household Hazardous Waste Wheel" (Durham, NH: undated).
20. Erickson, G., "Consumers Get in Touch With Packaging," *Packaging,* pp. 42- 51, June 1988.
21. Erol's, personal communication, Dec. 15-16, 1988.
22. Etter, R.M., "Reformulating Products and Proper Waste Disposal," *Chemical TIMES & TRENDS* 11(1):32-34,42, January 1988.
23. Fatkin, H., Health, Safety & Environmental Affairs, Polaroid Corp., personal communication, August 1988 and February 1989.
24. Fishman, A., "The 1986 Mail Order Guide," *Direct Marketing* 50(3):40-53,124-125, July 1987.
25. Food Engineering, "Interlocking Plastic Bottles Might Cut 6-pack Costs," *Food Engineering,* p. 37, March 1988.
26. Food Marketing Institute, "Preliminary Results of Loss Prevention Issues," *Loss Prevention Letter* 6(6):1-2, June 1989.
27. Fox, E., Corporate Packaging Development, Procter & Gamble, personal communication, February 1989.
28. Franklin Associates, Ltd., *Characterization of Municipal Solid Waste in the United States, 1960 to 2000 (Update 1988),* report prepared for the U.S. Environmental Protection Agency, Office of Solid Waste and Emergency Response (Prairie Village, KS: Mar. 30, 1988).
29. Franklin Associates, Ltd., *Characterization of Products Containing Lead and Cadmium in Municipal Solid Waste in the United States, 1970 to 2000, Executive Summary and Chapter 1,* final report prepared for U.S. Environmental Protection Agency, Municipal Solid Waste Program (Prairie Village, KS: January 1989).
30. Franklin, M.A., "The Potential Toxicity of Municipal Solid Waste," paper presented at *Municipal Solid Waste Source Reduction and Recycling Conference* (Hot Springs, VA: Mar. 23-25, 1988).
31. Gesellschaft für Verpackungsmarktforschung, "Packaging Without Plastic—Ecological and Economic

Consequences of a Packaging Market Free From Plastic (in FRG)" (Wiesbaden: Gesellschaft für Verpackungsmarktforschung mbH, 1987).

32. Gewiese, A., Bilitewski, B., and Okeke, M., "Abfallvermeidung-ein Modellversuch in Hamburg-Harburg im Jahre 1987," *Mull und Abfall*, pp. 104-120 (Berlin: Erich Schmidt Verlag, March 1989).

33. Goldberg, M., Safer, Inc., personal communication, August 1988.

34. Goosmann, G., Director, Federal Environment Agency, Federal Republic of Germany, personal communication, Apr. 14, 1989.

35. Greer, W.R., "Throw-aways: America's Lingering Fascination," *The Providence Journal*, May 11, 1987.

36. Guttman, E., Rhode Island Solid Waste Management Corp., personal communication, Feb. 20, 1989.

37. Hansen, T., "Today's Wastes Are Tomorrow's Resources," *Resources and Conservation* 12:193-201, 1986.

38. Hurst, K., and Relis, P., *The Next Frontier: Solid Waste Source Reduction* (Santa Barbara, CA: Community Environmental Council, Inc., 1988).

39. Illinois Hazardous Waste Research and Information Center, "Chemical Hazards in the Home" (Savoy, IL: undated).

40. Kinman, R.N., and Nutini, D.L., "Household Hazardous Waste in the Sanitary Landfill," *Chemical TIMES & TRENDS* 11(3):23-29 and 39-40, July 1988.

41. Lai, C.C., Selke, S.E., and Johnson, D.I., "Impact of Plastic Packaging on Solid Waste," paper presented at *Conference on Solid Waste Management and Materials Policy* (New York, NY: Feb. 11-14, 1987).

42. League of Women Voters of Washington, "Solid Waste Reduction and Recycling, A Handbook of Strategies Employed by Businesses in Washington State," prepared for Washington State Department of Ecology, Office of Waste Reduction (June 1988).

43. Lehrburger, C., *Diapers in the Waste Stream, A Review of Waste Management and Public Policy Issues* (Sheffield, MA: December 1988).

44. Lord, D., "Burnt Out Batteries," *Environmental Action* 20(2):16-19, September/October 1988.

45. Michigan State University, Cooperative Extension Service, "Backyard Composting," Extension Bulletin WM02 (New) (Lansing, MI: March 1987).

46. Moore, W.K., and Scott, D.L., "Beverage Container Deposit Laws: A Survey of the Issues and Results," *Journal of Consumer Affairs* 17(1):57-80, 1983.

47. National Association of Printing Ink Manufacturers, Inc., "Letter from J.E. Renson, Executive Director, to Office of Technology Assessment," Sept. 8, 1988.

48. National Electrical Manufacturers Association, personal communication, Feb. 16, 1989.

49. National Soft Drink Association, *Sales Survey of the Soft Drink Industry* (Washington, DC: 1986).

50. Neutragena, Public Affairs Office, personal conversation, July 27, 1988.

51. New York State Department of Environmental Conservation, *New York State Solid Waste Management Plan, 1987-88 Update* (Albany, NY: March 1988).

52. Nonwovens Industry, "End Use Markets for Nonwovens," *Nonwovens Industry*, p. 19, August 1988.

53. Obermeier, T., Ingenieurgemeinschaft Technischer Umweltschutz, Federal Republic of Germany, personal communication, Apr. 3, 1989.

54. Ontario Waste Management Advisory Board, "Environmental Aspects of Consumer Packaging, Phase I: An Overview" (Ontario: March 1978).

55. Organization for Economic Cooperation and Development, *Fate of Small Quantities of Hazardous Waste*, Environment Monographs No. 6 (Paris: August 1986).

56. Pennsylvania Resources Council, "What We Can Do To Promote Waste Reduction and Recycling" (Media, PA: undated).

57. Peterson, C., "A Waste Reduction Boom. . .In the Seventies!" *Waste Age*, pp. 100-106, February 1989.

58. Plastic Bottle Information Bureau, "Light-Weighting Plastic Milk Bottles," *The Plastic Bottle Reporter* 4(4):1-2, Fall 1986.

59. Rathje, W.L., Hughes, W.W., Archer, G., and Wilson, D.C., "Source Reduction and Landfill Myths," paper presented at *ASTSWMO National Solid Waste Forum on Integrated Municipal Waste Management* (Lake Buena Vista, FL: July 17-20, 1988).

60. Rayovac Corp., "Letter from R.L. Balfour, Vice President, to Office of Technology Assessment," Aug. 2, 1988.

61. Remes, B., American Western Corp., personal communication, July 1988.

62. Rhode Island Solid Waste Management Corp., *Annual Report 1986* (Providence, RI: 1986).

63. Rhode Island Solid Waste Management Corp., "Source Reduction Task Force Report" (Providence, RI: November 1987).

64. Rhode Island Solid Waste Management Corp., *Comprehensive Solid Waste Management Plan*, draft report (Providence, RI: December 1988).

65. Rhode Island Solid Waste Management Corp., "Source Reduction Ideas for Businesses, Source Reduction Tips" (Providence. RI: undated).

66. Rosen, C.J., Schumacher, N., Mugaas, R., and Proudfoot, S., "Composting and Mulching: A Guide to Managing Organic Yard Wastes," Minnesota

Extension Service, Department of Soil Science, University of Minnesota, AG-FO-3296 (St. Paul, MN: 1988).

67. Rosenberg, A., "Narrowneck Containers Take On the Heavyweights," *Recycling Today*, pp. 72-77, December 1988.

68. Schreiber, P., "Recycling of Polystyrene Packaging and Disposables in the USA: the Perceptions, Reality, and Possible Solutions," paper presented at *Recycle '88, International Management Forum* (Zurich, Switzerland: MAACK Business Services, 1988).

69. Selke, S.E., and Lai, C.C., "Considerations in Packaging Design—Recyclability Aspects," paper presented at *Fourth Annual Conference on Solid Waste Management* (New York, NY: Jan. 27-30, 1988).

70. Target Marketing, "Don't Rent My Name!" *Target Marketing* 10(9):16, September 1987.

71. Tuthill, R.W., Stanek, E.J., et al., "Degree of Public Support for Household Hazardous Waste Control Alternatives," *American J. of Public Health* 77(3):304-306, March 1987.

72. Twede, D., "Factors Influencing the Reduction of Distribution Packaging Waste," paper presented at *1988 Solid Waste Management and Materials Policy Conference* (Albany, NY: Legislative Commission on Solid Waste Management, Jan. 29, 1988).

73. Twede, D., "Opportunities for Public/Private Sector Cooperation to Minimize Packaging Waste," paper presented at *Rhode Island Solid Waste Management Conference* (Rhode Island: June 16, 1988).

74. U.S. Congress, Office of Technology Assessment, *Wood Use: U.S. Competitiveness and Technology*, OTA-ITE-210 (Springfield, VA: National Technical Information Service, August 1983).

75. U.S. Congress, Office of Technology Assessment, *Serious Reduction of Hazardous Waste*, OTA-ITE-317 (Springfield, VA: National Technical Information Service, September 1986).

76. U.S. Congress, Office of Technology Assessment, *Wastes in Marine Environments*, OTA-O-334 (Washington, DC: U.S. Government Printing Office, April 1987).

77. U.S. Congress, Office of Technology Assessment, *From Pollution to Prevention: A Progress Report on Waste Reduction—Special Report*, OTA-ITE-347 (Washington, DC: U.S. Government Printing Office, June 1987).

78. U.S. Congress, Office of Technology Assessment, *Identifying and Regulating Carcinogens, Background Paper*, OTA-BP-H-42 (Springfield, VA: National Technical Information Service, November 1987).

79. U.S. Congress, Office of Technology Assessment, "Workshop on MSW Reduction," July 14-15, 1988.

80. U.S. Congress, Office of Technology Assessment, *Issues in Medical Waste Management*, Background Paper, OTA-BP-O-49 (Washington, DC: U.S. Government Printing Office, October 1988).

81. U.S. Department of Commerce, Bureau of the Census, *Statistical Abstract of the United States, 1978*, 99th annual edition (Washington, DC: U.S. Government Printing Office, September 1978).

82. U.S. Department of Commerce, Bureau of the Census, *Statistical Abstract of the United States, 1988*, 108th edition (Washington, DC: U.S. Government Printing Office, December 1987).

83. U.S. Department of Commerce, International Trade Administration, *1988 U.S. Industrial Outlook* (Washington, DC: January 1988).

84. U.S. Department of Health and Human Services, *The Nature and Extent of Lead Poisoning in Children in the United States: A Report to Congress* (Atlanta, GA: Public Health Service, Agency for Toxic Substances and Disease Registry, July 1988).

85. U.S. Department of the Interior, Bureau of Mines, *Mineral Facts and Problems, 1985 Edition*, Bulletin 675 (Washington, DC: 1985).

86. U.S. Department of the Interior, Bureau of Mines, *Minerals Yearbook* (Washington, DC: 1986).

87. U.S. Environmental Protection Agency, *Resource Recovery and Waste Reduction, Fourth Report to Congress* (Washington, DC: 1977).

88. U.S. Environmental Protection Agency, *Report to Congress on the Discharge of Hazardous Wastes to Publicly Owned Treatment Works*, Office of Water Regulations and Standards, EPA/530-SW-86-004 (Washington, DC: February 1986).

89. U.S. Environmental Protection Agency, *Survey of Household Hazardous Wastes and Related Collection Programs*, Office of Solid Waste and Emergency Response, EPA/530-SW-86-038 (Washington, DC: October 1986).

90. U.S. Environmental Protection Agency, *Subtitle D Study, Phase I Report*, EPA/530-SW-86-054 (Washington, DC: Oct. 1986).

91. U.S. Environmental Protection Agency, *The Solid Waste Dilemma, An Agenda For Action*, Report of the Municipal Solid Waste Task Force, Office of Solid Waste (Washington, DC: February 1989).

92. Visalli, J., "The Similarity of Environmental Impacts From All Methods of Managing Solid Waste," paper presented at *Conference on Hazardous and Municipal Solid Waste Minimization* (Providence, RI: New England Section of Air Pollution Control Association, Feb. 7-8, 1989).

93. Washington State Department of Ecology, "Best Management Practices Analysis for Solid Waste, Eight Waste Generation Areas Findings, Volume

II,'' Office of Waste Reduction and Recycling, Publ. No. 88-33B (Olympia, WA: 1988).

94. Wirka, J., ''Design for a National Source Reduction Policy'' (Washington, DC: Environmental Action Foundation, January 1989).

95. Wilson, D.C., ''Ancient Trash, Modern Solid Wastes: An Archaeologist's Perspective on Reuse, Recycling, Waste, and Landfill Degradation,'' paper presented at *National Solid Waste Management Symposium* (Prescott, AZ: Apr. 10, 1989).

96. World Health Organization, *Environmental Health Criteria 1, Mercury* (Geneva: 1976).

Chapter 5

Recycling

CONTENTS

INTRODUCTION

Recycling is not a new phenomenon, at least not in concept. America's early settlers recycled as a matter of survival, turning corn husks into mattresses and old clothes into quilts. The materials conservation efforts so critical during World War II are not so distant that we have forgotten a time when used aluminum foil was carefully saved. In fact, most of us have recycled materials at some point in our lives—typically paper, aluminum, or glass.

But recycling is receiving increasing attention today as the Nation begins to grapple with the problems caused by MSW. Increased recycling is a goal for many State and local governments, private companies, and public interest groups. The topic of recycling is extremely complicated, and OTA believes it would be a disservice to oversimplify the facts. As a result, this chapter is long and detailed, but such detail is needed to understand the likely effectiveness of different recycling policy options.

Recycling actually consists of three different activities: collecting secondary materials, preparing those materials for market, and the actual recycling of the materials by manufacturing new products. The first section of this chapter briefly overviews recycling rates for different materials and presents information on collection and preparation. The second section discusses technologies and markets for individual secondary materials. The third section discusses pollutants associated with manufacturing processes that use virgin or secondary materials. The final section discusses general characteristics of commodity markets and barriers inhibiting the use of secondary materials.

How Much Do We Recycle?

It is difficult to provide accurate estimates of the amount of materials recycled in the United States because existing data for most materials are unreliable, especially in the MSW category. The lack of a consistent definition for MSW is a problem. Most observers agree that waste from residential, commercial, and industrial sectors should be counted, but what about junked automobiles, construction and demolition waste, and that portion of industrial waste that is disposed along with what is more commonly thought of as MSW?

Experts also disagree about how to account for waste from manufacturing processes, such as aluminum scrap from can-making and paper scrap from box-making. The manufacturing sector typically considers this waste as *post-consumer*. However, these portions of the scrap stream are not included in most accountings of MSW recycling—most observers consider them to be *pre-consumer*. Actually, manufacturing wastes are more appropriately divided into three categories:

- ''home scrap'' produced and reused inside a production facility,
- ''prompt industrial scrap'' produced in an intermediate stage of processing and returned to the basic production facility for reuse, and
- ''old scrap'' (post-consumer) generated by the product's final consumer.

This assessment considers the first two categories of scrap to be pre-consumer waste; almost all of this waste is recycled as common practice in manufacturing as a way to reduce materials procurement and disposal costs. The significant issue from an MSW perspective, then, is old scrap. Unfortunately, available statistics on recycled materials do not always provide information on all three categories of scrap. These problems are not confined to the United States (see box 5-A).

The most frequently reported estimate for a national MSW recycling rate is 10 percent (81). This does not include home and prompt industrial scrap, material recycled at the industrial and manufacturing level. This figure also does not include what modest recycling may take place at home, such as reuse of plastic containers or yard and food waste

---

Box 5-A—Recycling in Japan

Japan is known as a nation that recycles. Indeed, recycling has been practiced within the private sector for hundreds of years. However, the amount of MSW in Japan that is recycled is difficult to estimate for several reasons. First, neither the national government nor the private sector maintain aggregate recycling data or estimate an overall recycling rate. Second, the Japanese do not include materials that are recovered and recycled in their definition of MSW; instead they only include waste materials sent to landfills and incinerators (108,213).[1] This differs significantly from the definitions of MSW commonly used in the United States.

Some experts estimate that the recycling rate in Japan is around 50 percent (108,213). In contrast, OTA estimates that the rate may be as low as 26 to 39 percent, at least for materials for which data are available. Japanese officials also express varied estimates of the rate (108,180). Appendix A explains OTA's calculations and why its estimates differ from the estimate of 50 percent. The calculations indicate the great difficulties involved in estimating recycling rates.

Whether Japan recycles at a rate of 30 or 50 percent, it still sends a clear message that the United States could improve its current recycling rate of 10 percent dramatically. However, if the lower estimate proves correct it would indicate that high national recycling rates can be difficult to achieve, even in a country noted for its dependence on imports of raw materials, its homogeneous culture, and its propensity for citizen cooperation in community activities.

---

[1]Most Japanese municipalities require citizens to sort MSW into two categories—combustibles for incineration (e.g., paper, food waste, and sometimes plastics) and non-combustibles for landfilling (e.g., metals, glass, and sometimes plastics). Few recycling programs are conducted by municipal, prefectural, or national governments.

composting. In fact, no attempt has ever been made to estimate actual yard and food waste composting.

Glass recycling has increased considerably during the 1980s because of the efforts of glass manufacturers to increase the use of cullet, or waste glass; the recovery rate for glass in 1987 was estimated to be 15 percent (223) (figure 5-1). Paper and paperboard recycling have also increased; the American Paper Institute reports a recovery rate of 28.5 percent for all waste paper (this is higher than the Franklin estimate of 22.6 percent because it includes pre-consumer waste). Aluminum recycling has also increased; according to the Aluminum Association, recovery of aluminum from MSW is now around 43 percent.

Increases in recovery of ferrous metals, plastics, and yard waste also have been occurring as more communities and businesses implement recycling programs and build processing facilities. Changes are occurring so quickly that information may be outdated even as it is reported.

Preparing Materials for Recycling

MSW can be collected in a variety of ways: as mixed wastes, with commingled recyclables, or with separated recyclables. How materials are collected affects the kind of preparation needed before recovered materials can be manufactured into new recycled products. A variety of technologies and methods are used to sort recyclable materials, remove contaminants, and prepare materials for marketing. Sometimes, this preparation takes place at centralized facilities, commonly referred to as Materials Recovery Facilities (MRFs). A MRF can help reduce separation demands on waste generators and can respond relatively quickly to changing demands of materials markets. About 12 MRFs were in operation in the United States in mid-1989, and more are planned (100).

The choices of equipment and design for a MRF depend on the types of materials being recovered, the type and degree of contamination of incoming material, the requirements of the buyers, and the disposal method for waste that is not recycled. The major influence is the type of MSW handled—mixed v. commingled v. separated. Box 5-B describes examples of materials recovery facilities.

It is difficult to compare the quality and cost of different materials recovery systems without considering a broad array of variables such as the entire MSW management system for the area served, materials recovered, and market availability. Standard methods for evaluating performance are not available. Operational experience with the more automated processes used in U.S. MRFs is also limited.

Mixed MSW

The first step in preparing mixed MSW for processing is "previewing," where oversized materials, explosive materials, and materials that could damage the equipment are removed. Various unit processes can be used to recover recyclables from unsorted raw waste. Size reduction (or shredding) reduces the volume of the waste and prepares it for the segregation step, where components of the waste stream are separated from each other.[1] Following segregation the material is sent to market using many of the same techniques used for commingled or separated recyclables. After recovering recyclables and/or compostables from raw waste, residual material is either landfilled or incinerated. In some systems the residue is processed as refuse-derived fuel (RDF) prior to incineration. Some systems only recover metals and glass for recycling (in addition to preparing compost); other systems recover plastics, different paper fractions, and batteries (box 5-B) (also see ref. 1).

Facilities that handle mixed MSW have the advantage that no change in the collection system is required. The plant manager can determine which materials to recover, depending on market conditions. Mixed waste systems have the potential to remove a high percentage of metals and other recyclable and/or noncombustible materials from the waste stream. Separation can also improve the combustion efficiency of incineration and the quality of resulting ash.

The biggest disadvantages of mixed waste facilities are the relatively high energy requirements and high maintenance costs. The use of multiple mechanical processes may also require more time to adjust equipment to the incoming waste stream. Explosion hazards can be associated with the shredding and grinding steps, but these risks can be minimized with proper design and operation. A history of poor performance at mixed waste processing plants in the 1970s has made this type of technology fairly unpopular in the United States.

Figure 5-1—MSW Recycling Rates: Estimates by Franklin Associates and Industry

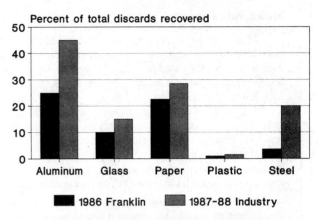

NOTE: Industry estimate for paper includes pre-consumer scrap; industry estimate for steel includes a higher total for white goods, as well as ferrous scrap recovered at incinerators.

SOURCES: American Paper Institute, Paper Recycling Committee, *1987 Annual Statistical Summary Waste Paper Utilization*, 2d ed. (New York, NY: July 1988); K. Copperthite, U.S. Department of Commerce, personal communication, 1988; Franklin Associates, Ltd., *Characterization of Municipal Solid Waste in the United States, 1960 to 2000 (Update 1988)*, final report, prepared for U.S. Environmental Protection Agency (Prairie Village, KS: March 1988); B. Meyer, Aluminum Association, personal communication, 1988; K. Smalberg, Steel Can Recycling Institute, personal communication, 1989; Society of the Plastics Industry, *Facts and Figures of the U.S. Plastics Industry* (Washington, DC: 1987); Society of the Plastics Industry, *Plastics A.D. 2000, Production and Use Through the Turn of the Century* (Washington, DC: 1987).

Refuse-derived fuel (RDF)—At many centralized facilities, the portion of the waste that is not recovered for recycling is converted into RDF. The RDF is then burned in a waste-to-energy incinerator to recover energy in the form of electricity or steam. Several kinds of RDF can be produced (including fluff, densified, and pelletized RDF), depending on the configuration of processes at a particular facility and on the specifications of RDF users.

An advantage of using RDF as a fuel, as opposed to mixed MSW, is that the properties of RDF are relatively consistent regardless of variation in MSW feedstock. Thus the incineration process can achieve

---

[1]**Size reduction** requires a relatively high amount of energy and maintenance, thus costs are a major factor in determining the amount of size reduction. It is also a process that is difficult to do manually. **Removal and segregation processes** may be combined in several ways, depending on the composition of the incoming wastes and the types of materials being recovered. Several types of technologies may be used including: air classification to separate light from heavy fractions, magnetic separation to remove ferrous metals, and screening to separate materials on the basis of particle size. Automated facilities to separate components of mixed waste are relatively new at the commercial level in the United States and have not as yet been proven as economical waste management methods. However, manual sorting can often substitute for automated methods, and source separation or manual methods are more effective for at least some materials (e.g., newspaper and glass).

Box 5-B—Examples of Materials Recovery Facilities

Mixed Waste Facilities

The Delaware Reclamation Plant, completed in 1983, processes solid waste and municipal sewage sludge from New Castle County, Delaware. The facility recovers ferrous metals, glass, and nonferrous metals, produces compost mixed with sewage sludge, and produces refuse-derived fuel (RDF). From the 500,000 tons of solid wastes and 60,000 tons of sewage sludge (20 percent solids) generated in the county each year, the facility produces about 130,000 tons of RDF and 250,000 tons of solid wastes. These solid wastes, which are landfilled, include ash from the RDF facility (which also accepts up to 60,000 tons of commercial waste), excess sludge, and solid wastes that have neither combustion capability nor materials recovery value (258). The facility markets the light ferrous fraction, aluminum, and a small portion of glass. Although high purity glass recovery is technically feasible, the cost of production far exceeds the current market value unless there is a nearby glass factory. The heavier ferrous fraction has no current market. The compost is used as landfill cover. Additional materials recovery prior to combustion could increase recycling and reduce the metals content of the ash.

MSW first passes through hammermills designed to shred up to 70 tons of waste per hour and equipped with explosion venting and suppression systems. After the hammermills shred the waste into 4-inch pieces, it is sent to air classifiers to separate the light from the heavy fractions. Magnets remove the ferrous material from the heavy fraction and a trommel screen separates glass. The organic matter removed in the trommel screens will eventually be sent to the humus processing section. The remaining, smaller fraction is further processed to separate the glass from the organics, paper, and plastics; the latter three also will be sent to the humus processing section. The glass fraction is crushed, screened, and reground. Then it is mixed with an amine acetate and removed through foam flotation; a magnetic separator removes fine ferrous contaminants from the glass once it has been dried. The remaining waste is sent to a secondary air classifier, where primarily nonferrous fraction is separated and sent to a trommel screen. The nonferrous material in this fraction (consisting of 60 percent aluminum) is recovered through eddy current separation (259).

The ORFA Corporation of America operates a facility in Philadelphia, Pennsylvania, that is designed to process about 90,000 tons of mixed MSW each year from the surrounding areas (182). The fully automated facility, completed in 1989, produces three products: ORFA Fiber, primarily composed of cellulose; granulate, consisting of glass, plastics, mixed sand, dust, grit, nonferrous metals and other dense substances; and ferrous metals. About 50 to 60 percent of the incoming waste becomes ORFA Fiber, about 18 percent becomes granulate, about 8 percent is ferrous metal, and the remainder is moisture and bulky waste. Uses for the Fiber include recycled paperboard, building board, kitty litter, and growing medium. Granulate is used as fill for strip mines, and ferrous metal is sold to local scrap dealers. Other ORFA facilities are planned, with expected capital costs of about $30 to $35 million for 132,000 tons per year of processing capacity. Tipping fees are expected to be about $85 per ton.

In the ORFA process, MSW is received in an enclosed tipping floor, where it is inspected for unacceptable materials such as bulky items or hazardous wastes. The MSW is then shredded and passed over a magnetic separator to remove ferrous metals. The shredded material is then screened to separate the light fraction and heavy fraction. The heavy fraction is sent to a hammer mill and the light fraction is sent to a high-speed cutting mill for further size reduction. The two fractions are then recombined. The combined fractions are dried in a natural-gas-fueled rotating drum dryer to approximately 5 percent moisture content. To reduce odor and stabilize complex organic compounds, the dried material is treated with ozone. The dry, sanitized, and stabilized material is screened and separated into coarse, medium, and fine grades before being sifted to separate the granulate from the ORFA Fiber. Coarse and medium fibers are baled and the fine fiber and granulate are stored in bins for shipment.

Commingled Recycables Facility

The Monmouth Recycling Corporation operates a facility in Long Branch, New Jersey that handles 70 percent of the containers recycled by the county, including glass, aluminum, and ferrous cans (216). The company has been in the recycling business since 1978, first as a buy-back operation for non-ferrous metals. It gradually expanded into glass in 1982 using manual separation of colors and contaminants, and in 1988 it began a commingled materials processing line.

Trucks are weighed before they dump their loads into a receiving pit. Materials are then pushed with a loader onto a conveyor where they are separated by several automated and manual steps. The conveyors pass over a magnet to remove ferrous metals; aluminum cans are removed by hand and dropped through a chute where they are automatically flattened and blown into a van for transport. Several people pick different colors of glass from the remaining materials and drop them in different hoppers where they move by conveyors to a primary crusher, pass under another magnet, through a secondary crusher and then through a vibrating screen. The system generates color-separated glass cullet with minor paper contamination.

Separated Recyclables Facility

Recycle America, a subsidiary of Waste Management, Inc., began operating a materials processing center in San Jose, California, in 1986. Residents of the city separate metal cans, glass bottles, and newspaper into three bins. The materials are loaded separately into different compartments of route trucks. Trucks arrive at a computerized scale and successively dump the different materials, allowing compilation of data on the tonnages of different materials collected on each route. Newspaper processing involves baling the materials. Glass is broken as it is initially unloaded, then it is moved by conveyor to allow manual removal of contaminants. The glass is then dropped again into containers for shipping. By this method the glass is compacted, without the use of a crusher, from 300 to 1,000 pounds per cubic yard. Metal cans are separated into ferrous metal and aluminum as the materials pass through a series of magnets. About 20 percent of the steel cans are discarded because labels have not been removed. The cans are then baled for shipment.

New England CRInc (NECRInc) operates a facility in Billerica, Massachusetts, that collects plastic, glass, steel, and aluminum beverage containers. The containers are separated, baled, and shipped to secondary aluminum smelters, glass manufacturers, etc. The company also operates two other similar facilities, two curbside recycling programs, and several drop-off programs around New England. It recently expanded its operations into Rhode Island, where it operates a facility that handles separated and commingled materials from a curbside collection program (newspaper is separated, while glass, plastic, and metal containers are commingled).

---

more thorough combustion and produce energy more efficiently. Among the disadvantages are the large amount of processing and energy needed to produce the fuel.

Commingled Recyclables

Technologies to separate commingled recyclables depend on the particular materials that are included in the mix. Some systems handle only glass and metal containers (box 5-B), while other facilities also sort paper and plastic. A combination of manual and automatic systems are usually used. Many of these same technologies are applicable to the segregation step for mixed waste.

The advantages of commingled collection are that some separation is already done and thus the amount of contamination that must be dealt with is reduced. Items that could pose a health hazard to workers are excluded (e.g., disposable diapers). One disadvantage of commingled collection is that it requires a different collection system than for the rest of MSW and is highly dependent on public participation (ch. 2).

Separated Recyclables

Even when recyclables are separated at curbside, some preparation of materials often is necessary to meet the needs of buyers. Thus, prepared materials often command a higher price than materials that would be delivered directly to market. Technologies to handle separated recyclables include automated or manual methods to remove contaminants as well as baling, shredding, or grinding equipment.

One advantage of processing separated recyclables is that much of the labor of sorting materials has already been done, and the equipment required is generally very simple. Equipment may include scales, conveyors, and balers, as well as other unit processes for separating materials such as magnets for separating ferrous and nonferrous metals.

A disadvantage of separated collection is that it, like commingled collection, requires a different collection system and is highly dependent on public participation. Specialized collection equipment (e.g., compartmentalized collection vehicles) is often needed.

RECYCLING: TECHNOLOGIES, MARKETS, RISKS

Recycling technologies vary considerably depending on the secondary material and the intended end product. For example, technologies to recycle used oil vary depending on whether the oil is intended to be reprocessed for use as fuel or re-refined and used again as a lubricant. This section provides an overview of technologies and markets for secondary materials—paper and paperboard products, glass, aluminum, batteries, iron and steel, tires, oil, plastics, and compost.

Paper and Paperboard Products

Paper and paperboard products account for a larger fraction of MSW than any other single category of material. An estimated 64.7 million short tons of paper and paperboard were used **and discarded** as MSW in the United States in 1986 (81).[2] If this figure is correct, paper and paperboard would account for 41 percent by weight of gross discards (ch. 3).

According to Franklin Associates (81), 14.6 million tons of paper and paperboard were recovered from MSW in 1986. By comparison, the American Paper Institute reports waste paper recovery in 1986 at 22.1 million tons (9). The difference between the two estimates is caused by how each accounts for pre-consumer waste (i.e., prompt industrial scrap) that is collected routinely by fabricators and shipped to paper mills for use in the papermaking process.

In 1987, total waste paper recovery (including pre-consumer waste) in the United States reached an all-time high of 24 million tons, a recovery rate of 28.5 percent (9). For comparison, total recovery of waste paper was only 12.6 million tons in 1970, a recovery rate of 22.4 percent. Recovery, and subsequent use, has shown a similar increase worldwide.

Recovered waste paper, or secondary fiber, is used to produce new paper products, construction materials, and miscellaneous products such as ani-

mal bedding, insulation, and cushioning. Growth in demand for these products worldwide has caused heightened demand for secondary fiber. Consumption of secondary fiber in the United States increased from 12.0 million tons in 1970 to 19.2 million tons in 1987, and exports increased from 0.4 million tons to 4.4 million tons over the same period.

In the United States, paper and paperboard mills are the major consumers of secondary fiber, accounting for 94 percent of the total in 1987 (9). OTA's evaluation of opportunities for increased paper recycling therefore begins with a description of trends in the U.S. paper and paperboard industry.

Structure, Conduct, and Performance of the Paper Industry

The paper industry is international and relatively competitive. The United States, with its abundant forest resources and low-cost production facilities, plays a major role in the world paper industry. Of the 238 million tons of paper and paperboard produced worldwide in 1987, the United States accounted for 74.4 million tons, or 31 percent (199).

Statistics alone, however, do not give a complete picture of U.S. standing internationally because many large U.S. paper companies own forest resources, pulp and paper mill capacity, and converting operations abroad (200).[3] The United States is headquarters for 26 of the world's largest 100 pulp and paper companies (in terms of 1987 sales from pulp, paper, and converting operations only). Of the 10 largest, 8 are U.S. companies. Total 1987 sales for the 100 largest companies amounted to $125.4 billion, of which U.S. companies accounted for 43.7 percent (200). Japanese companies accounted for the second largest share—14.8 percent.

The paper and allied products industry is scattered throughout the country, with establishments located in every State. The largest concentration of production is in the South, which accounts for about 35 percent of total production, by value. The North Central region and the Northeast account for about 25 percent each.

The regional distribution of the industry parallels that of domestic forest resources—the paper indus-

---

[2]One short ton equals 2,000 pounds. In this report, all references to tons refer to short tons unless otherwise noted.

[3]Converting operations refer to plants that transform paper and paperboard into products such as boxes or envelopes.

try locates its mills close to the major source of raw materials. As a result, many paper mills are in remote locations, where forestry and paper industries are the major employers.

According to the *1982 Census of Manufactures* (242), the industry consists primarily of large establishments. Nearly half of all the U.S. paper and paperboard mills are directly associated with a pulp mill. These integrated mills accounted for the bulk of paper and paperboard shipments. In 1982, the value of shipments from integrated mills amounted to $23.0 billion, or 75 percent of total mill shipments.

The paper industry generally keeps pace with the overall level of U.S. industrial production and exhibits relative stability. During the last recession, the industry's overall rate of decline was equal to or less than the average for all industries. Capacity utilization for most segments of the paper industry generally remains above 90 percent.

The **annual** average producer price indices for various paper products closely follow the index for all finished goods, but they are slightly more volatile. With the exception of wood pulp, all producer prices reported for paper products have increased by more than 50 percent since 1977 (250). The producer price index for wood pulp has fallen somewhat below the others and has exhibited greater volatility, particularly since 1981.

Data on **monthly** average paper product prices may be more meaningful, however. Beginning in July 1983, monthly data show that prices for waste paper are considerably more volatile than those for wood pulp (figure 5-2). This kind of relationship is typical of secondary materials.

The increased prices of paper products have benefited the industry. As recently as 1984, the profitability of the paper industry lagged well behind the rest of the economy. Over the last few years, however, the profitability of the paper industry has risen substantially, owing in part to cost-cutting measures, higher capacity utilization rates, and increased competitiveness associated with the decline in the value of the dollar (40,41) Despite this improvement, the industry's long-term returns-on-

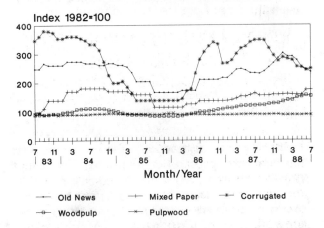

Figure 5-2—Producer Price Indexes: Waste Paper, Woodpulp, and Pulpwood

SOURCE: U.S. Department of Labor, Bureau of Labor Statistics, "Producer Price Indexes" (Washington, DC: January 1983-August 1988).

equity rates continue to be low relative to those for U.S. industry in general (3).

U.S. foreign trade in paper and allied products is substantial; in 1986, U.S. exports were valued at $4.9 billion, and imports at $7.8 billion. Of U.S. exports, wood pulp and paperboard accounted for the largest share (35 and 25 percent, respectively). Major destinations for U.S. paper product exports in 1986 were Japan, Canada, Mexico, and West Germany (225). Newsprint is by far the major product, accounting for 47 percent of total imports of paper-related products in 1986; wood pulp and printing and writing paper also account for significant shares (21 and 11 percent, respectively). Major sources of imports are Canada (accounting for 75 percent), Finland, West Germany, and Mexico (225).

The Use of Secondary Fiber in Production of Paper and Paperboard Products

The major grades of waste paper traded include old newspapers (ONP), old corrugated containers (OCC), mixed grades, pulp substitutes, and high grade de-inking.[4] The total amount of waste paper used and the proportion of each grade making up the total vary considerably by type of final paper product. For some paper products, waste paper is

---

[4]The Paper Stock Institute, a division of the Institute of Scrap Recycling Industries, Inc., identifies 49 standard grades and 31 specialty grades of waste paper, but statistics are not collected on that basis (185).

used in conjunction, and sometimes competes directly, with wood pulp. In some instances, the paper product is made from 100 percent waste paper.

Consumption of secondary fiber, or waste paper, in the production of *all* grades of paper and paperboard increased in the United States from 12.0 million tons in 1970 to 19.5 million tons in 1987. By weight, about 25 percent of the fiber raw material used to make paper and paperboard in the United States consists of secondary fiber.

The regional distribution of paper mills that consume waste paper differs somewhat from that of virgin paper mills, reflecting the comparative economics of raw materials transportation. Secondary fiber mills often are located to take advantage of the largest sources of waste paper—converting plants and large population centers. The five largest waste paper consuming States in 1986 were Wisconsin, California, Ohio, Michigan, and Pennsylvania (243).

Technologies of Recycled and Virgin Papermaking

Once it is received at a mill, waste paper is normally prepared or repulped by mixing it with water and beating it with a hydrapulper. This process mechanically separates the fibers from foreign materials and forms a fiber and water slurry. Plastics and any remaining foreign materials are filtered out of the slurry, which is then thickened. If de-inking is required, the pulp is diluted and sent to a series of flotation cells where the pulp is aerated so the ink migrates to the surface as a foam. This foam is often removed using a vacuum (70).[5] In some processes, de-inking is aided with the use of heat and chemical ink dispersants, detergents, solvents, or defoamers. Additional cleaning may be required to remove contaminants. The de-inked stock, about 4 percent fiber and 96 percent water, can then be used to form paper sheets, although some fiber refining or blending may be required. In some instances, the pulp must be bleached with chlorine gas, chlorine dioxide, sodium hypochlorite, hydrogen peroxide, oxygen, or other chemicals prior to papermaking (241). The use of coated waste papers results in the production of large amounts of sludge, which can amount to as much as 30 percent of the input by weight (3). This sludge then becomes industrial waste.

Pulping wood can be accomplished by mechanical or chemical methods.[6] Mechanical pulping involves grinding logs or wood chips, adding water to form a slurry, filtering, and cleaning. Sometimes the wood is heated or soaked in a chemical liquor to soften the fibers prior to grinding. In chemical pulping, which is used to make pulp for higher quality products, wood chips are cooked in chemical solutions containing caustic soda and sodium sulfide or sulfites of calcium, magnesium, ammonia, or sodium. The cooking process dissolves the lignin, which binds the fibers together. After cooking, the pulp is washed, then diluted, screened, and cleaned. The pulp can then be bleached. Often, pulps from a variety of woods are blended to attain specific qualities required for different products. The same equipment can be used for making paper both from wood pulp and from secondary fiber pulp.

The major difference between the costs of making virgin and recycled paper is in the pulping and stock preparation stages. Industry representatives generally agree that the capital cost of expanding papermaking capacity is estimated to average about $150,000 per ton of daily capacity if waste paper is used and about $500,000 to $1 million if wood is used. The cost of building a new mill is considerably greater than the cost of expanding an existing mill. For example, building a new mill for recycled paperboard can cost 50 percent more and take twice as long than expanding an existing mill. The cost differential for the fiber itself is much less important in the comparative economics of virgin versus secondary fiber than this capital cost differential.

Comparative Energy Consumption—Recycled fiber can be used to make various paper and paperboard products. Each product, however, has unique limitations on the amount of recycled fiber that can be used, and each one is produced by manufacturing processes that can differ in the amount of energy used.

For some paper products, using waste paper may require less energy than producing paper from virgin timber. These savings can result from reduced

[5]Waste paper is de-inked for most tissue and writing papers, but not for most paperboard products.

[6]According to API, U.S. woodpulp capacity is broken down as follows: 80 percent chemical, 10 percent semichemical, 10 percent mechanical (8).

energy demands in the process of making paper from waste paper and a reduced need to harvest and transport timber. They can be offset, however, by the energy needed to collect, transport, and de-ink the waste paper.

Estimates of the energy saved using waste paper vary greatly, however, and should be viewed with caution. In virgin papermaking, many process byproducts (e.g., lignin, bark, wood waste) are used to generate energy in the production process, thus reducing the need for purchased fuel. These types of byproducts are not produced in recycled papermaking. Many estimates of comparative energy consumption in papermaking do not account for this aspect of fuel use. Recycled paper and board often require more fossil fuel than virgin products.

Generalizations about relative energy consumption in virgin and recycled papermaking are difficult to make given the conflicting conclusions made by various studies of the subject. One study (99) estimated that most paper products require less energy to produce using recycled fiber than virgin fiber, but that most paperboard products require more energy if produced using recycled fiber (table 5-1). Data for tissue production from table 5-1 indicate a savings of 57 percent, while another study estimated savings of 41 percent (195). In contrast, Renard (206) reported a net energy loss of about 1 percent for the production of tissue from recycled fiber.

Other studies also address the total direct energy cost of using de-inked newspaper to produce new newsprint; these direct costs included electricity, heating water, and the introduction of inorganic additives (NaOH and NaOCl), but excluded the energy used to produce raw inputs (206). One study estimated direct savings of about 23 percent, or about 6.3 million Btu/ton. A more conservative study, however, concluded that using de-inked stock saved about 2.7 to 4.1 million Btu/ton, depending on the type of virgin pulp used.

In contrast, an analysis of primary versus secondary fiber use in linerboard production showed a net increase in energy cost when secondary fiber is used.

According to one study (113), "increased use of secondary fiber as opposed to increased kraft pulping capacity leads to reduced steam and electrical process-energy requirements per unit product but to slightly increased energy costs per unit product," based on using coal as an auxiliary fuel to replace wood residue fuel generated in primary fiber pulping.

An alternative approach to recycling waste paper is to recover the energy value in collected waste paper by using it as a fuel supplement. However, one analysis of waste paper used as a coal supplement in electric powerplants or to generate steam at paper plants found that recycling (with an optimum allocation of waste paper to efficient recycling options) was more energy efficient (99). In fact, that same analysis concludes that "the most energy efficient strategy of making paper is to increase the amount of source-separation and recycling (compared to the alternatives of burning or landfilling). The next most energy efficient use of scrap is to burn it for energy production and the least efficient is to land-fill it" (99).

Markets for Waste Paper, by Product Category

Every paper product that uses waste paper exhibits unique market characteristics. The major categories of products described here include the paper grades (fine printing and writing paper, newsprint, tissue, and packaging and industrial paper), the paperboard grades (unbleached kraft, semichemical, bleached paperboard, and recycled paperboard), and building paper and board.[7]

Fine Printing and Writing Papers—In 1987, U.S. mills produced 20.7 million tons of printing, writing, and related papers for use in publishing and office products (e.g., books, brochures, magazines, stationery, copy papers, accounting forms). Although most printing and writing paper is made from virgin fiber, about 1,375,000 tons of waste paper was used, for a waste paper **utilization rate** of about 6.6 percent (see figure 5-3).[8] About 74 percent of this waste paper was pulp substitutes, or cuttings from converting plants. The remainder consisted mainly of post-consumer high grade de-inking paper (e.g.,

---

[7]The use of waste paper for non-paper products is not described because reliable data are not available; these products include cellulose insulation, molded products (e.g., egg cartons and flower pots), cushioning material for packaging, animal bedding, and mulch.

[8]Utilization rate refers to the portion of waste paper used in total domestic production of the grade(s) under discussion.

Table 5-1—Estimated Energy Used To Produce Paper and Paperboard Products
(in million Btu per ton produced)

Product	From 100% virgin wood Energy use	From mixed recycled paper Minimum virgin fiber content	From mixed recycled paper Energy use	% change due to recycling
Paper products:				
Newsprint	44.33	0%	34.76	-21.6
Printing paper	67.72	16%	43.43	-35.9
Packaging paper	47.07	70%	43.48	-7.6
Tissue paper	68.52	0%	29.46	-57.0
Paperboard products:				
Liner board	14.46	75%	36.28	+150.9
Corrugated board	37.22	0%	36.28	-2.5
Box board	25.97	0%	36.25	+39.6
Food service board	29.19	100%	N/A	—
Other paper board	17.65	0%	36.32	+105.8
Construction board	31.71	65%	32.24	+1.7

SOURCE: T. Gunn and B. Hannon, "Energy Conservation and Recycling in the Paper Industry," *Resources and Energy* 5:243-260, 1983.

computer printout, tabulating cards, white ledger and forms).

Only a few printing and writing paper mills can de-ink waste paper and/or produce new paper that contains at least 50 percent waste paper. In 1983, 174 printing and writing paper mills with 18.6 million tons of capacity were operating in the United States, but only 12 mills had de-inking facilities (6). By 1988, mill capacity had increased to 22.7 million tons, but only 9 mills had de-inking facilities (one of which was not operating). A total of 18 mills, however, had the ability to produce printing and writing paper containing at least 50 percent waste paper; these mills had the combined capacity to produce about 1 million tons annually, or about 5 percent of the total (82).[9]

The majority of printing and writing paper mills are large, integrated world-class mills that use 600-ton-per-day papermaking machines. However, most mills that predominantly use waste paper as furnish—"secondary paper" mills—are smaller, older, and less efficient, typically using 70-ton-per-day machines. The secondary paper mills have been successful in producing high-quality recycled printing and writing paper that is comparable to virgin paper because they use very high-quality secondary fiber. According to paper industry representatives,

however, they can compete with the large integrated mills only because they can use lower cost secondary fiber.

Concerns have been expressed about the future supply and price of high-quality secondary fiber. Increased exports and increased competition from other types of paper mills (especially tissue) have driven up the price of some secondary fiber, making many grades economically marginal for the secondary paper mills. Since most of the highest quality waste paper appears to be collected already, a future increase in supply will be limited to increases in the rate of production of waste paper as a byproduct at converting plants. As a result, secondary paper mill representatives express reluctance to build new mills to produce more recycled printing and writing paper. One representative noted that just two new 600-ton-per-day paper machines (i.e., state-of-the-art technology) could consume the available annual supply of pulp substitutes.

This view is not held by all, however. During 1988, the Korean-owned Mi-Ho Paper Co. announced that it would build a new recycled printing and writing paper mill in St. Josephs, Missouri, that would use primarily secondary fiber. The business plan for the mill identifies reliable sources for the waste paper and also has most of the production

---

[9]The remainder of the 1,257,000 tons of waste paper consumed at printing and writing paper mills was presumably consumed in mills producing paper containing less than 50 percent waste paper.

earmarked for export. The capacity of the mill has not been reported, but it is expected to cost about $60 million to build, including land, insurance, and financing costs. The success of this venture will not be apparent for years to come, and many industry sources in the United States are skeptical.

In addition, some expansion of current recycled printing and writing paper capacity has occurred recently. One mill announced a 25-ton-per-day expansion at a cost of about $15 million (or about $600,000 per ton of daily capacity).

Therefore, the major barriers to increased use of secondary fiber in printing and writing paper appear to be supply of high-quality secondary fiber, technological constraints in the papermaking process, and high standards on the part of the consumer. Improvements in de-inking technology are required to allow the use of lower quality waste paper, such as that collected in office paper recycling programs. The industry is conducting some research in this area, but prospects for success are unknown. Additional research also is needed to improve the removal of contaminants (e.g., sticky adhesives and plastics), improve fiber treatment or refining, and find commercially viable ways to reduce or handle the low-solid sludge generated when recycling printing paper that has a thin clay coat. Some technology in use in Europe does allow the production of printing and writing paper from lower grade waste paper, but its quality is allegedly lower than U.S. standards for printing and writing paper. This paper, which can be called ''adequate for the purpose'' grade, is being produced in the Federal Republic of Germany, for instance, at a rate of about 140,000 tons per year (235). OTA is not aware of any imports of this type of paper into the United States.

Newsprint—Newsprint mills in the United States produced 5.8 million tons of newsprint in 1987. About 23 percent, or 1.4 million tons, was made from waste paper, virtually all old newspapers (ONP) (figure 5-3). Total U.S. production supplied less than half of total U.S. demand for newsprint, and 8.9 million tons of newsprint were imported in 1987, primarily from Canada.

In 1987, U.S. capacity to produce newsprint was about 5.9 million tons (8). The seven recycled newsprint mills in operation in 1987 had total annual capacity of 1.5 million tons (84). Most of these mills

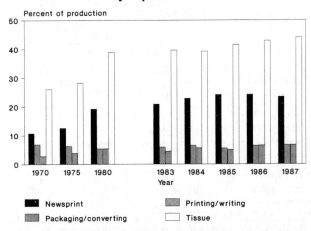

Figure 5-3—Waste Paper Utilization Rate, By Paper Product

SOURCE: American Paper Institute, "Waste Paper Utilization in Paper and Paperboard Manufacture" (New York, NY: individual yearly reports for 1970 through 1987); Paper Recycling Committee, *1987 Statistics of Paper, Paperboard & Wood Pulp* (New York, NY: August 1987).

are located very close to sources of secondary fiber—major metropolitan areas—to minimize transportation costs.

After 4 years of virtually no growth, the North American newsprint industry has embarked on a period of expansion. Within the next few years, 9 new newsprint machines, each with a capacity of 200,000 tons per year, will come on-line; 7 of these machines are in Canada. Most of this new capacity will use virgin fiber, mainly because the new machines are additions to current plants rather than developments at new sites. Most mills are located close to sources of wood pulp, so it is unlikely that it would be cost-effective to transport large amounts of ONP a longer distance to be used as furnish instead. This could change, however. For example, a new facility being built at a mill in Quebec will use ONP, magazines, and other forms of waste paper to produce newsprint pulp (47).

The major barriers to increased use of waste paper in newsprint appear to be lack of markets and higher levels of contaminants found in new supplies of ONP. Given current expansion plans, further increases in capacity would likely result in an overall reduction in the industry's capacity utilization rate. Of course, given the large volume of U.S. imports of newsprint, some of that displacement could occur in Canadian (or other foreign source) mills. Unless restrictions were placed on imports, however, there would be no assurance that U.S. capacity utilization would not be affected.[10]

Sufficient additional supply of ONP does exist to furnish new recycled newsprint capacity. It has been estimated that at least 700,000 to 800,000 tons of ONP would be available in the Northeast alone (123). However, questions exist as to the quality of the additional supply, particularly that generated by mandatory source separation programs. Garden State Paper, for example, has reported difficulty with contamination in ONP recovered from New Jersey's mandatory recycling program (123).

Finally, market volatility is an additional barrier to capacity expansion. Many analysts predict that the world supply of newsprint will outpace demand by 1990. With the possibility of recession increasing, the industry may see further investment in new machines as too risky.

Tissue—Tissue grade paper includes toilet and facial tissue, napkins, toweling, diapers, wipes, and other sanitary papers. U.S. mills produced 5.3 million tons of tissue in 1987. Approximately 2.4 million tons of secondary fiber was used to produce tissue, for a utilization rate of 44 percent. This is a significant increase from just over 25 percent waste paper utilization in 1970 (figure 5-3). All grades of waste paper are used to make tissue products, with high grade de-inking and pulp substitutes contributing the largest share—almost 75 percent. The lower grades, mostly post-consumer waste, generally are used to make industrial toweling and wipes for the "away-from-home" market.

Tissue production capacity in the United States has expanded steadily over the last decade, to about 5.8 million tons in 1988, and additional expansion is expected. An estimated 20 to 40 tissue mills make tissue products with about 25 percent recycled content or more (84). Highly proprietary technology has allowed some tissue mills to increase their consumption of de-inking grades of waste paper. Unfortunately, the potential to further increase

consumption of lower grades of waste paper cannot be determined quantitatively. However, tissue producers do not appear concerned by the possibility of reduced supplies of pulp substitutes, perhaps indicating a future tendency to rely less on these high grade fibers. Because most tissue products made with post-consumer waste paper are the coarser, "away-from-home" variety, increased use of such waste in tissue paper production depends to some extent on consumer preference. In blind tests on product quality and performance, consumers invariably pick the virgin product because it is whiter and softer (3). Whether consumers can accept a coarser product for home use is unknown.

Kraft and Packaging Paper—In 1987, U.S. mills produced 5.1 million tons of unbleached kraft and bleached packaging and industrial papers, mostly for making shipping bags and wrapping.[11] The waste paper utilization rate in producing these papers has averaged about 5 percent over the last decade (figure 5-3), with pulp substitutes and OCC being the major grades of waste paper used. Much of this waste paper is pre-consumer waste. According to the API (7), high grade secondary fibers from waste clippings at bag-making plants were the primary source of waste paper because packaging papers require high strength. Lower grade fibers and fibers recycled more than once do not exhibit the necessary strength characteristics.[12] Therefore, the use of waste paper in these products is not expected to increase.

Production of kraft papers, the largest share of this category, has declined over the last few years. The major market for these papers is grocery and merchandise bags, which have been losing about 5 percent of the market per year to plastics (197). Bans on plastic shopping bags, which have been implemented in several localities, could lead to increased domestic production of kraft papers.

Unbleached Kraft Paperboard—Production of unbleached kraft paperboard in the United States in 1987 amounted to 18.5 million tons. About 1.9 million tons of secondary fibers, mainly OCC and box plant clippings, were used to make products in

---

[10]Increased pressure is also being placed on Canadian newsprint mills to use more ONP. It appears likely that some displacement will occur there as a result of Canada's own recycling programs.

[11]Kraft paper, produced by a modified sulfate pulping process, is a relatively coarse paper with high strength characteristics. Unbleached grades are used primarily for packaging and wrapping; bleached kraft can be used to make many grades of paper including tissues and printing and fine papers.

[12]In the process of recycling paper, the wood fibers are broken and shortened, thus reducing their strength.

Photo credit: W. Johnson

Old corrugated cardboard typically is compacted and baled before being shipped to paper mills for recycling.

Figure 5-4—Waste Paper Utilization Rate, By Paperboard Product

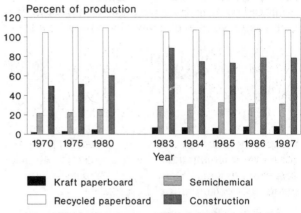

SOURCE: American Paper Institute, "Waste Paper Utilization in Paper and Paperboard Manufacture" (New York, NY: individual yearly reports for 1970 through 1987); Paper Recycling Committee, *1987 Statistics of Paper, Paperboard & Wood Pulp* (New York, NY: August 1987).

this category, for a waste paper utilization rate of 10 percent (figure 5-4). Most unbleached kraft paperboard is produced in the form of linerboard, which is used as the facing material in corrugated boxes and solid fiber boxes. The remainder is used to make folding cartons and other products. Demand for these products has remained strong in recent years, and linerboard in particular is expected to continue in high demand stimulated by projected strong growth in industrial production—corrugated containers are the most widely accepted shipping container.

Expansion of the use of secondary fibers in these mills is limited primarily by performance requirements.[13] Increased use of secondary fibers reduces the strength of the final product, thus limiting the amount of such fiber that can be used in linerboard mills. Some research is underway to enhance the strength of board made from OCC (e.g., using heat and higher pressure in board production, press drying in papermaking, separation of the linerboard from the weaker medium, and enhancement with chemical additives). However, additional research and development is needed (114). Box-makers continue to prefer virgin products because of their strength and durability; they often are specifically

requested by customers abroad, where they are valued as inputs to recycling processes.

One analysis indicated that favorable economics exist to increase the use of secondary fiber in the production of unbleached kraft linerboard (113). According to that study, the major economic advantage of secondary fiber is the relatively low capital cost. It is estimated that a 700-ton-per-day expansion at an existing linerboard mill would cost only $15.1 million for the secondary fiber process, compared with $113.7 million for the kraft pulping process (113).

Semichemical Paperboard—In 1987, U.S. mills produced 5.6 million tons of semichemical paperboard, primarily for use as corrugating medium (the center component or fluting material of corrugated boxboard). The waste paper utilization rate for this product has been about 32 percent over the last few years, an increase from only about 21 percent in 1970 (figure 5-4). Nearly all of the secondary fiber used to make semichemical paperboard consists of OCC.

Production of semichemical paperboard has increased steadily, but is expected to level off (199). Technically, more secondary fiber could be used in the production of corrugated boxes (and is used to

---

[13]Corrugated boxes are required to meet certain requirements for burst strength and sometimes stacking or compression strength as determined by standard industry tests.

make recycled paperboard for corrugated boxes). Many Asian mills are reported to use much larger proportions (if not 100 percent) of secondary fiber in their corrugated boxes. However, these boxes are of a much lower quality than those made in the United States, and limitations exist as a result of U.S. legal and technical shipping requirements. It is possible that these requirements could be changed to accommodate the use of more recycled fiber if greater care were used in shipping.

Semichemical paperboard production generally follows the same trend as kraft linerboard, the other major component of corrugated boxboard; demand is closely tied to industrial production.

Bleached Paperboard—Bleached paperboard is produced almost exclusively from virgin fiber. It is used primarily in sanitary packaging, such as milk cartons, and food service items, such as cups and plates, where it must meet very strict requirements. In 1987, 4.3 million tons of bleached paperboard were produced in the United States. Increased use of secondary fiber is unlikely in these products.

Recycled Paperboard—Almost half of all waste paper used in the United States is consumed in recycled paperboard. In 1987, 9.2 million tons of waste paper were used to make 8.6 million tons of recycled paperboard, a 100 percent recycled product (figure 5-4).[14] All grades of waste paper are used in the production of recycled paperboard, with OCC showing the largest increase (figure 5-5).

Recycled paperboard products include test liner, corrugating medium, filler chipboard for solid fiber boxes, folding cartons, rigid boxes, gypsum wallboard, paper tubes and drums, panelboard, set up boxes, tablet backing, and miscellaneous other products (8). Recycled paperboard has become more popular as industries attempt to lower costs. However, only slight increases in production capacity are expected to 1990.

Recycled paperboard continues to have strong competition from plastics and virgin paperboard. Major portions of the paperboard market were lost in recent years when diaper manufacturers converted packaging from folding cartons to plastic bags and when liquid detergent in plastic bottles began to replace cartoned granules. In higher priced con-

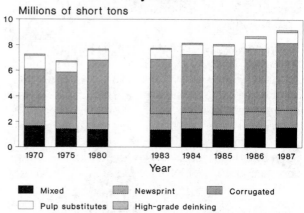

Figure 5-5—Waste Paper Use in Recycled Paperboard, By Grade

Millions of short tons

Legend: Mixed · Newsprint · Corrugated · Pulp substitutes · High-grade deinking

SOURCE: American Paper Institute, Paper Recycling Committee, *1987 Annual Statistical Summary Waste Paper Utilization*, 2d ed. (New York, NY: July 1988).

sumer products, where packaging accounts for a very small share of cost, manufacturers are reluctant to use recycled paperboard because the consumer may associate it with an inferior product. Strength and printability are generally the same for recycled and virgin paperboard, but recycled paperboard is used where lower quality is acceptable (114,264). **Thus, consumer preference appears to play an important limiting role in the increased use of recycled paperboard.** Some industry representatives, however, contend that sanitary and health considerations are the primary factor, followed by weight, economic, and performance considerations.

Construction Paper and Board—Production of construction paper and board in the United States declined from about 3 million tons in 1970 to 1.2 million tons in 1987. About 900,000 tons of waste paper of all grades were used to make construction paper and board in 1987 (figure 5-4). Products in this category include roofing, siding, wallboard, and insulation board. These markets have suffered competition from other materials, such as fiberglass, which is expected to continue.

Waste Paper Exports

The United States is the world's largest exporter of waste paper, and exports of U.S. waste paper have increased tremendously (figure 5-6). Concurrently, the importance of the export market for U.S. waste

---

[14]The process of repulping and cleaning the waste paper results in some shrinkage.

paper dealers also has grown. In 1970, only 3 percent of the waste paper recovered in the United States was exported. By 1987, exports had grown to 18 percent of recovery (9).

Major Markets—According to the Department of Commerce, more than half of U.S. waste paper exports in 1987 was destined for the industrializing countries of the Far East, particularly the Republic of Korea and Taiwan. Since 1970, U.S. exports to that region have increased fifteen-fold, a growth factor far greater than that exhibited by any other region. Mexico is also a large importer of U.S. waste paper, accounting for 18 percent of total U.S. exports in 1987.

The three largest consumers (i.e., Taiwan, Korea, and Mexico) accounted for 59 percent of total U.S. exports in 1987 (225). These countries have expanded papermaking capacity significantly in the last decade, based heavily on imported raw materials, particularly secondary fibers. Low labor costs have allowed them to import lower grade waste paper and sort it by hand for use in their paper mills. Their mills are relatively new and efficient, using technology imported from industrialized countries. Most of the paper produced in Taiwan and Korea is used internally, both for direct consumption and for packaging consumer goods for export.

The Japanese paper industry also consumes a large amount of secondary fiber, amounting to as much as 50 percent of total furnish. Japan accounted for 15 percent of U.S. waste paper exports in 1987.

The European market is expected to decrease in importance for U.S. exporters. U.S. waste paper exports to Europe declined from 402,800 tons in 1985 to 351,200 tons in 1986, as European recovery rates increased to supply their demand. In fact, waste paper markets in Europe experienced a glut in 1986, despite very strong performance by the European paper industry. This situation was particularly marked in West Germany, where mandatory collection of waste paper resulted in an oversupply of lower grades throughout the region and dampened prices considerably (202). Paper stock prices for the lower grades fell by 60 to 80 percent during the year (86). Increased West German exports to Korea and Taiwan have alleviated the European oversupply situation somewhat, but some concerns have been raised about the future ability of the Far East market

Figure 5-6—U.S. Exports of Waste Paper, By Grade

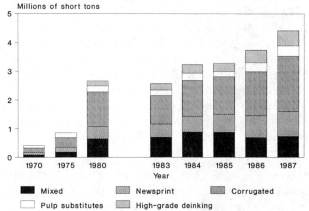

SOURCE: American Paper Institute, Paper Recycling Committee, *1987 Annual Statistical Summary Waste Paper Utilization*, 2d ed. (New York, NY: July 1988).

to absorb the increased supply of low grade waste. Overall, the potential for future increases in U.S. waste paper exports to Europe seems low.

Grades Exported—About 40 percent of U.S. exports of waste paper is OCC, which is in high demand because it is made from strong softwood fibers. Mixed paper and ONP each account for about 20 percent, with the remaining 20 percent split between pulp substitutes and high grade de-inking. These proportions have remained relatively constant over the last decade, with variations of about 5 percentage points (figure 5-6). For each grade, exports are equivalent to 20 to 30 percent of domestic consumption. Pulp substitutes, the highest valued waste paper, are the exception to this, with exports equivalent to only about 10 percent of domestic consumption.

Export demand for most grades of waste paper is expected to remain strong. Exports of most grades increased from 1986 to 1987 by more than 10 percent. Only mixed waste showed a lower growth rate, reportedly because of increased contamination from materials such as plastics and metals (203).

Although export demand is strong, increased supplies from States that recently have implemented recycling programs is reported to have reduced export prices. In the Northeast, where waste paper is a major export, prices for OCC and ONP declined in mid-1988 when New Jersey and other States increased their recycling. Although other factors may

Photo credit: R. Guttman

The United States is the world's largest exporter of waste paper. In 1987, 18 percent of the waste paper recovered in the United States was exported, with over half going to the industrializing countries of the Far East.

have contributed to the downward pressure on prices, by late 1988 some localities were having to pay waste paper dealers to take ONP. Waste paper export prices on the west coast also were affected to some extent, particularly since transportation costs there have risen (205).

The Glass Industry

About 11 million tons of glass containers are produced each year in the United States (52). According to industry sources, between 20 and 25 percent of each new glass container is produced from cullet, or waste glass. Of this, 50 to 55 percent is post-consumer cullet and the remainder is home scrap.[15] On that basis, the amount of cullet used in production would be 2.5 million tons, of which 1.3 million tons would be post-consumer cullet.

Glass discards were estimated to account for about 8 percent of MSW in 1986, or about 12.9 million tons. An estimated 90 percent of the glass was in the form of containers. With about 1.3 million

tons of cullet being recycled, this would represent a post-consumer glass recycling rate of 10 percent in 1986; the rate for 1988 is somewhat higher, at about 15 percent.

It is difficult to compare glass recycling rates in other countries. Most glass bottles in Europe and Japan are refillable. In the Netherlands, for example, over 90 percent of retail soft drink and beer sales are in returnable bottles, as required by law (194). In Japan, 66 percent of all bottles are collected and reused an average of three times; beer and some sake bottles are reused an average of 20 times (106).

The data on international glass recycling are conflicting. One study indicated that glass recycling rates for Europe, Japan, and the United States ranged from 10 to 53 percent, with Japan having a rate of only 17 percent (194). However, a 1983 survey in Japan indicated that about 54 percent of empty bottles and 52 percent of cullet were recovered (106). In Switzerland, enough glass was recycled in

---

[15]This is an estimate for 1986, used to be consistent with the rest of the statistics in this chapter; for 1987-88, 25 percent of each new container is cullet, 60 percent of which is post-consumer.

1986 to satisfy 75 percent of the raw material needs of the glass packaging industry. About 30 percent of West Germany's waste glass is collected, mostly in outdoor collection centers (115). In Sweden, glass recovery is only about 15 percent, even though more than 200 municipalities provide facilities for glass recycling (230).

Technologies of Virgin and Recycled Glassmaking

Glass can be manufactured entirely from virgin materials—primarily from silica sand, and other materials such as feldspar, limestone, and natural soda ash. In addition to making containers, silica sand is used to make flat glass, safety glass, pressed and blown glass, fiberglass, optical glass, and industrial glass. The largest end use for silica sand is containers, which consumed 69 percent of the silica sand produced in the United States in 1986 (246).

To improve melting efficiency in a glassmaking furnace, it is desirable to have at least 8 to 10 percent cullet in the furnace charge, with 25 percent cullet the most common mix. Varying the mixture of cullet and virgin material affects the chemical processes in the furnace, and can require changing the furnace temperature. Because of chemical differences, container cullet generally cannot be used to make most types of glass other than new containers and fiberglass.

Although cullet itself is 100 percent recyclable (one pound of cullet makes one pound of new glass), limitations exist on the amount of cullet that can be used as furnace feed. In general, glass produced from cullet must meet strict buyer specifications on quality and color (table 5-2). Color separation processes, however, usually are not 100 percent efficient, so that strict color specifications can act as a constraint to using large amounts of cullet.

It also is difficult to make glass entirely from cullet because cullet lacks "fining" agents that are needed to reduce bubbles in the glass. Little documentation is available on the amounts of cullet that can be used at various U.S. glassmaking facilities. One study of a European glassmaking facility indicated that, under good conditions, a maximum of about 70 percent cullet can be used in the glassmaking process to make flint glass (57). Higher mixes are possible, especially for colored glass (206), and

Table 5-2—Specifications for Furnace-Ready Cullet

- Only glass container glass is acceptable
- Permissible color mix levels—
  Flint glass
    95-100% flint; 0-5% amber; 0-1% green; 0-5% other colors
  Amber glass
    90-100% amber; 0-10% flint; 0-10% green; 0-5% other colors
  Green glass
    80-100% green; 0-20% amber; 0-10% flint or Georgia green; 0-5% other colors
- Glass must be free of any refractory materials. Grounds for rejection include:
    —presence of pottery, porcelain, china, dinnerware, brick, tile, clay, and so forth, larger than 1 inch.
    —presence of more than one particle of any of above materials larger than 1/8 inch, but less than 1 inch in a 200-pound sample.
    —presence of more than two grains of quartzite, sandstone, or sand pebbles larger than U.S. 16 mesh per 10 pounds of sample.
    —any clay particles larger than U.S. 20 mesh or more than 50 particles larger than U.S. 30 mesh per 10 pounds of sample.
    —any alumina silicate refractory heavy minerals larger than U.S. 30 mesh or more than 10 grains larger than U.S. 40 mesh per 10 pounds of sample.
    —presence of zircon, cassiterite, chrome, or similar refractory particles larger than U.S. 60 mesh.
- Glass must be free of metallic fragments and objects, dirt, gravel, limestone chips, asphalt, concrete, and excessive amounts of paper, cardboard, wrap, plastics, etc.
- Large amounts of excessively decorated glass must be kept separate.

SOURCE: Brockway, Inc., "Specifications for Furnace-Ready Cullet," unpublished manuscript (undated).

industry representatives contend that mixes of 80 percent or more are common (160). One glass manufacturer in Connecticut reportedly produced new container glass using 100 percent cullet for an extended period several years ago, but the highest level attained recently at that facility was 68 percent for making green glass. That same manufacturer reported that the biggest constraint to using more cullet was the difficulty in obtaining high-quality cullet from local suppliers (89).

Energy Consumption—To manufacture glass, four separate steps are used: melting, refining and conditioning, forming, and annealing. Energy is required to perform each step. In addition, energy is consumed in mining and transporting sand and other virgin materials. Mining and transporting can account for about 16 percent of total energy use when making glass from a mix of 15 percent cullet and the remainder virgin materials (table 5-3).

Table 5-3—Energy Consumption Associated With Manufacturing Glass (using 15% cullet)

Manufacturing component	Energy (million Btu/ton)	Percentage of total energy
Materials energy:		
Glass sand	0.50	3.2%
Feldspar	0.11	0.7%
Limestone	0.02	0.1%
Natural soda ash	1.85	12.1%
Subtotal	2.48	16.4%
Process energy:		
Melting	7.6	49.7%
Refining & conditioning	1.5	9.8%
Forming	1.3	8.5%
Post-forming	1.3	8.5%
Handling	1.1	7.1%
Subtotal	12.8	83.6%
Total energy	15.3	100.0%

SOURCE: M.L. Renard, *A Review of Comparative Energy Use in Materials Potentially Recoverable From MSW*, National Center for Resource Recovery, prepared for the U.S. Department of Energy, Office of Renewable Energy, DOE/CS/20167/12, March 1982.

The use of cullet produces energy savings because the heat required to melt cullet is only about one-half to two-thirds that required to melt virgin raw materials (206). In addition, increased use of cullet saves energy because fewer inorganic additives need to be mined. For example, soda ash accounts for 75 percent of the energy used in providing virgin materials and 12 percent of the total energy cost. These energy savings are offset some by the energy required to collect, beneficiate (i.e., remove contaminants such as aluminum), and transport the cullet. If 100 percent cullet is used, the total energy savings in processing amounts to about 15 percent, and an additional 16 percent is saved by avoiding mining and transportation of virgin materials (table 5-3) (206).

Markets for Glass Products

The production of glass items experienced a severe downturn during the recession of the early 1980s. Shipments of glass containers declined 16 percent from 1980 to 1985, primarily as a result of competition from aluminum and plastics. Although glass shipments increased in 1986, they again dropped in 1987. The industry has the potential to increase shipments, however, over the long term. Glass is competitive with other container materials because of the high-quality image it imparts to a product, its microwaveability, and its recyclability (52).

Because the unit price of silica sand is relatively low, cullet prices must remain low to compete. Nevertheless, average prices for industrial sand have increased over the past few years, reflecting higher mining costs (245) and increased demand. Although the potential supply of silica sand is large, land use restrictions and zoning regulations may limit its availability locally, especially in urban and industrialized areas. Restrictions on the availability of virgin materials could bode well for increased use of cullet in glass production in some areas. Current glassmaking technology would allow a substantial increase in cullet use.

Several non-glass markets for cullet exist, including ceramics, abrasives, industrial compounds, fillers, and glassphalt.[16] Initial processing of the cullet may be more important in some of these end uses than it is for glassmaking (236).

Consistently high quality and assured supplies of cullet are essential for all glass end-use products so manufacturers can control the mixture of cullet and virgin materials and produce new glass that consistently meets buyer specifications. **Therefore, the ability to increase the proportion of cullet in most end uses will be determined by improvements in the collection and beneficiation processes.**

The need to produce a consistent color glass for buyers limits the amount of color mixing that can be tolerated. Since two-thirds of the glass made in the United States is clear and only about one-tenth is green, color separation is an extremely important factor in increasing the use of cullet in glassmaking.

An adequate mechanical color separation technology has yet to be developed. Curbside collection of color separated glass containers usually results in higher quality cullet for glassmaking than that from glass separated at centralized processing facilities, where color separation is more difficult to control because of breakage.

Beneficiation removes contaminants (e.g., pieces of aluminum) from the cullet and crushes the cullet to a size suitable for the furnace. By 1989, at least 27

---

[16]Glassphalt is a product made with asphalt and glass.

beneficiation facilities, costing between $500,000 and $1 million each, will be on-line at U.S. glass container manufacturing plants. Newer facilities are significantly better at removing small pieces of aluminum (from neck rings and caps) in the cullet, thus allowing for larger proportions of cullet in the furnace feed (89). With increases in community collection of glass containers, glassmakers may build additional beneficiation facilities to assure consistent quality of the cullet supply.

Glass manufacturers in the United States have indicated a commitment to increasing the use of cullet in glass containers. In addition to those firms building new beneficiation facilities, at least one manufacturer has offered low interest loans to communities to build multi-material buy-back centers and help increase cullet supplies (236). Glass manufacturers feel that publicizing the image of glass as a recyclable material is an important factor in increasing consumption.

One end use where quality is less important is asphalt. Crushed glass can replace as much as 30 percent of the stone and sand used in a conventional asphalt mix (272).[17] Within this range, the product is of comparative strength and lower cost, taking into account revenues obtained for accepting the waste glass. Processing of glass to be used in asphalt requires only removing metal, plastic, and labels. The potential for cullet use in asphalt could be tremendous: the Nation uses approximately 1 billion tons of asphalt each year. The low cost of sand and gravel, however, limits the revenue potential of this market for cullet, especially compared with glass-making. Therefore, cullet is usually used in asphalt only when the quality is low or the distance to a glass plant is great.[18]

Fiberglass manufacturers also have considered the use of post-consumer cullet. The Mineral Insulation Manufacturers Association, however, reports that tests of mixed post-consumer cullet in fiberglass resulted in serious melting difficulties. These difficulties were caused by a variety of contaminants in the cullet, including organic matter, plastics, metals, and non-container glass (152). The manufacture of fiberglass, like glass containers, is subject to strict raw materials specifications. Although fiberglass manufacturers could use glass cullet in their process, it would need to meet standards at least as strict as those for cullet use in glassmaking and additional expenditures would be required for storage silos and materials handling equipment. Therefore, the near-term potential for post-consumer cullet use in fiberglass manufacturing on a national basis is relatively low.

The Aluminum Industry

Although aluminum comprises only about 1 percent by weight of MSW (about 1.8 million tons), its relatively high economic value can make it an important component of recycling programs. About 76 to 79 percent of the aluminum in MSW consists of aluminum cans, or used beverage containers (UBCs). The remainder consists of other aluminum packaging, such as foil and semi-rigid containers, discarded appliances, lawn furniture, and other items.

Aluminum can recycling has increased during the last two decades because of increased demand for aluminum, concerns about litter, the effects of deposit laws, and increases in energy prices (primary aluminum production is very energy-intensive). The aluminum that is diverted from MSW in the United States is almost totally used beverage containers. In 1988, 77.9 billion aluminum beverage cans were shipped and 42.5 billion cans weighing about 752,500 tons were recovered, representing an aluminum can recovery rate of about 55 percent (4). In terms of all aluminum discarded in MSW, this represents a 43 percent recovery rate—virtually all achieved through private collection efforts.[19]

Estimates of recovery rates in Europe and Japan for all aluminum in MSW (not just UBCs) range from 18 to 40 percent, with the highest rates in the Netherlands, Italy, West Germany, and Japan (194). These rates are lower than the U.S. rate, in part

---

[17]The Asphalt Institute believes that 20 percent may be a more realistic maximum, because of the lower bonding properties of glass relative to stone.

[18]New York City uses cullet that cannot be sold for glassmaking in its asphalt plant to substitute for up to 20 percent of the sand and gravel. It pays $10 per ton for the sand and gravel. The quality of the glassphalt is comparable to regular asphalt (28). In addition, a test glassphalt road in Baltimore has held up well in urban traffic for the last 5 years (10,210).

[19]Franklin (81) reported a recovery rate of 25 percent for aluminum from MSW for 1986. The discrepancy between their estimate and that of the Aluminum Association is at least partly because Franklin estimated that less than $1/2$ of the aluminum in MSW is in the form of UBCs (81).

because the use of aluminum beverage cans is lower in Europe and Japan. In Japan, estimates of recovery are between 25 and 32 percent for all aluminum (167,194) and about 40 percent for UBCs (49). Sweden has a deposit system on aluminum cans (ch. 8) and has achieved over 70 percent recovery (230,231).

In the United States, the recovered scrap metal is either returned to the domestic aluminum industry to be recycled into semifabricated products (e.g., can sheet) or castings, used as an oxidizing agent in steelmaking, or is exported. UBCs make up a substantial portion of this scrap. Of the UBCs diverted from MSW, 93 percent is used directly by can sheet manufacturers in the production of new can sheet. The Aluminum Association estimates that in 1988 713,000 tons of UBCs were consumed in domestic production of aluminum mill products and other uses and about 35,500 tons were exported.[20]

The production of secondary aluminum from post-consumer or old scrap by both primary and secondary producers in 1988 was 1,152,000 short tons (247). UBCs provided 60 percent of the raw material for this production, with the remainder coming from shredded auto parts and other old scrap such as old aluminum siding. This scrap material generally is bought and sold through a well-developed aluminum scrap dealers network.[21] Aluminum recovered from old scrap accounted for 20 percent of apparent U.S. consumption of aluminum in 1988, while net imports accounted for 7 percent (248).

Aluminum is imported in ingot and mill product forms primarily from Canada, with additional amounts from Japan, Venezuela, Brazil, and many other countries. Despite these imports, the United States has long been and continues to be the largest producer of primary aluminum in the world, as well as the world's largest market for aluminum products.

In 1989, 10 companies were making can sheet in the United States, and they were the major consumers of aluminum UBC scrap diverted from MSW. The majority of the UBC scrap is processed and melted directly by the can stock producer. In some cases, the material is shipped to another location, usually a secondary smelter, where it is melted and then returned to the can stock producer for final processing into new can sheet. More than 50 secondary aluminum producers are in operation in the United States.

The raw material for the primary aluminum producers is alumina, a refined product of bauxite. Only three sites in the United States refine bauxite into alumina. Small amounts of bauxite are imported—primarily from Guinea, Jamaica, and Australia—for making alumina in the United States, but most U.S. producers import alumina directly. Alumina is imported primarily from Australia, Jamaica, and Suriname. In many cases, U.S. aluminum companies own shares of bauxite and alumina operations in these exporting countries. Costs for transporting bauxite and alumina to the United States range from about \$3/metric ton (Guinea to U.S. Gulf coast) to almost \$20/metric ton (Australia to U.S. east coast) (249). One benefit of recycling aluminum is that it helps reduce dependence on foreign sources for raw materials.

Energy Consumption

Aluminum recycling has a natural economic impetus because of the high electrical energy costs associated with producing primary aluminum. The soaring energy costs in the 1970s further enhanced the energy conservation benefits. The recovery of aluminum from scrap saves about 90 to 95 percent of the energy required to produce the same product from alumina (195,206).

In the United States, electricity can account for up to 50 percent of the total cost of producing aluminum from virgin raw materials (155). For 1988, estimates of the U.S. Bureau of Mines show that the average electricity cost for U.S. aluminum smelters is 19.5 cents per pound of aluminum, compared with the total smelting cost of 59.1 cents. Energy also is required to mine, beneficiate, and transport raw materials such as alumina, aluminum fluoride, cryolite, calcinated petroleum coke, and electrode

---

[20]The Bureau of Mines' statistics on aluminum differ somewhat from those reported by the Aluminum Association, because of differences in accounting methods, definitions, and reporting procedures.

[21]The aluminum industry, like the paper industry, recycles a significant amount of scrap generated in the production of intermediate aluminum products (prompt industrial scrap); this scrap is not included in the statistics reported here. In 1988, 1.21 million tons of new scrap was consumed by the aluminum industry, according to the Bureau of Mines (247).

pitch. Smelting, however, is the most energy-intensive step in the process. The cost of smelting accounts for 85 percent of the total cost to produce aluminum in the United States.

In contrast, when aluminum is recovered from scrap the electrolysis step is eliminated, thus saving energy. In addition, none of the mining and beneficiation steps are required. Energy is required, however, to collect and transport the scrap. Estimates of energy consumption during secondary production range from 8.7 to 11.3 million Btu/ton, including the energy used for shredding and transportation (206).

Technologies of Aluminum Production

Bauxite, the ore from which alumina is made, is refined by dissolving it in a strong alkali solution, from which aluminum trihydrate is extracted to produce alumina, an oxide of aluminum. Primary aluminum production begins at the smelting stage, in which the alumina is dissolved in a large pot containing a molten bath of cryolite, and electrolysis is used to recover 99.7 percent pure aluminum. The aluminum is then alloyed with various elements to produce the qualities desired for specific end uses. This alloying stage is critical for most uses of aluminum.

In secondary aluminum production, scrap aluminum is melted in a furnace, to which alloying elements are added as needed, and subsequently cast into ingots or other aluminum products. New scrap is easy to recycle because the alloys are known and the user can readily separate it by alloy. Aluminum UBC scrap, a combination of similar alloys, is also easily reused, usually by melting and reforming it into new sheet stock. Generally, the only other material added to the furnace during melting of UBC scrap is primary aluminum, to provide the proper alloy and specifications for the final end-use product.

The presence of mixed alloys that may be found in different discarded aluminum products can pose a problem in the secondary production process. It is essential to control the alloy mix to meet strict product specifications.

The primary aluminum industry, in addition to being energy-intensive, is also capital-intensive.

The Bureau of Mines (249) estimates that the world average cost to build a new aluminum smelter would range from $3,000 to $4,000 per metric ton of capacity. Consolidated Aluminum Corp., however, announced the construction of an aluminum recycling facility in the United States in September 1988. The facility will have the annual capacity to produce about 45,000 metric tons of aluminum for a capital cost of $15 million, or about $330 per metric ton of capacity (204).

Markets for Aluminum

The United States is not only the largest aluminum producer, it is also the world's largest market for aluminum, consuming about one-fourth of the world's primary production in 1988. Aluminum industry shipments in the United States exceeded 8.2 million tons in 1988. By market, containers and packaging accounted for the largest share (27 percent) of shipments. Following in importance were transportation (21 percent), building and construction (18 percent), electrical (9 percent), consumer durables (8 percent), and other domestic uses (6 percent).[22] Exports represented 11 percent of U.S. industry shipments in 1988.

Most aluminum produced at secondary smelters is consumed in foundries to produce castings, and a smaller portion is used in steel mills as a deoxidizer. Because of the alloys used to make can sheet, UBC scrap is usually used by can-stock producers to make new can sheet (although other alloys can be produced by additional processing).

Sheet for beverage and food cans constitutes the largest share of the aluminum container and packaging sector, accounting for 82 percent of total shipments in 1988. The remainder consists mainly of foil for semi-rigid food containers, packaging, and consumer foil use. Shipments of aluminum sheet for cans increased from 925,500 tons in 1976 to 1,849,000 tons in 1988, mostly by displacing competing steel and glass, primarily for beer and soft drink cans. Aluminum cans now account for just over half of the entire beverage container market, but 95 percent of the beverage can subset of the market, compared with only about 5 percent of the food can market. Glass retains about one-quarter of the beverage container market, plastic nearly one-fifth,

---

[22]Market breakdowns provided by the Aluminum Association (4).

Photo credit: Office of Technology Assessment

Used beverage containers made from aluminum, shown here just before being compacted and baled for shipping, are recycled at a relatively high rate because of aluminum's high economic value.

and steel cans less than one-twentieth. Although the number of aluminum beverage cans has increased, cans now weigh less so total weight has dropped from 0.69 ounces per can in 1976 to 0.57 ounces per can in 1988.

Demand for aluminum beverage containers is expected to remain strong, because beverage manufacturers and retailers find aluminum a cost-effective packaging material. Growth in aluminum's container market share, however, is expected to slow (168). Some increased competition may also come from plastic, depending on the plastic industry's success in increasing the recycling and recyclability of their products.

Because all new primary aluminum production capacity is being constructed in countries with low electricity costs compared to the United States, U.S. aluminum producers will place increased emphasis on aluminum recycling. This will be particularly important if acid rain legislation is passed.[23] **As a result, post-consumer scrap can be expected to maintain its attraction for aluminum producers**

in the United States into the foreseeable future. In summary, the major barriers to increased recycling of aluminum from MSW are in the collection and transportation networks, the methods of segregating different forms of aluminum scrap, and the technologies for removing contaminants, such as food and dirt, from the scrap prior to melting.

Batteries

Two general types of batteries can be present in MSW—household (or dry cell) batteries and lead-acid automotive batteries. Recycling of these batteries is discussed here, while efforts to reduce the amount of potentially toxic substances in them (e.g., mercury) are discussed in chapter 4.

Household Batteries

Over 2 billion household batteries of all shapes and sizes are sold each year in the United States (153). Batteries can be classified into seven types: carbon/zinc (or LeClanche), alkaline or alkaline/manganese, mercury or mercuric oxide, silver oxide, zinc/air, nickel/cadmium, and lithium. Household batteries are a concern in the MSW system because many contain mercury or other potentially toxic metals (e.g., cadmium, nickel, silver). Some contain lithium, a metal that is reactive in the presence of water (140,153). These metals serve various purposes in the batteries. Mercury (mercuric oxide), for example, is used as a positive electrode in hearing aid batteries. It also is used to coat zinc electrodes, to prevent production of a gas that reduces battery performance, and to reduce electrical impedance and allow zinc to produce electricity more easily (16).

The amount of mercury in batteries has declined substantially in recent years (173) (ch. 4). The industry is now using proprietary substitutes, at least in part, for the mercury coating on zinc electrodes. Mercuric oxide batteries also are slowly being replaced by zinc/air batteries; between 1981 and 1987, the market share for mercuric oxide batteries declined from 72 to 58 percent, while the market share for zinc/air batteries increased from 14 to 40 percent. Zinc/air batteries, however, are sensitive to humidity and to fluctuations in oxygen availability,

---

[23]About one-half of U.S. aluminum production capacity is supplied with power from utilities that would be affected by acid rain legislation (44). Depending on what legislative provisions are enacted, power rates to smelters could rise by 12 percent. As a result, costs could rise by an estimated 2.5 to 4.0 cents per pound for most aluminum smelters and by as much as 7.7 cents per pound for those in Ohio and West Virginia (19).

two constraints that do not plague mercuric oxide batteries.

Separate collection of household batteries occurs to a limited extent in Japan, the United States, and several European countries (box 5-C). Batteries can be separated by hand (based on size, shape, weight) at households, retail outlets, or drop-off centers, and then sent to a refinery for processing. Batteries also can be segregated to some extent from mixed MSW at centralized processing facilities. Rechargeable batteries that are built directly into appliances, however, may be difficult to remove and collect.

Several collection programs exist in the United States (226), including the New Hampshire/ Vermont Solid Waste Program; the Environmental Action Coalition's program in New York City; the Household Hazardous Waste Project in Missouri; and programs in Bellingham, Washington, and Hennepin County, Minnesota. In general, batteries are collected in retail stores where new batteries are sold. The New Hampshire/Vermont program collected 9 tons of batteries from April 1987 through November 1988. The American Watchmakers Institute also has been collecting button batteries and using proceeds from their sale to fund scholarships for teaching watchmaking.

At least two organizations—the American Association of Retired Persons and the National Capital Poison Center—oppose legislative proposals to encourage collecting button batteries because of fears that children might ingest more batteries. They also fear costs of hearing aid batteries would increase (139,150). One suggestion is that States and the battery industry need to jointly sponsor research on the health and environmental risks associated with different management options and on the development of new processing technologies (134).

In theory, collected batteries can be processed to recover the metals. To recover mercury, for example, batteries can be heated to about 1,200° F to open them up and volatilize the mercury, which is then cooled, condensed, and refined (234). The steel casings of the batteries then can be removed and the remaining silver and zinc can be dissolved with hydrochloric acid. This precipitates silver chloride,

which is then reduced to silver powder (234). The remaining portion can be ground up, and some of the ferrous metals can be recovered with magnets.

In the United States, collected batteries are sent to at least two commercial processing facilities. At the Mercury Refining Co. (Mereco) in New York, mercuric and silver oxide batteries are processed to recover mercury and silver (153,154). Nickel/ cadmium batteries are marketed to facilities in Europe. Lithium batteries are sent to a company in Buffalo, New York, that treats the lithium to make it less reactive and then sends the batteries to hazardous waste landfills. Mereco also takes carbon/ zinc, zinc/air, and alkaline batteries; until technologies for processing these are economical, however, it is cheaper to send them to a hazardous waste landfill. The Environmental Pacific Corp. in Oregon takes in all batteries (67,260). The company either recovers metals itself or sells the batteries to smelters for metals recovery. Residues from processing are sent to smelters or hazardous waste facilities for further treatment.

Lead-Acid Automotive Batteries

About 75 million lead-acid automotive batteries reach the end of their useful lives each year in the United States; by 1990, this number is expected to reach 80 million (133). These batteries are of particular concern because all automotive batteries contain lead and sulfuric acid, which pose potential environmental and health risks when landfilled or incinerated.

Historically, used auto batteries have been collected and recycled for their lead content, as well as for the plastic casings. (About half of a battery's weight, 18 to 19 pounds on average, is lead.) Recently, however, several factors reduced the recycling rate for auto batteries and increased the prospects that some may be ending up in MSW landfills.

Recovery of auto batteries is not mandated in most States, so the primary motivation for collection is profit from the sale of the lead.[24] The price for this scrap lead depends on the price of unwrought lead and the cost of processing scrap lead into usable forms. After 1979, lead prices dropped precipitously

---

[24]Rhode Island placed a $5 charge in lieu of trade on all vehicle batteries; Minnesota, Pennsylvania, Florida, and Wyoming all have legislation requiring that retailers who sell batteries accept spent batteries; and California has regulations governing the management of lead-acid storage batteries.

Box 5-C—Household Battery Management in Europe and Japan

Collection and Recycling in Europe

Battery collection programs have been initiated in at least 11 European countries. Some are run by industry and/or trade associations, and some by municipalities (137,183). In the Netherlands, for example, mercuric oxide batteries have been collected since 1978, and most communities now have depots for batteries (14,122).

The presence of collection systems, however, does not mean that batteries are recycled. In the Netherlands and Denmark, batteries are stored temporarily, sent to a manufacturer for reprocessing, or exported to West or East Germany, where they are put in salt mines or landfilled with industrial wastes (115,137). This is partly because recycling plants designed for batteries have not demonstrated long-term economic success. Two plants in France and one in Sweden were unable to operate profitably on the basis of recovering mercury alone. Several institutes are conducting research on sorting and processing technologies (e.g., 256,257).

The European Community Commission

In 1987, the European Community Commission issued a proposal that called for labeling batteries, collection of used batteries, and prohibitions on the marketing of certain batteries. The proposal also called for a 70 percent reduction in mercury in batteries (85 percent for alkaline/manganese batteries), replacement of mercury batteries by zinc air and lithium batteries, and deposit systems (69). The battery industry, which previously agreed to reduce mercury in alkaline/manganese batteries by 85 percent, estimates that the mercury in batteries discarded in Europe will decline by 86 percent between 1985 and 1992 (69).

Household Battery Management in Sweden

The Swedish Environmental Protection Board, concerned about consumption of mercury from fish by children and pregnant women, estimated that up to one-third of background levels of mercury during the late 1970s and early 1980s came from incineration of batteries (106). Incineration of wastes in general was estimated to account for 55 percent of known mercury emissions in Sweden in 1985 (138,174). However, mercury also comes from anthropogenic emissions from continental Europe and from natural emissions (e.g., geothermal areas) (138).

In 1983 the government began a voluntary collection program that encouraged the 27 cities with incinerators to collect batteries (14,15,106,115,174). By 1987, the government's goal of collecting 75 percent of mercury oxide, alkaline, and nickel/cadmium batteries had not been met, so it expanded the effort into a nationwide voluntary program, including extensive education and the placement of collection receptacles at offices and public areas. The educational campaigns and management of collected batteries are funded with a surcharge on all mercury oxide, alkaline, and nickel/cadmium batteries. The government is studying mandatory deposit systems, and in 1989 it banned all alkaline batteries containing over 0.025 percent mercury, effective in 1990 (137).

Some collected carbon/zinc batteries are sent to ordinary landfills in Sweden (sometimes to separate areas at the landfills) (137,173). All other batteries are sent to the SAKAB Mercury Distillation Demonstration Plant. Almost 300 tons of batteries are now in storage at SAKAB. Nickel/cadmium batteries are sorted and sent to another facility for recovery of the nickel and cadmium.

The SAKAB Demonstration Plant was built to test the feasibility of recovering mercury from batteries; mercury oxide batteries were used because of their high concentrations of mercury (106). The plant handled 100 kilograms per day. It is not operating now because it was not commercially viable at that size; the parent company, however, is still interested in developing the facility (137). Concerns were expressed that manual sorting would increase health risks for workers (14,15).

The effect of collecting batteries on the levels of mercury in incinerator emissions is not clear. Three years after the collection program began, the amount of mercury emitted from the Stockholm incinerator reportedly had declined 80 percent, to a total of 150 kilograms in 1986 (106). The pollution controls at the facility also were upgraded at this time, however, so it is impossible to determine how battery collection affected emissions.

West Germany: Voluntary Agreement

In 1987, the German government and a trade association representing the electrical industries reached a voluntary agreement regarding batteries (87,93). Manufacturers and importers agreed to reduce mercury levels in alkaline/manganese batteries from current levels of 0.5 percent by weight to 0.15 percent by 1990, with an option to reduce the level to less than 0.10 percent by 1995. Manufacturers also agreed to accept returned button batteries (e.g., from watch-makers and camera shops), although there is some confusion about whether other batteries must also be collected.

If the number of returned batteries is deemed insufficient, the government could impose a mandatory deposit on the sale of new household batteries (ch. 8). The Federal Environmental Agency is concerned that after the minimum mercury concentration per alkaline/manganese battery is attained, the total level in all batteries will increase again as the market share of these batteries increases.

If the European Community Commission proposal is adopted, then this more stringent German agreement might be dropped because it would interfere with trade within the European Community.

Collection and Recycling in Japan

Past experience with Minamata disease, a debilitating human disease caused by mercury consumption, makes mercury a major issue in Japan (106). In the early 1980s, the government reached an agreement with manufacturers to reduce the amount of mercury in batteries by five-sixths between 1983 and 1986. Two household battery collection programs also were established. About three-fourths of Japanese municipalities collect cylinder-shaped batteries, while battery manufacturers collect button-shaped batteries at retail stores. However, collection rates have been low (9 percent by weight of cylinder-shaped batteries and 27 percent by number of button-shaped batteries) and did not increase during 1987 and 1988 (179). As of 1985, over 750 municipalities simply stored cylinder-shaped batteries, 47 mixed them with concrete and landfilled the material, and about 550 sent them to a processing facility located at Itomuka, on the northern island of Hokkaido. Button-shaped batteries also were shipped to Itomuka.

The Itomuka facility is a demonstration mercury recycling plant that began operating in October 1985. It is a joint venture between the Clean Japan Center (CJC), Mitsui Metals Engineering Company, and Nomura Kosan Company (50,109). Participating municipalities pay transportation costs and a tipping fee to cover operating costs. The plant's purpose is to demonstrate the technical and economic feasibility of recycling mercury-containing wastes—mostly batteries, but also fluorescent lamps, thermometers, and mirrors (109). The plant can handle 20 tons per day. Batteries are separated by size and shape, and then a proprietary process separates cylinder-shaped batteries by weight. Thermal treatment and recovery techniques are used to separate metals (e.g., volatilization, distillation, and condensation of mercury; magnetic recovery of ferrous materials). Gas emissions are treated with a wet scrubber and electrostatic precipitator (109). Wastewater is evaporated until salts are crystallized out, then recirculated instead of being discharged. OTA was unable to obtain data on air emissions.

The plant processed an estimated 7 percent of the household batteries used in Japan annually, recovering mercury, zinc and managanese (in combination), and iron. Problems have occurred with the condition of incoming batteries, fluctuations in supply, and the battery dismantling process (50). As of November 1988, the facility was operating at a loss (179). In particular, the zinc residues (consisting of zinc, manganese, and other materials), which make up 54 percent by weight of the incoming batteries, are not being marketed because the price of zinc had fallen too low. The arrangement with the CJC is scheduled to end in August 1989.

Whether these collection efforts have had any effect on mercury levels in remaining MSW is unclear. A more important factor may be the significant decline in mercury used in household batteries.

from more than 50 cents to about 18 cents per pound. As a result, many scrap dealers could not realize a profit from the collection and sale of discarded automotive batteries.

In addition to low prices, the costs of collecting and processing batteries increased as a result of environmental regulations. For secondary smelters,[25] operating costs of full compliance with environmental regulations existing in 1988 were estimated at 6.8 cents (in 1987 dollars) per pound of refined lead produced (118).[26] Also, as of January 1985, EPA designated spent lead-acid batteries as a hazardous waste under RCRA. Costs associated with RCRA compliance can range from $100,000 to $200,000 per processing facility. Many scrap collectors and dealers refused to continue handling batteries for fear of incurring liability under Superfund.

The specter of increasing costs, ever-increasing regulation, and low lead prices caused a significant reduction in the number of people willing to

[25]Secondary lead smelters are the facilities that reprocess the lead from spent batteries.

[26]Environmental regulations considered include those for particulates, water, and health and safety. The particulates standard of 1.5 micrograms per cubic meter of lead in ambient air was used in the calculation.

participate in battery recycling. This caused a reduction of U.S. secondary lead smelting capacity from 1.4 million tons per year in 1980 to 882,000 tons per year in 1986.

On the other hand, in 1987 about 1.25 million tons of lead were consumed in the United States. Automotive batteries are the largest end-use, accounting for more than three-quarters of total consumption. Most of the demand is supplied by domestic smelters, and about two-thirds of this is from secondary smelters, despite the reduction in secondary smelting capacity. In 1987, 725,000 tons of lead were produced at secondary smelters from old scrap (about 90 percent from batteries), while 412,000 tons of lead were produced at primary facilities.[27] Significant quantities of lead are also imported, principally from Canada and Mexico, amounting to about 15 to 20 percent of U.S. consumption. The United States also imports some batteries for the replacement market and as original equipment in imported autos and exports about 2.5 to 3 million new batteries per year.

What happens to the unrecovered batteries has not been documented. Between 1980 and 1986, an estimated 98 million batteries containing 900,000 tons of lead went unrecovered (184). Some probably are being discarded in MSW, some are being stored in garages or elsewhere, and some may have been exported as scrap and toll smelted in Mexico.[28]

Recycling rates for auto batteries are difficult to calculate. In 1965, the recycling rate was estimated to have reached a peak of 96.6 percent (201). In the early 1980s, the estimated rate dropped sharply to a low of about 57 to 66 percent. Recycling rates then began to rise again, reaching an estimated 80 percent or more between 1984 and 1986 (128,269).[29]

At a 1986 rate of 80 percent, a reported 556,200 tons of lead was recovered from discarded batteries, representing 44 percent of total U.S. lead consumption. Obviously, auto batteries are a very important

source of lead, despite a relatively large lead reserve base.[30]

The amount of unrecovered batteries may have decreased during 1987 and 1988, as a result of increases in lead prices and high demand (figure 5-7). Average annual lead prices increased from 19 cents per pound in 1985 to 36 cents per pound in 1987, as demand increased by 90,000 tons (248).[31] Corresponding lead recovery from batteries increased from 542,800 tons in 1985 and 556,200 tons in 1986 to 648,900 tons in 1987. Some portion of this increase is very likely to have come from "inventoried" batteries stored in garages and basements, so recycling rates calculated using historical methods could be misleading. The increase could also be attributable to the enhanced efforts of secondary smelters and battery manufacturers to collect and recover discarded batteries to help reduce the public's concern about batteries entering landfills. Recovery rates for 1987 are estimated at about 82 to 83 percent (133,184).

Continued increases in battery recycling may be evidenced by a rise in the utilization of secondary smelter capacity from 76 percent in 1986 to 83 percent in 1987. Concern exists about the adequacy of secondary smelter capacity, however. Some analysts worry about the allegedly poor financial condition of some firms operating the smelters. About 110,000 tons of existing secondary capacity will probably be lost if more stringent water protection regulations are enacted. However, planned expansions will increase capacity to about 1 million tons by the early 1990s. Because battery manufacturers view secondary smelters as an important component of the battery consumption chain, they are interested in expanding U.S. capacity to recover lead from discarded batteries.

To this end, certain battery manufacturers have approached the two major primary lead producers, Doe Run and Asarco, about refitting currently closed primary smelters to process battery scrap. Prefeasi-

---

[27]An additional 58,000 tons or so of lead were produced from purchased new scrap, including drosses (this is in addition to home scrap).

[28]Some secondary smelters have agreements with landfill operators to accept lead-acid batteries that do reach the landfill, but the extent to which this occurs is unknown (143).

[29]One study (201) estimated a rate of 69.5 percent in 1985, but another analyst (269) speculated that this lower estimate was based on data which have since been revised.

[30]According to the Bureau of Mines, the United States accounts for nearly 20 percent of the world's lead reserve base.

[31]Although 36 cents was the posted price in 1987, analysts believe that producers were offering substantial discounts to consumers.

bility studies were conducted in 1988 on converting the Buick smelter in Missouri, which has capacity to process 140,000 tons per year of primary lead. The decision has been made to retrofit Buick to accept battery scrap, but the work is not expected to be completed until mid-1990. Similar retrofits are being considered for primary smelters in Glover, Missouri; East Helena, Montana; Omaha, Nebraska; and El Paso, Texas.

Another avenue for discarded batteries is the export market. Despite EPA's designation of spent batteries as hazardous waste, the United States is exporting this lead scrap to Brazil, Taiwan, and Canada.[32] In 1986, about 65,000 tons of scrap batteries were exported. Some of this scrap is used to produce new batteries that compete with U.S. producers.

The proliferation of discount battery outlets has increased the incidence of home battery replacement. Because the home mechanic may not be aware that spent batteries can be returned and recycled, there is a greater chance that they will not enter the collection chain. Unless the home mechanic is educated or otherwise induced to return the spent battery to the retailer or a collection center, batteries will continue to elude the recycling process.

In all member countries of the Organization for Economic Cooperation and Development (OECD), consumers can trade in old automotive batteries for a discount off the purchase of a new battery (183). The trade-in discount essentially amounts to a deposit that is refunded when a new battery is purchased. Statistics on recycling rates in all OECD countries are not available. The Association of European Accumulator Manufacturers estimated the average European battery recycling rate at about 80 percent in 1986-87; the rate for the Federal Republic of Germany was estimated at 75 percent in 1986 (85). In comparison, normal battery recycling rates in Japan have been estimated as nearing 100 percent (112). It is interesting to note, however, that when lead prices declined in 1986, Japanese recovery rates dropped to about 90 percent. It is likely that spent batteries were stockpiled for later sale at higher prices.

Figure 5-7—Battery Recycling Rates and Lead Prices

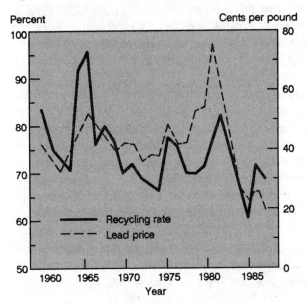

SOURCE: Putnam, Hayes & Bartlett, Inc., "The Impacts of Lead Industry Economics and Hazardous Waste Regulations on Lead-Acid Battery Recycling: Revision and Update," prepared for Office of Policy Analysis, U.S. Environmental Protection Agency (Washington, DC: September 1987).

Iron and Steel Scrap

The amount of ferrous (iron-based) scrap in MSW was estimated to be 11.0 million tons in 1986, or 7.0 percent of total gross discards (81). About one-fourth (2.8 million tons) of the ferrous scrap fraction consisted of steel packaging such as food and beverage cans. Another one-fourth (2.8 million tons) consisted of major appliances (i.e., "white goods"), and the remainder was products such as small appliances, toys, tools, and furniture. Serious questions have been raised about the accuracy of these estimates, particularly concerning the kinds of products included in the definition of MSW (ch. 3). Industry representatives contend that these estimates seriously understate the amount of ferrous material in MSW by excluding junked automobiles, office equipment, and worn out fixtures from commercial and institutional establishments.

According to the Franklin estimates, only about 400,000 tons of ferrous scrap were recovered from

---

[32]Spent batteries that are shipped for recycling do not require a manifest for domestic shipments (see 40 CFR 266.80), and thus are not subject to the RCRA requirement in Sec. 3017 for bilateral agreements for the export of hazardous waste.

MSW in 1986, a recovery rate of only 3.6 percent. Most of this consisted of packaging (100,000 tons) and white goods. A recovery rate of only 3.6 percent for MSW ferrous scrap is deceptively low. Depending on what materials are included, the rate could be higher than 20 percent.[33] In addition, junked automobiles are an important source of ferrous scrap, and large amounts are currently recycled in the United States. The Institute of Scrap Recycling Industries (ISRI) estimates that as much as 8 million tons of ferrous scrap was generated from recycling old automobiles in 1986. This material is not included in Franklin's definition of MSW, but if the current, well-developed system for processing junked autos deteriorated, some of them could become part of MSW. Some analysts do include this source of scrap in calculating MSW recycling rates for other countries (e.g., for Japan; see appendix).

Reported recovery rates for ferrous scrap from MSW in other countries vary greatly, ranging from 9 percent in China to more than 40 percent in Belgium and Luxembourg; countries with more iron ore reserves tend to have lower rates (167). How much of these amounts refer to industrial scrap, however, is unknown.

The Franklin estimate of 400,000 tons of ferrous scrap recovered from MSW in the United States is a relatively insignificant portion of the total ferrous scrap consumed in the United States. The total amount of ferrous scrap recovered from all sources in the United States amounted to about 66 million tons in 1986. Almost three-quarters of that total was consumed by the steel industry, one-quarter was consumed by the ferrous castings industry, and a small portion was consumed in uses such as copper precipitation and ferroalloys production. In addition, 12 million tons of ferrous scrap were exported in 1986, principally to the Republic of Korea, Japan, Turkey, Spain, and Taiwan (36).

Technologies for Using Ferrous Scrap in Steelmaking

Some of the ferrous scrap recovered from MSW is prepared for shipping by baling—the scrap is flattened and packaged to produce bales that weigh around 75 to 80 pounds per cubic foot. The density and packaging of the scrap influence the transportation costs and consequently the economics of recycling. Transportation cost is an extremely important factor in the recycling of ferrous scrap because the scrap has a relatively low value per ton.

In the past, scrap was melted primarily at mills owned by large integrated steel companies (i.e., those owning iron ore mines, ore pelletizing operations, coke ovens, blast furnaces, steelmaking furnaces, and steel fabricating plants). These mills melt the scrap material in blast furnaces along with iron ore and coke to produce hot metal. Scrap is also used in basic oxygen or open-hearth steelmaking furnaces along with hot metal to produce raw steel.

Electric arc furnaces (EAFs), developed around the turn of the century, are seeing increased use as a result of advances in the technology during the last 20 years. Modern EAFs reduced the time needed to produce a ton of steel from 180 to 70 minutes and reduced the electricity consumption from 630 kWh per ton to 430 kWh per ton (63). The reduced electricity consumption makes raw steel production by melting scrap in EAFs considerably more economical (approximately 25 percent) than by the iron ore-blast furnace-basic oxygen furnace route (124). EAFs use virtually 100 percent scrap to make steel. About 60 percent of all the ferrous scrap now consumed in the United States is melted in EAFs.

The improvements in EAF technology have nurtured the rise of "minimills." Minimills use relatively small EAFs (100,000 tons per year capacity for a minimill operation v. 2 million tons per year for an integrated producer) to produce certain steel products. These mills are not integrated, and because they are not dependent on iron ore supplies they can be located away from traditional steelmaking loca-

---

[33]Franklin does not estimate the recovery of white goods separately. However, if all of the remaining 300,000 tons of ferrous scrap recovered were white goods, then the implied recovery rate for white goods would be only about 11 percent. However, the steel industry estimates that 75 percent of white goods are collected separately and routinely delivered to auto shredders for processing (219). This would mean that 2.1 million tons of white goods were recovered, plus the 100,000 tons of packaging estimated by Franklin to have been recovered, as well as an additional 100,000 tons of miscellaneous ferrous scrap recovered from separation at waste-to-energy plants, as estimated by the steel industry. This total of 2.3 million tons of ferrous scrap represents a 21 percent recovery rate.

tions. This flexibility has helped improve productivity and lower costs; minimills can produce their products for about 15 percent less than integrated steel producers (158). The largest advantage enjoyed by the minimills, however, is in the capital cost of building a mill. The Bureau of Mines (37,245) estimates the capital cost per annual ton of raw steel capacity is less than $400 for EAF production from scrap v. $1000 for the iron ore-blast furnace-basic oxygen furnace route.

Detinning—The major source of **post-consumer** scrap steel from MSW is "tin cans," which are actually steel with a light tin coating intended to prevent rusting. However, the tin is generally considered an undesirable contaminant in steelmaking, so these cans must be detinned (as well as cleaned of other contaminants such as glass and aluminum). In the detinning process, the tin is removed either chemically or electrolytically. Tin residues typically cannot exceed 0.05 percent if the can is to be remelted into steel.

Energy Savings—Estimating current energy savings associated with producing steel from scrap v. iron ore is difficult because the relevant data are mostly from studies performed in the 1970s. The estimates presented here are averages of a mix of steelmaking processes; the mix is based on data from the 1970s and is not representative of present industry conditions.

Energy savings associated with producing raw steel from scrap v. ore were estimated to average around 75 percent, based on the 1970s data for an EAF using 100 percent scrap (206). However, the savings for the production of finished steel were estimated to be lower, about 45 percent. The energy used to mine and process the ore was estimated to be about 3 percent of the total energy cost to produce finished steel. When the total amount of energy required to mine, beneficiate, transport, and process both ore and scrap was included, the savings from using scrap were estimated to be between 47 and 59 percent (206).

More recent data indicate that energy requirements in the steel industry declined by about 16 percent from 1972 to 1981. At least some of this decrease can be attributed to the increased use of

EAFs. Also, further energy efficiencies have been gained. In 1983, the total energy required to produce a ton of raw steel amounted to 21.7 million Btus, down from 25.7 million Btu in 1973 (245). Energy from coal amounts to about half of the total, and EAFs use most of their energy in the form of electricity and natural gas.

Overall Use of Scrap

Scrap is an important raw material to the steel industry. In 1986, U.S. steel mills consumed 49.7 million tons of scrap and 44.3 million tons of new pig iron (made from iron ore) to produce 81.6 million tons of raw steel. Franklin estimates that only 0.4 million tons of the ferrous scrap consumed to produce raw steel in 1986 was recovered from MSW.[34] Almost all of the scrap consumed was obtained from sources other than MSW—about 40 percent from home scrap; 40 percent from old scrap; and 20 percent from prompt industrial scrap. The old and prompt industrial scrap are purchased from brokers, dealers, and company-owned plants.

Several trends have caused an increase in the importance of purchased obsolete and prompt industrial scrap. The first is the growing use of EAFs by minimills. EAF capacity in the United States has grown from 23 percent of the total in 1978 to 36 percent in 1988. Over 200 EAFs are in operation in the United States, and they produced 27 million tons of carbon steel in 1987.

The second factor causing increased demand for scrap is the use of continuous casting, which now accounts for about 60 percent of raw steel production (36). Continuous casting reduces the generation of home scrap, compared with that of traditional ingot casting, and increases the yield from about 75 to 88 percent. Because a certain amount of scrap is used in basic oxygen steelmaking processes for temperature control, the advent of this technology has increased the demand for purchased scrap. These changes can be seen by comparing the consumption of purchased scrap and home scrap with the production of raw steel, steel mill products, and steel castings. In 1982, 24 million tons of home scrap and 24 million tons of purchased scrap were consumed to produce steel mill products and castings. In 1987, despite an increase in raw steel and castings production, use of

---

[34]The steel industry estimates that 2.3 million tons of ferrous scrap were recovered from MSW (see footnote 33).

home scrap declined to 20 million tons but use of purchased scrap increased to 38 million tons (36).

Potential Markets for MSW Ferrous Scrap

Because much of the ferrous scrap in MSW (as defined in this study) is in the form of tin-plated steel cans, the detinning industry is an important potential market. Detinners are primarily interested in recovering tin, but they also increase the value of the remaining steel in the process. Detinners can sell the clean ferrous scrap to steel mills at prices set for relatively high-quality scrap. Small amounts also are sold to copper producers in the southwest, who use the scrap to precipitate copper from copper sulfate solutions. This market may decline as new copper recovery technologies are developed.

In 1986, about 550,000 tons of tin-plate scrap was processed to recover about 1,250 tons of tin. Most of this processed scrap was pre-consumer—tin plate scrap from can manufacturers and rejected tin plate from tin plate producers. Only a small amount consisted of post-consumer can scrap from MSW.

Detinning capacity is limited and confined mainly to the Midwest. Other plants are located in Maryland, Texas, Arizona, Utah, California, and Washington. The limited availability of detinning facilities is one reason why most MSW recycling programs do not include tin cans. However, detinning capacity is expanding (186). The construction of two new detinning plants was announced in 1988—one in New Brunswick, New Jersey, and one in Houston, Texas (266). The detinning industry has indicated an interest in processing increased amounts of post-consumer can scrap.

Small amounts of tin can scrap can also be used directly to produce lower grade steel products, such as reinforcing bar.[35] It is not known what portion of recovered steel cans is used in this manner, however. In 1988, 19 integrated steel mills announced that they were willing to purchase post-consumer tin cans for direct use in their furnaces (129). Because the steel mills can accept bales of scrap that are more dense than those that detinners can accept, the mills could have a transportation cost advantage. However, as of early 1989, the prices the steel mills were willing to pay for tin cans did not provide enough

incentive for recyclers to collect the material in large quantities.

The steel industry has also indicated a willingness to accept bimetal cans (steel body and aluminum top). Until recently, the 150,000 tons of post-consumer bimetal beverage cans discarded each year have had a relatively small market—in 1986 only about 5 percent were recycled. However, evidence of increased bimetal can recycling rates by steel mills is not available, and some observers remain skeptical about the potential for this market (187).

Steel producers, primarily in the eastern United States, have initiated a public relations campaign to promote recycling of both tin-plated and bimetal cans. Major steelmakers formed the Steel Can Recycling Institute to promote this type of recycling.

The steel industry has placed less focus on other ferrous components of MSW. Generally, these materials can be shredded or baled and sold to steel mills or exported through scrap processors or brokers. The quality of the scrap is very important in determining price and locating a purchaser. Scrap from alloys formed by blending rare metals is difficult to market, because few products are able to tolerate such contamination. The United States has never faced a severe shortage of ferrous scrap, and it has been estimated that 800 million tons of ferrous scrap (probably lower grade) have been stored in the last 30 years because of lack of demand (36).

In 1986, domestic steel mills and ferrous foundries purchased 42 million tons of ferrous scrap, while export markets purchased an additional 12 million tons. In 1987, total domestic purchases increased to 48 million tons, while exports dropped to 11 million tons. Ultimately, the potential market for ferrous scrap depends on the worldwide demand for steel, which was strong in 1987 and 1988. In the United States alone, raw steel production is relatively high, responding to strong demand in the home market (and voluntary restraint agreements on imports). U.S. capacity utilization was 79 percent in 1987, compared with just 64 percent in 1986. As an indirect result of this strong demand for steel, the Bureau of Mines' composite price for No. 1 heavy melting scrap increased from $72 per metric ton in

---

[35]Tin causes embrittlement of the steel, which is intolerable in the higher grade steel products. In general, the quantity of non-detinned scrap that can be used depends on the overall tin content of scrap used and the specifications of the end product.

1986 to $84 per metric ton in 1987 and to $114 per metric ton in July 1988. Planned capacity expansions abroad, however, will put downward pressure on these prices, and the steel market in general, in the long term.

Special Problem Materials

Steel Drums—Fifty-five gallon steel drums are another source of ferrous scrap. However, mills have refused to accept these drums based on fears about the potential presence of hazardous wastes and potential liabilities under Superfund (97). To counter this, ISRI proposed that drum suppliers certify that the drums are clean and indemnify the recyclers against the possible liability associated with handling the drums. According to ISRI, this has worked fairly well and has created an incentive for suppliers to ensure that drums are clean before they are delivered to the recyclers.

Some small supplier companies that cannot afford to indemnify recyclers have chosen to contract with drum reconditioning firms to clean the drums, either for reuse or disposal. The reconditioners act as intermediaries between the drum suppliers and the recyclers. They accept the drums, which have been certified to be free of RCRA-regulated hazardous waste, clean the drums, and send them to scrap processors. Steel mills apparently are willing to accept drums from scrap processors that follow these procedures.

White Goods—The term "white goods" refers to large appliances such as refrigerators, washers, and dryers. They typically contain large amounts of steel and are a traditional source of ferrous scrap. They are discarded at an estimated rate of about 2.8 million tons per year (81). Recovery rates were discussed above.

Recycling of discarded appliances usually begins with shredding, which helps separate metallic from non-metallic materials (e.g., rubber, glass, plastic, and dirt). Scrap dealers typically shred white goods using the same equipment used for automobiles. State-of-the-art shredders can separate the discards into ferrous metals, nonferrous metals, and nonmetallic waste. Once shredded, the scrap is sent to processors where stainless steel and nonferrous metals are recovered, to steel mills where it is melted into new steel or steel alloy products, or to foundries where it is melted into new castings products.

The major environmental problem associated with recycling white goods is that polychlorinated biphenyls (PCBs) are present in the electrical capacitors of some appliances produced or repaired prior to 1979. When these appliances are shredded, the capacitors are crushed and leak PCB-contaminated oil over the shredder fluff (i.e., the nonmetallic waste produced when the appliances are shredded).

EPA clarified its policy on PCB-contaminated fluff in a letter to ISRI on July 18, 1988. EPA stated that the Toxic Substances Control Act (TSCA) rules that regulate waste contaminated with PCBs at concentrations of 50 ppm or more (40 CFR 761.60) are applicable to shredder fluff. These regulations require that PCB-contaminated waste be disposed at a landfill, incinerator, or "alternative method which can achieve. . .no unreasonable risk," in compliance with standards in the regulation.

This action immediately reduced the number of scrap handlers willing to accept white goods and caused others to accept them only under restrictive conditions. ISRI, for example, recommended that its members stop handling and processing appliances or fluorescent lighting fixtures unless they were evaluated prior to processing to be sure that PCBs are not present (116). In response to ISRI's advisory, EPA issued a press release indicating that it did not believe that many pre-1979 appliances still exist in the waste stream, and therefore they should not pose a problem for scrap processors.

In Connecticut, the Department of Environmental Protection formally notified landfill operators, scrap dealers, and municipalities that shredding old appliances is illegal, unless the electrical capacitors that contain PCBs are removed. This, in turn, has led some scrap dealers to notify municipalities that they will no longer accept appliances without some means of guaranteeing that they do not contain PCBs. Some Connecticut towns have developed programs to remove electrical capacitors that contain PCBs from appliances prior to shredding and to ship the capacitors out of state at a cost of about $500 to $700 per barrel, or about $2 per capacitor.

The presence of chlorofluorocarbons (CFCs) in refrigeration systems could pose similar regulatory problems for scrap processors. CFCs contribute to the depletion of stratospheric ozone, and recycling of white goods containing CFCs may be regulated in the future. According to ISRI, data are not available indicating either the amount of CFCs that typically remain in non-operational refrigerators or air-conditioners when they are delivered for recycling or the potential for release of CFCs during processing.

Tires

Between 200 and 250 million waste tires are discarded annually in the United States. Once discarded, they can provide breeding habitat for rats and mosquitoes and present a serious fire threat (94). In 1983, for example, a scrap tire fire in Winchester, Virginia, smoldered for months and produced 250,000 gallons of an oil-like liquid that contaminated the dump. Some alternatives to landfilling exist for scrap tires, including physical recycling, chemical recycling, and waste-to-energy.

Physical Recycling

Several methods are available to physically recycle the whole tire or some fraction of it. Whole tires have been used for landscape borders, highway trash barriers, artificial reefs, and erosion control (95). Retreading of used tires also occurs, but the market for retreaded tires has declined considerably in the last 10 years and is expected to decline even more in the future. In 1978, 31 million tires were retreaded and sold, while in 1986 this figure declined to only 15 million. By 2005, only 6 million tires are expected to be retreaded and sold (176).

Some used tires have been processed into specialized industrial products and household items such as doormats. However, these processing techniques are limited to fabric-belted tires, which have been losing their market share to steel-belted models (95).

Mechanical or cryogenic processes have been developed to break tires into fine particles, known as crumb rubber. Crumb rubber can replace virgin rubber in carpet backing, asphalt, and friction break materials (95). An innovative crumb rubber plant with a capacity to process 3 million tires a year has been built in a remote part of Minnesota. The facility, operated by Rubber Research Elastomerics

and capitalized with public funds, is attempting to increase the marketability of the crumb rubber by adding various polymers. During 1988, however, the plant operated at less than one-third of its production capacity, because there was limited demand for the product. In the first 9 months of 1987, the plant processed only 100,000 tires and lost $1.5 million. It expects to process about 750,000 tires in 1990 (196). The remote location of the plant may act as a deterrent to potential markets and the company operating the plant is seeking to expand to other locations in the United States.

Chemical Recycling

Scrap tires can be converted into gas, oil, and char through a process known as pyrolysis (thermal decomposition in the absence of oxygen) (ch. 6). The tires are heated to 1,000° F to 1,800° F to volatilize the oil and gas, separating them from the carbon (char) and inorganic materials (e.g., steel). Condensation at various temperatures, along with filtration, allows the recovery of oil and gas fractions.

Chemical reclamation has also been used in the past to recover the rubber. However, since the composition of tires has changed from primarily rubber to synthetic elastomer blends, this process has become less economical.

Waste-to-Energy

Scrap tires also can be incinerated to recover energy. Different technologies can be used, including fluidized beds, rotary kilns, and cement kilns. Depending on the facility, either whole tires or tire-derived-fuel (TDF) can be used. Cement kilns and facilities that use rotary kilns can burn both whole and shredded tires. Facilities equipped with fixed or traveling grates tend to burn TDF, since this fuel burns more rapidly and evenly than whole tires. However, the steel belts in tires can cause problems in the combustion chamber when TDF is burned. Consequently, many shredding operations that prepare TDF for incinerators, paper mills, or cement kilns remove as much steel as possible.

During combustion, up to 15,000 Btu per pound of scrap tires can be generated. In the past, the costs of competing fuels, such as wood chips and coal, have caused prices of TDF to drop and processors to lose money. Between 1986 and 1987, for example, the price of TDF dropped from $35 to $33 per ton.

One company that produces TDF had to increase its tipping fee for accepting waste tires by 63 percent (tipping fees vary considerably, ranging from $8 to $100 per ton) (196).

Only one cement manufacturer, in Redding, California, is burning tires as the primary fuel. Often, however, tires are used to supplement other fuel sources in cement kilns. In German and Japanese cement operations, up to 20 percent of the coal typically used to fire the kilns has been replaced by whole tires.

Similarly, two Firestone Tire plants, one in Illinois and one in Iowa, use a pulsating floor technology to burn tires along with other solid waste (105). At these facilities, the fuel (tires and mixed combustible solid waste) is forced into the primary combustion chamber with a hydraulic ram and then forced along the hearth with pulses of air. Gases produced by this process are burned as they pass through three subsequent combustion stages.

In fluidized bed incinerators, gasses are blown through the bed containing the solid fuel; the fuel can include MSW combined with shredded tires. The velocity of the gas is such that it counteracts the forces of gravity and places the fuel in suspension. This provides a high rate of mixing of air and fuel.

A recently constructed powerplant in Modesto, California, burns scrap tires to generate electricity. This technology was developed and used for 12 years in West Germany prior to installation at the Modesto facility. The plant cost $41 million to build, burns 19,200 tires a day at 2,000° F, and generates 15 megawatts of electricity. Pollution control equipment includes a lime slurry scrubber, baghouse filters, and a thermal DeNOx process (ch. 6). Air emissions reportedly are below California's permitted limits (232). A centralized computer system has been installed to monitor emissions and to maintain temperatures at 2,000° F in case of an upset. Steel and zinc oxide are recovered from the ash residues; the steel is sold to a scrap dealer, while zinc oxide is sold to Zinc Corp. of America (148). Gypsum recovered from the lime slurry is sold to cement and fertilizer manufacturers.

The company that runs the Modesto plant is being sued, however, by the California Attorney General and a number of environmental groups, which claim that the tire pile at the plant constitutes a nuisance. Moreover, the company has encountered opposition to the siting and construction of additional facilities along the east coast. Despite local opposition, a larger, 25-megawatt facility has been given siting approval in Sterling, Connecticut. A tire incinerator in New York also has been proposed, but it has not yet been sited.

Used Oil

Approximately 700 million gallons of used vehicle oil are generated in the United States every year, and an additional 500 million gallons of used lubricants are generated by industrial operations (144). Of the vehicle oil, more than 360 million gallons is generated at households by individuals who change their own oil (13). Much of this oil from households is disposed in the trash, on the ground, or down sewers.

Two-thirds of the total of 1.2 billion gallons of used oil are recycled, mostly by burning it as fuel. To reprocess used oil for burning, it usually undergoes dewatering through distillation or evaporation, or chemical treatment to produce a suitable fuel.

An alternative to burning used oil as fuel is to re-refine it, which happens to about 100 million gallons of used oil per year. Re-refining essentially removes various additives and contaminants in used oil—detergents, dilutants, combustion byproducts, heavy metals, metal deactivators, lead scavengers, anti-oxidants, and compounds designed to maintain viscosity. Additives can comprise up to 25 percent of lubricating oil. Although re-refining technologies can cope with these additives, the contamination of used oil with hazardous waste constituents can hamper re-refining processes (34).

To re-refine used oil, it typically undergoes three stages of distillation (34): water removal, high-temperature removal of light hydrocarbons (fuel constituents), and high-temperature and vacuum separation of the lubricant from contaminants. After distillation, the oil is finished by a clay contact process and filtered to remove coloring and odor-causing constituents. However, this step also creates a clay-oil sludge that eventually must be disposed. A finishing process that creates less sludge residual, but that is more costly, is hydrofinishing. In this process, the distilled oil is catalytically hydrogenated at temperatures between 600 and 700° F; this produces a higher quality lubricant with less loss of oil than does the clay contact procedure.

EPA prohibits the burning of "off-spec" oil without prior notification to the Agency. Off-spec oil is used oil containing more than any of the following: arsenic, 5 ppm; cadmium, 2 ppm; chromium, 10 ppm; lead, 100 ppm; and total halogens, 4,000 ppm. In addition, the used oil may not have a flashpoint that is less than 100° F. EPA also regulates the burning of used oil contaminated with PCBs under TSCA, which places the burden of proving that the oil does not contain PCBs on the persons handling it.

Some contaminants separated from the lubricant in the distillation process often are used as asphalt extender. However, many of the contaminants removed during re-refining, such as detergents, combustion byproducts, and heavy metals, result in a solid or hazardous waste. Moreover, the water removed during the initial distillation phase is contaminated with hydrocarbons and must be treated and discharged.

An additional environmental hazard caused by re-refining used oil is posed by operations that have gone out of business. In the 1960s, numerous operations went bankrupt because of the increased use of additives in oil, which necessitated the use of more sophisticated and costly re-refining technologies. The re-refining industry expanded in the 1970s, in response to the oil "crisis," but capacity has been declining again for the last decade. Abandoned operations can leave behind leaking surface impoundments, storage tanks, and other disposal units that can pose substantial threats to surface water and ground water (34).

Plastics

The presence of plastics in landfills, on streets, and in marine waters has raised tremendous controversy. Plastics comprise an estimated 7.3 percent by weight of MSW, or 10.3 million tons (81); this percentage is similar in other industrialized countries, where plastics constitute between 5 and 10 percent of MSW. About half of the plastics discarded in the United States, or 5.6 million tons, was equally divided between containers and packaging. These nondurable goods are the target for almost all

of the current concern about plastics in MSW and provide a useful starting point for discussing prospects for increasing the relatively low level of plastics recycling. Box 5-D provides an introduction to the properties and types of plastics.

Structure of the Primary Plastics Manufacturing Industry

The plastics manufacturing industry is growing and thriving. Between 1981 and 1986, it had one of the highest compound growth rates of any industry and maintained a positive balance of trade (along with only one other commodity group, chemicals) (220). In 1986, about 22 million tons of plastics were sold in the United States in several market sectors (figure 5-8, table 5-4). Production of many commodity plastics is currently operating at or near capacity. After about 4 years of relatively stable prices, resin prices rose by 50 to 100 percent from 1987 to 1988, and small users had difficulty insuring a stable supply of some resin types. Prices reflect world supply and demand. Prices have flattened in recent months and some analysts predict that prices may soon drop (3).

The industry is categorized into two major groups (in the Standard Industrial Classification codes), one for plastics materials and resins and one for miscellaneous plastics products. In 1986, these two groups were among the 15 largest manufacturing industries in the United States (220). Fewer than 300 companies manufacture plastic resins in the United States, and fewer than 25 companies manufacture each of the commodity plastics. On the other hand, the number of processors of plastics into finished products is on the order of 10,000.

One trend in the use of plastics has significant implications for MSW management—in particular, the growing demand for single-service, convenience products in response to changing demographics and lifestyles. Plastics are expected to comprise an increasing share of the packaging and consumer/institutional markets, especially at the expense of more traditional materials (paper, glass, and metal). Thus, greater amounts and a larger proportional share of plastics will be disposed of as MSW. However, plastics are normally lighter than the products they replace and in most cases they are also less bulky (ch. 4).

Figure 5-8—Plastics Markets, 1986 (millions of tons)

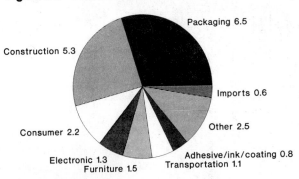

Packaging 6.5
Construction 5.3
Imports 0.6
Consumer 2.2
Other 2.5
Electronic 1.3
Furniture 1.5
Transportation 1.1
Adhesive/ink/coating 0.8

NOTE: Total U.S. Market Sales = 22 million tons.
SOURCES: Office of Technology Assessment, after Society of the Plastics Industry, *Facts and Figures of the U.S. Plastics Industry* (Washington, DC, 1987); Modern Plastics, "Materials 87," *Modern Plastics*, pp. 55-65, January 1987.

Status of Post-Consumer Plastics Recycling

Most experts agree that recycling in the United States is constrained by the lack of collection of plastics. In 1986, less than 100,000 tons of post-consumer plastic discards—less than 1 percent of the amount in MSW—were recycled. This increased to about 125,000 tons in 1988.

Given the variety of plastics, however, it is appropriate to consider sales and discards of specific types. Current recycling of post-consumer plastic wastes is focused almost entirely on containers made of two resins, polyethylene terephthalate (PET) and high-density polyethylene (HDPE). These containers are relatively easy to identify and are not degraded significantly by reprocessing. In 1986, 65,000 tons of PET from soft drink containers were collected for recycling, up from 4,000 tons in 1979 (21). This comprises about 20 percent of the PET used for soft-drink bottles and about 10 percent of U.S. PET sales in 1986. PET collection increased to 75,000 tons in 1987.

Total estimated HDPE collection in 1986 was about 30,000 tons, about 1 percent of U.S. HDPE sales. Roughly half of the recycled HDPE came from base cups for PET soft drink containers (22). An estimated 17,000 tons of HDPE from milk jugs were recycled in 1986 (157). This is only 5 percent of the HDPE used in milk bottles. HDPE collection in 1987 is estimated to be 36,000 tons, again divided equally between milk jugs and base cups from PET soft drink containers (22).

Photo credit: Office of Technology Assessment

Current recycling of plastics from MSW focuses on containers made from polyethylene terephthalate (PET) and high-density polyethylene (HDPE), which are relatively easy to identify and are not degraded significantly by reprocessing. Only about 1 percent of the plastic in MSW is now recycled.

The recycling of other post-consumer plastics in the United States is negligible. Efforts are focused on nondurable goods, especially containers and packaging: some small-scale recycling of mixed plastics is occurring; polystyrene (PS) recycling began in 1989 at two pilot-scale plants; and more limited experiments are underway on post-consumer polyvinyl chloride (PVC). Most PVC recycling efforts are focused on contaminated pre-consumer waste. Post-consumer recycling tends to focus on finding ways to reuse PVC bottles (115,000 tons per year in the United States). These bottles are more difficult to identify than PET and HDPE bottles, and are used mostly for products with a low turnover rate, such as shampoo and vegetable oil (135). PET is replacing PVC in some bottles. FDA is preparing an environmental impact statement (EIS) for its proposed action to establish the safe conditions for use of PVC. The EIS will evaluate, among other things, the potential effects of PVC on post-consumer recycling programs (53 *Federal Register* 47264, Nov. 22, 1988).

Recycling of post-consumer plastics from durable goods, such as old appliances and furniture, is also

Table 5-4—Major U.S. Resin Markets, 1986 (millions of pounds)

Markets	Thermoplastics								Thermosets	Total
	LDPE	PVC	HDPE	PP	PS	PET	Engineering	Other		
Packaging	5,605	497	3,560	1,128	1,360	747	15	5	97	13,014
Building/construction	213	4,711	522	34	418	0	84	154	4,541	10,677
Consumer/institutional	507	277	783	732	1,296	608	31	31	233	4,498
Electrical/electronic	421	478	147	277	360	0	236	332	307	2,558
Furniture/furnishings	71	380	16[a]	1,103	47	0	10	425	923	2,975
Transportation	0	149	232	237	0	0	123	477	1,020	2,238
Adhesives/inks/coatings	231	83	38	24	0	15	0	977	285	1,653
Imports	715	201	45	25	17	0	0	134	118	1,255
Other	760	467	821	1,162	814	0	132	216	714	5,086
Total[b]	8,523	7,243	6,164	4,722	4,312	1,370	631	2,751	8,238	43,954

[a]Polyethylene in transportation and furniture/furnishings markets assumed to be HDPE.

[b]These estimates calculated by OTA differ from those of SPI (1987) and Modern Plastics (1987) because of nondisclosure of market information and exclusion of polyurethene data by SPI and inclusion of import data by OTA.

SOURCES: Office of Technology Assessment; after Society of the Plastics Industry, *Facts and Figures of the U.S. Plastics Industry* (Washington, DC, 1987); Modern Plastics, "Materials 87," *Modern Plastics*, pp. 55-65, January 1987.

negligible. Some of these materials, such as old appliances, are handled by scrap dealers but the plastics components are usually discarded.[36]

An estimated 95 percent of clean, pre-consumer industrial scrap from processing and from off-spec virgin thermoplastic resins is recycled, comprising as much as 10 percent of all production (56). The amount of contaminated industrial scrap material, or obsolete product inventories and overruns, that is recycled is unknown, but significant.[37] This off-spec material is often used as an inner layer with virgin material as the outer layers.

The number of companies involved in recycling post-consumer plastic wastes is small, but growing. Most are relatively small operations. A few large companies are involved in recycling post-consumer plastics, and several large resin producers are announcing plans for new recycling plants. Also, the number of traditional scrap dealers and brokers dealing with post-consumer plastics appears to be increasing.

Current Products and Markets—Post-consumer plastic wastes, especially plastic bottles, can be recycled into products that replace or supplement virgin materials, or that replace other materials such as lumber, concrete, or metal. HDPE, for instance, is recycled into lumber substitutes, base cups for soft drink bottles, flower pots, pipes, toys, pails and drums, traffic barrier cones, golfbag liners, kitchen drain boards, milk bottle crates, soft drink bottle carriers, trash cans, and signs (222).

PET is recycled into dozens of products (222). Some examples include strapping, scouring pads, fence posts, parking space bumpers, industrial paints, paint brushes, fiberfill for pillows, ski jackets, sleeping bags, carpet fibers, rope, sails, and tire cord. PET is also used to produce: polyol used in making urethane foam and furniture; unsaturated polyester used in making boat hulls, bath tubs, swimming pools, automobile exterior panels; engineering plastics used for appliance parts and automotive components; and thermoformable sheets used to produce six-pack carriers for soft drink bottles, nonfood containers, and audiocassette cases. New uses are frequently introduced, such as transparent egg cartons.

One of the major products made from mixed plastics is plastic "lumber." Plastic lumber is being used for posts, poles, marine pilings, dock surfaces and piers, and also for nonstructural applications such as decking, agricultural pens, fences, park benches, and parking space bumpers.[38] Based on ongoing experiments, some of the properties of plastic lumber appear to be superior to wood, while others are not (21). Superior properties include its resistance to rot, water, chemicals, and insects, as well as its lack of splintering and its ability to hold nails better and in any direction (unlike wood, which only holds nails well across the grain). However, plastic lumber loses strength when heated and does not hold screws as well as wood; as a result, carpentry joining may be a problem in hot weather if the plastic softens slightly. This probably can be overcome by using bolts to join pieces together.

Some post-consumer plastics are being exported to Asia and Europe. There are currently no PET reclaimers on the west coast so plastics collected there are shipped to Asia, which is cheaper than shipping to east coast reclaimers. Several east coast companies also export some of their collected post-consumer plastics. Data are not available on the size of post-consumer plastic export markets.

Recycling in Japan and Europe—In Japan, recycling of post-consumer plastics has always been low and has declined recently because of: the difficulties of separating pure plastics from MSW; the poor quality of products from mixed plastics using technologies available in the early 1980s; and the high cost of collection, separation, and processing (170). As a result, the number of Japanese municipalities with plastics recycling programs declined from 25 in 1982 to 1 at the end of 1988. PET, the most common resin recycled in the United States, is used only in small quantities in Japanese products. However, interest in post-consumer plas-

---

[36]Limited research on technologies to reuse plastic components recovered from automobile and appliance shredder residues is underway (189,190,191). The problems faced are similar to recycling other post-consumer plastics but are more difficult to overcome because of the variety of plastics mixed together. Suggested markets for these materials are similar to those proposed for other mixed plastics.

[37]Industry is very secretive about how much of this scrap is recycled and in naming sources because of the price advantage gained using this material.

[38]One parking space bumper, or car stop, consumes 400 PET beverage bottles including caps, labels, and base cups left on the bottles (31).

Box 5-D—Introduction to Plastics

Definition of Plastics

Plastics are chemicals—long-chain polymers—made from fossil fuels and chemical additives. Most polymers have little practical value without a small percentage of additives that give the plastic materials useful properties.

Additives impart physical properties to meet specific applications and improve processing. Over 4,000 individual types of additives exist, including a variety of mineral and chemical derivatives. Additives can be classified into four major types: reaction controls (e.g., catalysts, initiators, auxiliary processing materials); processing additives (e.g., blowing agents and lubricants); stabilizers (e.g., antioxidants, heat stabilizers, light or ultraviolet stabilizers, preservatives); and performance additives (e.g., fillers and reinforcements, plasticizers, colorants, impact modifiers, flame retardants, antistatic agents, coupling agents) (96).

The majority of additives are inert fillers such as calcium carbonate; many (e.g., reaction controls and processing additives) are used in manufacturing processes and do not remain with the finished polymer. Most additives are used in very small quantities, usually less than 1 percent. Exceptions include "plasticizers" (i.e., chemicals added to impart flexibility) that can account for 40 percent of some plastics products, including wire and cable insulating material and artificial leather made from PVC. Colorants can represent 1 to 10 percent of some plastics.

Concern about the disposal of plastics and their additives in MSW has focused primarily on the use of metal additives, particularly lead and cadmium used as heat stabilizers in PVC and as colorants in other plastics. Heavy metal stabilizers are used primarily in nonpackaging markets such as PVC wire and cable insulating material, furniture film, floor tiles, and pressure pipes. Heavy metal colorants are applicable to a wide variety of thermoplastics. Only a small percentage of PVC is used in packaging and containers (table 5-4).

In addition to questions about heavy metals, however, questions also exist about the environmental fate of other additives when plastic wastes are discarded. Of particular concern is the use of organic and halogenated chemicals (e.g., phthalate esters, which account for roughly 70 to 75 percent of plasticizers). Phthalate esters are considered priority pollutants by EPA under the Clean Water Act. Because these additives do not become a permanent part of the polymer molecule, they are more susceptible to migration than many other additive types.

Additives used in plastic food packaging are subject to premarket approval by the Food and Drug Administration (FDA). FDA conducts safety evaluations of food additives and considers the amount of additive that can migrate to food and the toxicity of the additive. Extraction tests are required for new food additives or new applications to determine migration potential and this data is used to review the environmental effects of disposal. Some additives may be automatically considered acceptable to FDA if they are included on the list of substances "generally recognized as safe."

Properties of Plastics

The properties of plastics make them highly desirable to manufacturers and consumers, particularly for packaging. Although plastics often cost more to produce than alternative materials, their properties may make plastics more cost-effective and the preferred material for particular uses. As a result, plastics have been replacing glass, aluminum, steel, and paper for many uses.

In general, plastics are light-weight and inert; they resist breakage and are not subject to environmental deterioration (121). They also can be tailored to suit almost any specific need—rigid, flexible, stretchable, insulating, sterilizable, breathable, impermeable, transparent, transluscent, opaque, colored, etc. Compared to alternatives, plastics also are relatively cheap to transport because of their light weight.

Plastic Types

Plastics can be classified into four groups: commodity thermoplastics, engineering thermoplastics, thermosets, and multicomponent plastics. This classification is based on the uses of plastics that affect their presence in MSW, their relative cost, sales volume, and properties that affect their potential for recycling.

1. *Commodity thermoplastics* are produced at low cost, in high volumes. They include the five resins that account for about two-thirds of all plastic sales (table 5-4): low-density polyethylene (LDPE), high-density polyethylene (HDPE), polyvinyl chloride (PVC), polypropylene (PP), and polystyrene (PS). They also include polyethylene terephthalate (PET), which has only recently been used in sizable quantities for packaging. Other commodity thermoplastics include acrylonitrile butadiene styrene (ABS) and nylon. In general, commodity thermoplastics are candidates for recycling because they soften when heated and can be remolded. PET and HDPE are the predominant post-consumer resins that have been recycled in the United States.

   No current data quantify the amounts of resins found in MSW in the United States. However, it can be assumed that polyethylene (LDPE and HDPE), PP, and PS are major plastic components of MSW. PVC and PET are probably present in lower quantities because of their more limited use in short-lived markets such as packaging and consumer/institutional products. Limited information indicates that MSW in Europe is comprised of roughly 60 percent PP and polyethylene (i.e., polyolefins) (29).

2. *Engineering thermoplastics* are produced at high cost, in low volumes. Examples include polycarbonate (Lexan) and polytetrafluoroethylene (PTFE or Teflon). Engineering thermoplastics are used in the construction, electric/electronic, and transportation markets (220,221). These plastics are not considered a major component of MSW. In general, the higher the price of a thermoplastic, the greater the driving force to recycle it. PTFE, a relatively high-priced resin, is one of the few plastics that has been recycled in significant quantities (12). Engineering thermoplastics are targeted for increased recycling by at least one major manufacturer. For example, in 1987 General Electric announced a campaign to recycle one of its engineering thermoplastics, polycarbonate, into structural panels, building insulation, and other long-life construction markets.

3. *Thermosets*, compared to thermoplastics, are low-volume materials, but they still comprise about 20 percent of the U.S. plastics market. Two resins, phenolic and polyurethane, are sold in sizable quantities (1.4 million tons and 1.3 million tons, respectively), predominantly for long-lived products such as building insulation. The major markets for thermosets are building and construction, transportation, and furniture and furnishings (table 5-4). Unlike thermoplastics, thermosets generally are not considered recyclable because they do not soften when heated and thus cannot be remolded. However, they can be recycled as a filler.

4. *Multicomponent plastics and laminations* are combinations of different plastics or of plastics and other materials such as paper or metal foil. These materials are primarily used for packaging. In 1988 about 1.3 million tons of plastics were used in multicomponent films and semi-rigid sheets and almost two-thirds of this amount was used for food packaging (39). This type of packaging is expected to expand significantly in the coming years because it offers increased shelf life, reduced need for refrigeration, and the feasibility of using food processing methods that result in improved flavor and texture. Multicomponent plastics provide an economical way of combining the needed properties of different materials. For example, recently available plastic ketchup bottles are made from several plastics— including an exterior plastic for appearance and strength, an adhesive to hold different plastics together and attach the label, a special oxygen barrier plastic, and an interior plastic to resist fats and acids. This combination of materials makes these plastics technically difficult to recycle except into mixed plastic products.

tics recycling remains high, especially given recent technological advances.

The outlook may be more encouraging in Europe, although the current rate of plastics recycling is low. In West Germany, over 20 sorting plants have been built in the last decade (106). Many of the new mixed plastics recycling technologies originated in Europe and numerous plants are now in operation and being planned.

Plastics Reclamation Technologies

Theoretically, any type of plastic—either as single resins, separated from other plastic types, or as mixed plastics, combining several different resins or a few resins with similar properties—can be recycled. Single resin recycling can only be done with thermoplastics (box 5-D), which can be re-molded easily because they melt when heated. Mixed plastics recycling can be done with thermo-plastics, multicomponent plastics and laminations, and thermosets. Technical limits on the quantities of different resins that can be used in mixed plastics depend on the specifications required for the final product. Additives can be used to improve the compatibility of different resins.

Numerous proprietary techniques are being used to recycle plastics. Some techniques are available commercially; except for initial preparation steps to remove contaminants they do not differ substantially from the equipment used to fabricate some products from virgin resins.

Initial Preparation—Initial preparation of separated plastic containers may include washing and separation to remove unwanted materials. Separation methods are based primarily on differences in physical properties such as density. Automated techniques are suitable for mixtures of relatively pure polymers, but not complex mixtures of products containing many types of plastics or plastics that are altered by fillers or coatings (42). The resin recovered after separation is usually in the form of flakes or pellets.

Separated HDPE milk jugs may require removal of labels and closures. PET bottles, however, require much more sophisticated washing and separation steps. Most PET bottles have base cups made from HDPE, caps made from aluminum or polypropylene, and a paper or plastic label with adhesive. Thus, a typical PET bottle is composed of 70 percent PET, 24 percent HDPE, 1 percent aluminum, and 5 percent label and adhesive (192). PET bottles without HDPE base cups are also available.

Some separation technologies are available commercially. For example, the HDPE/PET reclamation process developed by the Center for Plastics Recycling Research (CPRR) at Rutgers University is available for licensing at a nominal cost. Investment costs for the system are $2.0 million to produce 5,000 tons and $2.5 million to produce 10,000 tons of 99.9 percent pure PET each year (48). Some separation technology is proprietary, however. One proprietary system uses a solvent (1,1,1-trichloroethane) to separate PET from aluminum in a closed system that is claimed to minimize environmental releases (164).

Processing Into Usable Plastic Products—The basic technologies used to make products from virgin resins are also used to recycle large amounts

of clean, pre-consumer industrial scrap. They also can be used to make products from clean, post-consumer single resins. They basically involve melting and extruding it into objects or pellets (42). Prior to extrusion, the recycled plastic may be mixed with additives to improve processing and enhance properties and/or mixed with virgin resin. Additives are discussed in box 5-D.

Two basic technologies for processing mixed post-consumer plastics are also available from Europe. A third technology has been patented by a U.S. company. One of these technologies, the Extruder Technology I (ET/I), is used in 12 European and 3 U.S. plants. ET/I has the advantages of moderate price and modular design. The basic extruder and molds costs $300,000 for a capacity of 175 to 400 pounds per hour. In general, the system including preparation equipment (grinder, shredder, densifier, blenders, and conveyors) costs $375,000 to $450,000 (29). A second technology, the Recycloplast Technology, is used in three plants in Germany; other European plants are being negotiated and the first U.S. plant began operations in Atlanta, Georgia, in spring 1989. Recycloplast is more costly than ET/I, and the German plants use about 30 percent industrial scrap to improve quality control and broaden the range of end products. Equipment costs vary depending on the size of the operation and the amount of preparation equipment needed for preliminary cleaning. A typical plant has a capacity of 5,000 tons per year on three shifts; plant and installation costs are $5 to $6 million, with 15 percent of that cost earmarked for pollution control (30). One company, Polymer Products, began commercial operations in Iowa in late 1986 after patenting an upgraded version of another European technology. Its process accommodates a wide variety of mixed plastics with varying degrees of contamination and produces lumber substitutes, metal substitutes, and concrete substitutes (31).

Another new technology can produce high-quality polyolefin resin (i.e., all types of polyethylene and polypropylene) from mixed plastics. One version of this technology was developed by the German company AKW Equipment and Process Design. The technology involves grinding, magnetic separation to remove metals, granulating into flakes, liquid separation to remove minerals, washing, air separation to remove PS, PVC and others from the lighter PE and PP, drying, mixing, and then extruding into pellets. The end product is a pelletized polyethylene raw material containing less than 5 percent polypropylene. According to tests on MSW plastic waste samples from Massachusetts and Rhode Island, the final product performs very similar to virgin PE. It cannot be used for film or plastic bags, but is suitable for making bottles (32). The first industrial-scale AKW plant in West Germany produces 4,000 to 6,000 tons per year. Polymer Resource Group, Inc., a joint venture between AKW and ITC Inc., has announced plans to open a plant in the Baltimore-Washington area. Similar technology (Transplastek) is producing bottle-grade polyolefins in Quebec, Canada.

Chemical dissolution systems to recover specialized plastic resins are also being marketed. This technology involves adding chemicals that cause the plastic to dissolve in water. After dissolution, the particles theoretically can be recovered and reused. As of 1988, this technology had been developed to be applicable to acrylics, styrenes, and other resins. Current economics are not favorable for producing polyethylene, and further technical development would be required to do so, but these technical problems do not appear insurmountable (27). Commercial products include coatings to protect new automobiles that can be hosed off when they reach the showroom and a bottle label that can be readily removed by washing. Products being studied include laundry bags that would dissolve when put through a washing machine cycle with the laundry and plastic backings for diapers that could be flushed down toilets (27).

Technical Constraints—Several factors constrain the use of recycled plastics in making new products. Among the most important are the presence of contaminants and the effects of natural degradation processes.

Contaminants in collected plastics include paper, metals, other plastics, residual products, adhesives, pigments, and dirt. These substances can make a plastic technically difficult to recycle. In addition, the Food and Drug Administration (FDA) has stated that it cannot authorize the safe use of recycled plastics for use in contact with food unless additional information is provided to resolve the uncertainties about these contaminants (110). The FDA did not object, however, to a request to use recycled plastics as an outer layer in a multi-layer food package when it was demonstrated that there was little likelihood that contaminants in the recycled layer would migrate through the food contact layers.

In general, the performance of recycled resins is not as good as virgin resins. Reprocessing and environmental exposure degrades some of the beneficial properties of some plastics, such as durability and dimensional stability, so recycled plastics usually are used in products with less demanding applications than the original products.

Degradation of some properties can be overcome with the use of additives, by making the recycled product thicker, or by coextrusion (making a product with a recycled core and a virgin outer layer). For example, garbage bags made from recycled plastic (usually industrial scrap) are generally thicker than garbage bags made from virgin resin. A pilot plant in France is coextruding recycled PVC bottles with virgin PVC to make pipe.

Infinite recycling is technically impossible, however, because degradation eventually occurs (55). Thus, while recycling recovered plastics defers the need to use other management techniques, it does not eliminate the need for eventual disposal. Ideally though, recycled products would have long-lived utility, especially relative to the short-lived utility of plastic packaging.

Energy Consumption—The production of virgin plastics accounts for a relatively small percentage of total energy consumption in the United States. According to a recent EPA report, current domestic production uses 5 percent of the oil and less than 1 percent of the gas consumed by the Nation (252). Plastics production accounts for the dominant use of three major feedstocks—in 1985, 72 percent of the ethylene produced, 59 percent of the propylene, and 76 percent of the benzene (220).

Plastics production is not limited to the use of petroleum and natural gas. Depending on the techniques used, different raw materials, such as coal, can be used to produce feedstocks (130). However, history and relative economics make oil and gas the current materials of choice.

Making products from recycled plastics can result in considerable energy savings compared to virgin plastics production. Table 5-5 shows the production energy used for the major commodity thermoplastics. It takes about 1,000 to 2,000 Btu per pound to melt these plastics (11).[39] Therefore, recycling these resins would save 92 to 98 percent of the energy needed to produce single virgin resins (excluding energy used to collect and transport recycled resins).

The manufacture and use of plastics products may require less energy than the manufacture and use of nonplastic alternatives, based on data from 1978 in a study conducted for a plastics industry association (80). Based on 1978 production data, the study estimated that using plastics instead of alternative materials would result in energy savings of about 71 percent. The study concluded that plastics products save nearly as much energy as they consume, primarily because their light weight is beneficial in terms of raw materials used and in subsequent transportation costs. The use of some plastic products also can result in significant energy savings; for example, automobiles with plastic parts are lighter and have improved fuel efficiency.

Materials Cost Comparisons—A general rule of thumb states that recycled resins must be priced 33 to 50 percent lower than virgin material before a fabricator will find it worthwhile to use them (212). However, supply-demand-price relationships are not well established and decisions about using recycled resins depend on the unique circumstances of the individual fabricator. For many low-priced, high-volume plastic products, small savings in raw material costs may make a big difference in profits.

The price of post-consumer plastic bottles varies by color, cleanliness, the way it is packaged (i.e., baled or ground), and geographic area. Once the material is reprocessed, the price is also determined by its quality and the geographic region, form (i.e., flakes or pellets), additive content, and color. According to the CPRR and the Plastics Recycling Foundation, post-consumer plastic bottles can be sold for about 6 cents per pound (prices as of 1987), and reclaimed PET can be sold profitably for 25 cents per pound in flake form or 30 cents per pound in pellet form. For comparison, virgin PET pellets sell for about 56 cents per pound (192).[40] Recycled HDPE from base cups can be sold for 17 cents per pound, compared to virgin resin at about 40 cents per pound.

Barriers to Increased Recycled Plastics Use

As stated earlier, lack of collection is the major factor limiting plastics recycling. This opinion is widely held by plastics manufacturers and recycling businesses, based on their experience and on market studies for PET, HDPE, and mixed plastics. The lack of technologies to separate different plastic types and product quality are also problems in some instances.

Available markets have not yet been a problem for recycled plastics, largely because of the limited collection that has taken place. As discussed below, market studies for HDPE, PET, and mixed plastics show enormous potential, compared to current levels of recycling, but it remains to be seen whether these markets can be developed to use a significant quantity of the plastics in MSW. Information is not available on potential markets for other single resins.

Collection—The major methods now used to collect plastic bottles for recycling are bottle deposit systems for PET containers and curbside collection. Drop-off programs are also used in some jurisdictions to collect HDPE milk jugs, but such programs are very limited and are usually located near a reprocessor to avoid transportation costs. A buy-back system for plastics has been in operation in the Bronx since 1983 (145).[41]

Bottle deposit systems have been the most successful method for collecting PET soda bottles. This method is used by 9 States, and in 1986, 98 percent of collected PET was from bottle bill States (159). However, the plastics, beverage, and food store and many other industries are generally opposed to deposit systems (ch. 8) and have been effective at

---

[39]Energy requirements for the PET/HDPE reclamation process developed by CPRR are 820 Btu/pound (48). The ET-1 process requires 1,910 Btu/pound, including auxiliary equipment, according to manufacturer's information.

[40]This translates into $600 per ton, making recycled plastics far more valuable than many other recycled materials, such as newsprint at $40 per ton and glass at $30 per ton.

[41]The responsible company, R2B2, will buy any separated, identifiable plastic brought to its door. Materials purchased for up to $0.10 per pound have subsequently been sold at $0.015 to $0.31 per pound to domestic and export markets. For a six month period in 1988, plastics sales totaled $50,000 and revenues averaged $200/ton. More plastics were recovered than used beverage cans.

Table 5-5—Energy Requirements To Produce Selected Plastics

Plastic	Production energy (Btu/lb)	Feedstock (%)	Electricity (%)	Oil and natural gas (%)
LDPE	38,500	73	17	10
HDPE	36,500	75	10	15
PS	34,300	69	4.5	26.5
PET	48,700	51	10	39
PVC	25,600	49	26	25

SOURCE: Argonne National Laboratory, *Energy and Materials Use in the Production and Recycling of Consumer-Goods Packaging*, ANL/CNSV-TM-58, prepared for U.S. Department of Energy (Argonne, IL: February 1981).

preventing bottle bills from being adopted in other areas.

One technology, the reverse vending machine, is being used to collect PET bottles in some bottle deposit States. These machines shred the bottles for later shipment to reprocessors. The next generation of machines, scheduled for distribution at the end of 1989, is expected to be able to separate clear from colored PET, which can enhance the value of the product. The new machines will also accept HDPE milk jugs and all other plastic containers. Plans are to sell clear PET and HDPE separately for reprocessing and make the other plastics that are collected into a plastic lumber product (60).

Experts consider curbside collection of PET and HDPE the simplest way to start a community plastics recycling program (227). Limited curbside collection of plastics now occurs, but it is the likely future direction of plastics recycling, primarily because of opposition to deposit legislation. Also, curbside recycling is increasing for other materials and the costs of including plastics are perceived not to be excessive (ch. 2). More than 60 curbside programs are known to include plastics (33).

Major Collection Problems—Concerns about plastics collection programs include the space used by uncompacted plastic bottles, the variety of plastics found in post-consumer waste, and the costs of collection and processing.

The difficulty of collecting rigid containers that have high-volume and low-weight has limited curbside collection of post-consumer plastics. For example, adding plastics to an existing collection program can be a problem if the collection equipment is not designed to handle resilient materials that are not easily crushed. The space required to collect plastic bottles also can reduce the number of households that a collection truck can stop at before the truck is full; one estimate of the potential reduction is 30 percent for uncompacted plastic bottles and 17 percent for bottles compacted 50 percent before collection (227). Several companies are working to develop on-truck densification equipment and at least six projects are underway or pending to use on-truck densification of plastics in curbside collection (33).[42] One alternative being studied by plastics processors and waste management companies is to attach densifiers or compactors to existing collection trucks to allow subsequent sorting of flattened whole plastic bottles. Although transporting shredded or ground plastics would take up less space, on-truck granulators pose several problems including safety hazards to operating personnel and poor marketability of reground mixed resin (33).

The variety of plastics in MSW is a concern because only PET and HDPE resins have much of a market at present, and single resins have a much higher value than mixtures of resins. Collection of single resins is problematic because of the difficulty in identifying and separating different resins. Limited information from curbside collection programs that include separation of plastics shows a measurable amount of contamination with other wastes. For example, a pilot study in Rhode Island found 6.5 percent contamination with other materials, with 18 percent of the contamination being other plastic containers (125). Another pilot study in Westchester, New York, found 14 percent contamination (107).

---

[42]Sites include Nepean, Ontario; Seattle, Washington; Rhode Island; Winona, Minnesota; and several Chicago, Illinois suburbs.

To help resolve the identification problem, the Society of the Plastics Industry (SPI) is sponsoring a voluntary coding system to get manufacturers to label the resins on bottles and jars. One concern about this labeling system is the difficulty of reading codes after bottles have been flattened to facilitate collection.

Separation Technologies—Most separation of plastics is now done manually. New technologies could be developed to improve the separation of different plastic types. Research on new automated approaches to separating plastic containers made from different resins is now underway at CPRR. The center is studying ways to identify resin types based on bar codes using photoelectric beams, machine vision, and near infrared technology (79). Other innovative approaches may be applicable to a wider variety of resins and plastic products. For example, additive "tags" could be put into all types of virgin resins to facilitate automatic identification and sorting (163). Chemical separation techniques are also under investigation, including a project at Rensselaer Polytechnic Institute to use selective solvent dissolution and flash devolatilization to recover individual polymers. An automated approach to separating PET and PVC plastic bottles is used in Europe, where many more PVC bottles are used than in the United States. The technology uses an electromagnetic scanning technique to detect the chlorine in PVC (135).

The breakeven cost of collection and processing is a major concern. Unless avoided costs of tipping fees for other disposal options are included in an analysis, recycling plastics does not appear to be financially viable from a collector's viewpoint (ch. 2). For example, according to one study handling costs for deposit systems (including collecting, crushing, baling, and shipping to reprocessors) can range from $0.20 to $0.40 per pound of PET (42). These costs are greater than the recent scrap value of PET bottles, which ranges from $0.05 to $0.10 per pound.

One market analysis for post-consumer HDPE milk bottles estimated that processing and transportation costs ranged from $0.03 to $0.49 per pound for transporting material 100 miles to market, depending on the type of processing equipment used (granulators or balers) and the amounts processed

each year (157). Granulators produce a higher priced product than balers, but this may change as purchasers discover that they can more easily determine contamination levels with baled materials. In some cases, the costs can be less than revenues for selling collected HDPE; some sellers have noted a rise in some areas from around $0.06 per pound in 1987 to $0.15 per pound in 1988 (145).

Another study of plastics collection programs concluded that even without specific cost estimates, most operators believed that it was worthwhile to collect plastics (145). This opinion was based on the improving resale value of plastics and the willingness of the public to participate in collection programs. Higher participation rates were found for "user-friendly systems," especially those that included some combination of containers, minimal preparation requirements, public education, frequent pick-ups, and a broad range of targeted plastics.

Quality of Recycled Plastics—Quality control is a major concern that affects the willingness of manufacturers to use recycled materials. According to studies sponsored by CPRR, many potential users of recycled plastic resins are unaware of the progress being made in recycling technologies for post-consumer plastics (20). CPRR has also found that many recycling success stories are kept secret because of the competitive nature of the business. This leads to duplication of research efforts.

Standardized tests, such as those developed by the American Society for Testing and Materials (ASTM), are used within the plastics industry to provide basic information on the properties of plastic materials. Test results on different generic virgin plastic types are published. The tests, however, do not necessarily provide precise information on how a fabricated product will perform under various conditions (59). Given potential variations in the life-history of plastics that are recycled, such as exposure to sunlight, heat, and other environmental factors that may degrade plastics properties, it may be difficult to generalize about the performance of recycled products without quality control testing. Standardized methods are needed to test performance, quality assurance, and contaminants in recycled resins to ensure the reliability of these materials. ASTM is preparing a guidance document to address these concerns (79).

The quality control programs used by recyclers, for both finished products and source materials, often are considered proprietary. For example, Wellman, Inc. maintains its own laboratory and testing facilities to determine the suitability of recycled source materials, including their potential for new products. The Coca-Cola Co. and Pepsico consult with Wellman, Inc. and other PET recyclers when they are planning potential changes in PET bottles, such as labels, adhesives, or barriers, to note any impacts on recyclability.

Another key issue is the impact of degradable plastics on recycling efforts. Recyclers of plastic bottles are concerned that the presence of degradable plastics in post-consumer plastic wastes could cause deterioration of recycled products and complicated liability problems, hurting and potentially killing current plastic recycling efforts. Producers of degradable plastics disagree, contending that degradables would not be a problem and that potential adverse effects could be minimized by carefully considering the properties of the recycled product and/or by modifying reprocessing technologies to accommodate the presence of degradables. OTA has not found any data to demonstrate whether the presence of degradable plastics would cause a problem for recycling plastics. The issue of degradable plastics is explored further in box 5-E.

Potential for Increased Recycling

Several factors work in favor of an increase in the recycling of post-consumer plastics. At present, commodity plastics production is operating close to capacity and prices of virgin resins have almost doubled in the past year. As a result, demand for plastic resins is very high and is expected to increase over the next decade (221).

Political and institutional factors—especially the threat of bans on particular plastics products, and State and local initiatives to increase recycling—are stimulating the plastics industry to expand recycling opportunities. Various industry representatives have formed lobbying coalitions to promote recycling (and/or incineration) of plastics. New industry programs are being announced frequently, making it difficult to present an up-to-date picture in a document like this. Some companies are working to increase the availability of plastics for recycling by helping communities study collection options. Some companies are setting up programs with waste haulers to collect plastics for reprocessing (e.g., Wellman/Browning-Ferris Industries and DuPont/Waste Management, Inc.).

Industry has established two pilot programs for recycling foam polystyrene. Amoco Foam Products Co., McDonald's, and wTe Corp. are collecting unseparated post-consumer wastes from 20 McDonald's restaurants in the New York City area for recycling. The waste is separated and washed, and PS is cut into fluff and then sent to be repelletized at another location. Then it will be mixed with virgin PS to produce building foundation protection board for construction uses. In another pilot-scale program, Mobil Chemical Co. and Genpak Corp. will recycle PS collected by New England Container Recovery, Inc. (NECRInc) from schools and institutions and fast-food restaurants. The recycled PS can be reused in products such as coat hangers, flower pots, wall and building insulation, and protective packaging.

Research and Development—Many industry and government groups are sponsoring research on recycling technologies and collection systems. Worldwide patent activity indicates that innovation is occurring in reclamation technologies. For example, 450 patents covering equipment, processing, and products (for polymers that include plastics, rubber, and textiles) were issued from 7 industrialized countries in 1986, 1987, and the first 2 months of 1988 (169). Almost half of this activity (212 patents) focused on recycling products into alternative uses.

Twelve major resin suppliers of the Council for Solid Waste Solutions, a division of SPI, have each pledged $1 million a year for the next 3 years for research, development, and lobbying on plastics reuse. Research areas will include technology to minimize the costs of collecting, sorting, and reprocessing post-consumer plastics packaging (165). Producers and users of specific resins are also joining together to sponsor research. For example, the Vinyl Institute supports research on PVC recycling, and the Polystyrene Packaging Coalition is coordinating research activities on PS. NECRInc, Wellman, Inc., Eaglebrook Plastics, Inc., and Waste Management, Inc., are sponsoring joint projects to develop on-truck densification units to overcome

Box 5-E—Degradable Plastics and MSW

Most plastics are inert and designed to resist attack by microorganisms. The relative impermeability of plastics and high molecular weights tend to make plastics nondegradable (98). However, plastics can be designed to be degradable, either by physical, chemical, and/or biological means.

Two factors are driving the sales and development of degradable plastics: legislative mandates and economics. Legislative mandates can require degradable products to be used (e.g., connecting devices for containers—such as 6-pack rings—are required to be degradable in 17 States and EPA must establish similar regulations under Public Law 100-556 by 1990). Many of these laws were passed as a result of concerns about plastic litter on land and later over the entanglement of marine and land-based animals.

Alternatively, legislation can ban or threaten to ban the use of nondegradables (e.g., nondegradable fast-food packaging) because of concerns about MSW management capacity (254). For example, legislation has passed to require the use of biodegradable materials in at least two States and two localities to help with MSW management or to increase the nonfood use of surplus agricultural commodities.[1] As of May 1989, at least 31 States had legislation introduced concerning mandates for degradable products, recycling, packaging, taxes on packaging, and waste reduction (ch. 8).

Economic factors have stimulated the development of degradable products that may be more cost-effective to use than their nondegradable alternatives. For example, the use of degradable plastic agricultural mulches can save farmers the cost of removing a nondegradable mulch. However, degradable plastic products cost about 8 to 14 percent more than comparable nondegradable products (238). Degradable plastics may also provide a market for surplus agricultural commodities.

It is not clear whether degradable plastics can actually help solve MSW disposal problems, or whether degradables might actually aggravate existing problems and constrain emerging solutions like recycling. It is also unclear whether they degrade into environmentally safe byproducts. Little information is available to shed light on these issues, and this hinders the development of degradable materials. In addition, legislative bans or restrictions may have little impact on actual MSW management, because the products usually subject to bans make up a very small portion of MSW and substitutes for banned or restricted products may require more disposal capacity.

The expanded use of degradable plastics for solving MSW problems is questionable until the uncertainties about what happens to them when they are landfilled, incinerated, or mixed with nondegradable materials for recycling are answered. One role which appears promising is the use of degradable plastic bags for collecting yard wastes as part of a composting program. Other applications that may be appropriate include the use of degradables for specialty products such as agricultural mulch (where some operational economies are associated with its use) and possibly products that cause severe litter problems or become marine debris.[2]

Another concern is that some people may see degradable plastics as a "license to litter." Other observers see waste in allowing plastics to degrade into "nothing" when they have such a high energy value for incineration.

Types of Degradable Plastics

Biodegradable Plastics—There is no formal definition of biodegradable plastic, but it generally indicates a plastic that can be broken down by biological means (i.e., the metabolic activities of microorganisms such as bacteria and fungi). As the term is used, it does not necessarily mean complete biodegradation, which would be breakdown into carbon dioxide and water. Two related terms also are used. Biodisintegration is the biological breakdown of plastic into smaller sized (but not molecular) particles. Biodisfiguration occurs when the surface of the material becomes blemished or contaminated by the growth of microorganisms, but no structural changes in the material occur.

---

[1]Minnesota; Iowa; Berkeley, California; Suffolk County, New York.

[2]Another specialty use of degradable plastics, using different technologies than those discussed here, is for medical applications (e.g., sutures and time-release capsules).

A number of technologies to make plastics biodegrade are being marketed or developed. One approach is to add biodegradable materials such as starch to the resin. At least three starch-based/polyethylene technologies are available for licensing or sale.[3] These technologies vary in the amount of starch used, the types of additives used to ensure degradation and shelf-life, and the need for special processing. They also vary in their claimed effectiveness, whether the starch is metabolized and thus the remaining plastic loses strength and disintegrates, or whether other chemical reactions occur that break down the plastic component into smaller particles (of lower molecular weight) that can eventually be metabolized. One firm has combined photodegradable and biodegradable technologies.

Another approach is to develop plastics entirely with biodegradable materials, referred to as "second generation" biodegradable plastics. Materials of this type are claimed to degrade into products that are naturally present in the environment. At least one technology of this type, bioengineered bacteria-synthesized resins, is being produced on a pilot scale.[4] Other products still under development include plastics made from lactic acid.

The rate of biodegradation depends on the presence of microorganisms, temperature and moisture conditions, starch content, and additives used (271). For example, one firm predicts that one of its starch-based products, with a shelf-life of 2 years, will biodegrade within another year into small particles (centimeter-sized or less) when the product is placed in a bacteria-rich, moist environment, and that it will continue to biodegrade depending on its composition (146). Biodegradable plastic bags are now being tested for applicability to yard waste composting operations and suitability for food contact use. Special attention is being given to degradation byproducts and toxicity.

Photodegradable Plastics—Photodegradable refers to plastics that break down in the presence of ultraviolet (UV) light. These plastics are made by including chemicals that make the polymer sensitive to UV light (e.g., carbon monoxide, vinyl ketone, nickel, cobalt, iron) in the structure of the photodegradable plastic (98).[5] Upon exposure to sunlight, the plastic absorbs radiation and the sensitizing chemicals cause reactions that break the long plastic chains into smaller segments of the polymer. However, other cross-linking reactions may occur and make some portions of the material less susceptible to degradation (53). The subsequent biodegradation rate depends on the chemical make-up of the original polymer, particle size, and molecular weight (98). Some plastics also use "photo-initiated oxidation," in which sensitizing chemicals continue the degradation process after initial exposure to UV light, including after burial.

Sensitizing chemicals can be selected to cause a reaction only when exposed to particular wavelengths of light. For example, plastics can be made to degrade when exposed to a sufficient amount of sunlight, but not behind window glass since glass blocks UV penetration.

The rate of photodegradation depends primarily on UV intensity (which varies seasonally, with latitude, and time of day), length of exposure, and, to a minor extent, on thickness of the plastic (98). The time lag between exposure to UV and degradation can be controlled in the manufacturing process or the fabrication process, depending on the technology; different formulations show degradation to dust-sized particles in periods ranging from 48 hours to 1 year.[6]

---

[3]These include: 1) Archer Daniels Midland additive that is used to make PE that contains 6 percent cornstarch, an unsaturated polymer, and a very small quantity (ppm) of transition metal catalyst; 2) St. Lawrence Starch masterbatch additive with 6 to 15 percent starch and a fatty acid (an earlier patent from the developer of the ADM material); and 3) Agri-Tech Industries compounds with 20 to 80 percent starch, plus polyethylene, polyethylene co-acrylic acid, urea, ammonia, and various additives depending on the application.

[4]Poly(hydroxybutyrate-valerate), or PHBV, is produced by Imperial Chemical Industries (ICI). Current production is about 100 tons per year of a resin with properties similar to polypropylene, at a cost of $15 per pound. ICI's goal is full-scale production of 10,000 tons per year, at a cost of $1.50 to $2.00 per pound.

[5]Carbon monoxide is incorporated during the manufacture of the resin, while vinyl ketone or metallic salts are incorporated as additives during fabrication.

[6]The 48-hour degradation resulted when 6-pack rings containing 13 percent ethylene carbon monoxide were tested. Commercial degradable 6-pack rings, however, use only 1 percent carbon monoxide to maintain product integrity and function in differing climatological conditions (121,142). As another example, "Plastigone" agricultural mulch can be designed, using metal additives, to last between 30 days and 1 year (104).

(continued on next page)

After photodegradation occurs, it is unclear whether subsequent biodegradation will be complete. Some investigators have predicted complete biodegradation in 1 year for PP and 10 years for PS (made with vinyl ketone comonomers), based on laboratory tests of biological oxygen demand (98), but other reviewers of the same tests and data question whether the biodegradation would be complete (271).

Chemical Dissolution—Plastics also have been developed that will dissolve when a chemical is added with water. After dissolution, plastic particles theoretically can be recovered and recycled back into plastics products. The developers claim the particles are similar to detergent additives, flocculants used at wastewater treatment plants, and soil conditioners, and that they are not harmful to the environment (18).

Problems With Degradable Plastics

Lack of Standard Definitions and Testing Methods—One fundamental question about degradable plastics is what the term really means. ASTM is developing standard definitions for different degradable plastics and standard tests to evaluate degradability. This work will likely result in de facto industry standard definitions within 2 years (171). More research will likely be required to develop standard testing protocols.

Without standard definitions, it can be difficult to determine what is really meant when a product is called photodegradable or biodegradable, and under what environmental conditions and timeframe the claim is valid. In general, it can be assumed that a product marketed as photodegradable or biodegradable will become brittle and break into fragments in the presence of ultraviolet light or microorganisms, respectively. It is not clear what size the fragments will be and what will happen next—whether the material will ultimately degrade into inert dust-sized particles, into organic intermediates, or eventually into biomass, carbon dioxide, and water. It is also not clear what will happen to any additives such as colorants. The General Accounting Office (254) pointed out the need to develop standard definitions and testing methods to assure consumers of satisfactory products and to facilitate manufacturers' compliance with legislation.

Uncertain Performance and Safety—Many important questions about the rate and timing of degradation in different environments and about the environmental safety of degradation products have either not been addressed or the research is only now underway. For example, FDA is concerned about the possibility of a shortened shelf-life of degradable food-packaging material. In evaluating the safety of new additives in food-contact materials, FDA must consider potential problems such as enhanced migration of food-packaging components as a consequence of accelerated degradation of the polymer (111). As another example, little is known about what happens to plastics when they biodegrade. It is not known how specific fungi and bacteria degrade particular plastics, if nonbiodegradable materials affect the microbes in any way, how sunlight affects biodegradable plastics, and how physical and chemical aging affect the properties of biodegradable plastics (270). Whether biodegradable plastics, including their nondegradable components, cause any hazards to animals (e.g., invertebrates, fish, birds, mammals) is unknown. Although much of the interest in degradable plastics has been stimulated by concerns about marine litter, few tests have been conducted on the degradability of available plastic products in seawater (175). Limited seawater testing of the deterioration of photodegradable material now used in 6-pack rings, as well as polyethylene and polystyrene products commonly found as marine debris, has been completed by the Research Triangle Institute for the Northwest and Alaska Fisheries Center. Scientists are now concerned that degradable plastics in marine waters may serve only to substitute one hazard for another. That is, with the use of degradable plastics, the hazard of ingesting plastic fragments may replace the hazard of entanglement in nondegradable plastics. Tests of degradability of some products in landfills are also planned (147).

A few communities (e.g., Urbana, Illinois, and Lincoln, Nebraska) are testing biodegradable mulch/trash bags for disposal of leaves and grass clippings. Results of the first year pilot study in Nebraska raised questions about the rate of degradation of the bags and fate of color additives (102). A second year of testing is planned with more rapidly degrading bags and alternative collection of yard waste in large trash containers. Preliminary tests of garbage bags made of a photo-initiated oxidation material showed that only bags of leaves on top of a pile began to degrade (46). It may be difficult to ensure the adequate exposure to UV prior to burial so the bags will continue to degrade once buried or landfilled.

Uncertain Impact on Recycling—One concern about degradable plastics is that expanding their use might adversely affect plastics recycling. The plastics industry (i.e., those who produce nondegradable plastics) contends that if degradable plastics get mixed into the post-consumer plastic waste stream destined for recycling, they might threaten the physical integrity of products made from recycled plastics. In turn, this could cause complicated liability problems for product manufacturers and potentially reverse current increases in the recycling of plastics.

Technical experts who work with degradable plastics disagree. They contend that potential adverse effects will vary depending on the particular degradable plastic, but that the problems will be minimized by: 1) dilution of the degradable material in the overall volume of MSW; 2) addition of appropriate steps to the recycling process (e.g., separation of degradables, chemical treatment, use of additives) to negate any effects of degradable materials; or 3) careful consideration of the intended uses and properties of the recycled products. They consider quality control of the incoming resin, processing, and the final product as the key to avoiding adverse impacts of degradable plastics on recycling.

Markets for Degradable Plastics—Commercial products made with degradable plastics include 6-pack ring carriers, agricultural mulches, and trash bags. Sales of these products are approximately $100 million per year, less than 0.1 percent of the overall $150 billion plastics market in the United States (104).

Over half of all degradable plastic sales are of polyethylene beverage packaging rings. About 30 percent of these 6-pack rings are photodegradable, as required now by various State laws (104). This market share is expected to rise as Public Law 100-556 is implemented; this law requires EPA to regulate the use of certain degradable ring-type devices by 1990, and it asks for a report on the feasibility of expanding the requirements to other packaging systems.

The market shares for other degradable plastic products are very limited to date, but some may be growing. For example, degradable garbage bags have captured 10 percent of the market in New York City, Boston, and Hartford (104). Several communities are distributing degradable bags for yard waste collection. Many additional potential products are being investigated for degradable plastics, including films, bottles, and other containers.

---

some of the problems associated with collecting high-volume plastic containers.

The Plastic Recycling Foundation, another industry group, had a budget for 1988 of $1.2 million. Much of this funding (along with funds from the New Jersey Commission on Science and Technology, Rutgers University, other States and universities, and the National Science Foundation) has been awarded to the CPRR. The Center's total 1988-89 research budget was $2.3 million. Over half of the funds will support research on reclamation, end use markets, sorting, and collection. The remaining funds were used for pilot plant experiments and information services (193).

Projected Markets for Single and Mixed Resins—An estimated 6.2 million tons of plastic containers and packaging are projected to be discarded in 1990 and this is expected to increase to 8.2 million tons by 2000 (81). If market projections are realized for recycled PET and HDPE, by the mid-1990s the Nation could achieve a 10 percent recycling rate for plastic containers and packaging. If recycled plastic products could capture a significant share of the treated lumber market, plastics could achieve a 25 to 40 percent recycling rate for packaging over the next decade. However, if recycling rates are calculated by comparing the amount recycled with all plastics discarded, rather than with containers and packaging discards, then plastic recycling rates will more likely be around 5 percent by the mid-1990s, if only the projected HDPE and PET recycling is realized, or between 15 and 20 percent if the treated lumber market is captured.

Additional market development will be necessary to accommodate expanded collection of post-consumer plastics. Expanding the use of recycled plastics to replace some virgin resin markets, tap nonplastics markets, and attract the interest of particular industries (e.g., automotive and construction) will require some effort.

PET—Projections of the amount of PET that might be recycled by 1993 range from about 300,000 to 350,000 tons, or at least 50 percent of all PET beverage bottles (22,172). This would replace up to 4 percent of virgin PET sales. These increased amounts could be sold easily in established and newly developing markets. For example, Wellman, Inc., the company that now recycles about 75 percent of all recycled PET beverage bottles, claims it could use two to three times the number of available bottles, and it plans to more than double the size of its operation by 1990 (211). Wellman, Inc. has also recently announced plans to work with Browning-Ferris Industries, a major waste hauler, to collect PET bottles. Dow Chemical Co. has announced plans for a joint venture to reprocess 25,000 tons of PET and HDPE per year into high-value building materials like roofing shingles by 1990. Dow is one of the first producers of commodity thermoplastics to move into the recycling business (165).

HDPE—In 1987, approximately 36,000 tons of HDPE were collected for recycling, up from about 30,000 tons in 1986 (22). The current potential market for recycled HDPE is estimated to be about 200,000 tons (54) and is projected to be as much as 330,000 tons by 1993; if the latter level were achieved, almost 6 percent of virgin HDPE sales would be displaced. The use of recycled HDPE is expected to increase and expand into new markets including nonfood bottles (193). The Proctor & Gamble Co. plans to include 20 to 30 percent recycled HDPE in non-food bottles (166).

Mixed Resins—Products from mixed plastics are technically capable of replacing a portion of the treated lumber market, especially decorative landscape ties and erosion control applications (21). This

market was estimated at 1.8 million tons per year. However, it is questionable how much and how rapidly mixed plastics markets can be developed. Investment in technologies for mixed plastics recycling is very limited in the United States. OTA could only identify four U.S. businesses using post-consumer waste to produce mixed plastics products (Polymer Products in Iowa; Processed Plastics, formerly Summit Steel Processing Corp., in Michigan; NECRInc in Massachusetts; and CPRR in New Jersey). Both NECRInc and CPRR began operations in early 1988 and the CPRR facility is a research/pilot-scale operation.

Plastic lumber from mixed resins may also have to compete with plastic lumber products made from single resins, both recycled and virgin. The appearance and properties of these single resin products can be controlled more easily than similar products made from mixed plastic wastes, and thus may be able to tap more specialized markets.

Composting

Composting refers to the process of biological decomposition of solid organic materials by micro-organisms (mainly bacteria and fungi). "Compost" is the stabilized, humus- or soil-like product.[43] Composting has been popular for years because compost products help improve soil structure. Now it is gaining favor as an MSW management method because, in addition to stabilizing organic materials, it can divert them from landfills and reduce some of the risks associated with landfilling and incineration (chs. 6 and 7). (Another way of handling organic materials involves anaerobic bacteria, but this process does not produce compost; see box 5-F).

Composting involves manufacturing a product, just like other industrial practices, and its effectiveness depends on how well the decomposition process is designed and controlled. To maximize the rate of microbial activity within a mass of organic materials, factors such as temperature and moisture must be controlled. With proper controls, composting can occur rapidly, yield a product that meets end-use quality specifications, and reduce the original volume of the materials by more than 50 percent.

---

[43]"Stabilized" refers to the point at which microbial activity reaches a low and relatively constant level.

The biodegradable organic materials in MSW include yard wastes (i.e., leaves, grass clippings, weeds, prunings), food wastes, and paper from residential, commercial, and institutional uses. Yard wastes make up 10 to 30 percent of MSW, although this portion varies greatly geographically and seasonally; food waste constitutes another 5 to 10 percent (ch. 3).

A critical decision has to be made prior to composting—whether to keep the organic materials, particularly yard wastes, separate from other components of MSW, or to begin with mixed MSW and extract the organic materials later for subsequent composting.[44] Yard wastes that are kept separate from the rest of MSW can be handled and composted easily—they require fewer controls on the composting process itself and yield products that tend to have low levels of contaminants. This is especially true for leaves, and many facilities have been dedicated solely to leaf composting. However, the disadvantage is that separate collection of yard wastes is necessary. In contrast, mixed MSW must be mechanically sorted into different portions prior to composting (43).[45] The disadvantages of mixed MSW systems are that mechanical separation involves more equipment and higher capital and operating costs, subsequent composting requires greater control, and the resulting product tends to have higher levels of metals. Mixed MSW systems can be desirable, however, because they handle the entire waste stream and do not require special collection efforts.

Biological Decomposition

Microorganisms, or microbes, are the essential agents of decomposition. To maximize the rate of microbial activity, the composting process must be designed to properly control factors such as temperature, oxygen and nutrient availability, physical substrate, moisture, and pH (43,71-76,90,178,229).

Temperature is a key factor controlling the composting process because the microbes that decompose organic material can survive and function efficiently only at certain temperatures. As microbes decompose organic material, they generate

---

Box 5-F—Anaerobic Systems

Anaerobic systems use bacteria that do not need oxygen (i.e., anaerobic bacteria) to convert organic materials into saleable methane gas and carbon dioxide. Anaerobic systems do not produce compost. They can be attractive, however, because methane gas can be an alternative to natural gas (38). Several methane recovery systems are operating in Europe and Japan, and laboratory-scale research has been conducted in the United States (62).

One demonstration plant in Florida was built specifically to test methane production from MSW (38,188,263). The plant processed up to 100 tons of MSW per day and was operated for research purposes between 1978 and 1988. The plant had "digestor" reactors that used fermentation and other anaerobic reactions to yield methane and carbon dioxide; these reactions required careful control of parameters such as temperature and pH (188). The methane gas was purified to remove acid gases, water vapor, and other impurities.

In France, the Valorga Company opened its first plant in 1981, with a 60-ton-per-day capacity (115). This plant mechanically separates glass and metals, then the organic wastes (i.e., food and paper) undergo anaerobic fermentation in the digesters. The resulting methane gas is captured. About 30 percent of the MSW remains after processing and is incinerated. A new plant designed to handle about 300 tons per day (including sewage and industrial sludge) cost about $19 million (115). The plant was not fully operational as of October 1988, and only the sale of gas (to Gas France, which is a 20 percent owner) and scrap ferrous metals had been arranged; no buyers had been found for cullet or the compost-like product ("digestate"). The plant appears to have some problems with materials becoming contaminated during the mechanical separation

---

heat as a metabolic byproduct. The organic material loses its original identity and eventually becomes stabilized, at which point microbial activity ceases and heat generation subsides. However, the material can retain excessive heat, and if temperatures rise above 60° C before the material is stabilized the

---

[44]Yard and food wastes also can be composted or mulched in backyards. OTA considers this to be a form of waste prevention (ch. 4).

[45]Most mixed MSW composting operations use mechanical processes (e.g., screens, magnets, air classifiers, trommels, hammermills, and shredders) and/or handsorting to remove materials such as tires and bricks, recover recyclable materials such as glass and ferrous metals, reduce particle size, and mix the waste.

Photo credit: Office of Technology Assessment

Composting, the decomposition of solid organic materials by microorganisms, is gaining favor as a management method because it diverts materials from landfills and reduces some risks associated with landfilling and incineration. Its effectiveness depends on how well the decomposition process is designed and controlled.

microbes begin to die and further microbial activity is severely limited. In practical terms, then, temperatures sufficient for microbial activity must be maintained, but excessive temperatures must be prevented. Deliberate removal of heat from the material often is essential, although low-level leaf composting appears to be an exception. According to some researchers, current EPA guidance on composting leads to inhibitively high temperatures and improper functioning (73,74,75,76).

Because composting relies on aerobic bacteria (i.e., bacteria that require oxygen), sufficient oxygen must be available, either from air in the spaces between particles or from air immediately outside the waste mass. Sufficient aeration results in greater microbial activity, faster and more complete decomposition, and more control over odors and pathogens (43,71,72). Excessive aeration can reduce temperatures below those best for maximum microbial activity; insufficient aeration leads to overheating, minimal activity, and foul odors.

In general, if temperatures are maintained properly and the mass of materials is ventilated, then oxygen availability is assured. Ventilation can be accomplished effectively by blowing air through the

mass (i.e., forced aeration) and to some extent by mechanically agitating the mass (i.e., turning, stirring, or tumbling). In some cases, ventilation is conducted in conjunction with temperature controls (71-76). Agitation also helps control temperature and moisture, reduce particle size, and increase bacterial access to nutrients by replacing "used" substrate with "fresh" material.

Curing and Finishing—Once initial composting is complete, composted materials must still be "cured" to ensure that the product is stabilized (i.e., biological activity is low enough so few odors are present). Depending on the system, this can take several months or more. After curing, compost can be "finished" or upgraded to meet market specifications by using methods such as screening, pulverization, destoning, pelletization, and crumbling (207). Compost also can be enhanced by adding nitrogen, mixing with peat or other products for use by nurseries, or blending with other soils for landscaping (43).

System Configuration

The configuration of a composting system refers to the layout of equipment and machinery used for handling materials and for ventilation, along with any enclosing structures or special features (71,72). These features can be combined in numerous ways.

General Terminology—The language of composting configurations typically uses terms such as windrow, static pile, and in-vessel or reactor systems. However, this terminology has been criticized for overemphasizing the physical design of a composting facility and underemphasizing the biological decomposition process (71,72). According to critics, any of these configurations might be compatible with effective, ventilation-based control of the process, so the terms do not indicate the key factors affecting the biological process. OTA agrees that the process is more important than design; the design of a particular facility will depend more on the needs of a particular community (e.g., location, costs). The terminology is still widely used, however, so the terms are described briefly.

Windrow and Static Pile Systems—Windrow and static pile systems typically process material in an unconfined area, and the product is stored in piles to undergo further stabilization. The size and depth of windrows and piles are limited by several factors, particularly compaction, ability to ventilate and agitate, moisture, and temperature (43,71-76). In windrow systems, compostable material is placed in elongated piles or "windrows" and then is agitated to increase aeration. In static pile systems, large piles are formed over a network of perforated pipes that pull (i.e., vacuum) or force (i.e., inject) air through the material (207).

In-Vessel Systems—"In-vessel" or "reactor" systems process material in confined structures. A few of these systems have operated for over 30 years (43,68,178,224). Most systems co-compost sewage sludge with the organic portion of MSW (24,90,215). Sewage sludge increases the moisture content and adds nitrogen, which helps the growth of microbes, but it also can increase odor problems and potential contamination with metals. Additional research is needed on the quality of compost products obtained from co-composting operations.

Configurations for Leaf Composting—Leaf composting can be accomplished with relatively simple system configurations. For example, most leaf composting systems do not require deliberate ventilation (71,72), although they can be designed with this feature. This simplicity is attractive because leaves are a significant waste management problem in some communities. In some areas, for example, leaves and grass clippings can comprise over 60 percent of the MSW generated at residences during summer and fall (88,207,229).

Although leaf composting systems are generally simple, a range of configurations still can be used depending on the needs of a particular community (228,229). In **minimal** technology systems, the only activity is turning large piles of leaves once a year; compost is produced in 2 to 3 years. A large buffer area is needed, however, because the piles become anaerobic and odorous. In **low-level** systems, front-end loaders turn smaller piles several times a year so the piles do not become anaerobic as readily; compost is produced in 1 to 2 years. In **intermediate** systems, piles are watered periodically and turned by specially designed machines; compost is produced in 6 to 12 months. **High-level** systems produce compost in less than 6 months by grinding leaves before composting, providing more aeration and turning, and controlling temperature and moisture.

Minimal and low-level systems thus require less management and expense, but more time and space. Intermediate and high-level systems require more control over the biological processes, but more capital investment.

Operational Problems

Odors—Odors usually indicate that the process of biological decomposition is not proceeding properly. Odor generation can be controlled, however, through proper temperature controls and agitation. Grass clippings often cause odor problems because their high moisture, nitrogen, and organic content makes them decompose rapidly, which can lead to anaerobic conditions (229). As an alternative, homeowners can leave clippings on lawns after mowing, as long as they are not too thick (208).

Leachate—Leachate formation can occur when the moisture content of the composting material is too high. Source-separated organic materials, for example, tend to have a higher moisture content than does mixed MSW (77,115). Leachate can be collected several ways, including conducting operations on a paved surfaced designed to collect leachate or by collecting runoff in sedimentation ponds (43,233). Important questions are whether heavy metals are leached from compost and whether organic chemicals (e.g., pesticides) are present and leachable (see "Pollution From Primary and Secondary Manufacturing Processes" below).

Pathogens, Plants, and Fungi—Various pathogens (e.g., bacteria such as *Salmonella*, parasites such as *Ascaris*) can be present if composting is not well controlled. The existence of pathogens varies with the type of waste, but potential contamination is higher when co-composting with sewage sludge occurs. Some microbes also can be released into the air on dust particles and aerosols generated during composting (43); health effects related to inhalation of *Aspergillus fumigatus*, for example, have been of concern, although none have been documented (228). Weed seeds and fungi also can be present in yard waste and sewage sludge and thus can reduce final product quality. In general, temperatures over 50° C, maintained throughout the entire composting pile for a sufficient time, are needed to destroy pathogens and weed seeds (71,72,91,178); composting cannot continue above 60° C, however, or the microbes needed for decomposition begin to die.

Operational Facilities

Mixed MSW Facilities—At least six mixed MSW composting facilities currently operate in the United States (table 5-6), and one additional facility is being built in Minnesota. Most of the composting facilities that operated in the 1950s and 1960s closed because of economic or technical problems (90,207,252). About three dozen additional projects are in the planning, design, and bid stages (207). Portland, Oregon, for example, began negotiations in July 1988 to build a $23 million composting facility (120,265); the facility would process 180,000 tons of waste and produce about 100,000 tons of compost annually.

Five of the existing facilities are publicly owned, and at least three co-compost with sewage sludge. The Delaware facility is designed to process 1,000 tons of MSW and 350 tons of sewage sludge per day; the planned Minnesota facility also will be large, with a capacity of over 1,000 tons per day. The other facilities are relatively small and began operating only recently (43). The Delaware facility and the facility under construction in Minnesota are designed with front-end mechanical separation. Besides separating various materials for recycling (e.g., metals, glass) and producing RDF (from plastics and paper), the Delaware facility can produce about 180 tons of finished compost per day (24); the operators expect to market about half of the output to the fertilizer industry.

Limited information is available about the costs of mixed MSW composting. Total capital costs for existing facilities range from $700,000 (1987 dollars) for the Minnesota facility to $73 million (1983 dollars) for the Delaware facility (161,252); this corresponds to about $13,000 to $54,000 per ton of design capacity. Aside from size, differences in capital costs are related to equipment specifications, construction and insurance costs (43), and storage space requirements (237). Operation and maintenance costs have been estimated to range from about $17 to $33 per ton (43).

Mixed MSW composting has been more common in Europe than in the United States, and a few facilities have proven successful over long periods of time (23,68,106,141).[46] However, many facilities (e.g., in Belgium, Switzerland, West Germany, the Netherlands, and Sweden) have had difficulties marketing their products (23,106,115). Mixed MSW composting has declined in Sweden, which had a high rate, because of problems with heavy metals and marketing (23). Even before this, many Swedish facilities simply transported much (between 61 and 80 percent) of their compost to landfills (23,115).

Yard Waste Programs—Many communities in the United States compost yard wastes, especially leaves. Yard wastes are collected several ways, including using front-end loaders to pick up bags, vacuuming from curbsides, and using packer trucks to empty waste bins. No estimate of the total number of yard waste facilities exists, but hundreds are known, for example, in New Jersey, Michigan, Wisconsin, and Minnesota (88,151,161). As of December 1988, New Jersey alone had 180 permitted facilities, most for leaf composting; the State uses a manual on leaf composting as its guidance document for such facilities (229). In Massachusetts, about 25 percent of all municipalities participate in yard waste composting programs (209). However, these States have not estimated the amount of yard waste handled, and most do not have specifications regarding the quality of final products from such programs. Numerous reports describe local programs (e.g., 25,217,233).

Few data are available on the costs of yard waste composting. In one study of eight municipal operations, collection and transportation costs to the municipality ranged from $0 (where residents or landscapers dropped wastes off at a facility) to over $80 per ton, and processing costs ranged from $4 to $23 per ton (233). In general, collection and transportation costs were 1 to 11 times greater than processing costs. For leaf composting, operating costs for low-level systems are estimated to range from $2 to $4 per cubic yard (228).

Composting of yard and food wastes that have been separated from other MSW is increasing in Europe (77,115,103,156). In West Germany, for example, in 1988 at least 71 source separation projects existed for organic wastes (93,218). These projects served an estimated 430,000 households,

---

[46]One study indicated that France had over 100 composting facilities in operation (194). However, most of these plants probably are sludge composting or co-composting plants (136).

Table 5-6—Operational Mixed MSW Composting Facilities in the United States

Location	Year opened	Processing capacity (tpd of MSW)	Type of composting system	Co-compost with sludge
Wilmington, DE	1984	1350	In-vessel	Yes
Sumpter County, FL	1988	65-100	Windrow	NA[b]
Dodge City, KS	1987[a]	30	Windrow	NA
St. Cloud, MN	1988	50	In-vessel	Yes
Fillmore County, MN	1987	25	Windrow	No
Portage, WI	1986	30	In-vessel	Yes

[a]Not commercially operating; run for research and demonstration by vendor.
[b]Information not available.

SOURCES: Cal Recovery Systems, Inc., "Composting Technologies, Costs, Programs, and Markets," contract report prepared for U.S. Congress, Office of Technology Assessment (Richmond, CA: January 1989); Ron Albrecht Associates, Inc., "Composting Technologies, Costs, Programs and Markets," contract report prepared for U.S. Congress, Office of Technology Assessment (Annapolis, MD: December 1988).

and they composted an estimated 200 pounds per person of organic wastes each year. Heidelberg's program is one of the largest, serving over 100,000 people (78,115).

Food Wastes—No MSW facilities in the United States are used solely for composting food waste (252). Some U.S. companies, however, collect and process certain food wastes. For example, one operation in Virginia collects waste grease, bones, fat, and offal from slaughterhouses, restaurants, and supermarkets and processes it into an animal feed additive (126). In New Jersey, some farmers are licensed to collect food wastes and feed them to swine (58).

Products, Markets, and Standards

The main value of finished compost is its humus-like characteristic, which can help improve soil by adding organic matter and increasing water-holding capacity. The positive effects of compost on plant growth and yield are well documented (178,194). The nutrient content of compost is low relative to chemical fertilizers, however, so compost usually is not used as a fertilizer unless it has been chemically enhanced (43,178,267). Compost products are used by many businesses (e.g., private landscapers and contractors, vineyard operators, farmers, golf course operators, topsoil and nursery industries), public institutions (e.g., public works and parks departments), and some individual homeowners (207).

In general, municipalities should not expect composting to be profitable; revenues from the sale of compost products can only partially offset operating costs (71,72,267) (see ch. 2). Gross wholesale revenues for yard waste compost products exhibit a wide range, from $0 (when given away for free) to $25 per ton (233). Products that cannot be sold or distributed usually have to be used as cover material at landfills.

General Market Demand—Each end use of compost requires that the product meet certain specifications. As a result, consistent quality, as well as consistent availability, are critical in determining marketability (43). Mixed MSW, or organic waste from previously mixed MSW, usually contains small pieces of glass and plastics, stones, and other objects. Mechanical screening processes can remove much, but not all, of these materials. Whether these contaminants are a problem depends on the end use of the product.

In general, products with consistently high quality are required for food production and horticultural uses, while products with lower quality can be used for revegetation and landfill cover (71,72). A top-grade product generally has dark color and earthy smell, minimal pathogens and toxic substances, uniformly small particle size, and proper nutrient and moisture content (43).

The potential market for compost products is impossible to quantify, but proponents contend that existing markets are small relative to their potential (24,43,61). However, compost must compete with sewage sludge compost and other products (e.g., sawdust, fish processing wastes, peat products, manure, bark, natural topsoils). Almost 200 sludge composting facilities are operating or are being planned, and competition is likely to increase in the

Northeast and mid-Atlantic regions (2). Many compost products are only marketed locally because their weight and bulkiness (e.g., 700 to 1,000 pounds per cubic yard) makes transport expensive and energy-intensive.

The market for compost in large-scale agriculture is small, because compost is not intended to be used primarily as a fertilizer and because of its bulkiness. Given increasing concerns about depletion of organic matter in soil, however, some analysts consider farmers to be a strong potential market for using compost as a soil conditioner (43,237). Overall energy use in agriculture also might decrease if compost could help reduce dependence on energy-intensive chemical fertilizers and lower the energy needed for soil preparation (61).

The potential market for compost in landscaping (horticulture) and smaller scale agriculture (e.g., row crops and orchards) may be large (43). Market evaluations indicate that landscape contractors and suppliers, sod services, nurseries, and retailers of soil conditioners are likely to show increased interest in bulk compost (237). Homeowners represent another potentially large market for bagged products. Marketing surveys, however, indicate that many individuals are reluctant to use composts made from MSW and sewage sludge (43).

Standards—Many States require composting **facilities** to obtain permits from the relevant environmental or health agencies (161,207). For mixed MSW facilities, permits can require hydrogeological site investigations, studies of odor dispersal, and monitoring plans. Some States (e.g., Florida, Massachusetts, New Jersey, and New York) require water pollution controls. Local regulatory agencies also may issue permits to address storm water and sediment control.

Yard waste facilities tend to be regulated less stringently than mixed MSW facilities. For example, Michigan, Pennsylvania, Texas, Virginia, and Wisconsin do not require community operations to obtain a permit, and New Jersey recently made it easier for small operations to obtain permits. Some proponents suggest that these facilities continue to be less stringently regulated (88). Although this approach would provide incentives for yard waste composting, it would not necessarily ensure protection of human health and the environment or the

production of compost products that meet specifications.

State policies regarding the use of compost **products** vary widely (43). Regulations for products from mixed MSW are based on EPA guidelines (40 *CFR* 257) and Department of Agriculture standards (e.g., for chemical quality) originally developed to address the application of sewage sludge to land (177,207). The guidelines set the maximum rates at which metals can be added to soil, based on the fate of metals and their impact on the food chain, soil properties, and crop types. More research is needed on the extent to which leaching of metals and uptake by plants occurs.

Few States have developed standards for different classes or uses of compost. Similarly, few standards exist to regulate organic chemicals (e.g., pesticides) in compost products. Some States, however, are beginning to regulate these products (table 5-7). For example, Minnesota has proposed standards to control the levels of contaminants in compost products. Under these rules, Class I compost, made without sewage sludge and containing metal and PCB levels below specified limits, would be safe for unrestricted use. Class II compost, either made with sewage sludge or containing levels of metals and PCBs above the limits, would be restricted according to soil properties and land use.

Future composting regulations could be designed in several ways. For example, they could require testing of compost products (e.g., for toxicity) or they could specify performance standards to be met by composting processes and facilities.

Another problem is the lack of guidelines or standards to help municipal buyers of composting technologies evaluate claims about decomposition rates and product quality (43,72). Some vendors of mixed MSW systems claim, for example, that they can produce a stable compost product in a relatively short time (less than 2 weeks in some cases).

Pollution From Primary and Secondary Manufacturing Process

Proponents of recycling have made many claims about the relative levels of pollution generated by primary and secondary manufacturing processes, often arguing that recycling reduces pollution. In

Table 5-7—Selected State Standards for Compost Products
(parts per million dry weight)

Substance	Minnesota[a] Class I	New York[b] Class I[d]	New York[b] Class II[d]	Massachusetts[c] Class I[d]	Massachusetts[c] Class II[d]
Boron				300	300
Cadmium	10	10	25	2	25
Chromium	1000	1000	1000	1000	1000
Copper	500	1000	1000	1000	1000
Lead	500	250	1000	300	1000
Mercury	5	10	10	10	10
Molybdenum				10	10
Nickel	100	200	200	200	200
Zinc	1000	2500	2500	2500	2500
PCBs	1	1	10		

[a]For any compost made without sewage sludge; if levels are met, unrestricted use is permitted.
[b]For sewage sludge and mixed MSW compost.
[c]For sewage sludge, mixed MSW, and yard compost.
[d]Class I refers to food crops; Class II refers to non-food crops.

SOURCES: Cal Recovery Systems, Inc., "Composting Technologies, Costs, Programs, and Markets," contract report prepared for U.S. Congress, Office of Technology Assessment (Richmond, CA: January 1989); M. Mayer, H. Hofer, and U. Maire, "Trends in Yard Waste Composting," *BioCycle* 29(6): 60-63, July 1988; Minnesota Pollution Control Agency, "State Solid Waste Policy Report, A Focus on Greater Minnesota, Background Paper XII: Composting," Office of Waste Management Grants and Assistance, draft report (St. Paul, MN: December 1988); C.J. Rosen, N. Schumacher, R. Mugaas, and S. Proudfoot, *Composting and Mulching: A Guide to Managing Organic Wastes*, Minnesota Extension Service Report AG-FO-3296 (St. Paul, MN: 1988).

general, recycling may result in fewer pollutants when the entire MSW system is considered. In particular, if recycled products replace products made from virgin materials, potential pollution savings may result from the dual avoidance of pollution from manufacturing and from subsequent disposal of replacement products made from virgin materials.

However, it is usually not clear whether secondary manufacturing produces less pollution per ton of material processed than primary manufacturing. Such an analysis, which is beyond the scope of this report, would have to examine all the pollutants produced during each step in production, as well as pollution generated while providing energy to the process itself and for transporting materials. It would also be necessary to account for the effects of water and raw materials use on ecological systems. Definitive research has not been conducted, however, on all the relevant primary and secondary materials processes. To provide a starting point, this section reviews some comparisons of manufacturing using recycled versus virgin materials. Box 5-G briefly illustrates some of the pollutants generated in secondary manufacturing processes.

Numerous publications have documented pollutants emitted from manufacturing processes that use virgin materials (e.g., 131). In the mid-1970s, EPA concluded that recycling of waste materials generally resulted in less pollution than did manufacturing from virgin materials (251).

This generalization does not necessarily hold true in all cases. Using EPA data on paper production processes, for example, one researcher found no clear difference in measurements of chemical and biological oxygen demand and of total suspended solids in water effluents from recycling and virgin materials processes (262). The EPA data also indicated that 5 toxic substances "of concern" were found only in virgin processes and 8 were found only in recycling processes; of 12 pollutants found in both processes, 11 were present in higher levels in the recycling processes.

This researcher also noted that EPA's analyses of pollutants from virgin materials processing did not account for pollution from mining, timbering, and transportation (262). He concluded that "there are clear materials and energy conservation benefits to recycling, [but] the picture regarding environmental benefits and risks is complex, especially when

Box 5-G—Pollutants Generated in Secondary Manufacturing Processes

Heavy Metals

Iron and Steel Recycling—Solid wastes produced by iron and steel foundries that primarily use ferrous scrap can contain lead, cadmium, and chromium; these wastes may be classified as hazardous (181). Sludges from core-making processes and baghouse dusts also are hazardous in some cases, depending on emission controls and the quality of incoming metal. Oman (181) cited one study indicating that "9 out of 21 foundries generated emission control residuals which would be considered as a hazardous waste on the basis of EP toxicity for lead." Air emissions also are common. Electric arc furnaces, which normally operate on 100 percent scrap, avoid some air emission problems because they do not use coke oven gases as a heat source; however, they can emit high levels of particulates if they use scrap with high concentrations of dirt, organic matter, and alloys (131).

Aluminum Recycling—When aluminum scrap is melted, associated substances (e.g., painted labels, plastic, and oil and grease) are burned off. The resulting air emissions can contain particulate matter in the form of metallic chlorides and oxides, as well as acid gases and chlorine gas (261). Similar types of emissions are likely from plants that smelt other scrap metals.

Paper Recycling—Printing inks often contain pigments that contain heavy metals such as lead and cadmium (261). These and other metals can be present in wastewater and de-inking sludge from paper recycling; for example, de-inking sludges have been reported with lead concentrations ranging from 3 to 294 ppm (dry weight) (64).

Materials Recycling Facilities (MRFs)—Very little testing has been conducted at MRFs to determine levels of pollutants. Even the results of testing that has been done at one facility that handles sorted paper, glass, and metals are ambiguous. At that facility, air withdrawn from within the building (i.e., prior to emissions controls) exhibited relatively low emission rates (in terms of pounds per hour) for cadmium, chromium, lead, mercury, and nickel (117,262). However, actual concentrations of the metals in the emissions were high. No data were available about emissions after air pollution controls or on heavy metal concentrations in dust that settled in or around the plant.

Composting—Concentrations of heavy metals tend to be higher in compost from mixed MSW composting facilities than from compost made from separately collected organic wastes, primarily because mechanical separation cannot remove all metals. Compost from MSW that is co-composted with sewage sludge also tends to have high metal concentrations. Sewage treatment processes remove metals from effluent and concentrate them in sludge, and this emphasizes the role industrial pretreatment programs can play in reducing the metals entering treatment plants (240). The concentrations of metals in mixed MSW compost and co-compost samples vary from site to site (161). In some cases, zinc and lead exceeded State limits (26), while in other cases lead levels were lower than the limits. Problems also have been noted with heavy metals in mixed MSW compost in Europe (23,92,101,115,132,149,156). In one West German study, average concentrations of seven heavy metals were almost always lower in compost made from source-separated organic waste; in some cases they were essentially the same as soil concentrations (77,78). More research is needed on the composition of leachate from compost products under different conditions.

Dioxins

Dioxins can be produced at paper mills, as a byproduct of pulp bleaching, and can be present in the effluent or sludge (241). Limited testing by EPA has shown that concentrations of 2,3,7,8-TCDD in sludges from two mills that use waste paper are relatively low, ranging from 2 to 37 parts per trillion (17).

Dioxins also have been detected in post-pollution control emissions from certain secondary metals smelting facilities. For example, dioxins have been reported in post-control emissions from (127):

- steel drum reclamation;
- scrap wire reclamation (combustion to remove wire insulation, with afterburner);[1] and
- metals recovery from electronic scrap such as telephones and circuit boards (combustion, with afterburner and baghouse).

Other Organic Chemicals

Paper—Inks that need to be removed during recycling also contain acrylics, plastics, resins, varnishes, defoamers, and alcohols, some of which are discharged in wastewater. Paper recycling processes, particularly those with a bleaching step involving chlorine, also are known to discharge effluents that contain various chlorine-based compounds, including carbon tetrachloride, dichloroethane, methylene chloride, and trichloroethylene (261). In addition, the dispersing agents used in the de-inking processes (e.g., detergents and emulsifiers) end up in the sludge.

Plastics—Residues from the recycling of plastics are difficult to assess without knowing the specific details of proprietary systems used to wash materials and remove contaminants. Wash water and air emissions may be contaminated by residues from other products associated with recycled plastic, such as food or pesticides. At least one PET reclamation system planned to operate at a scale of 25,000 tons per year by 1990 will use 1,1,1-trichloroethane to remove residues. This toxic solvent is a well-known groundwater contaminant (239). However, according to Dow, the developer of the technology, the solvent is used in a closed system that will not result in release to the environment (165).

Compost—Few data are available on organic chemicals in compost. Compost from the Delaware facility has been found to contain PCBs in concentrations up to 5 parts per million (42), which is below the allowable limit of 10 parts per million set in Delaware's regulations. Questions have been raised about chemicals in grass clippings, particularly nitrogen from fertilizers and organic chemicals from pesticides (228). Many of these chemicals are insoluble and may bind to particles instead of being leached into groundwater, but there is little data to evaluate this. It also is unclear whether they could be taken up in food crops grown on compost containing the chemicals (228).

Chlorine and Sulfur

Chlorine and sulfur are common components in many products and chlorine is used in some recycling processes, so it is not surprising that both elements are found in residues at recycling facilities. For example, Visalli (262) calculated that uncontrolled emissions from one secondary aluminum smelter contained 1.7 pounds of hydrogen chloride and 1.8 pounds of SO_2 per hour.

---

[1]It is likely that dioxins and furans are produced from burning plastic wire coating. Wire scrap makes up a small percentage of total metal scrap processed.

---

specific hazardous pollutants are taken into account.''

Paper

Virgin pulp processes generate various liquid and gas residues, depending on the type of paper, type of pulping process, and extent of bleaching (131). In general, large amounts of mill effluent are generated and this contains suspended solids, dissolved organic solids, various chemicals, and high BOD. Wastewater generated in the bleaching stage can contain dioxins, chlorine dioxide, hypochlorite, and other bleaching chemicals and byproducts. Spent liquor generated in the pulping process can contain a wide variety of chemicals; the liquors often are burned in a recovery furnace or fluidized bed. Other byproducts from the virgin paper process also can be used to generate energy. Gas emissions include chlorine, chlorine dioxide, sulfur dioxide, particulates, and hydrogen sulfide. Metals from de-inking are present in sludge residues; the concentration of lead in these sludges appears to be in the same range as in sludges from mills that use secondary fibers (64).

Aluminum

At primary aluminum smelters, one major concern is with the "potliners"—pots lined with carbon that serves as the cathode and that contain compounds of aluminum, fluorine, and sodium. The potliners are replaced every 4 or 5 years, and disagreement has arisen over whether used potliners should be listed as a hazardous waste under RCRA. As of August 1988, EPA has been required to list potliners as hazardous waste. The aluminum industry claims, however, that potliners can be used to fire cement kilns, among other things, and therefore should not be considered a "waste." The designation of potliners as hazardous waste discourages this recycling. Most aluminum smelters in 1989 are disposing of spent potliners in hazardous waste landfills.

Steel

Various residues are generated during the steps necessary to produce steel (e.g., coking, sintering, ironmaking, steelmaking, rolling, and finishing steps) (131). Air emissions from coke ovens, for example, contain particulates and sulfur dioxide. Wastewater from steelmaking contains suspended and dissolved solids, oxygen-demanding substances, oil, phenols, and ammonia. Solid waste residues also are common, particularly from open hearth and oxygen furnaces. One study (131) modeled production processes and estimated that using less scrap and more ore would result in increased generation of phenols, ammonia, oxygen-demanding substances, sulfur dioxide, and particulates, and decreased generation of suspended solids.

Plastics

Once a resin is produced, the environmental risks associated with fabricating products from the resins are the same whether the resin is produced from virgin or secondary materials. However, primary production processes generate air emissions, wastewater, and solid waste. The types and amounts of these wastes vary with different processes and types of plastics, and some are managed as hazardous waste. According to one analysis, five of the six chemicals whose production generates the most hazardous waste in the United States are chemicals commonly used by the plastics industry (268).

In general, air emissions are highest during the initial processing and recovery steps for monomers, solvents, catalysts, and additives. Wastewater associated with the primary production process can contain suspended monomers, co-monomers, polymers, additives, filler particulates, soluble constituents, and solvents that are washed or leached from the plastic. Solid waste is produced at various points, mostly from spillage, routine cleaning, particulate collection (from feeding, handling, grinding, and trimming processes), but also from production errors and a few production process byproducts. It can contain mostly polymers and small quantities of plasticizers, fillers, and other additives.

Some emissions are associated with the reprocessing of secondary plastic materials. For example, volatile air emissions can be generated during the heating of plastics, and residues can be contained in the rinse water used to cool the remelted resins.

Barriers to Increased Recycling

Nature of Commodities Markets

One important factor in any commodity-based industry is the volatility of markets. This volatility creates heightened uncertainty in evaluating the financial viability of a business venture, discouraging growth to some extent. Markets for both primary (or virgin) and secondary (or recovered) materials are subject to this volatility to varying degrees. Therefore, the nature of commodity markets, and the causes of their volatility, should be considered when barriers to increased recycling are evaluated.

Both primary and secondary materials are used as inputs in one or more "downstream" production processes. As such, the demand for most raw materials is based on factors far removed from the immediate use of the materials as an input for another product. For instance, demand for packaging materials depends on the demand for the multitude of products for which packaging is used. This means that demand for a raw material is not very sensitive to its own price, especially in the short run. Rather, the demand for raw materials is more strongly dependent on current technology and the availability of substitute and other inputs in an intermediate product, as well as final consumer preference factors (45).

When considering market manipulation in an attempt to stimulate recycling, it is essential to consider these demand factors for basic raw materials. **Because demand factors can be in a constant state of flux, with a market having many actors and an increasingly global nature, it is very difficult to externally control or balance the markets for these raw materials, whether primary or secondary.**

The demand for raw materials often is volatile because of the "distance" between the production of the raw material and final consumption. This volatility is sometimes more marked for secondary than for primary materials, resulting in even greater price fluctuations. This is particularly true when the secondary material is a marginal supply (i.e., the least desirable and first to be cut during business downturns). In those markets, secondary materials prices are always more volatile than those for primary inputs, although they generally exhibit similar longer term trends. This situation applies most to iron and steel scrap, lead scrap, and lower grades of waste paper, and is dependent on the industrial infrastructure and the regulatory regime.

In any waste management program, the ultimate fate of waste, including materials that can be recovered, largely depends on the costs of different management options. Recycling, of course, competes with landfilling and incineration. Moreover, markets for materials recovered from MSW depend on demand for recycled products. Where primary manufacturing produces less costly goods, demand for recycled goods will tend to be lower, creating an economic environment that favors disposal. Consequently, recycling must compete simultaneously with primary manufacturing and traditional waste disposal methods.

Types of Constraints to Increased Use of Secondary Materials

Materials recovered from MSW can be used to produce a variety of new products. In some of these products, secondary or recovered materials compete as inputs only with their primary or virgin counterparts, while in others they compete with different virgin or secondary materials. The relationship between similar primary and secondary materials must be understood to assess the potential for increased consumption of materials recovered from MSW.

Markets for secondary materials are, for the most part, competitive, and they operate under a complex set of dynamics. **Any attempt to provide specific incentives to increase the use of secondary materials should recognize that the dynamics of these markets, and the barriers impeding them, are different for each material.** The nature of the barriers determines the types of policy options likely to be most effective.

Both economic and noneconomic barriers exist to increased recycling (83). **Economic** barriers are factors that limit markets through economic forces, such as:

- the costs of raw materials, capital, and labor;
- the costs of transportation;

- new business or capacity expansion decisions; and
- end-product prices.

These economic factors can be broadly classified as supply-side or demand-side factors. Supply-side factors affect the procurement and processing of raw materials prior to manufacturing. Demand-side factors affect the end users of goods in the commercial, institutional, and household sectors. Mills and other recycled materials manufacturing establishments are at the pivot point of the system, being direct participants in both supply-side and demand-side factors.

The degree to which each secondary material is used is determined by a unique set of market factors. For example, old newspapers are relatively easy to collect, and little doubt exists that current rates of collection could be increased. However, the two primary end products for ONP—recycled paperboard and newsprint—are sold to limited markets. Competitive products made of virgin materials serve most of those markets, and the market share for recycled products has declined in the last decade. Thus, ONP is demand-side limited, and this limit must be removed if more ONP is to be recycled.

An evaluation of demand-side or supply-side limiting factors for secondary materials is presented in table 5-8. The most opportune incentive points in the system that might help increase recycling also are presented. In the example of ONP, incentives to end users would be most effective. In contrast, old corrugated containers present a different situation. Products made from recycled OCC compete well against products made of virgin materials in many markets. In this instance, incentives to collectors and processors of OCC and to primary manufacturers to use OCC would likely result in increased recycling. One group of materials—plastics—is listed as being both supply-side and demand-side limited. Postconsumer plastics recycling is in its infancy, and many problems need to be worked out at all points in the system.

Economic barriers can be related to technical issues, on both supply and demand sides. Technical barriers are often related to material quality, which can limit the substitutability of secondary materials for virgin materials. One example can be found in recycled printing and writing paper. These papers

**Table 5-8—Overview of the Recycling System for Various Materials:
Limiting Factors and Incentive Points**

Materials	Limiting factors		Appropriate incentive points		
	Supply	Demand	Collection/ processing	Mills	Industrial/ commercial consumers
Old newspapers		x	x	x	x
Old corrugated containers	x		x	x	
Office papers	x		x		
Mixed papers		x		x	x
Plastics	x	x	x	x	x
Glass	x		x		
Tin cans	x		x		
Aluminum	x		x		
Used oil		x		x	x
Tires		x		x	x

SOURCE: Franklin Associates, Ltd., "Economic Incentives and Disincentives for Recycling of Municipal Solid Waste," contract prepared for U.S. Congress, Office of Technology Assessment (Prairie Village, KS: 1988).

are generally about 50 percent secondary fiber, consisting mostly of pulp substitutes (pre-consumer waste). Greater quantities of post-consumer waste cannot be used, however, because of the inability of the current process to sufficiently remove contaminants in the waste paper.

Similar technical constraints exist for the use of scrap in steelmaking. Currently unremovable contaminants in some iron and steel scrap (particularly post-consumer) compromise the strength of the final steel product, thereby limiting the amount of scrap that can be used and the types of products in which it can be used. Post-consumer plastics, too, face similar constraints concerning contaminant removal.

Relative cost also can act as an economic barrier. Whether a cost differential results from higher transport costs, subsidies to the virgin material, or higher processing and handling costs, the outcome is that the manufacturer will minimize costs in the production process by choosing the lowest cost material. In some cases, this turns out to be the virgin material.

Finally, the manufacturer may be unable to obtain secondary materials because they have not been removed from the waste stream in large enough quantities. The glass industry claims that this factor alone inhibits greater recycling of glass cullet. Collection is a serious problem for plastics.

Noneconomic barriers to increased recycling can be caused by value judgments in the decisionmaking process. These factors include the attitudes of manufacturing personnel or consumers, attitudes about quality control, and long-standing corporate policies and procedures.

Some noneconomic factors are demand-related. Some consumers are unwilling, either for real or perceived quality deficiencies, to buy products made from secondary materials. The preference for a virgin content product is based not on an inability of the secondary material to perform, but on the desire of the consumer to have a "more attractive" product. In other cases, the consumer is not even aware of the existence of secondary materials in the product, and is therefore unable to make a decision on that basis. For example, it is impossible to distinguish between primary and secondary aluminum.

Another example of the importance of noneconomic factors is illustrated with writing paper. Consumers prefer bright white paper, which is more difficult to produce if the paper has a high post-consumer waste content (above about 10 to 15 percent). It is likely that lower brightness paper would be sufficient for many uses, but people view this as a sign of inferior quality.

Supply-related noneconomic barriers exist where the manufacturer is unwilling to obtain secondary materials to use as inputs in the production process. Such unwillingness is more common in vertically structured industries, where the source of the virgin raw material is owned by the manufacturer. This barrier is difficult to overcome because the industrial infrastructure is built around this long-held economic relationship. Unwillingness may also be a result of the manufacturer being unaware of technical advances in reprocessing technologies. This problem has been noted for plastics.

Concerns about liability under Superfund legislation also act as an additional barrier to increased recycling. Scrap handlers and processors increasingly are unwilling to handle scrap materials contaminated with known hazardous substances. This has long been a concern for lead-acid battery recyclers, and it is becoming one for auto scrap processors as air bags containing sodium azide and other nonmetallic materials are used more widely.

Tilts in the Playing Field

Recycling must compete simultaneously with primary manufacturing and traditional disposal options, yet various government actions have given economic advantages to these alternatives that in the end make recycling less appealing. These actions have resulted in market choices that, when **all** the costs are accounted, are inefficient in the economic sense.

In the competition between primary and secondary materials manufacturing, the costs of raw materials are not always accurately reflected in the price paid by the manufacturer. For example, the government sometimes uses subsidies to supplement the cost of producing some raw materials, such as timber. In these cases, the total costs of producing finished goods are not all internalized to the manufacturer. In addition, the cost of managing waste residuals produced during the manufacturing process is not always internalized, contributing to inefficient market decisionmaking. For example, if an industry emits chemicals to the environment, there may be human health and environmental costs, but these costs are unlikely to be reflected in the price of the manufactured good.

External Costs of Manufacturing—When industrial facilities fail to control the release of pollutants to the environment, an external cost is incurred because the detrimental effects of that pollution on human health and the environment are not accounted for in the cost of production. The failure to internal-

ize these costs can affect the relationship between primary and secondary materials. Because the relative level of pollution from primary and secondary production processes is not always clear, it is not possible to determine how these external costs affect the choice between primary and secondary materials. Those facilities generating more pollution will have an advantage because they are avoiding more external costs. Where primary facilities produce higher levels of pollution than secondary facilities, the primary facilities thus will have an unfair advantage.

In addition, the reduced energy consumption associated with recycling certain materials, such as aluminum and some types of paper, could have indirect pollutant savings by reducing overall fossil fuel consumption. The burning of fossil fuels has been linked to problems such as acid rain and global warming. Although these externalities have not been quantified, they can be important considerations in the choice between virgin and secondary materials.

Federal Subsidies for Virgin Materials—The history in the United States of preference programs or subsidies for natural resources dates back to early in this century, when the development of natural resources was encouraged to fuel economic growth. Preferences granted within the Federal tax system are among the most visible—programs such as depletion allowances for mineral mining and petroleum production, and special tax treatment of capital gains from the sale of timber. These programs have been used for decades to stimulate, and sometimes help maintain, these sectors of the economy. As a result, the programs have become embedded in the economic system and are now an integral part of the industrial infrastructure and economics of natural resource development and production.

Federal expenditures for natural resources tax programs are summarized in table 5-9. The tax preferences most relevant to recycling are the percentage depletion allowances for minerals, oil, and gas and the special treatment of income for the timber industry. Studies conducted in the 1970s on the effects of these preferences indicated that they have not significantly discouraged the use of secondary materials; recent studies on the issue have not been conducted (83).

Table 5-9—Estimated Costs for Special Tax Treatment for Virgin Materials Production, Fiscal Years 1980 to 1989ª (millions of dollars)

	FY80	FY81	FY82	FY83	FY84	FY85	FY86	FY87	FY88[b]	FY89[b]
Natural resources and environment:										
Expensing of exploration and development costs, nonfuel minerals	27	31	30	62	65	85	88	35	34	37
Excess of percentage over cost depletion, nonfuel minerals	493	506	466	531	589	493	500	410	318	293
Capital gains treatment of iron ore	27	25	24	45	44	32	31	10	—	—
Subtotal—minerals	548	563	519	638	698	610	618	455	352	330
Capital gains treatment of timber income	740	756	808	831	997	610	690	290	10	—
Expensing of multi-period timber growing costs	—	—	—	—	—	—	—	130	256	279
Investment credit and seven-year amortization for reforestation expenditures	—	—	12	34	49	53	57	210	203	195
Subtotal—timber	740	756	820	864	1,046	663	747	630	468	474
Total—minerals and timber	1,288	1,319	1,339	1,503	1,744	1,272	1,365	1,085	820	804
Energy:										
Expensing of exploration and development costs for oil and gas	2,980	3,419	3,428	2,639	1,978	519	639	(675)	(400)	(172)
Excess of percentage over cost depletion for oil and gas	2,041	2,656	2,667	1,944	1,771	1,659	1,936	1,030	743	618
Total—energy	5,021	6,075	6,095	4,582	3,750	2,178	2,575	355	343	446

NOTE: The corporate and individual tax categories have been combined for all years to give a total. In the energy category, the individual benefits dominate substantially; in FY85, 86, 87, 88, and 89 the corporate benefit is negative for expensing of exploration and development costs.
aPresented in constant dollars using an implicit price deflator with 1987 as the basis.
bTo bring these values to constant 1987 dollars, implicit price deflators were projected for each based on the historical trend.

SOURCE: Franklin Associates, Ltd., "*Economic Incentives and Disincentives for Recycling of Municipal Solid Waste*" contract prepared for U.S. Congress, Office of Technology Assessment (Prairie Village, KS: December 1988); U.S. Office of Management and Budget, *Budget of the United States Government* (Washington, DC: U.S. Government Printing Office, individual budgets for fiscal years 1982 through 1989).

Depletion Allowance—Historically, percentage depletion allowances date back to the Internal Revenue Act of 1913 and to World War I, which placed heavy demands on the minerals industry. In 1932, depletion allowances were extended to all primary metals industries to help them recover from the depression. During World War II, depletion allowances were extended to nonmetallic minerals. In each case, it was understood that the tax preferences would likely be repealed after the difficult period ended. But when it came time to give up the subsidies, the industries fought to keep them and they have succeeded to this day.

The percentage depletion allowance enables minerals producers to deduct a percentage, between 5 and 22 percent depending on the mineral, of the value of mineral production in computing taxable income from a mineral property (subject to a limit of 50 percent of taxable income). The significance of percentage depletion allowance is that the deduction is based on production, not on the amount of capital invested in developing the property.

The basic premise for depletion allowances is that the natural resource base depletes over time, just as a production facility depreciates. In effect, a depletable resource is capital. The Federal Government provides the depletion allowance to encourage industry to undertake the risky endeavor of exploring for resources that are ever more difficult to find. Higher allowances allegedly reflect the higher costs and difficulty of replacement. These allowances help ensure an adequate supply of mineral resources to domestic industry, a factor some people consider important to national security.[47]

It should be noted that the minerals industries pay special taxes, in effect reducing the benefits of Federal incentive programs. State severance taxes are the most widely known special taxes on minerals. A severance tax is an excise tax levied on the quantity or value of production. The amount of the tax varies by State, but it can amount to a significant financial burden for a mining enterprise.[48]

Special Treatment of Income for the Timber Industry—Income from timber can be broken down into two components: 1) real income from the production of timber, and 2) income from increases in the price of standing timber. Both types of income qualify under capital gains. It has been argued that annual increases in the value of timber are no different than other agricultural production except for the longer growth period and thus should be taxed as ordinary income. The timber industry argues, however, that this longer growing period entails unusual risks and thus the increase in the value of standing timber should receive preferential tax treatment.

The Tax Reform Act of 1986 lowered the Nation's overall tax rates. It also eliminated the preferential rate structure from capital gains treatment for corporations and individuals. Even though the differential tax rate between ordinary income and net capital gains was eliminated beginning in 1988, capital gains remains as a concept in the tax law. Thus, for other tax reasons timber owners often continue to distinguish between ordinary income and capital gains.

The tax costs listed in table 5-9 seem to show that as costs for capital gains treatment of certain timber income decrease, costs for other programs, such as expensing of multi-period timber growing costs, increase. Why these increases appear is unclear. (It should be noted that the budget estimates published from year to year vary for a given year of a program, so the latest year was used. Although these data may be inaccurate, they are the only data available on the costs of these tax programs.)

The first example of a program that appeared to increase tax costs for the government was the expensing of multi-period timber growing costs. For all industries except timber, the Tax Reform Act requires that if production extends for 2 or more years, the producer must capitalize interest. This exemption allows the timber industry to distribute interest for capital costs over the entire production period. This multi-period expensing for the timber industry is not a new program. Therefore, it is surprising that the budget reports such tax cost increases in 1987.

---

[47]The National Materials and Minerals Policy, Research and Development Act of 1980 declares it U.S. policy to promote an adequate supply of materials to maintain a strong economy.

[48]A study conducted in 1980 indicated that the State tax burden can reach 40 percent of the total taxes paid by the mines examined (253).

The Federal Government historically has given preferences or subsidies for the extraction and use of virgin materials. Tax preferences are among the most visible—depletion allowances for mineral mining and petroleum production and special treatment of capital gains from timber sales.

The second program that appears to increase tax costs is investment credit and reforestation expenditures. Under this program, the direct costs incurred by a company to reforest a site for commercial production can be amortized over a 7-year period rather than capitalized and recovered when the timber is cut in 20 or 30 years. These direct costs are also eligible for a special 10 percent tax credit as long as the investments in timber stands are not depreciable. The overall cost of this program jumped from $57 million in 1986 to $210 million in 1987. The Tax Reform Act did not change the provisions governing reforestation amortization and credit. These incentives have been available to taxpayers since January 1, 1980, up to a limit of $10,000 per year, and primarily benefit small- and medium-sized landowners.

Two additional programs, not included in table 5-9, also benefit the timber industry: below-cost government timber sales and technical support from the Department of Agriculture. The sale of timber by the Federal Government has been under fire for several years. These sales can be seen as a form of subsidy because the Federal Government sells timber on Federal land at less than market value. The timber industry argues that the reason for the reduced pricing is the additional expense incurred by the purchaser to build roads to access the timber, roads which can then be used by everyone.

The Forest Service, a part of the Department of Agriculture, carries out a number of technical assistance programs designed to improve timber management. These programs include fire protection, insect and disease control, and forest management. The costs of these programs have not been quantified.

Effects of Virgin Materials Subsidies on Recycling— Several studies carried out in the mid- to late-1970s analyzed the effects of subsidies for virgin materials on recycling of secondary materials (83). These studies are dated, however, so current conditions and differences in the tax codes must be taken into account when examining their conclusions. In addition, these studies did not address glass and plastics.

In general, the studies concluded that while tax benefits for mining and timber growing did exist, they did not significantly discourage or reduce the use of secondary materials. Some studies evaluated the potential effects of tax benefits on virgin materials supply (table 5-10). The tax benefits were estimated to have affected the price of virgin materials by varying degrees. Under the most likely scenario, subsidies were estimated to affect the price of virgin paper by 1 percent, copper by 5 percent, and steel by 2 percent.

The effect of subsidies on secondary materials is more difficult to describe. Two studies on the effects of eliminating virgin materials subsidies estimated that increases in the recycling of secondary materials would be relatively small (table 5-10). In recent years, in fact, the real increase in recycling has been significantly higher than these estimated increases, independent of the tax differences.

From these analyses, conducted prior to tax reform, it appears that tax preferences for virgin materials did not significantly inhibit increases in recycling. Furthermore, the tax preferences address national needs well beyond the issues of recycling and MSW management. Any consideration of removing the tax preferences must carefully examine the costs as well as the benefits associated with such an action. Nevertheless, it is apparent that virgin materials producers enjoy tax benefits not available to secondary materials, thus creating some inefficiency in the market.

Recycling v. Other Management Methods— Several factors distort the economic environment and thus affect decisionmaking among MSW management alternatives. For instance, through the Public Utility Regulatory Policies Act (PURPA) and Federal tax laws the Federal Government has promoted the use of waste-to-energy facilities as a method to manage MSW; no comparable incentives are available for recycling. Another factor that distorts economic decisionmaking is the failure to internalize external costs of recycling, incineration, and landfilling.

Public Utility Regulatory Policies Act and the Promotion of Incineration Facilities—PURPA was enacted to encourage the generation of electricity by non-utility producers (ch. 8). Under PURPA, the Federal Energy Regulatory Commission (FERC) established rules requiring utility companies to purchase electrical energy generated by qualifying independent generators at guaranteed rates. The rates are determined by the States and are based on "avoided costs," the price the utility would have to pay if it were to generate the power itself or buy it from another supplier. In some states, these rates are calculated based on the cost of building new generating facilities.

The intended effect is to provide a guaranteed market at a "fair" price for power generated by MSW incinerators. Although these provisions provided strong incentive to build waste-to-energy facilities in the past, they are currently under review. If FERC restricts electricity purchases at rates above current costs, MSW incineration and recycling will compete on a more equal basis.

Federal Tax Laws Favoring Incineration—In addition to PURPA, certain Federal tax laws provide incentives for private ownership of MSW incinerators that recover energy, including an investment tax credit, an energy tax credit, and a rapid depreciation schedule. Along with these incentives, the availability of tax-exempt industrial development bonds also encouraged the building of such facilities by private parties. Most MSW incinerators built during the last decade or so enjoyed the advantages of these incentives.

The Tax Reform Act of 1986 substantially reduced the financial incentives (other than those accruing through PURPA) favoring private ownership of MSW incinerators. As a result, it now may be more cost-effective for such facilities to be municipally owned, since tax-exempt financing is still available for municipalities. (Despite this change, waste-to-energy companies appear willing to finance new facilities.) By comparison, it is not clear that municipal tax-exempt financing is available for materials recycling operations. If a facility recovers materials from mixed waste, it is a waste treatment facility and therefore eligible for tax-exempt financing. However, if the facility processes source-separated waste materials having value, the equipment and facilities used to handle these materials generally may *not* be financed with tax-exempt

Table 5-10—Estimated Effects of Tax Subsidies on Virgin Materials Prices and of Eliminating Virgin Materials Subsidies on Recycling of Secondary Materials

Material	Increase in virgin material price as a result of tax subsidies		Increase in use of secondary materials with subsidy elimination
	Maximum possible impact	Most likely impact	
Paper	+4.2%	+1.0%	0.04-0.6%
Steel	+3.0%	+2.0%	0.4-2.0%
Copper	+6.0%	+5.0%	0.4%
Aluminum	+2.2%	—	1.0%
Lead	+3.0%	—	0.8%

SOURCE: Environmental Law Institute, *Impact of the Federal Tax Code on Resource Recovery* (Washington, DC: 1976); Environmental Law Institute, *Evaluation of Economic Benefits of Resource Conservation* (Washington, DC: 1978); JACA Corp., *Barriers to the Use of Secondary Materials*, report prepared for U.S. Bureau of Mines (Fort Washington, PA: 1977); Franklin Associates, Ltd., "Economic Incentives and Disincentives for Recycling of Municipal Solid Waste," contract prepared for U.S. Congress, Office of Technology Assessment (Prairie Village, KS: 1988).

bonds (83). This disallowance of tax-exempt financing for recycling facilities is discriminatory and favors incineration with energy recovery over recycling. Of course, recent efforts to reduce the incentives for incinerators will also reduce the importance of this point.

External Costs of Waste Management—Failure to internalize health and environmental costs can distort the market with respect to choosing between recycling and other management methods. If recycling, landfilling, and incineration are not adequately regulated, then their health and environmental risks and costs may not be fully accounted for. As a result, management decisions could be made on the basis of information that does not explicitly encompass all of these costs. In such cases, the costs of managing and cleaning up pollutants could be spread indiscriminately to those individuals and ecosystems exposed to pollutants, irrespective of how the benefits are distributed.

Because quantifying external costs is difficult, however, it is unclear whether any one management method is currently favored over other methods because of a failure to internalize these costs. In a practical sense, then, the most that can be done is to ensure that each management method is protective of human health and the environment and that environmental regulations are designed to explicitly address all management methods.

APPENDIX 5-A: CALCULATING THE RATE OF RECYCLING IN JAPAN

As noted in the text, some experts estimate that the recycling rate in Japan is around 50 percent, while OTA estimates that the rate could be as low as 26 to 39 percent, at least for materials for which data are available. These estimates all are based on data published by the Clean Japan Center, a quasi-governmental agency that runs recycling education and demonstration projects, about the generation of MSW and the recycling of individual materials. This appendix explains OTA's calculations and why its estimates differ from the estimate of 50 percent. If nothing else, the calculations indicate the great difficulties involved in estimating recycling rates.

Recycling rates cannot be calculated unless the total amounts of recycled, incinerated, and landfilled materials are known. No aggregate data on total recycling in Japan are gathered, and calculations of the amount of material that is recycled require making assumptions about some materials, particularly steel. These calculations then must be linked with estimates about MSW sent to landfills and incinerators. As shown below, the calculations can become somewhat tortuous.

Estimates of the amount of MSW sent to landfills and incinerators in Japan range between 40 and 60 million metric tons each year. The lower figure is based on an estimate that about 110,000 metric tons of MSW are generated per day (49). The higher figure is based on a recent estimate that the per-capita generation rate may have risen to as high as 3.0 pounds per day (51).

Information on recycling indicates that in 1984 about 9.7 million metric tons of waste paper (a recovery rate of about 50 percent), 8.7 million metric tons of bottles, and 24,000 tons of aluminum cans (41 percent recovery) were recovered (49). In addition, about 75,000 metric tons of compost were produced and 220,000 metric tons of plastics were collected in 1984. The Plastic Waste Management Institute indicates that there is little recovery of plastics from post-consumer materials (170), so this plastic may have been industrial scrap. Although data are not available for textiles for 1984, we do know that 724,000 metric tons of textiles were collected in 1981 (49). Data are not available for other commodities such as non-can aluminum, household batteries, rubber, and leather. Based on the above figures, one estimate of the amount of materials collected for recycling, excluding steel and materials for which data are unavailable, is 19.4 million metric tons.

The primary reason for the discrepancy in the estimates of Japanese recycling rates is the way in which steel recycling is treated. The 50 percent figure includes steel from the residential and commercial sectors **and** from industry. OTA's estimate of 26 to 39 percent includes steel only from the residential and commercial sectors (even this has problems, however, such as what to do about junked autos). In particular, Hershkowitz and Salerni (108) indicated that 27.7 million metric tons of steel were recovered in 1983, but their analysis did not indicate how much was industrial scrap v. post-consumer material. The analysis considered 12.2 million metric tons as industrial scrap, leaving 15.5 million metric tons recovered from post-consumer material (214).

However, if the 15.5-million-ton figure is added to the amounts of other recovered materials (paper, glass, aluminum, etc.) and to the estimates for MSW generation, then the total amount of post-consumer material would be between 75 and 95 million metric tons. The steel portion alone then would comprise 16 to 21 percent of this total. Most industrialized countries, however, have a total metal content in post-consumer material of 10 percent or less, and generally about half of the metal is not steel. On this

Table A-1—Estimated Rates of Recycling in Japan

Scenarios: estimates of total MSW generation and assumptions of steel recovery	Calculations under different scenarios			
	Estimated steel recovery[b] (mmt)	Total materials recovery[c] (mmt)	Total post-consumer material[d] (mmt)	Estimated recycling rate
40 mmt MSW[a]				
5% steel, 50% recovery	1.5	20.9	60.9	34.3%
10% steel, 100% recovery	6.3	25.7	65.7	39.1%
60 mmt MSW				
5% steel, 50% recovery	2.1	21.5	81.5	26.4%
10% steel, 100% recovery	8.4	27.8	87.8	31.7%

[a]mmt = million metric tons
[b]Based on solving equation discussed in text
[c]Based on adding the estimated amount of steel (column 2) and the amount of other recovered materials (19.4 mmt).
[d]total materials recovery, plus MSW generation
[e]Based on (column 3/column 4) x 100

SOURCE: Office of Technology Assessment, 1989.

basis, the 15.5 million-ton-figure poses problems. In addition, it is unclear whether the figure includes construction scrap or obsolete scrap (e.g., railroad cars) that is not considered as MSW. This indicates the great effect that different definitions can have on estimates of MSW recycling rates.

OTA re-estimated the amount of steel on the basis of the following assumptions: 1) post-consumer materials contain 5 percent metal; 2) all of that metal is steel; and 3) about half of the steel is recycled (based on an estimate that less than 50 percent of steel cans in post-consumer materials are recycled) (49). Estimates of the amount of steel in post-consumer materials can then be calculated by solving the equation:

X = 0.05 [0.5 X + 19.4 + Y] million metric tons, where:
X is the steel (in million metric tons) in all post-consumer material;
0.05 represents the 5 percent assumption;
the figures in [] represent total post-consumer material;
0.5 X represents the 50 percent recovery of steel;
19.4 represents recovery of other materials; and
Y represents MSW generation.

Using this equation, estimates of the amount of steel in post-consumer material are between 3.0 million metric tons (using Y=40 million metric tons) and 4.1 million metric tons (using Y=60 million metric tons), and the amount of recovered steel would be 1.5 to 2.1 million metric tons, respectively (table A-1). No data are available to confirm or refute the underlying assumptions, however. One measure of how sensitive the analysis is to error is to assume that the amount of steel in post-consumer materials is actually 10 percent and, furthermore, that all steel is recovered for recycling. Using the same procedures, the relevant figures for total **and** recycled steel would range between 6.3 million and 8.4 million metric tons of steel. A potentially important source of error in the estimates is that the higher generation data are from 1988, while most of the material recovery data are from 1984. If the amounts of materials recovered rose between 1984 and 1988, then OTA's estimated recycling rates would underestimate the actual recycling rate.

Using these data, estimates of the percentage of post-consumer materials (i.e., MSW generation plus total materials recovery) that is recycled range from 26 to 39 percent (table A-1). The figures could be somewhat higher if other materials were included or if material recovery rates were higher in 1988 than in 1984.

CHAPTER 5 REFERENCES

1. Abert, J.G., *Municipal Waste Processing in Europe: A Status Report on Selected Materials and Energy Recovery Projects*, World Bank Technical Paper No. 37 (Washington, DC: The World Bank, 1985).

2. Albrecht, R., "How To Succeed in Compost Marketing," *BioCycle* 28:26-27, September 1987.

3. Alexander, J., James River Co., personal communication, February 1989.

4. Aluminum Association, *Aluminum Statistical Review* (Washington, DC: 1989).

5. American Paper Institute, "Waste Paper Utilization in Paper and Paperboard Manufacture" (New York, NY: individual yearly reports for 1970-87).

6. American Paper Institute, "Attachment B to Letter Submitted By the American Paper Institute to the EPA Concerning 'Guidelines for Federal Procurement of Recycled Paper'" 4-5-83 (New York: June 1983).

7. American Paper Institute, Paper Recycling Committee, "Paper Recycling and Its Role in Solid Waste Management" (New York, NY: 1987).

8. American Paper Institute, Paper Recycling Committee, *1987 Statistics of Paper, Paperboard & Wood Pulp* (New York, NY: August 1987).

9. American Paper Institute, Paper Recycling Committee, *1987 Annual Statistical Summary Waste Paper Utilization*, 2d ed. (New York, NY: July 1988).

10. Anderson, A.B., Asphalt Institute, personal communication, 1989.

11. Argonne National Laboratory, *Energy and Materials Use in the Production and Recycling of Consumer-Goods Packaging*, ANL/CNSV-TM-58, prepared for U.S. Department of Energy (Argonne, IL: February 1981).

12. Arkles, B., "Recycling Polytetrafluoroethylene," in *Symposium on Polymers and Ecological Problems*, J.E. Guillet (ed.) (New York, NY: Plenum Press, 1972), pp. 121-138.

13. Arner, R., "Used Oil Recycling: State and Local Collection Programs," *Resource Recycling*, pp. 22-23+, May/June 1989.

14. Backman, M., and Lindhqvist, T., "Pantsystem for Batterier," Lunds University, TEM Naturvardsverket Report No. 3489 (Sweden: 1988).

15. Backman, M., and Lindhqvist, T., "The Question of Battery Deposit Systems in Sweden," unpublished manuscript, March 1988.

16. Balfour, R.L., Rayovac Corp., personal communication, July 1988.

17. Barney, J., "Summary of Dioxin Data for Paper Mill Sludges," U.S. Environmental Protection Agency, Region 5, Water Quality Branch (Chicago, IL: Sept. 25, 1987).

18. Belland Plastics, *We Develop Plastics That Dissolve, If and When You Want Them To* (Solothurn, Switzerland: June 1988).

19. Bennett, J., *The Potential Impact of Acid Rain Legislation on the Domestic Aluminum Smelting*

Industry, Bureau of Mines Open File Report 58-88 (Washington, DC: 1988).

20. Bennett, R.A., "Market Research on the Plastics Recycling Industry," Center for Plastics Recycling Research Technical Report #17 (Piscataway, NJ: Rutgers, The State University of New Jersey, 1988).

21. Bennett, R.A., "New Applications and Markets for Recycled Plastics," paper presented at *Recyclingplas III, Plastics Recycling as a Future Business Opportunity* (Washington, DC: Plastics Institute of America, Inc., May 25-26, 1988).

22. Bennett, R.A., University of Toledo, personal communication, April 1989.

23. Biles, S., "A Review of Municipal and Hazardous Waste Management Practices and Facilities in Seven European Countries," working paper prepared for German Marshall Fund of the United States (Washington, DC: February 1987).

24. BioCycle, *The BioCycle Guide to In-Vessel Composting* (Emmaus, PA: The JG Press, Inc., March 1986).

25. BioCycle, "Composting Projects for Grass Clippings," *BioCycle* 29(5):47, May/June 1988.

26. BioCycle, *Composting Municipal and Industrial Wastes*, draft manuscript, 1988.

27. Bouzianis, M., Belland, personal communication, August 1988.

28. Braun, I., New York City Division of Resource Recovery, personal communication, 1988.

29. Brewer, G., "European Plastics Recycling, Part 1," *Resource Recycling* 6(2):14-17, May-June 1987.

30. Brewer, G., "European Plastics Recycling, Part 2," *Resource Recycling* 6(3):16-19, July 1987.

31. Brewer, G., "Mixed Plastics Recycling: Not a Pipe Dream," *Waste Age*, pp. 153-160, November 1987.

32. Brewer, G., "European Plastics Recycling, Part 4," *Resource Recycling* 6(6):18-19,41, November/December 1987.

33. Brewer, G., Earth Circle, personal communication, February 1989.

34. Brinkman, D.W., "Used Oil: Resource or Pollutant?" *Technology Review*, pp. 47-51,70, July 1985.

35. Brockway, Inc., "Specifications for Furnace-Ready Cullet," unpublished manuscript (undated).

36. Brown, R., "Iron and Steel Scrap," in *1987 Minerals Yearbook* (Washington, DC: Bureau of Mines, 1988).

37. Brown, R., Bureau of Mines, personal communication, 1989.

38. Burnett, W.M., "Methane From Wastes—Gas Research Institute Perspective," *Bioconversion: A New Technology for Waste and Sludge Disposal—Workshop Proceedings*, ANL/CNSV-TM-174 (Chicago, IL: Argonne National Laboratory, February 1986), pp. 65-70.

39. Business Communications Co., Inc., "Multicomponent Films and Sheet: Changing Markets, Technologies and Materials, PROSPECTUS" (Norwalk, CT: December 1988).

40. Business Week, "Business Week Scoreboard Special," *Business Week*, entire issue, Mar. 22, 1985.

41. Business Week, "Business Week Top 1000," *Business Week*, Apr. 15, 1988.

42. Cal Recovery Systems, Inc., "Evaluation of Plastics Recycling Systems" (Richmond, CA: July 1988).

43. Cal Recovery Systems, Inc., *Composting Technologies, Costs, Programs, and Markets*, contract report prepared for U.S. Congress, Office of Technology Assessment (Richmond, CA: January 1989).

44. Cammarota, D., U.S. Department of Commerce, personal communication, 1988.

45. Campbell, G.A., "Theory of Mineral Demand," *Economics of the Mineral Industries*, 4th ed. (New York, NY: American Institute of Mining, Metallurgical, and Petroleum Engineers, Inc., 1985).

46. Carlson, A.W., and Mimeault, V.J., "Degradable Concentrates for Polyolefins," paper presented at *Symposium on Degradable Plastics* (Washington, DC: Society of the Plastics Industry, June 10, 1987).

47. Carter, M.G., "Newsprint," *Presstime*, pp. 33-41, May 1988.

48. Center for Plastics Recycling Research, "Technology Transfer Manual: Plastics Beverage Bottle Reclamation Process" (Piscataway, NJ: Rutgers, The State University of New Jersey, September 1987).

49. Clean Japan Center, *Recycling '87, Turning Waste into Resources* (Tokyo: 1987).

50. Clean Japan Center, "Test Report of Demonstration Plant for Recycling Mercury Containing Wastes" (Tokyo: August, 1988).

51. Clean Japan Center, "Waste Volume on the Rise and Measures Against It," *Clean Japan* 14:6-10, February 1989.

52. Copperthite, K., U.S. Department of Commerce, personal communication, 1988.

53. Cornell, J.H., Kaplan, A.M., Rogers, M.R., "Biodegradability of Photooxidized Polyalkylenes," *Journal of Applied Polymer Science* 29:2581-2597, 1984.

54. Crawford, M., "There's (Plastic) Gold in Them Thar Landfills," *Science* 241:411-412, 1988.

55. Curlee, T.R., *The Economic Feasibility of Recycling, a Case Study of Plastic Wastes* (New York, NY: Praeger, 1986).

56. Curry, M., Plastics Institute of America, personal communication, May 1988.

57. Dalmijn, W.L., "Glass Recycling Prospects and Limitations," *Resources and Conservation* 14:195-204, 1987.

58. Derr, D.A., Price, A.T., Suhr, J.L., and Higgins, A.J., "Statewide System for Recycling Food Waste," *BioCycle* 29(5):58-63, May/June 1988.

59. Desk-top Data Bank, "Plastics, Edition 8, Thermoplastics and Thermosets" (San Diego, CA: D.A.T.A., Inc., 1986).

60. DeWoolfson, B., ENVIPCO, personal communication, January 1988.

61. Diaz, L.F., Golueke, C.G., and Savage, G.M., "Energetics of Compost Production and Utilization," *BioCycle* 27(8):49-54, September 1986.

62. Diaz, L.F., Savage, G.M., Trezek, G.J., and Golueke, C.G., "Biogasification of Municipal Solid Waste," *J. Energy Resources Technology* 103:180-185, June 1981.

63. Douglas, J., "The Rise of Electric Steelmaking," *EPRI Journal*, pp. 15-21, April/May 1988.

64. E.C. Jordan Co., "Pulp and Papermill Sludges in Maine: A Characterization Study" (Portland, ME: September 1984).

65. Environmental Law Institute, *Impact of the Federal Tax Code on Resource Recovery* (Washington, DC: 1976).

66. Environmental Law Institute, *Evaluation of Economic Benefits of Resource Conservation* (Washington, DC: 1978).

67. Environmental Pacific Corp., "Letter from D.L. White, Recycling Program Coordinator, to M. Steinwachs, Household Hazardous Waste Project," Feb. 1, 1989.

68. Ernst, A.A., "30 Years of Refuse/Sludge Composting," *BioCycle* 29(6):34-35, July 1988.

69. Europile, "EC Commission Proposal for a Council Directive Concerning Batteries and Accumulators Containing Dangerous Substances," position paper (Bern: no date).

70. Evans, J., "Cascades' Deinking Plant Producing High Grade Market Pulp From Waste," *Pulp and Paper*, pp. 55-57, April 1988.

71. Finstein, M.S., Miller, F.C., and Strom, P.F., "Waste Treatment Composting as a Controlled System," in *Biotechnology, Vol. 8*, H.-J. Rehm and G. Reed (eds.) (Weinheim, FRG.: VCH Verlagsgesellschaft, 1986), pp. 363-398.

72. Finstein, M.S., Miller, F.C., and Strom, P.F., "Monitoring and Evaluating Composting Process Performance," *J. Water Pollut. Control Fed.* 58:272-278, 1986.

73. Finstein, M.S., Miller, F.C., Hogan, J.A., and Strom, P.F., "Analysis of EPA Guidance on Composting Sludge, I. Biological Heat Generation and Temperature," *BioCycle* 28(1):20-25, Jan. 1987.

74. Finstein, M.S., Miller, F.C., Hogan, J.A., and Strom, P.F., "Analysis of EPA Guidance on Composting Sludge, II. Biological Process Control," *BioCycle* 28(2):42-47, Feb. 1987.

75. Finstein, M.S., Miller, F.C., Hogan, J.A., and Strom, P.F., "Analysis of EPA Guidance on Composting Sludge, III. Oxygen, Moisture, Odor, Pathogens," *BioCycle* 28(3):38-44, March 1987.

76. Finstein, M.S., Miller, F.C., Hogan, J.A., and Strom, P.F., "Analysis of EPA Guidance on Composting Sludge, IV. Facility Design and Operation," *BioCycle* 28(4):56-61, April 1987.

77. Franke, B., "Composting Source Separated Organics, *BioCycle* 28(6):40-42, July 1987.

78. Franke, B., Institut fur Energie und Umweltforschung, Federal Republic of Germany, personal communication, Nov. 1988.

79. Frankel, H., Center for Plastics Recycling Research, personal communication, April 1989.

80. Franklin Associates, Ltd., "Total Energy Impacts of the Use of Plastics Products in the U.S.," prepared for Society of the Plastics Industry (Prairie Village, KS: Jan. 15, 1981).

81. Franklin Associates, Ltd., *Characterization of Municipal Solid Waste in the United States, 1960 to 2000 (Update 1988)*, Final Report, prepared for U.S. Environmental Protection Agency (Prairie Village, KS: March 1988).

82. Franklin Associates, Ltd., "Paper Mills With the Potential To Produce Products Meeting the EPA Minimum Content Standards: Printing-Writing Paper, Tissue Papers, Cotton Fiber content Papers" (Prairie Village, KS: July 29, 1988).

83. Franklin Associates, Ltd., *Economic Incentives and Disincentives for Recycling of Municipal Solid Waste*, contract prepared for U.S. Congress, Office of Technology Assessment (Prairie Village, KS: December 1988).

84. Franklin, W., and Hunt, R., "Background Documentation For Minimum Content Standards," Final Report under Subcontract to Midwest Research Institute for U.S. Environmental protection Agency (Prairie Village, KS: March 6, 1987).

85. Gabrisch, R., "Factors Affecting the Economics of Battery Recycling in the Federal Republic of Germany," special meeting of the Recycling Subcommittee of the International Lead and Zinc Study Group, Sept. 9-11 (Washington, DC: March 1988).

86. Garcia, D.A., "U.S. Wastepaper Consumption and Export Shipments Continue To Rise," *Pulp and Paper*, pp. 114-117, February 1987.

87. Genest, W., "Used Batteries in the Federal Republic of Germany—Status and Trends," unpublished paper from Federal Environmental Agency (Berlin: March 1988).

88. Glenn, J., "Encouraging Yard Waste Utilization," *BioCycle* 29(7):49-50, August 1988.

89. Gloxin, A., Diamond-Bathurst, personal communication, 1988.

90. Golueke, C.G., "Cycles of Community Waste Composting," in *The BioCycle Guide to In-Vessel Composting* (Emmaus, PA: The JG Press, Inc., March 1986), pp. 57-62.

91. Golueke, C.G. and Diaz, L.F., "Composting and the Limiting Factor Principle," *BioCycle* 28(4):22-25, April 1987.

92. Goosmann, G., "Municipal Solid Waste Management in the Federal Republic of Germany," *Federal Environment Agency, Federal Republic of Germany, A Selection of Recent Publications (Vol. 2)* (Berlin: Federal Environment Agency, 1988), pp. 118-126.

93. Goosmann, G., Federal Environment Agency, Federal Republic of Germany, personal communication, Oct. 1988 and April 1989.

94. Grady, J.C., "Tire Disposal Problem May Be Short-Lived," *Waste Age*, pp. 34-44, January 1987.

95. Gray, T.A., "The Evolution of Scrap Tire Disposal," *Resource Recovery/Cogeneration World*, No. 1, pp. 33-36, 1988.

96. Greek, B.F., "Plastics Additives: Less Performing Better," *Chemical and Engineering News* 66:35-37, June 13, 1988.

97. Griswold, P., "Drums Back Up As Industry Avoids Risks," *Recycling Today*, pp. 60-61+, December 1987.

98. Guillet, J.E., "Polymers With Controlled Lifetimes," *Symposium on Polymers and Ecological Problems*, J.E. Guillet (ed.) (New York, NY: Plenum Press, 1972), pp. 1-26.

99. Gunn, T.L., and Hannon, B., "Energy Conservation and Recycling in the Paper Industry," *Resources and Energy*, pp. 243-260, May 1983.

100. Guttentag, R., and Arnold, H., "What is a MRF?" *Waste Alternatives/Waste Reduction and Recycling*, Summer 1989, pp. 37-46.

101. Haggin, J., "More Awareness Sought Concerning Role of Metals in Pollution," *Chemical & Engineering News* 64(36):37-42, Sept. 8, 1986.

102. Hanlon, G., Lincoln, NE, personal communication, April 1989.

103. Hansen, T. and Hirsbak, S., "Co-composting and Source Separation in Denmark," *BioCycle* 28(6):60-61, June 1987.

104. Heppenheimer, T.A., "Plastics Makers Clean Up From Litter," *High Technology Business*, pp. 30-32, August 1988.

105. Hershey, R.L., "Energy From Waste Tires," paper presented at *Wastes-To-Energy '87: Exploring the Total Market*, 1987.

106. Hershkowitz, A., *International Experiences in Solid Waste Management*, contract prepared for U.S. Congress, Office of Technology Assessment (Elmsford, NY: Municipal Recycling Associates, October 1988).

107. Hershkowitz, A., Municipal Recycling Associates, personal communication, December 1988.

108. Hershkowitz, A., and Salerni, G., *Garbage Management in Japan, Leading the Way* (New York, NY: INFORM, 1987).

109. Hirayama, N., Gotoh, S., and Yajima, T., "Recovery of Mercury and Other Metals From Used Dry Battery Cells—the CJC Demonstration Plant in Hokkaido, Japan," *Conservation & Recycling* 10(4):237-241, 1987.

110. Hoffmann, B., U.S. Food and Drug Administration, personal communication, September 1988.

111. Hoffmann, B., U.S. Food and Drug Administration, personal communication, February 1989.

112. Ideta, S., "Recovery of Old Batteries in Japan," Special Meeting of the Recycling Subcommittee of the International Lead and Zinc Study Group, Washington, DC: Sept. 9-11, 1987, March 1988

113. Ince, P., and Klungness, J., "Economics of Increasing the Use of Recycled Fiber in Linerboard," *Tappi Journal* 67(8):62-65, August 1984.

114. Ince, P., and Klungness, J., U.S. Forest Products Lab, Madison, WI, personal communication, 1989.

115. Institute for Local Self-Reliance, *Garbage in Europe: Technologies, Economics, and Trends* (Washington, DC: May 1988).

116. Institute of Scrap Recycling Industries, "ISRI Board Recommends That Industry Stop Processing, By Any Method, White Goods Containing Capacitors," press release (Washington, DC: July 26, 1988).

117. Interpoll Laboratories, Inc., "Results of the December 9 and 10, 1987 Air Emission Characterization Test at the Resource Recovery System Facility in Groten, Connecticut," Report No. 7-2468 (Circle Pines, MN: Feb. 10, 1988).

118. Isherwood, R.J., et al., *The Impact of Existing and Proposed Regulations Upon the Domestic Lead Industry*, BOM OFR 55-88 (Denver, CO: August 1988).

119. JACA Corp., *Barriers to the Use of Secondary Materials*, Report Prepared for U.S. Bureau of Mines (Fort Washington, PA: 1977).

120. Johnson, B., "Portland: First in the West to Send Waste Long Distance," *World Wastes* 31(10):21,23,26,32, October 1988.

121. Johnson, R., "An SPI Overview of Degradable Plastics," in *Proceedings of Symposium on Degradable Plastics* (Washington, DC: The Society of the Plastics Industry, Inc., June 10, 1987), pp. 6-13.

122. Joosten, J.M., "Memorandum on the Prevention and Recycling of Waste Products," The Netherlands National Institute of Public Health and Environmental Protection (Bilthoven, The Netherlands: Sept. 27, 1988).

123. Josephs, J., Garden State Paper Co., personal communication, June 1988.

124. Katzman, M.T., "From Horse Carts to Minimills," *Public Interest* 92:121-135 (Oak Ridge, TN: Oak Ridge National Laboratory, 1988).

125. Keller, J., "Recovery of Post Consumer Plastics Through Curbside Collection, Two Rhode Island Case Histories," paper presented at *New England Recourse Recovery Conference*, Rhode Island Department of Environmental Management (Providence: June 9, 1988).

126. Kelly, J., "A Guy Who Just Won't Spill His Guts," *The Washington Post Magazine*, pp. 20, 22, Nov. 27, 1988.

127. Kelly, W.E., "Measurement of Dioxins and Furans in Combustion Flue Gases: Results and Problems," paper presented at *International Municipal Waste Incineration Workshop* (Montreal: Oct. 1-2, 1987).

128. Kettle, P., and Stuart, C. "Recycling Lead: The Challenge Ahead," *Secondary Recovery of Lead and Zinc*, special meeting of the Recycling Subcommittee of the International Lead and Zinc Study Group, Washington, DC: Sept. 9-11, 1987.

129. Kieb, R.E., U.S. Steel, personal communication, 1989.

130. Kirk-Othmer, *Encyclopedia of Chemical Technology: Concise Version* (New York, NY: John Wiley & Sons, 1985).

131. Kneese, A.V., and Bower, B.T., *Environmental Quality and Residuals Management* (Baltimore, MD: Johns Hopkins University Press, 1979).

132. Koser, W.S., "European Composting Study Tour," *BioCycle* 29(6):26-28, July 1988.

133. Larrabee, D., U.S. Department of Commerce, personal communication, 1988.

134. Leach, C., Vermont Department of Environmental Conservation, personal communication, Feb. 10, 1988.

135. Leaversuch, R.D., "PVC Recycling, Landfill Fodder? It Doesn't Have To Be," *Modern Plastics*, pp. 69-73, March 1989.

136. Levasseur, J.P., and P. Mousty, "Accelerated Co-composting of Refuse and Sludge," in *The BioCycle Guide to In-Vessel Composting* (Emmaus, PA: The JG Press, Inc., March 1986), pp. 129-131.

137. Lindhqvist, T., TEM, University of Lund, Sweden, personal communication, February 1989 and March 1989.

138. Lindqvist, O., "Occurrence and Turnover of Mercury in the Environment—A Swedish Research Project," paper presented at *Elmia-Waste 88 Conference* (Jonkoping, Sweden: June 13-17, 1988).

139. Litovitz, T., "Letter from T. Litovitz, Director, National Capital Poison Center, Washington, DC, to Senator M.J. Tully, New York State Senate," March 30, 1988.

140. Lord, D., "Burnt Out Batteries," *Environmental Action* 20(2):16-19, September/October 1988.

141. Lutz, W., "International Perspective on Composting," *BioCycle* 25(2):22-25, March 1984.

142. Lynch, M., Illinois Tool Works, personal communication, Feb. 1989.

143. Magdits, L., Exide Corp., personal communication, 1988.

144. Males, E., "A Slippery Beast: EPA's Evolving Used Oil Regulations," *Lubrication Engineering*, pp. 162-166, March 1987.

145. Massachusetts Department of Environmental Quality Engineering, "Plastics Recycling Action Plan for Massachusetts" (Boston, MA: July 1988).

146. Matlock, M., Archer Daniels Midland, personal communication, December 1988.

147. Matlock, M., Archer Daniels Midland, personal communication, March 1989.

148. Mattheis, A.H., "How To Make 40 Million Tires Disappear," *Waste Age*, pp. 46-52, January 1988.

149. Mayer, M., Hofer, H., and Maire, U., "Trends in Yard Waste Composting," *BioCycle* 29(6): 60-63, July 1988.

150. McHugh, J.R., "Letter from J.R. McHugh, American Association of Retired Persons Pharmacy Service, to Assemblyman M.D. Hinchey, Assembly of New York," May 4, 1987.

151. McShane, E., New Jersey Department of Environmental Protection, personal communication, Dec. 1988.

152. Mentzer, K., Mineral Insulation Manufacturers Association, personal communication, March 1989.

153. Mereco, "Household Battery Information Package" (Latham, NY: Mercury Refining Co., Inc., undated).

154. Mereco, "Letter from the Mercury Refining Co., Inc. to Office of Technology Assessment," Dec. 21, 1988.

155. Meyer, B., Aluminum Association, personal communication, 1988.

156. Michigan Department of Natural Resources, *European Study Tour, Composting and Recycling*, report on trip conducted Oct. 10-24, 1987 (Lansing, MI: 1987).

157. Michigan Department of Natural Resources, *Market Study for Recyclable Plastics—Background Report*, prepared by Resource Integration Systems Ltd. (Toronto, Ontario: February 1987).

158. Miles, G., "U.S. Minimills Launch a Full-Scale Attack," *Business Week*, pp. 100-102, June 13, 1988.

159. Milgrom, J., "Polyethylene Terephthalate (PET) Bottles Status Report," paper presented at *Recyclingplas II, Plastics Recycling as a Future Business Opportunity* (Washington, DC: June 18-19, 1987), pp. 97-108.

160. Miller, C., Glass Packaging Institute, personal communication, 1988.

161. Minnesota Pollution Control Agency, "State Solid Waste Policy Report, A Focus on Greater Minnesota, Background Paper XII: Composting," Office of Waste Management Grants and Assistance, draft report (St. Paul, MN: December 1988).

162. Modern Plastics, "Materials '87," *Modern Plastics*, pp. 55-65, January 1987.

163. Modern Plastics, "Key Role for Additives, Upgrade Polymer Recycle," *Modern Plastics*, pp. 85-90, October 1988.

164. Modern Plastics, "Resin Supplier, in Joint Reuse Venture, Plans 50-million-lb./yr. Recycling Operation," *Modern Plastics*, pp. 22-24, November, 1988.

165. Modern Plastics, "Solid Waste Disposal Program Approved," *Modern Plastics*, pp. 116-118, November 1988.

166. Modern Plastics, "As Recycling Gains Momentum, More Resins Suppliers Get In On the Action," *Modern Plastics*, pp. 170-171, June 1989.

167. Mulvey, F.P., "A Look at Recycling Programs Here and There," *1987 W-T-E- Recycling Annual*, pp. 29-39, 1987.

168. Munts, S., "Beverage Container and Life Cycle Trends," draft manuscript (Washington, DC: U.S. Bureau of Mines, 1989).

169. Naar, R.Z., "Worldwide Recycling Technology: a Patent Perspective," *Recyclingplas III—Conference, Plastics Recycling as a Future Business Opportunity* (Washington, DC: Plastics Institute of America, Inc., May 25-26, 1988), pp. 3-8.

170. Nakane, K., Iijima, R., and Motonaga, H., Plastic Waste Management Institute, Tokyo, personal communication, April 1988.

171. Narayan, R., Purdue University, personal communication, April 1989.

172. National Association for Plastic Container Recovery, "Recycling Plastic Containers" (Charlotte, NC: undated).

173. National Electrical Manufacturers Association, personal communication, February 1989.

174. National Energy Administration and National Swedish Environment Protection Board, "Energy From Waste," Summary of a Study by the National Energy Administration and National Swedish Environment Protection Board (Stockholm, 1987).

175. National Oceanic and Atmospheric Administration, *Report of the Interagency Task Force on Persistent Marine Debris* (Washington, DC: May 1988).

176. National Tire Dealers and Retreaders Association, personal communication, 1989.

177. Naylor, L.M., and Kuter, G.A., "Metals in Organic Wastes: Problems or Benefits?" (Lebanon, CT: International Process Systems, Inc., Compost Facts, May 1988).

178. Obeng, L.A., and Wright, F.W., *The Co-composting of Domestic Solid and Human Wastes*, World Bank Technical Paper Number 57, Integrated Resource Recovery Series (Washington, D.C.: The World Bank, March 1987).

179. Ogasawara, H., Clean Japan Center, personal communication, April 1988 and November 1988.

180. Ogasawara, H., Clean Japan Center, "Letter to the Office of Technology Assessment," March 23, 1989.

181. Oman, D.E., "Waste Minimization in the Foundry Industry," *Journal of Air Pollution Control Association* 38(7):932-940.

182. ORFA Corp., "Introduction to the ORFA Process and ORFA Corporation of America" (Philadelphia, PA: January 1988).

183. Organization for Economic Cooperation and Development, *Fate of Small Quantities of Hazardous Waste*, Environment Monographs No. 6 (Paris: August 1986).

184. Palmer, J., *A Cleaner Environment: Removing the Barriers to Lead-Acid Battery Recycling* (St. Paul, MN: GNB Inc., October 1988).

185. Paper Stock Institute of America, "Paper Stock Standards and Practices," Circular PS-86 (New York, NY: National Association of Recycling Industries, Inc., April 1986).

186. Pederson, A., AMG Resources, personal communication, 1988.

187. Pedigo, B., "The Resurgence of the Bi-Metal Beverage Can," *Resource Recycling* 8(1):22-23,74, March/April 1989.

188. Pfeffer, J.T., "R&D Data Base for System Development," in *Bioconversion: A New Technology for Waste and Sludge Disposal—Workshop Proceedings*, ANL/CNSV-TM-174 (Chicago, IL: Argonne National Laboratory, February 1986), pp. 71-79.

189. Plastics Institute of America, Inc., *Plastics Recycling as a Future Business Opportunity* (Washington, DC: June 20, 1986).

190. Plastics Institute of America, Inc., *Recyclingplas II, Plastics Recycling as a Future Business Opportunity* (Washington, DC: June 18-19, 1987).

191. Plastics Institute of America, Inc., *Recyclingplas III, Plastics Recycling as a Future Business Opportunity* (Washington, DC: May 25-26, 1988).

192. Plastics Recycling Foundation and Center for Plastics Recycling Research, *Plastics Recycling: A Strategic Vision* (Washington, DC: undated).

193. Plastics Recycling Foundation, *Annual Report* (Washington, DC: 1988).

194. Pollock, C., *Mining Urban Wastes: The Potential for Recycling*, Worldwatch Paper 76 (Washington, DC: April 1987).

195. Porter, R., and Roberts, T. (eds.), *Energy Savings By Wastes Recycling* (London: Elsevier Applied Science Publishers, 1985).

196. Powell, J., "Tire Recycling Bounces Along," *Resource Recycling*, pp. 22-23,70, July 1988.

197. Pulp and Paper, "Outlook '88: U.S. Paper Industry Should Perform Fairly Well Even If Economy Slows Down," *Pulp and Paper*, pp. 52-69, January 1988.

198. Pulp and Paper, "High Consistency Pulping of Broke, Wastepaper Cuts Cycle Time, Costs," *Pulp and Paper*, p. 24, April 1988.

199. Pulp and Paper International, "Annual Review," *Pulp and Paper International*, pp. 48-56, August 1988.

200. Pulp and Paper International, "Listing of the Top 100 Paper Producers Worldwide," *Pulp and Paper International*, pp. 54-59, September 1988.

201. Putnam, Hayes & Bartlett, Inc., "The Impacts of Lead Industry Economics and Hazardous Waste Regulations on Lead-Acid Battery Recycling: Revision and Update," prepared for Office of Policy Analysis, U.S. Environmental Protection Agency (Washington, DC: September 1987).

202. Recycling Today, "Distortion in Competition in the Waste Paper Market as a Result of Government Intervention," *Recycling Today*, p. 46, September 1986.

203. Recycling Today, "Straight Talk About Strong Markets," *Recycling Today*, pp. 56-58,103, April 1988.

204. Regan, B., "Aluminum Recycling Unit Planned," *American Metal Market*, p. 2, Sept. 14, 1988.

205. Relis, P., Gildea Resource Center, personal communication, December 1988.

206. Renard, M.L., *A Review of Comparative Energy Use in Materials Potentially Recoverable From Municipal Solid Waste*, prepared for U.S. Department of Energy (Washington, DC: National Center for Resource Recovery, Inc., March 1982).

207. Ron Albrecht Associates, Inc., *Composting Technologies, Costs, Programs and Markets*, contract report prepared for U.S. Congress, Office of Technology Assessment (Annapolis, MD: December 1988).

208. Rosen, C.J., Schumacher, N., Mugaas, R., and Proudfoot, S., *Composting and Mulching: A Guide to Managing Organic Wastes*, Minnesota Extension Service Report AG-FO-3296 (St. Paul, MN: 1988).

209. Roy, N., Massachusetts Department of Environmental Quality Engineering, personal communication, November 1988.

210. Rural and Urban Roads, "Crushed Glass 'Aggregate' Used in Baltimore 3R Job," *Rural and Urban Roads*, pp. 36-37, March 1983.

211. Sabourin, D., "Wellman Plastics Recycling Operation," paper presented at *Recyclingplas III, Plastics Recycling as a Future Business Opportunity* (Washington, DC: May 25-26, 1988).

212. Sabourin, D., Wellman, Inc., personal communication, May 1988.

213. Salerni, E., "Solid Waste Management in Japan: Lessons for New York," staff report to the New York State Legislative Commission on Solid Waste Management (Albany, NY: 1987).

214. Salerni, E., Schillinger, Salerni, & Boyd, Inc., "Letters to the Office of Technology Assessment," June 15, 1988 and Feb. 25, 1989.

215. Savage, G.M., and Golueke, C.G., "Major Cost Elements in Co-composting," *The BioCycle Guide to In-Vessel Composting* (Emmaus, PA: The JG Press, Inc., March 1986), pp. 133-137.

216. Scheinberg, A., "Commingled Materials: Efficiency on the Processing Line," *Biocycle* 29(3):36-37, March 1988.

217. Seattle Engineering Department, Solid Waste Utility, *Draft Environmental Impact Statement: Waste Reduction, Recycling and Disposal Alternatives* (Seattle, WA: May 1988).

218. Selle, M., Kron, D., and Hangen, H.O., "Die Biomullsammlung und-kompostierung in der Bundesrepublik Deutschland, Situationsanalyse 1988," translation provided by G. Goosmann, Federal Environment Agency (West Germany: 1988).

219. Smalberg, K., Steel Can Recycling Institute, personal communication, 1989.

220. Society of the Plastics Industry, *Facts and Figures of the U.S. Plastics Industry* (Washington, DC: 1987).

221. Society of the Plastics Industry, *Plastics A.D. 2000, Production and Use Through the Turn of the Century* (Washington, DC: 1987).

222. Society of the Plastics Industry, *Plastic Bottle Recycling Directory and Reference Guide* (Washington, DC: 1988).

223. Stack, E.G., "Statement of E. Gifford Stack, Vice President, Solid Waste Programs, National Soft Drink Association, Before the Subcommittee on Transportation and Hazardous Materials of the House Committee on Energy & Commerce" (Washington, DC: National Soft Drink Association, July 12, 1989).

224. Stahlschmidt, V., "Can Composting Compete With Controlled Tipping?" *BioCycle* 25:34-38, March 1984.

225. Stanley, G., U.S. Department of Commerce, personal communication, November 1988.

226. Steinwachs, M., "Battery Collection Programs," paper presented at *Third National Conference on Household Hazardous Waste Management* (Boston, MA: Nov. 3, 1988).

227. Stephensen, D., "Impact of Plastics on Curbside Recycling," paper presented at *Recyclingplas III, Plastics Recycling as a Future Business Opportunity* (Washington, DC: May 25-26, 1988).

228. Strom, P.F., "A Discussion of the Basics of Composting, Yard Waste Composting, Equipment Options and Problem Solving," presentation at *Yard Waste Composting Workshop*, 7th National Recycling Congress (St. Paul, MN: Sept. 27, 1988).

229. Strom, P.F., and Finstein, M.S., *Leaf Composting Manual for New Jersey Municipalities* (New Brunswick, NJ: Rutgers University, revised edition, October 1986).

230. Swedish Association of Public Cleansing and Solid Waste Management, *Solid Waste Management in Sweden* (Sweden: Malmo, February 1988).

231. Swedish Ministry of the Environment, "Offical Government Paper 1986/87:157 on Waste Management, Etc." (Sweden: May 7, 1987).

232. Synk, R., "Tire Waste-to-Energy Technology in the USA and Wast Germany," unpublished manuscript (Atlanta, GA: Fichner, USA, Inc., 1988).

233. Taylor, A.C., and Kashmanian, R.M., "Study and Assessment of Eight Yard Waste Composting Programs Across the United States," U.S. Environmental Protection Agency, EPA/530-SW-89-038 (Washington, DC: April 1989).

234. Taylor, K., Hurd, D.J., and Rohan, B., "Recycling in the 1980s: Batteries Not Included," *Resource Recycling* 7(2):26-27,58-60, May/June 1988.

235. Tron, A.R., "Recycling of Wastepaper in the UK—An Overview" (United Kingdom: Department of Trade and Industry, Recycling Advisory Unit, July 1987).

236. Trunick, P., "Low Public Awareness Limits Supplies of Recycled Glass," *Recycling Today*, pp. 46-48, April 1988.

237. Tuttle, R., Earthlife Sales Co., personal communication, December 1988.

238. U.S. Congress, Congressional Research Service, "Degradable Plastics," Issue Brief IB88067 (Washington, DC: June 8, 1988).

239. U.S. Congress, Office of Technology Assessment, *Protecting the Nation's Groundwater From Contamination*, OTA-O-233 (Washington, DC: October 1984).

240. U.S. Congress, Office of Technology Assessment, *Wastes in Marine Environments*, OTA-O-334 (Washington, DC: U.S. Government Printing Office, April 1987).

241. U.S. Congress, Office of Technology Assessment, *Technologies for Reducing Dioxin in the Manufacture of Bleached Wood Pulp*, OTA-BP-O-54 (Washington, DC: U.S. Government Printing Office, May 1989).

242. U.S. Department of Commerce, Bureau of the Census, *1982 Census of Manufactures* (Washington, DC: 1984).

243. U.S. Department of Commerce, Bureau of the Census, "Pulp, Paper, and Board," Current Industrial Reports, MA26A(86) (Washington, DC: 1986).

244. U.S. Department of Commerce, *1988 U.S. Industrial Outlook* (Washington, DC: 1988).

245. U.S. Department of the Interior, Bureau of Mines, *Mineral Facts and Problems* (Washington, DC: 1985).

246. U.S. Department of the Interior, Bureau of Mines, "Sand and Gravel," *1986 Minerals Yearbook* (Washington, DC: 1986).

247. U.S. Department of the Interior, Bureau of Mines, "Mineral Industry Survey, Aluminum" (Washington, DC: 1988).

248. U.S. Department of the Interior, Bureau of Mines, *Mineral Industry Yearbook*, preprint (Washington, DC: 1988).

249. U.S. Department of the Interior, Bureau of Mines, "Memorandum from H. Bennett to D. Rogich," November 1988.

250. U.S. Department of Labor, Bureau of Labor Statistics, "Producer Price Indexes" (Washington, DC: January 1983-August 1988).

251. U.S. Environmental Protection Agency, Office of Solid Waste Management Programs, *First Report to Congress, Resource Recovery and Source Reduction*, Report SW-118, 3rd ed. (Washington, DC: 1974).

252. U.S. Environmental Protection Agency, Office of Solid Waste, Municipal Solid Waste Task Force, *The Solid Waste Dilemma: An Agenda for Action, Appendix A*, draft report (Washington, DC: September 1988).

253. U.S. General Accounting Office, *Assessing the Impact of Federal and State Taxes on the Domestic Minerals Industry* (Washington, DC: June 1981).

254. U.S. General Accounting Office, *Degradable Plastics, Standards, Research and Development, Report to the Chairman, Committee on Governmental Affairs, U.S. Senate* (Washington, DC: September 1988).

255.. U.S Office of Management and Budget, *Budget of the United States Government* (Washington, DC: U.S. Government Printing Office, individual budgets for fiscal years 1982 through 1989).

256. University of Lund, "How Will the Used Battery Problem Be Solved?" seminar arranged by TEM (University of Lund, Sweden) and Center of Cleaner Technologies (Technological Institute, Denmark) (Sjobo, Sweden: Dec. 12, 1988).

257. van Gemert, W.J.T., and Kolster, B.H., "Treatment of Spent Batteries," translation of paper 85-014786/GJ-55 (Apeldoorn, The Netherlands: Organisatie voor Toegepast-Natuurwetenschappelijk Onderzoek, February 1986).

258. Vasuki, N., and Canzano, P., "State of the Art Materials Recovery Systems: Options and Economics," *Energy Progress* 8(4):209-219, December 1988.

259. Vasuki, N., Canzano, P., and Pase, J., "Delaware Reclamation Project," *Journal Resource Management and Technology* 12(1):3-10, January 1983.

260. Villendre, J., Oregon Department of Environmental Quality, personal communication, Mar. 30, 1989.

261. Visalli, J., "Environmental Impact Considerations in Recycling Solid Wastes," *Journal of Resource Management and Technology* 14(4):241-245, December 1985.

262. Visalli, J., "The Similarity of Environmental Impacts From All Methods of Managing Solid Waste," paper presented at *Conference on Hazardous and Municipal Solid Waste Minimization* (Providence, RI: New England Section of Air Pollution Control Association, Feb. 7-8, 1989).

263. Walter, D.K., "Anaerobic Digestion of Municipal Solid Waste To Produce Methane," *Bioconversion: A New Technology for Waste and Sludge Disposal—Workshop Proceedings*, ANL/CNSV-TM-174 (Chicago, IL: Argonne National Laboratory, February 1986), pp. 1-63.

264. Ward, D., Hershman Recycling, personal communication, June 1988.

265. Watson, T., "Yard Waste Composting," *Resource Recycling* 7(2):18-19,52, May/June 1988.

266. Watson, T., "A Force in Detinning," *Resource Recycling* 7(7):18-19,51-54, January/February 1989.

267. Williams, T.O., and Epstein, E., "Creating Markets for Solid Waste Compost," *Resource Recycling* 7(2):20-21,56-57, May/June 1988.

268. Wirka, J., *Wrapped in Plastics: the Environmental Case for Reducing Plastics Packaging* (Washington, DC: Environmental Action Foundation, August 1988).

269. Woodbury, W., Bureau of Mines, personal communication, 1988.

270. Wool, R.P., "Center for Biodegradable Plastics," proposal submitted to National Science Foundation (Urbana, IL: January 1988).

271. Wool, R.P., and Cole, M.A., "Microbial Degradation of Polymers," draft manuscript (Urbana, IL: July 1988).

272. World Wastes, "Economics Paves Path For Long Island Glass Recycler," *World Wastes*, p. 48, March 1988.

Chapter 6

Incineration

CONTENTS

Boxes

Figures

Tables

INTRODUCTION

Garbage has been burned for centuries. Until the last few decades, the burning typically was uncontrolled (i.e., in a dump, field, or backyard drum or pit) or only marginally controlled (i.e., in very simple incinerators). The Clean Air Act of 1970 in essence banned uncontrolled burning, however, and so a new generation of incinerators came into use.

The goals of MSW combustion are to burn fuel and chemically convert carbon to carbon dioxide and hydrogen to water. It also helps destroy pathogens and toxic chemicals (178). Solid waste managers find incinerators attractive because of this and because they can reduce the volume of MSW, so that less landfill capacity is used.[1] Other advantages are that incineration does not require changes in existing collection systems and it can be linked with energy recovery processes. Newer incinerators are more efficient and they emit less air pollution than their predecessors because they have better control of combustion and better pollution control equipment.

Despite these improvements, which are acknowledged by proponents and opponents alike, public opposition to incineration has increased. People are concerned about the mobilization of metals in MSW and the creation of new chemical compounds that might affect human health and the environment. Rising costs, the reliability of facilities, and the effects of incineration on the feasibility of recycling are also concerns.

TYPES, NUMBERS, AND CAPACITY

Types of Incinerators

Three basic types of incinerators are used to burn most MSW (152). Mass burn systems are large facilities (usually over 200 tons per day) that burn mixed MSW. Refuse-derived fuel (RDF) systems generally are large facilities that process MSW into a more homogeneous fuel that is then burned. Together, mass burn and RDF systems account for about 90 percent of current and planned incineration capacity (32). Some smaller, modular systems also burn unprocessed MSW; they usually consist of modules manufactured at a factory and assembled onsite. Other processes (e.g., pyrolysis, fluidized bed combustion) are used only to a small extent. In addition, several companies have proposed incinerating MSW at sea.

Mass Burn Systems

Mass burn systems burn unprocessed, mixed MSW in a single combustion chamber under conditions of excess air (i.e., more than is needed to complete combustion if the fuel could be uniformly burned) (figure 6-1). Most systems store MSW in a pit and move it about with an overhead crane, which also can remove oversized items (152). Many mass burn incinerators, including most new ones, are designed to recover energy (see ''Energy Recovery'').

Mass burn systems are designed specifically to handle unprocessed MSW, which is extremely heterogeneous. Most burn the MSW on a sloping, moving grate (175). The movement (e.g., vibrating, reciprocating, or pulsing) helps agitate the MSW and mix it with air, and causes it to tumble down the slope; many proprietary grates have been designed. Some systems use a rotating (or rotary) kiln rather than grates to agitate the waste and mix it with air. Many new mass burn incinerators use computer

---

[1]The percentage of MSW that is diverted from landfills by a given incineration facility is probably on the order of 60 to 70 percent. Some MSW (e.g., bulky appliances) is not burned and may be landfilled. In addition, about one-fourth by weight of the MSW that is sent to a furnace still remains behind in the form of ash, which usually is landfilled.

Figure 6-1—Diagram of a Modern Mass Burn Facility

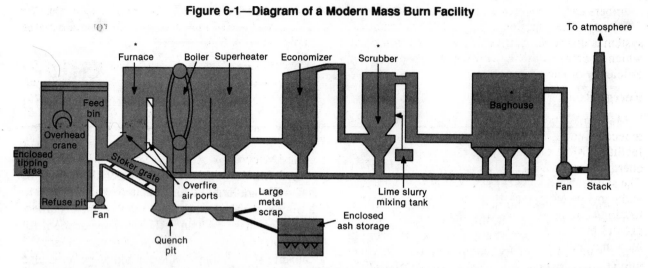

SOURCE: U.S. Environmental Protection Agency, *Municipal Waste Combustion Study, Report to Congress*, EPA/530-SW-87-021a (Washington, DC: June 1987).

systems to precisely control grate movement, underfire air, and overfire air.[2]

RDF Systems

Some facilities process MSW by mechanical means to produce a more homogeneous fuel. This fuel is known as refuse-derived fuel or RDF (152). Several types of RDF can be made—coarse, fluff, powder, and densified. These differ in the size of the particles and whether or not the material is compacted under pressure (densified) into uniform pellets, briquettes, or similar forms.

RDF can be burned in two types of boilers (152). It can be used as the sole or primary fuel in "dedicated" boilers, or it can be "co-fired" with conventional fossil fuels (e.g., coal and oil) or even wood in existing industrial or utility boilers. This can be an advantage because it avoids the need for a new boiler. The densified form is easier to handle and burns more evenly; it can even replace coal in some furnaces (152,178). RDF can be produced at one location for use at an offsite boiler, which allows for flexibility in locating processing facilities.

Boilers using RDF can recover energy (see "Energy Recovery"). In addition, materials such as steel and glass recovered during the initial process-ing can be sold (ch. 5). However, the quality of these recycled materials generally is lower than that of materials recovered from source separation systems.

Modular Systems

Modular systems are small, factory-fabricated plants, generally custom-designed to fit a particular application. They generally can process up to several hundred tons of MSW per day. Because they are small and can be modified relatively easily to handle particular waste streams, they often are used for on-site industrial and medical waste combustion, as well as off-site medical waste combustion (172). Modular systems are similar to mass burn systems in that they use unprocessed MSW, but they feature two combustion chambers and initially move MSW through the system with a hydraulic ram (152). Modular systems have attracted growing interest in less populated areas of the country.

The primary chamber of a modular system is operated in a slightly oxygen deficient ("starved" air) environment. The wastes are vaporized in this chamber and the resulting gases are sent to the secondary chamber. In modern facilities, the secondary chamber operates in an "excess" air condition to cause ignition and combustion of the gases. The rate at which the gases are inducted through the

---

[2]Underfire air is supplied from below the grates and initiates combustion. Overfire air is supplied from above the grates and mixes with gases given off during volatilization and helps continue their combustion.

chambers can be controlled to improve destruction efficiency. One disadvantage of the two-chamber system is that waste burnout is not always complete, which increases ash quantities and reduces the efficiency of energy recovery (175).

Energy Recovery

Many mass burn and RDF systems are designed to recover energy and are known as **waste-to-energy** facilities. Most operate by transferring the thermal energy from the hot gases to water in a boiler (152). The steam that results can be used to turn a turbine and generate electricity, or it can be used in district heating/cooling systems (i.e., networks of underground pipes that distribute steam or hot water to buildings and industries).

Recovery efficiency usually is based on the total amount of steam or electricity produced or the amount of energy in MSW that is converted into electricity. However, an evaluation of total net energy balance should also include the energy used for construction and operation, transportation and processing, and pollution controls.

The financing of waste-to-energy facilities has been aided by the Public Utility Regulatory Policies Act, or PURPA (see "Factors Affecting Future Growth" and ch. 8). One question, however, is how much energy ultimately stands to be recovered from these processes. Given three assumptions (that 25 percent of the Nation's MSW is incinerated, that the average heat value is 5,000 Btu per pound, and that 50 percent of heat value can be recovered and converted into electricity), a rough estimate is that waste-to-energy facilities could ultimately generate about 0.1 quadrillion Btu, or only about 0.2 percent of total U.S. energy production. The assumed 50 percent recovery probably is high for electricity, but low for steam.

Reliability

Reliability refers to the average percentage of operating capacity that is used. Vendors claim that mass burn systems have a reliability of about 85 percent, and in practice some have achieved 90 to 95 percent. (Reliability cannot approach 100 percent, because standard maintenance requires periodic shutdowns.) The newest mass burn facilities seem capable of achieving high reliability rates, based on their performance so far in Europe, Japan, and the United States. This may be one reason for the widespread use of incineration in Europe and Japan (table 6-1; box 6-A).

Combustion "upsets" can cause temporary increases in emissions. These problems can be caused by changes in MSW composition (e.g., in moisture) that affect combustion efficiency, or by failures of plant power, instrumentation, and emissions controls. For example, a failure of one portion of the pollution controls at a California facility caused a short-term, 100-fold increase in concentrations of metals emissions (66). Combustion upsets occasionally lead to the temporary closure of facilities (124). Data are not available on the relative frequency of upsets, however. Combustion problems do not necessarily require shut-down; instead, they often can be controlled relatively quickly by adjusting air supply and changing the rate at which the MSW advances down the grate. Such adjustments are easier with computerized control systems (65).

RDF systems generally have not been as reliable as mass burn systems because of the greater complexity of their processing systems. Many systems developed in the 1970s had frequent and substantial technical problems and needed significant modification; some have been closed down altogether. Nonetheless, some RDF systems have operated reliably once start-up problems were overcome (1). New RDF facilities have performed well, but it remains to be seen how reliable and economical they will be over time.

Other Combustion Technologies

Several other technologies have been used to a small extent to burn MSW, and others have been proposed. Their use in the future depends on numerous factors, not least of which is relative cost.

Fluidized Bed Combustion—Fluidized bed combustion (FBC) differs from mass burn and RDF combustion in that the fuel is burned in "fluid suspension"—entrained along with intensely hot particles of sand in an upward flow of turbulent air (122). To date, it has been used primarily to burn sewage sludge, industrial waste, and coal (108).

"Bubbling" FBC designs retain the material near the bottom of the furnace, while "circulating" designs allow material to move upward and then be returned near the bed for further combustion. These

Table 6-1—Estimates of the Percentage of Post-Recycling MSW Incinerated in the United States, Japan, and Europe, by Weight[a]

Country	Percent incinerated	Year
Denmark	55	1985
France	37	1983
Italy	11	1983
Japan	67	1987
Netherlands	38-42	1985
Sweden	51-55	1985, 1987
Switzerland	75	1985
United Kingdom	9	1983
United States	15	1986
West Germany	22-34	1985, 1986

[a]These figures refer to incineration **after** recycling (e.g., of source-separated glass, paper, metals) has occurred.

SOURCES: Franklin Associates, Ltd., *Characterization of Municipal Solid Waste in the United States, 1960 to 2000 (Update 1988)*, final report prepared for the U.S. Environmental Protection Agency (Prairie Village, KS: March 1988); A. Hershkowitz, *International Experiences in Solid Waste Management*, contract prepared for U.S. Congress, Office of Technology Assessment (Elmsford, NY: Municipal Recycling Associates, October 1988); Institute for Local Self-Reliance, *Garbage in Europe: Technologies, Economics, and Trends* (Washington, DC: 1988); C. Pollock, *Mining Urban Wastes: The Potential For Recycling*, Worldwatch Paper 76 (Washington, DC: Worldwatch Institute, April 1987); Swedish Association of Public Cleansing and Solid Waste Management, *Solid Waste Management in Sweden* (Malmo, Sweden: February 1988).

designs are reported to provide more consistent combustion because of the extreme turbulence and to require lower combustion temperatures than do mass burn and RDF systems (122).

Pyrolysis—Pyrolysis is the chemical decomposition of a substance by heat in the absence of oxygen; it generally occurs at relatively low temperatures (900 to 1,100 °F, compared with around 1,800 °F for mass burn). The heterogeneous nature of MSW makes pyrolysis reactions complex. Besides producing a solid residue that must be managed, pyrolysis also produces liquid tar and gas that are potentially marketable energy forms. The quality of the fuel products depends on the material fed into the reactor (e.g., moisture, ash, cellulose content) and operating conditions (e.g., temperature and particle size).

The term "pyrolysis" is sometimes applied to certain MSW facilities built in the 1970s with grants from EPA. These facilities generally were unable to produce quality fuels in high quantities (7). They were not true pyrolysis plants, however, because they used a starved-air design, somewhat like current modular plants. True pyrolysis for MSW management still attracts attention in other countries (box 6-B). One 50 ton-per-day pilot plant also has been tested in California (197). It uses a patented dry distillation process, with high temperatures in the absence of oxygen, to generate volatile gases that can be burned in a boiler.

At-Sea Incineration—Another concept, first proposed in the 1960s (59), involves burning MSW onboard a ship at a specified ocean site. One proposed system includes: 1) an incineration ship stationed more than 100 miles off-shore; 2) transfer of MSW in enclosed barges, with waste exchanges via conveyor and vacuum systems to avoid spillage; 3) rotary kilns designed to account for ship rolling; 4) dry scrubber and fabric filter emission controls; 5) on-ship solidification of ash into blocks for reuse on land, or barging of unprocessed ash to land for landfilling; and 6) energy recovery to provide power for operations (102).

Proponents contend this could be used when land-based incinerators cannot be sited and that its costs might be competitive, particularly in the Northeast (103). Potential human health risks should be less than those associated with land-based incinerators because of the at-sea location. However, potential risks to the marine environment would increase incrementally (171). No at-sea-incineration can occur without a permit under relevant regulations, and it does not appear that such regulations will be developed in the near future (85,171).

Current and Projected Capacity

Based on an estimated MSW generation rate of 160 million tons a year (ch. 3) and current incineration capacity, OTA estimates that incineration accounts for about 15 percent of current MSW management in the United States; this estimate is slightly higher than EPA's estimate of 10 percent. In some other industrialized countries, incineration is much more prevalent (table 6-1).

Existing Facilities

Estimates of the number of MSW incinerators in the United States vary because surveys use different definitions (e.g., some include only waste-to-energy facilities) and because the operational status of some facilities changes over time. Two databases indicate

---

Box 6-A—Incineration in Europe and Japan

Some European countries and Japan use incineration to manage much more of their MSW than does the United States (table 6-1) (also see boxes 6-B, 6-C, and 6-E). In Japan, over 1,900 municipalities (almost two-thirds of all municipalities) have incinerators of some sort. The majority of European facilities and about one-fifth of all Japanese facilities are mass burn, waste-to-energy facilities, and almost all are publicly owned. They typically handle from 250 to 1,200 tons per day (95), which is smaller than many planned U.S. facilities. However, some facilities are larger—for example, one in Rotterdam has a 3,100-tons-per-day capacity (98). Old incinerators in many countries are being closed or retrofitted with modern pollution controls.

Regulations on emissions are perhaps most stringent in West Germany (95,98), where multi-field ESPs are common and fabric filters and scrubbers are increasingly used. Sweden has the most stringent dioxin emission goal in the world and the government has noted that many questions about dioxin pathways and effects remain (98). National regulations in Japan are less comprehensive, but advanced technologies and well-disciplined workers have achieved results at new facilities that appear acceptable to the general public.

Some European (e.g., in West Germany and Austria) and Japanese facilities conduct continuous monitoring (11,95). At these facilities, information about different parameters is relayed via telephone to a centralized computer at the regulatory agency. When emissions violate a permit level or air standard, the regulatory staff can undertake more detailed monitoring to verify and pinpoint the problem.

Some operators in West Germany and Switzerland are required to undergo substantial training at schools run by the Boiler Manufacturers Association (94,95). However, the U.S. licensee of a West German company maintains that this is not the norm in West Germany and that certification is not required (76). Instead, operators learn on-site under the direction of engineers with extensive knowledge of the systems. Similarly, worker training programs in Japan are variable and are not formally required.

The increasing proportion of plastics in MSW is a concern to many countries. More plastic increases the caloric value of MSW, possibly beyond the capabilities of older incinerators (95); some German and Japanese incinerators built before the 1970s were designed to burn MSW with caloric values lower than today's typical values. Chlorinated plastics also can contribute to HCl emissions. Japanese officials feel these problems can be controlled, either through source separation of plastics or use of pollution controls. In 1982, over 1,600 Japanese municipalities separated plastics from combustible waste. However, new incinerators have been equipped with scrubbers to control HCl emissions, and the number of cities separating plastics from combustibles had declined to just over 1,000 in 1988, a trend that is expected to continue (164).

---

that over 160 operating MSW incinerators existed in 1988, with a total design capacity of about 70,000 tons per day (194,196).

Of the 166 operating facilities listed in one database, 123 were waste-to-energy plants (39 mass burn, 24 RDF, 52 modular, 1 FBC, and 7 unknown) with a capacity of 58,000 tons per day (194).[3] The remaining 43 incinerators (22 mass burn, 17 RDF, and 4 unknown) had a capacity of 14,000 tons per day. Mass burn systems accounted for 56 percent of capacity, RDF and FBC systems accounted for 34 percent, and modular systems accounted for 10 percent. The FBC facility uses both MSW and sewage sludge as fuel (122). Over 40 percent of the Nation's MSW incineration facilities were located

in New England and the mid-Atlantic region; less than one-tenth were located in the Rockies or farther west. The States with greatest incineration capacity were, in order, Florida, New York, Massachusetts, Ohio, and Virginia.

Future Facilities

It is also estimated that some 45 facilities were being built as of 1988 (24 mass burn, 9 RDF, 8 modular, 1 FBC, 1 gasifier, and 2 unknown), with a total capacity to burn 42,000 tons of MSW per day. Almost half were located in the mid-Atlantic and Northeast regions. Mass burn accounted for 61 percent of the design capacity being built, RDF 32 percent, and modular 4 percent (194).

---

[3]These numbers are greater than an earlier EPA estimate of 111 total incineration facilities (73 of which recov ed energy) and a U.S. Conference of Mayors estimate of 76 waste-to-energy facilities (168,175,177).

Box 6-B—Pyrolysis in West Germany

Three MSW pyrolysis plants operate in West Germany. One is a commercial plant in Burgau, located in the state of Bavaria, northwest of Munich. It processes about 35,000 metric tons of MSW per year, after some paper, glass, cans, and batteries are removed. The Bavarian and federal governments provided capital costs, as well as operating costs for the first 2 years. The county now owns and operates the plant, and citizens pay operating fees based on the volume of MSW they generate.

Daily operations at the Burgau facility began in 1985. MSW is shredded and fed into a rotary drum kiln, where it is indirectly heated and pyrolyzed. The resulting gases are burned with oxygen in a secondary chamber to heat the kiln or put through a heat exchanger to produce steam and electricity. Pollution controls consist only of a filter. According to the plant manager, emissions detected during tests (for particulates, SO_2, HCl, HF, carbon monoxide, total dioxins) in 1987 were all below applicable national standards (113). Ash amounts to about 16 to 27 percent by volume (40 to 45 percent by weight) and is landfilled separately from other MSW.

A small pilot plant also is located northwest of Munich, in the town of Aalen. Privately owned and operated, it only processes one metric ton per day. It differs from the Burgau facility because it mechanically processes MSW with a crusher, magnet, air classifier, and hammermill before pyrolysis. The wet organic material is diverted to an anaerobic decomposition process. The remaining dry "fluff" is pyrolyzed in a rotary drum kiln. Because the kiln is operated at about 1,100 °F, the operators expect few metals or metal oxides to be emitted. The ash is vitrified and then landfilled by itself. However, a tar byproduct might be considered hazardous under U.S. regulations (120).

Another unique feature is that the gases from pyrolysis gas are sent to a gas cracking column, which breaks down long-chain hydrocarbons (including, theoretically, dioxins and furans) into smaller fractions, and then to a wet scrubber for cooling and neutralization.

The front-end mechanical processing and the gas cracking make this system complex. The costs of front-end processing are considerable, and the quality of separation can be problematic. However, the system has several advantages, for example, relatively high heating value of the processed fuel, potential recovery of some metals, and potentially low emissions. The operators also report that it produces a low volume of ash (4 to 8 percent), but this figure does not reflect the material removed during the initial processing of the MSW.

If these 45 facilities are completed, then about 210 facilities will be operating in the next few years. About 80 other facilities are under contract, and perhaps 100 more are in early planning stages (168,194,195). About 23,000 tons per day of new capacity is expected to become operational during the years 1990 through 1992 (33).

At the same time, however, at least 30 planned or proposed facilities have been canceled or postponed in recent years, representing a total potential investment of over $3 billion—including facilities in Austin, Gainesville, Los Angeles, Philadelphia, San Diego, San Francisco, and Seattle (15,99,141). In California, where at least 30 projects were once considered, only three are now operating (in Commerce, Long Beach, and Stanislaus). One survey concluded that in 1987, the capacity of previously ordered units that was canceled was larger than the amount of capacity added through openings of new facilities (116).

Factors Affecting Future Growth

Estimating the number of incinerators that may exist in the future is difficult, particularly for facilities that are planned but not yet being built (116). Public opposition and uncertainties regarding emissions and ash management have slowed projects and probably will continue to cause some cancellations or delays (101). In addition, the nature of financing (including bond status, tax changes, and PURPA) is changing and could affect future use of this MSW management method.

Public Opposition

Although some facilities are being sited, usually in or near populated areas to reduce transportation costs, intense public opposition to the development of new incineration facilities is common throughout the country. This opposition is based on several concerns:

- potential human health and environmental risks from emissions and ash;
- whether recycling is being supported to the maximum extent possible;
- lack of early public involvement in decision-making (63) (see ch. 8);
- facility reliability and the quality of operator training;
- impacts on property values and traffic patterns; and
- contentions that sites are sometimes selected to avoid middle- and higher-income neighborhoods that have sufficient resources to fight such development (92).

Financing Mechanisms

MSW incinerators currently operating or being built represent an estimated capital investment of about $14 billion (124). They are capital-intensive, and the largest facilities can cost over $500 million. Major factors affecting total costs include size, pollution controls, differences in vendor designs, land prices, and labor costs.

Most projects are financed with bond issues, and financing arrangements typically account for tax incentives and revenues from sales of steam or electricity under the provisions of PURPA (ch. 8). The following sections discuss how financing decisions might be influenced by the status of bond issues and changes in tax laws and (potentially) PURPA.

Status of Bond Issues—According to some analysts, some major investment firms are limiting the types and availability of bonds they issue to support MSW incineration because of concerns about financial risks and liabilities (3). Other analysts, however, conclude that bond availability is not declining (71). Typically, about two-thirds of the bonds issued for an MSW incinerator are used to build the facility; the other one-third is used to cover other costs, including bonds on contractor performance. Some investment firms, however, are now less willing to bond contractor performance (10). In some cases, other contractor firms have been willing to manage this share of the bond.

The nature of financing may affect the size of incineration facilities. The 1986 Tax Reform Act lowered the amount of bonds that can be issued for privately owned incinerators and decreased tax benefits (17). As a result, some analysts expected fewer bonds to be issued. Instead, the number of bond issues increased in 1986 and remained steady in 1987 (10,196), possibly because some planned projects were grandfathered by the act. However, the dollar volume of these bonds decreased significantly, especially in 1987, perhaps indicating a trend toward smaller facilities. It may be several years before actual effects can be ascertained.

Changes in Tax Policies—From the late 1970s through 1986, private investors could regain part of their investment in MSW incinerators by depreciating investments over 5 years and taking a 10 percent investment tax credit (18,55). Tax-exempt industrial development bonds and pollution control bonds also were allowed. As a result, privately owned facilities often could afford to charge users lower tipping fees than if a city or county owned the facilities (9).

The 1986 Tax Reform Act reduced the investment tax credit, placed limits on tax-exempt bonds issued for private activities, and created a minimum tax on the interest earned on some otherwise tax-exempt bonds (17). This changed the nature of financing, which in turn could affect the ownership status of some new facilities. In particular, other sources of financing are now needed to fund equipment that cannot be covered by tax-exempt bonds, such as electricity generating equipment. As the costs of such equipment increase, financing them with taxable bond issues will require increased tipping fees to cover bond repayment. There is no consensus on whether municipally owned projects will be more cost-effective than privately owned ones.

Effect of PURPA—Before PURPA was enacted in 1978, owners of small non-utility power generators (including MSW waste-to-energy facilities, windmills, and other generators) did not have guaranteed markets for their power. PURPA changed this by requiring utilities to buy electricity from these generators at rates equal to the estimated cost the utility would incur to generate the electricity itself—the "avoided cost" (124,141,170). The Federal Energy Regulatory Commission (FERC) let the States establish actual avoided cost rates, but it permitted them to set rates higher than full avoided costs if they wished to encourage cogeneration and small power production (170).

In designing incineration facilities, planners assume that the revenues from energy sales will partially offset the cost of operating the facility. The PURPA guarantee may have been an important factor in the development of MSW waste-to-energy facilities, especially before the 1986 tax changes, but there is no evidence that such facilities would not have been built anyway, since they still could have sold electricity or steam on the open market.

PURPA has not been popular among electric utilities and has caused some problems for municipalities. Utilities feel that the law forces them to buy power inefficiently, often at higher cost, and some have argued for changes in PURPA regulations (124).[4] Some municipalities have suffered financial losses as a result of long-term avoided-cost contracts with utilities, which allow a utility to buy electricity from the city or county at a rate adjusted for the price of oil. In some cases, when oil prices have dropped, so did revenues to municipalities; because these revenues were used to offset operating costs, tipping fees sometimes had to be increased to make up the difference (165).

In April 1988, FERC reversed its position and ruled, in a case involving the New York Public Service Commission, that States can no longer impose rates exceeding avoided costs on wholesale electricity purchases in interstate commerce. The rationale given was that exceeding avoided cost could adversely affect costs to utilities and consumers (ch. 8). FERC also argued that waste-to-energy vendors no longer needed the competitive advantages associated with rates that exceed avoided cost, even though it acknowledged that this ruling might delay the development of many new projects. The ruling is being contested by the Public Service Commission.

Uncertainty in Standards

MSW incinerators are subject to some Federal regulation under the Clean Air Act (see "Regulatory Status") and EPA has issued guidance on pollution controls considered to be "Best Available Control Technology" (BACT). However, EPA is not scheduled to propose regulations concerning emissions until late 1989 and it will not propose regulations

concerning ash until Congress clarifies whether or not ash is to be managed as a hazardous waste.

In the absence of national standards for MSW incinerators, some States have issued varying emissions and ash management guidelines and standards. These guidelines change, causing uncertainty in the incinerator industry and the financing community and making it difficult to design and finance new facilities.

The regulatory status of ash is particularly uncertain. For example, if ash is regulated as a hazardous waste, disposal costs are likely to be higher. Potential liabilities from improper disposal also could be high: if it turns out later that ash was hazardous and disposed of improperly, an incinerator owner or operator might be penalized under CERCLA—regardless of whether the owner or operator thought the waste was not hazardous (161)—and might be asked to pay for cleaning up such sites.

Possible Trends

How an improved, more certain regulatory climate would affect the development of MSW incinerators is unclear. Some analysts think it would decrease public opposition and thus cause an increase in new construction (116,136,200), especially as MSW generation increases and landfill capacity decreases. Others expect siting and permitting difficulties to continue and that the growth rate of new construction will be slower (199).

There also is no consensus about trends in ownership. Most waste-to-energy incineration facilities now are publicly owned but privately operated (31). Most new plants may continue to be publicly owned, but some analysts note that tax-exempt bonds still can be used to finance facilities (even when operated by private firms) and contend that both public and private ownership are viable options (72). In most cases, publicly owned plants still would be designed, built, and operated by private firms under long-term contracts (18).

Trends in the size of new facilities are difficult to predict. Small modular facilities (e.g., less than 500 tons per day capacity) might fit the majority of local management needs because most communities gen-

---

[4]For example, utilities in California tend to oppose the purchasing of electricity from small generators (141).

erate less than this amount and because political factors may deter development of larger facilities (126,196). In addition, when new incinerators are planned in conjunction with future recycling capabilities, smaller facilities may be sufficient. In contrast, however, cost factors could motivate small communities to develop larger regional facilities that service multiple communities.

POLLUTANTS IN AIR EMISSIONS

The Combustion Process

MSW combustion involves several stages (152). First, the heat in the furnace evaporates the moisture in the MSW and volatilizes many components. In most systems, the volatile gases are ignited in the presence of oxygen to begin actual combustion. When combustion of the volatile gases is complete, ideally the carbon content of the MSW has been oxidized to carbon dioxide.

Achieving good combustion depends on thorough mixing of the waste to make it more homogeneous and to distribute air, good grate and furnace design to aid in mixing and combustion, and proper operating conditions (65,140). Three important operating variables are oxygen, residence time, and temperature. Moreover, the overall way that the system responds to changes in incoming fuel and these variables is critical.

Oxygen Levels and Distribution

In mass burn and RDF systems, oxygen for initial combustion is introduced from below or near the grate (i.e., **underfire** air) and then additional **overfire** air is mixed into the rising gases to achieve more complete combustion. Too much air can lower temperatures and decrease combustion. Without enough overfire air, however, pockets of gas that were not burned near the grate may escape the furnace without being combusted, even if temperatures are high (189). Thus efficient combustion requires properly distributed underfire and overfire air. In modular systems, the primary chamber is operated in a slightly oxygen-deficient condition, and oxygen is added in the secondary chamber.

Residence Time

In general, flue gases should remain in the combustion zone (i.e., residence time) for at least 1 to 2 seconds (20,65). However, residence time may be less important than adequate mixing because combustion is virtually instantaneous once fuel and oxygen are well-mixed at sufficient temperatures.

Temperature

A minimum temperature is needed to completely burn MSW. For mass burn and RDF systems, a mean temperature of 1,800 °F at the "fully mixed height" is considered adequate (20,65,178). This is an area above the overfire air injection zone where mixing of the waste theoretically is complete. However, these high temperatures may increase the volatility of metals and cause greater emissions of nitrogen oxides (NO_x) (178). In addition, even if high temperatures destroy organic compounds such as dioxins, these compounds can be formed during post-combustion processes (see "Fate of Substances Before Pollution Controls").

The operating temperature in the primary chamber of modular systems typically is lower, between 1,000 to 1,400 °F, depending on the waste being handled and how the MSW is fed into the system (i.e., in batches or on a continuous basis). To destroy organic compounds efficiently, temperatures in the secondary chamber need to be higher, around 1,800 °F (126).

Overall System Response

Most waste-to-energy facilities are designed to produce a relatively constant output of steam heat for electricity production (e.g., point B in figure 6-2). These systems respond to variations in fuel moisture and heat value (133). However, these responses only occur within a certain range. For example, a facility can only produce higher outputs of steam heat for short periods before harming the equipment; therefore, if the heat input is too high, fuel must be introduced at a lower rate (point A). If the MSW is too wet, some energy in the fuel will be used to evaporate moisture, so the system must burn more fuel to produce the same amount of heat for energy recovery (point C). The maximum amount of fuel is limited by the design of the grate and the minimum heat content of the fuel; beyond a certain point (point D), much less heat will be released (i.e., the boiler

Figure 6-2—Relationship Between Heat Input and MSW Throughput

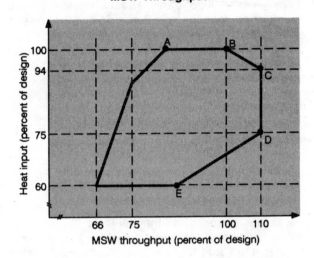

SOURCE: Ogden Projects, Inc., "Ogden Haverhill Associates' Responses to Information Requests by the Haverhill Board of Health, Set V" (Emeryville, CA: Nov. 10, 1987).

will not operate efficiently). New facilities use automatic computer control systems to help achieve greater consistency in this process. For example, one system has two independent, automatic control loops that respond to the amount of steam being produced (133). The first loop adds more combustion air in appropriate locations; the second loop senses the air/fuel ratio and adjusts the feed rate of the fuel.

General Characteristics of Air Emissions

If MSW consisted only of carbon and hydrogen, then complete combustion would yield only CO_2 and water. However, other substances are present in MSW. In addition, combustion is never totally complete and new substances can be formed during the burning process. As a result, flue gas typically contains many substances, including carbon monoxide (CO), particulate matter, nitrogen oxides (NO_x), chlorinated hydrocarbons (e.g., dioxins), other hydrocarbons (e.g., volatile organic chemicals such as polycyclic aromatic hydrocarbons), acid gases (e.g., hydrogen chloride or HCl), and metals (e.g., mercury and lead).

The ranges of concentrations of these substances in emissions have been studied extensively. EPA reported a wide range of pollutant concentrations for different systems (table 6-2). However, it is difficult to establish which data come from facilities without specific pollution controls or from older facilities. Thus the data overall should not be viewed as representative of modern facilities.

There is no question among various observers, however, that older facilities, especially ones without computerized combustion controls or new pollution controls, tend to have relatively high emissions. This is confirmed by data compiled from emissions tests at individual facilities (table 6-3). Among mass burn systems, for example, the data clearly show that newer facilities with advanced pollutant controls emit fewer pollutants than do older facilities.

Among newer facilities, it is not clear whether mass burn and RDF systems differ. In theory, RDF facilities might exhibit lower levels of metals, since some noncombustibles are removed during preprocessing. However, insufficient data are available on metals emissions from both systems to discern any differences.[5] The limited test data available also do not indicate any significant differences in dioxin emissions between new RDF facilities and new mass burn facilities.

Fate of Substances Before Pollution Controls

Dioxins, Furans, Other Organic Chemicals

Many organic chemicals can be present in the flue gases, mostly in trace amounts. Public attention has focused on two large groups of compounds known as chlorinated dioxins (dibenzo-p-dioxins, or PCDDs) and chlorinated furans (dibenzofurans, or PCDFs). Some of these compounds are highly toxic to laboratory animals under certain conditions, and EPA considers one form, 2,3,7,8-tetrachloro-p-dibenzodioxin or TCDD, a probable human carcinogen (173).

Dioxins and Furans—Dioxins and furans are present in emissions for two reasons. First, trace amounts usually are present in incoming MSW. Dioxins are present as contaminants in bleached paper products such as coffee filters, sanitary

---

[5]Some experiments show that preprocessing or curbside separation may lead to fewer metals emissions at RDF facilities (see "Separation Prior to Collection or Combustion"), but not whether these emissions are less than at mass burn facilities.

Table 6-2—Concentrations of Substances in Emissions, as Reported in EPA Municipal Waste Combustion Study[a]

Substance	Type of Facility		
	Mass burn	Modular	RDF
Metals (ug/Nm³)			
Arsenic	0.452-233	6.09-119	19.1-160
Beryllium[b]	0.0005-0.327	0.0961-0.11	20.6[d]
Cadmium	6.22-500	20.9-942	33.7-373
Chromium (total)	21.3-1020	3.57-394	493-6660
Lead[c]	25.1-15400	237-15500	973-9600
Mercury[b]	8.69-2210	130-705	170-441
Nickel	227-476	1.92-553	128-3590
Dioxins/furans (ng/Nm³)			
2,3,7,8-TCDD	0.018-62.5	0.278-1.54	0.522-14.6
TCDD	0.195-1160	1.02-43.7	3.47-258
PCDD	1.13-10700	63.1-1540	53.7-2840
2,3,7,8-TCDF	0.168-448	58.5[d]	2.69[d]
TCDF	0.322-4560	12.2-345	31.7-679
PCDF	0.423-14800	96.6-1810	135-9110
Acid gases (ppm)			
HCl	7.5-477	159-1270	95.9-776
HF	0.620-7.21	1.10-15.6	2.12[d]
SO₃	3.96-44.5	—	—
Criteria pollutants[c] (ppm)			
Particulate matter (mg/Nm³)	5.49-1530	22.9-303	220-533
SO₂	0.040-401	61-124	54.7-188
NOₓ	39-376	255-309	263[b]
Carbon monoxide	18.5-1350	3.24-67	217-430

[a]Concentrations normalized to 12 percent CO_2; note that subsequent measurements (see table 6-3) are not included.
[b]National Emission Standard for Hazardous Air Pollutants (NESHAP) promulgated.
[c]National Ambient Air Quality Standard (NAAQS) promulgated.
[d]Data available for only one test.

SOURCE: U.S. Environmental Protection Agency, *Municipal Waste Combustion Study, Emission Data Base for Municipal Waste Combustors*, EPA/530-SW-87-021b (Washington, DC: June 1987).

napkins, and milk containers and in chlorophenols and chlorobenzenes used to make pesticides and wood preservatives (173). One study found levels of dioxins in MSW ranging between 3 and 5 parts per billion (189). These incoming amounts might not be burned and instead could pass into the flue gas. This probably is not common, however, because modern facilities are capable of extremely high destruction efficiencies for dioxins and furans during combustion, making it highly unlikely that they would pass through the furnace undestroyed (178).

Second, dioxins and furans can be formed from other compounds in MSW. Three possible pathways have been suggested: 1) direct conversion of precursors during combustion; 2) synthesis during combustion from other, nonprecursor organic compounds and a chlorine donor; and 3) catalysis, after combustion and in the presence of fly ash particles, of undestroyed precursors into dioxins/furans.[6] The first pathway does not seem important during normal operating conditions (155). More research has been conducted on the second and third pathways because of concerns that chlorinated plastics such as polyvinyl chloride (PVC) are major contributors of chlorine and that catalyzed reactions may be the major mechanism for dioxin formation.

Formation During Combustion—Plastics do not appear to play a major role in the formation of dioxins and furans within the combustion chamber. This issue was studied, for example, at a small modular facility in Pittsfield, Massachusetts (129,189). Test results indicated that:

---

[6]Precursors are chlorinated, aromatic compounds with structures similar to dioxins or furans (e.g., phenols, benzenes) (140). Nonprecursor compounds include chlorinated aliphatic and nonchlorinated aromatic compounds.

Table 6-3.—Pollutant Concentrations During Emission Tests at Individual MSW Incinerators

Type & location	Year open	Test date	APC[a]	Dioxins[b] (ng/Nm³)	NOₓ (ppmdv)	CO (ppmdv)	Particulates[c] (gr/dscf)	Hydrocarbons (ppmdv)	SO₂ (ppmdv)	HCl (ppm)	References
Mass burn											
Alexandria/Arlington, VA		1987	ESP	0.761	207	20	0.0012-0.0017 (total)				Hahn & Sofaer 1988
Babylon, NY	1988	1988	DS/FF	0.206	85-119	13-15	0.0033-0.0066 (total)	<1-3	21-36		Hahn et al. 1989
Bristol, CT		1988	DS/FF	0.076-0.103	278-281	18-20			5-22		Hahn & Sofaer 1988, Ogden 1988
Chicago, IL	1970	1987	ESP	3.845		20	0.0047 (total)		2 (SOₓ)		Siebert et al. 1987
City of Commerce, CA	1987	1987	DS/FF, DeNOx	0.029 (Eadon)	116			8		11	Caponi & Carry 1988
Hillsborough Co. FL	1986	1987	ESP	0.098-0.28	322-329; 319	9-11	0.003-0.006 (front)		40-103 mg/Nm³	28-85 mg/Nm³	Hahn & Sofaer 1988
Hogdalen, Sweden	1986	1986	DS/FF		446-538 mg/Nm³	14-23					Hahn & Sofaer 1988, Ogden 1986a,b
Malmo, Sweden		1986-7	S/FF				0.007 (total); 0.011 (total)	<1-3	8-66	4-39	Siebert et al. 1987; U.S. EPA (ref. 183)
Marion Co., OR		1987-8	DS/FF	0.031-0.094	271-306	8-16	0.001-0.004 (front)				Hahn & Sofaer 1988, Siebert et al. 1987
Munich North, West Germany	1984	1984	DS/ESP	6.576			0.006 (front); 0.010 (total)		22 (SOₓ)	28	Hahn et al. 1985
North Andover, MA	1985	1987	ESP		261-294	2-5	0.002-0.003 (front); 0.003-0.007 (total)				Siebert et al. 1987
Pinellas Co., FL		1987	ESP				0.052 (total)		84-312		Signal 1987
Pittsfield, MA	1981		EGF	1.421							Siebert et al. 1987
Saugus, MA	1975		ESP	9.228							Siebert et al. 1987
Stanislaus Co., CA	1988	1988	DS/FF, DeNOx	0.053-0.058	93-113	42-43	0.0022-0.0055 (total)	3-4	3-4	1-3	Hahn & Sofaer 1989
Stapelfeld, West Germany	1979		ESP/WS	2.027			0.005 (total)				Siebert et al. 1987
Tulsa, OK	1986	1986-7	ESP	0.697-0.806	332-367	15-22		<1-1			Hahn & Sofaer 1988, Seibert et al. 1987
Westchester, NY	1984		ESP	1.623			0.043 (total)				Siebert et al. 1987
Wurzburg, West Germany	1984	1985	DS/FF	0.374-0.431	261	35	0.004 (front); 0.010 (total)	<1			Hahn & Sofaer 1988, Hahn et al. 1986, Siebert et al. 1987
Zurich, Switzerland	1978	1987	ESP	1.3-1.5			0.002 (total)			28	Seibert et al. 1987, Clarke 1988
Refuse-derived fuel											
Mid-Connecticut, CT	1988	1988	S/FF	0.027	188		0.005 (total)	<1	4	2	Boley 1988
Biddeford, ME	1987	1987	DS/FF	0.040	202	83	0.008 (total)	0.4	5	10	Ferraro & Parenteau 1988
Circulating fluidized bed											
Duluth, MN				0.12; 0.090 (Eadon)	110-168	73-96	0.003 (<2 microns)			<1	Clarke 1988
Gotaverken, Norway				0.3-0.7							Minott 1988

[a]APC (air pollution controls); DS = dry scrubber; EGF = electrified granular bed filter; ESP = electrostatic precipitation; FF = fabric filter; S = scrubber; WS = wet scrubber

[b]Dioxin measurements in terms of total EPA Toxic Equivalents (at 12% CO_2), unless noted otherwise; Nm^3 = normal cubic meters of gas at 0 °C and 1 atmosphere of pressure.

[c]"Front" refers to particulate material collected on the air pollution control equipment; "back" refers to material that condenses after being emitted; "total" refers to both.

SOURCE: Office of Technology Assessment, 1989, after references in last column (listed in bibliography).

- PVC levels were not correlated with the formation or concentrations of dioxins or furans at any measurement location;
- highest dioxin/furan concentrations in the chamber occurred at low operating temperatures (1,350 to 1,400 °F), and high concentrations also occurred at high operating temperatures (over 1,750 °F);
- dioxin concentrations increased as excess oxygen levels increased; and
- varying moisture levels had no significant effect on dioxin concentrations.

These data suggest that, at least within the combustion chamber, low operating temperatures were more important than PVC concentrations in contributing to dioxin and furan formation. Whether high operating temperatures play a role is unclear, however. The importance of low temperatures is further indicated by data from Westchester, New York, where dioxin and furan concentrations during "cold start" conditions (i.e., when the furnace was not preheated with auxiliary fuels before combustion of MSW) were at least 20 times greater than during normal operations (104). However, at the facility in Marion County, Oregon, dioxin and furan concentrations during startup were greater in the boiler but not in the stack (183,185), indicating that small perturbations in the furnace or boiler may not affect subsequent stack emissions.

One review of laboratory- and full-scale tests concluded that laboratory tests are not representative of actual conditions in large incinerators and tend to yield contradictory results (114). The same review criticized the relative lack of test data from full-scale tests, especially a lack of duplicate runs. For example, the tests from Pittsfield, Massachusetts, did not sample a wide range of PVC concentrations nor provide large sample sizes. More research needs to be conducted in field situations to see what typically happens at high temperatures and different oxygen and chlorine concentrations, at various incinerators (e.g., large mass burn and RDF facilities), and under atypical operating conditions.

Even if PVC was correlated with dioxin and furan formation, there are many other sources of chlorine in MSW—wood, bleached paper, treated textiles, chlorinated solvents, and common metallic chlorides (e.g., sodium or calcium chloride) (19,65,112)

(ch. 3). High levels of hydrogen chloride emissions, which indicate the presence of chlorine, were typical of MSW incinerators even before the proportion of plastics in MSW started growing.

Catalysis on Fly Ash Particles—Several tests (at Pittsfield and a modular starved-air facility on Prince Edward Island, Canada) indicate that dioxin/furan concentrations leaving the boiler are greater than those leaving the combustion chamber, which is located before the boiler (50,51,129). Because the flue gases begin cooling after they leave the combustion chamber, this indicates that dioxin and furan formation occurs **after** combustion in cooler parts of the system.

Post-combustion formation, which was postulated in 1981 (154), occurs when precursors not destroyed during combustion react at lower flue gas temperatures and in the presence of fly ash particles to form dioxins and furans (68,178). The fly ash acts as a catalyst, with the precursors condensing onto the particles. Condensation appears to be more frequent on smaller particles (i.e., less than 10 microns), perhaps because of differences in carbon content, reactive sites, or surface area (189). Additional research is needed on the relationship between dioxin concentrations and particle size because smaller particles may be more difficult to capture in pollution controls (see "Controlling Air Emissions") (27,201).

Laboratory experiments have begun to pinpoint actual mechanisms of post-combustion dioxin and furan formation. They show, for example, that dioxins and furans can be catalyzed from chlorophenols at 550 to 840 °F and from chlorobenzenes and PCBs at 1,000 to 1,200 °F (74,75). However, they also show that oxygen concentrations affect the outcome: fly ash catalyzed **formation** when oxygen was in surplus, but it catalyzed **decomposition** of dioxins and furans (particularly more highly chlorinated ones) when oxygen was deficient.

Other Organic Chemicals—Limited information is available on the formation and destruction of organic chemicals beyond dioxins and furnas. Several laboratory studies show that numerous organic chemicals are emitted during the combustion of polystyrene, polyethylene, and PVC (89,90,91) and during pyrolysis of vinylidene chloride, used to make plastic wrapping film (206). Field tests conducted at two facilities in Canada—a pilot-scale mass burn facility in Quebec City and a modular facility on Prince Edward Island—show that chlorobenzenes, chlorophenols, PCBs, and polycyclic aromatic hydrocarbons (PAHs) were present in emissions (50,52).

Nitrogen Oxides

Nitrogen oxides (NO_x), which are precursors to ozone, can be formed during incineration in two ways (178). Nitrogen in the MSW itself (i.e., "fuel" nitrogen) can be converted into NO_x via oxidation, depending on the peak operating temperature of the flame, chemical structure and amount of the nitrogen, and the presence and distribution of oxygen (24,189). This is known as **conversion**. In addition, nitrogen in the flue gases can react at high temperatures with oxygen to produce NO_x (178). This is known as **thermal fixation**.

The relative importance of conversion and fixation depends on the design and operation of the incinerator and the nitrogen content of the fuel. Yard and food wastes, for example, are major contributors of fuel nitrogen. At the typical operating temperature in MSW incinerators of around 1,800 °F, NO_x formation appears to occur primarily by conversion (24).

Acid Gases

Acid gases emitted from MSW incinerators include sulfur dioxide (SO_2), hydrogen chloride (HCl), and minor gases such as sulfuric acid, hydrogen bromide, and hydrogen fluoride. In general, concentrations in uncontrolled emissions are related to concentrations of elemental chlorine, sulfur, bromine, and fluorine in the original MSW (29,178). These elements are present in many components of MSW (e.g., sulfur from wallboard and tires). MSW tends to be low in sulfur and to produce less SO_2 than does combustion of oil or coal (152).

Hydrogen chloride emissions have been of concern because of potential effects on: 1) humans (i.e., through respiration); 2) the environment (i.e., as an acid gas); and 3) incinerators and nearby structures (e.g., through corrosion). Although the role of PVC in dioxin and furan formation has generated much attention, combustion of PVC and other chlorine-containing materials appears to be more important in HCl production. For example, up to 99 percent of the chlorine in PVC can be released during combustion

and used to form HCl. At the Pittsfield facility, higher amounts of PVC were correlated with increased levels of HCl (i.e., over 1,200 ppm) in the combustion gases (129).

Particulate Matter

Particulate matter is generated in two ways (20). **Solid particles** consist of noncombustible or uncombusted materials from the original MSW (e.g., metals, components of glass such as silicates, and inorganic oxides). **Condensable** particles are substances that are vaporized or formed into gases during combustion but that later cool and condense into or onto particles (20). Most metals in particulate matter are common, nontrace metals; for example, about 90 percent of the particulate metals measured at one facility were calcium, iron, aluminum, and silica (81).

Particulates are emitted if they are entrained into the flue gases leaving the furnace (i.e., they become fly ash) and are not captured by pollution control equipment. Aside from their effects on visibility and general air quality, particles are important because the small ones typically emitted by MSW incinerators (i.e., less than 10 microns) can be inhaled by humans and deposited in the respiratory system (128). Moreover, organic compounds (e.g., dioxins and furans) and trace heavy metals can adsorb onto them.

Trace Metals

Metals are not destroyed by combustion, but they can be altered into different forms depending on the metal (e.g., its possible speciation forms, boiling point, and vapor pressure) (118). Metals that have a high boiling point and do not volatilize easily are likely to become incorporated into bottom ash; iron, for example, tends to be mostly in bottom ash, although it is also found in fly ash.

Metals with lower boiling points are more likely to become entrained in the flue gas and, depending on temperatures and pollution controls, to be emitted from the stack or be present in captured fly ash. The higher operating temperatures needed to destroy organic chemicals can increase metal volatilization rates and the potential for emissions.

Some metals (e.g., aluminum and calcium) are volatilized in the form of metallic oxides, sulfates, or chlorides. Most "heavy" metals (e.g., zinc, lead, cadmium, mercury, and arsenic), however, are volatilized in elemental form (20,65). Volatilized metals are entrained in the flue gases, but as the gases cool the metals condense either onto fly ash particles or by themselves into a homogeneous material known as fume. Mercury is an exception among the heavy metals, however; it is often present in flue gases in the form of mercury chloride. Mercury chloride has a lower condensation point than elemental mercury and other metals, so the gases have to be cooled to a greater extent before mercury chloride will condense onto fly ash particles (see "Controlling Air Emissions").

The distribution of metals in relation to the size of fly ash particles varies by metal. For example, one study showed that 75 to 90 percent of lead, cadmium, and arsenic was found on particles smaller than 8.3 microns (81). Particles smaller than 1.3 microns accounted for 76 percent of the arsenic, but only 18 percent of the cadmium and 29 percent of the lead. Particles smaller than about 1 micron can be respired into human lungs (particularly the alveolar region), and particles less than 10 microns in size can be deposited in other parts of the respiratory system (128). Larger particles also can pose potential risks through food chain pathways and through direct ingestion following inhalation (see "Risks From Air Emissions").

Controlling Air Emissions

Pollutants present in flue gases can be controlled in several ways: 1) separation of materials from MSW prior to combustion; 2) destruction during combustion; and 3) removal from flue gases by using pollution control equipment. This section describes the effects of separation prior to combustion, emissions controls for individual pollutants, and the relationships among different operating conditions, pollutant controls, and removal efficiencies.

Separation Prior to Collection or Combustion

The effects of presorting MSW on incineration depend on what is separated and what incineration parameters are measured. Only limited information on these effects is available, mostly from theoretical calculations and a few small-scale experiments.

Effect on Organic Chemical Emissions—Given current information and the importance of post-combustion catalysis, it is difficult to identify specific precursors or chlorine donors that could be removed to lower concentrations of dioxins and furans. The relative importance of different chlorine donors or precursors of dioxins and furans is unknown, and the data available do not indicate a significant relationship between the amount of PVC in MSW and subsequent levels of dioxins and furans.

One experiment at some relatively old U.S. facilities showed that presorting certain materials (e.g., aluminum, iron, glass/grit, and auto batteries) from MSW reduced total, but **unabated**, hydrocarbon concentrations in the flue gases at these facilities by a factor of 1 to 4. This probably occurred because the more homogeneous sorted MSW allowed more complete combustion (159). However, no data are available to determine whether similar reductions would have occurred had the facilities been equipped with advanced pollution controls. The idea that presorting helps seems logical, but research is needed on the effects of removing various products on emissions and ash (22) and to see if these results can be generalized to other facilities, especially new ones with advanced air pollution controls.

Effect on Metal Emissions—Metals in flue gases, as well as in fly and bottom ash, potentially can be reduced by removing certain MSW components prior to collection. In Sweden and Japan, for example, household batteries are collected because of concerns about mercury emissions (ch. 5) (143). After battery collection was initiated in Sweden, air emissions of mercury from the Hogdalen facility dropped 60 percent (203); however, the facility also was retrofitted with pollution control equipment during this period, so it is unclear how much of the reduction can be attributed to the removal of batteries. Household batteries are a major source of mercury in MSW in the United States (ch. 4); programs to collect these batteries are increasing, although reprocessing of the batteries is not common (ch. 5).

Actual metal concentrations in the flue gases tended to decline after presorting at some older U.S. facilities (159). For seven metals, the average decrease was more than 30 percent, including 70 percent for mercury and 90 percent for beryllium. Results were variable, however, and chromium increased at one facility. Again, however, it is unclear what effect presorting would have at facilities equipped with advanced pollution controls. One researcher suggests that presorting may prove to be more effective at older facilities than at modern facilities (77); however, research at modern facilities is still needed.

Effects on Other Parameters—Presorting was estimated to increase the heat value of MSW at the affected facilities by about 25 percent, lower ash content by about half, and decrease carbon monoxide emissions by a factor of 2 to 3 (159,160). In addition, removing corrugated paper (which has a relatively high sulfur content) might reduce SO_2 emissions. The effects of presorting may not always be dramatic, however, depending on what is removed. For example, calculations regarding a hypothetical facility indicated that recycling all yard waste and 50 percent of plastics and paper would reduce heat value by only 4 percent (88).

Dioxins

Because dioxins and furans in flue gases condense onto fly ash particles if the gases are cooled sufficiently, they can be controlled by the air pollution controls that remove particulate matter. These controls—scrubbers, fabric filters, and electrostatic precipitators (ESPs)—are described below (see "Particulate Matter").

In general, newer MSW facilities equipped with scrubbers and fabric filters or with new ESPs have low dioxin emissions, as much as two orders of magnitude lower than older facilities (table 6-3; figure 6-3). The combination of a scrubber and fabric filter can remove 97 to 99 percent of the total dioxins present in post-combustion flue gases (65,87,112,127).[7] Some mass burn, RDF, and FBC facilities have achieved levels that are lower than the Swedish goal of 0.1 ng/Nm³ of 2,3,7,8-TCDD Toxic Equivalents (table 6-3).[8] Initial tests on uncontrolled emissions at a pilot-scale pyrolysis facility did not detect dioxins or furans (197).

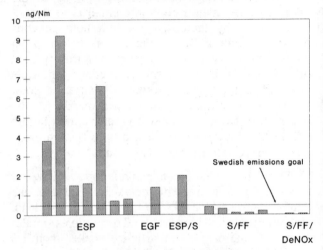

Figure 6-3—Dioxin Emissions From Mass Burn Incinerators Equipped With Different Pollution Controls

KEY: ESP=electrostatic precipitator; EGF=electrified granular bed filter; S=scrubber; FF=fabric filter; DeNOx=Thermal DeNOx.
SOURCE: Office of Technology Assessment, 1989.

The scope of available test data is limited, however, because tests usually are performed soon after construction. Little information exists on the ability of these incinerators to achieve low emissions levels over a period of 20 or more years.

In addition, little is known about what happens when a facility is not operating properly. For example, when the facility in Commerce, California, was not running optimally during one test, dioxin emissions were 5 to 50 times higher than during tests conducted under optimal conditions (139).

Several new techniques might help reduce dioxin and furan emissions. For example, some Swedish facilities are studying the effect of adding chemicals such as lime (8). Another possibility is adding ammonia to the flue gas to neutralize copper chloride, which may be important in the catalysis of dioxins and furans on fly ash (75,192). However, some facilities that add ammonia (e.g., Commerce, California) exhibit similar dioxin concentrations as do facilities without this feature (e.g., Marion County, Oregon, and Bristol, Connecticut). Some analysts suggest that fluidized bed gasification of

---

[7]Data from a pilot-scale facility in Quebec City, Canada, indicate that scrubbers and filters also can exhibit high removal efficiencies (over 99 percent, depending on the flue gas temperatures) for other organic chemicals such as chlorobenzenes and polycyclic aromatic hydrocarbons (52).

[8]The compound 2,3,7,8-TCDD is considered to be the most toxic dioxin. The toxicities of other dioxins usually are compared with 2,3,7,8-TCDD and expressed as "Toxic Equivalents" (173). However, there are several methods of calculating Toxic Equivalents. The Swedish goal is based on the "Eadon Method." The equivalent goal when calculated by the "EPA Method" is 0.2 ng/Nm³.

RDF may result in dioxin emissions that are only a fraction of the Swedish goals (112,153,154). This technology, developed for coal gasification into synfuels, converts RDF into a low-Btu gas that is cleaned in a scrubber and burned to generate electricity.

Nitrogen Oxides

Typical **uncontrolled** emissions of nitrogen oxides (NO_x) from mass burn facilities range from 200 to 370 ppm (table 6-3). Based on limited data, emissions from RDF facilities appear to be around 200 ppm or less and perhaps are even lower for FBC facilities. Among mass burn plants, higher combustion efficiencies result in lower emissions of organic chemicals such as dioxins and slightly more conversion of fuel-bound nitrogen into NO_x (178). In general, NO_x emissions tend to decrease during colder months because the MSW contains less yard waste (and therefore less fuel nitrogen). This suggests that separating yard wastes prior to combustion could help control NO_x (24).

Three types of controls have been demonstrated at full-scale MSW facilities, although they are used only at a few locations. Combustion modification and Thermal DeNOx work during combustion, while selective catalytic reduction works after combustion. These controls are capable of reducing NO_x levels to below 100 ppm in some cases (table 6-3). In addition, wet scrubbing is being explored as a way of controlling NO_x. (See ref. 24 for more information on existing and emerging technologies.)

Combustion modification means changing design and operating features to avoid conversion of elemental nitrogen to NO_x. Typical modifications include:

- changing grate and furnace design to enhance combustion;
- varying the speed of MSW input to dampen changes in Btu values;
- automatic computer controls;
- auxiliary burners in the furnace;
- two chambers, with starved air conditions in the primary chamber; and
- using fluidized bed incinerators, at temperatures lower than those used in mass burn

Photo credit: Office of Technology Assessment

Emissions of nitrogen oxides, which are precursors to ozone, can be reduced by separating yard wastes prior to combustion and by using pollution controls. Shown here is the catalyst from a selective catalytic reduction system, currently used in Japan but not in the United States.

incinerators, to decrease the chance of thermal fixation (21,24).

A variation, **flue gas recirculation**, involves injecting the cooler gases leaving the boiler back into the combustion chamber to reduce operating temperatures. Tests at a Tokyo, Japan, facility showed a 25 percent removal rate, while tests at the mass burn facility in Long Beach, California, showed a 10 to 20 percent removal rate (21,24). Similar results were reported from a small modular facility in Rutland, Vermont, during performance tests, but not during subsequent compliance tests.

Selective catalytic reduction (SCR) involves injecting ammonia (NH_3) into the flue gases just before they enter a metal-based catalyst (box 6-C). The NH_3 reacts with nitrogen oxide gases to form nitrogen, thus precluding NO_x emissions, and the catalyst enables the reactions to occur at lower temperatures (178). SCR can potentially reduce NO_x by over 70 percent; Mitsubishi, for example, will guarantee NO_x removal efficiency of 70 to 85 percent for MSW facilities in Europe, depending on the local requirements for NO_x reduction. SCR has not been used in the United States.

Thermal DeNOx is a form of selective noncatalytic reduction that involves injecting NH_3 into the upper furnace, where it reacts with NO and NO_2 to produce nitrogen and water.[9] Three California facilities use this method (Commerce, Long Beach, and Stanislaus). The Commerce facility has achieved an average of 45 percent NO_x removal (16). Thermal DeNOx and SCR systems are compared in box 6-C. Another selective noncatalytic reduction method in the early stages of commercialization is the injection of urea into the furnace and boiler (23,24). The potential advantages are that urea is less toxic than ammonia and that liquid urea mixes more readily than gaseous ammonia with the NO_x.

Acid Gases

Acid gases cause corrosion of internal furnace components, a major problem in early MSW incinerators, and they also can contribute to air quality problems (e.g., corrosion of buildings and acid rain). They can be controlled with ''scrubbers,'' which add alkaline reagents that react with the gases to form salts that are then collected and landfilled (65).

Wet, dry, and spray dry scrubbers add the reagent after the boiler (see figure 6-1). With dry injection, the reagent is added into or before the boiler. In general, spray dry and dry scrubbers have several advantages over wet scrubbers: they do not require wastewater treatment and they reduce corrosion and energy consumption (20). However, these scrubbers are relatively new and research is needed on their long-term effectiveness. Some observers suggest that wet scrubbers may be appropriate in modular facilities that operate on a batch basis (e.g., for medical waste) (126). Others note that dry injection may be well-suited for retrofitting facilities because it tends to be less costly than retrofitting with other scrubbers (56). Hydrogen Chloride

Wet scrubbers use a liquid, alkaline absorbent. Under optimal conditions, they can remove about 95 percent of HCl and 85 percent of SO_2 (20). They use less reagent but much more water than do dry scrubbers; this necessitates de-watering of residues and subsequent wastewater treatment. They also can be affected by corrosion, so corrosion-resistant materials are needed in duct work, tanks, and other equipment (56). In addition, because wet scrubbing may cool the flue gases to as low as 120 °F, plumes leaving the stack do not rise very high, leading to increased ground-level concentrations of pollutants. Reheating is needed to get more dispersion and comply with ambient air quality regulations (76).

Flue-gas condensation, a related technology that has been used in combination with ESPs in Europe, involves reducing flue gas temperatures to as low as about 100 °F by direct contact with water droplets or by a heat exchanger (20,65). Theoretically, this results in condensation of acid gases, as well as organic chemicals and volatile metals, onto particles that can be collected (20).

Dry scrubbers inject lime in a dry state into the flue gases. They use more reagent than wet scrubbers but do not have wastewater problems. At one facility in Claremont, New Hampshire, removal efficiencies for HCl and SO_x were reported to be 90 and 70 percent, respectively.

Spray dry (or wet-dry or semi-dry) scrubbers spray an atomized liquid such as a lime slurry into the flue gases; the water evaporates, leaving only dry particles (16,65). The process reduces flue gas temperatures below 300 °F, which aids in removing acid gases and causes some organic chemicals and metals to condense on particulate matter. These can then be collected by particulate controls (20,65). Removal efficiencies for HCl and SO_2 are high under optimal conditions. At the Commerce, California, facility, removal of HCl and SO_x averaged 98.8 percent; at the Munich North facility in West Germany, removal of HCl and SO_x averaged 95 and

---

[9]''Thermal DeNOx'' was developed by Mitsubishi Heavy Industries in Japan and licensed in the United States to the Exxon Corp. (21).

76 percent, respectively. However, if flue gas temperatures drop too low, condensation and subsequent wetting of the particles and, in some cases, clogging of the sprayer, can occur.

Dry (or furnace sorbent) injection systems inject a dry absorbent such as lime powder into the boiler or the original MSW, prior to production of flue gases (56). This avoids the use of water and excessive cooling of the flue gases (22). However, because the gases are not cooled, there is no additional control of metals or dioxins via condensation on particles. Dry injection systems have been used at about 50 facilities in Japan and at least one facility each in Canada and Sweden (65). At a circulating fluidized bed incinerator in Sweden, fueled with RDF and equipped an ESP, HCl was reduced by 77 to 94 percent during tests in 1986 (122).[10] After the ESP was replaced with a fabric filter, both HCl and SO_2 were reduced by about 95 percent during tests in 1988 (2). However, excessive lime injection also caused an increase in NO_x emissions.

Particulate Matter

After combustion, some particles become incorporated in bottom ash while others are entrained in the rising flue gases. One way to increase the portion in the bottom ash is to reduce the vertical velocity of air introduced from below the grate (i.e., underfire air). This may be most possible in modular facilities, which use less air in the primary chamber (22). Once particles become entrained in the flue gases, however, the primary control method is to remove them (along with metals and other substances that have condensed onto them) with a collection device positioned near the end of the incinerator. Two devices are common: electrostatic precipitators and fabric filters (i.e., baghouses).

Electrostatic precipitators (ESPs) electrically charge particles and pass them between parallel plates of opposite charge so that the particles are drawn to the plates (65). The plates are shaken periodically and the particles fall into hoppers. ESP removal efficiency is greatest when the surface area of the plates is large and flue gas velocity is slow (65). Newer ESPs with 3 to 5 fields of plates appear

to perform more efficiently than 2-field ESPs. For example, 7 of 15 facilities with 3- and 4-field ESPs achieved emissions levels of less than 0.01 grains per dry standard cubic foot (gr/dscf) during emissions tests conducted from 1984 to 1988 (20). At the Pinellas, Florida, facility, removal efficiencies were greater than 99.7 percent during emissions tests (158).

Fabric filters or baghouses consist of an array of cylindrical bags, through which the flue gases are filtered (65). In most systems, the layer of dust or "cake" that builds up on the bags increases the efficiency with which particles are collected, but only to a point: too much cake lowers efficiency. In general, removal efficiencies are enhanced if flue gas temperatures are lowered before reaching the filters (20).

Combining a fabric filter with a dry or spray dry scrubber is particularly effective. The scrubber reduces acid gases (which degrade the baghouse), reduces "blinding" of the baghouse by wet particles, and cools the gases, while the filter cake helps absorb particles (20,65). During tests conducted from 1984 to 1988, 15 of 17 facilities with this combination had emissions below 0.010 gr/dscf, and all had emissions below 0.011 gr/dscf (22). In some cases, emissions were reduced to below 0.005 gr/dscf, with a removal efficiency of over 99.99 percent (table 6-3) (65,84,127). Whether these levels can be maintained consistently is unknown. In addition, if the temperature in the baghouse is too low, then calcium chloride formed in the scrubber will condense, which can increase blinding (56).

Particle Size, ESPs, and Filters—Some analysts contend that fabric filters are more efficient than ESPs in collecting particles smaller than 2 microns (i.e., ones that penetrate most easily into the lungs) and that they are not as sensitive to changes in flue gas volumes and velocities (20,65,87,112,178). For example, data from the 1970s indicate that 98 percent of particles over 2 microns, but only about 93 percent of those smaller than 2 microns, were captured by ESPs (21).

Research on coal-fired plants showed that fabric filters generally had greater removal efficiencies

---

[10]Because these facilities typically use limestone particles in the fluid bed to help distribute heat evenly, some of the reported neutralization of acid gases might result from this design feature rather than the dry injection process.

Box 6-C—Selective Catalytic Reduction

Selective catalytic reduction (SCR) is a technology capable of removing more than 70 percent of the NO_x normally emitted from MSW incinerators. It involves injecting ammonia (NH_3) into the flue gas just before the gas enters a special catalyst. The NH_3 reacts with nitrogen oxide gases (NO and NO_2) to form nitrogen and water instead of NO_x. The catalyst enables these reactions to occur at lower temperatures (178).

SCR is used at two Japanese facilities. The Iwatsuki facility opened in 1987, while the Tokyo facility opened in 1983 and was retrofitted with SCR in 1987. The Iwatsuki facility is small, with a capacity of 130 tons per day, and is equipped with a dry scrubber, fabric filter, and SCR system. The SCR system was installed in anticipation of future lower national NO_x standards and to meet local public demands. Fly and bottom ash—about 15 percent by weight of the original MSW—are mixed with sludge from the facility's wastewater plant, then mixed with cement and sent to a lined monofill.

Emissions Control and Catalyst Efficiency at Iwatsuki

SCR removed 80 percent of NO_x during initial testing at Iwatsuki (167). According to Mitsubishi Heavy Industries (MHI), the SCR manufacturer and plant designer, the system currently removes 50 to 60 percent, with NO_x concentrations of 30 to 60 ppm, because the municipality only requires that level. These emissions are lower than typical NO_x emissions from U.S. facilities, which tend to have higher uncontrolled levels of NO_x to begin with, and lower than emissions at facilities using Thermal DeNOx (204). According to MHI, operating at a lower control level requires less NH_3 and reduces operating costs.

A potential problem with catalysts in general is that they become less efficient over time, due to "poisoning" with alkaline metals or "blinding" with particulate matter (76). MHI calculated that catalyst activity at Iwatsuki had decreased by only 1 to 2 percent after one year of operation, and it expects the catalyst to function efficiently until activity has been reduced by 20 to 30 percent.[1]

Another potential disadvantage is the presence of white plumes caused by ammonia "slip." Slip occurs when excess NH_3 and HCl are released from the stack as gases and react in the atmosphere to form NH_4Cl, which is visible at concentrations greater than 10 ppm. At Iwatsuki, this is avoided by carefully controlling the rate of NH_3 injection. According to MHI, 80 percent NO_x removal without ammonia slip can be achieved by injecting 2 kg per hour.

Using SCR at U.S. Facilities

Deciding to use SCR at U.S. facilities hinges on: 1) the need to reheat the flue gases, and the costs of doing so; 2) capital and operating costs of SCR itself; 3) long-term performance; and 4) local NO_x requirements.

Reheating Flue Gases—Most Japanese incinerators are small and they use the heat they produce for local steam heating (e.g., for greenhouses and community swimming pools) rather than electricity generation. Flue gases typically exit the boiler at 600 to 700 °F, are cooled, and pass through a fabric filter. At Iwatsuki, the gases then pass through the SCR at a temperature above 430 °F, the temperature required to operate the catalyst efficiently.

In contrast, most large U.S. facilities produce electricity. In these facilities, the flue gases would be too cool to operate efficiently when they reached an SCR system and would require reheating. This is because the gases leave the boiler, pass through economizers or other heat exchangers to convert heat into electricity, and then exit the economizer well below 430 °F (76). Additional cooling to around 300 °F prior to entering the scrubber and filter is required by some States (e.g., New York), primarily because the controls operate more efficiently at those temperatures. MHI's configuration for a proposed California facility required that the SCR be placed **after** a scrubber and filter, in part to reduce blinding and poisoning by metals.

MHI also would guarantee the proposed SCR system only if flue gas temperatures entering the catalyst were 428 °F or higher at all times. Because the flue gases would be cooler than 430 °F before they reached the SCR, they would have to be reheated with an auxiliary burner. After passing through the SCR, the gases then would have to be recooled to less than 300 °F prior to emission (but not less than 270 °F, to avoid formation of $CaCl_2$). This reheating and recooling adds to total costs.

An alternative is to place the SCR right after the boiler, which would eliminate the need for reheating. This might cause problems with blinding of the catalyst, but MHI used a similar arrangement at its Tokyo plant, where the SCR is placed after an ESP but before a wet scrubber (109). In this situation, reheating was not necessary.

Capital and Operating Costs—The SCR system at Iwatsuki cost approximately about $570,000, or $4,400 per ton of capacity.[2] For comparison, the fabric filter system had capital costs of about $3.4 million, or $26,000 per ton of capacity. Operating costs for the SCR consist of the cost of ammonia, about $32,000 annually (about $240 per ton of capacity). According to MHI, initial costs for new plants and retrofitting costs for old plants are similar, assuming space is available.

Capital costs for a system with the SCR placed after a scrubber and filter are greater than if the SCR is placed nearer the boiler because of the extra equipment needed to reheat and recool the flue gases. The cost of a complete SCR system at the proposed California facility was estimated, in 1987, to be about $13 million (76). The SCR catalyst was to cost $7.6 million; auxiliary equipment (burners, etc.) $0.5 million; ductwork and support steel $1.65 million; and construction $3.3 million. This would have increased the capital cost of the entire facility by about 8 percent. The additional operating costs for the SCR system were estimated to be roughly $150,000 per year.

Long-Term Catalyst Performance—Data on catalyst performance at MSW incinerators are limited to pilot tests from Tokyo and one year of operating data from Iwatsuki. In the pilot test, the catalysts were sampled periodically at different temperatures and NH_3/NO_x ratios. About 80 percent NO_x reduction was achieved for 2,000 hours of operation (the length of the test) (167). The plant now has operated for a total of 16,000 hours with 80 percent removal efficiency (110). As noted above, the SCR system at Iwatsuki exhibited a decrease in activity of only 1 to 2 percent after one year of operation, and MHI expects it to function efficiently until activity has been reduced by 20 to 30 percent.

Whether the current rate of decrease will continue is unknown. Although it looks promising, the SCR system at Iwatsuki has only been operating for 2 years. In addition to normal gradual decreases in activity, catalysts can be degraded suddenly by thermal shocks (e.g., from startups and shutdowns) (76). MHI, however, does not consider this to be important.

Local NO_x Controls: SCR or Thermal DeNOx?—The value of SCR at U.S. facilities would depend on local air quality standards. If the objective is to maximize NO_x removal, then SCR is the best technology available. However, if the objective is to meet established standards for NO_x, then other controls, particularly Thermal DeNOx, can be used at less expense. Under typical operating conditions, Thermal DeNOx can reduce NO_x by about 40 percent. At the Commerce, California, facility, for example, tests show an average removal rate of 44.5 percent; a rate as high as 60 percent was achieved when NH_3 was injected at a slightly greater rate (16). In all tests, ammonia slip was reduced by particulate controls (spray dryer and baghouse) to less than 3 ppm.

Thus Thermal DeNOx removes less NO_x than SCR. It also constrains reactions to a smaller temperature range (1,700 to 1,800 °F) (16), and so requires greater control over operating conditions. However, the capital and operating costs of Thermal DeNOx are considerably lower. The capital costs of the system at Commerce were approximately $250,000 (about $660 per ton of design capacity) (204). Operating costs also are relatively low; a compressor costs about $100,000 annually and ammonia injection costs are only about $2 to $3 per day.

Despite the lower costs of Thermal DeNox, SCR still may be appropriate in some situations. For example, Clean Air Act regulations state that new plants cannot make additional measurable impacts when an area already is in violation of annual and hourly standards for NO_2. In southern California, which already violates these standards, the South Coast Air Quality District defines the measurable impact for NO_2 as 19 mg/Nm^3. After estimating that Thermal DeNOx would reduce the measurable impact to between 50 and 100 mg/Nm^3, Ogden Martin Systems, Inc., suggested using an SCR system at a proposed MSW incinerator.

---

[1]Another SCR manufacturer, Takuma Industries, also concluded that reduction of catalyst efficiency by metals was not yet a problem; the Takuma Hamamatsu facility showed NO_x reductions from 150 to 45 ppm during emissions testing.

[2]Conversions into U.S. dollars are based on exchange rate of 125 yen/dollar.

than ESPs (111). However, that research also showed that an ESP combined with a scrubber exhibited better removal than the fabric filter. The investigators concluded that both systems could achieve low levels of particulate emissions. Other investigators also contend that fabric filters are sensitive to changes in flue gas volumes and velocities, for example, that increased gas volumes would increase the pressure within the bag and cause more particles to migrate through it (56).

Trace Metals

Most volatilized metals condense at temperatures below 570 °F. When flue gases are cooled below this temperature, many of the metals will condense, usually onto fly ash particles. These can be collected by ESPs or baghouses. High, but in some instances variable, removal efficiencies have been reported for most metals (except mercury):

- over 99 percent removal of 26 metals at Quebec City, Canada (equipped with scrubber/filter) (52);
- over 99 percent of 12 metals at a Japanese facility with a baghouse (30);
- 98 percent of cadmium, lead, and zinc at a German facility with a spray dry scrubber/ESP system (20);
- over 99.7 percent for chromium and cadmium, 98.6 percent for lead, and 23.0 to 89.7 percent for nickel, at Marion County, Oregon (183); and
- between 88.4 and 99.9 percent for 12 metals at Commerce, California, with all but lead below detection limits (16).

Mercury and mercury chloride have lower condensation points than other metals, but if temperatures are low enough some will condense onto particles and be removed by particulate controls. Limited test data indicate that as temperatures decrease below 285 °F, mercury removal tends to increase. For example, removal efficiencies ranged between 91 and 97 percent at temperatures of 230 to 284 °F at the Quebec City, Canada, facility, but no removal occurred when temperatures were over 390 °F (52). In contrast, no removal was detected at the Commerce, California, facility even when flue gas temperatures were around 270 °F (16). At the Bristol, Connecticut, facility, mercury emissions were about 10 times lower than permit levels (134).

No significant difference appears to exist between the capability of new ESP-based systems and scrubber/filter systems to remove most metals. In general, flue gas temperatures appear to have a greater effect than the type of control technology (52,118). However, scrubbers may be more effective in removing mercury; much of the mercury in flue gases is mercury chloride, and the lime used in scrubbers may react with this compound and increase removal rates (21).

Failures in even small parts of pollution control equipment can have dramatic short-term effects. At the Commerce, California, facility, for example, several metals (arsenic, cadmium, lead, mercury, and zinc) showed a 10- to 100-fold increase in emissions when one bag in the baghouse fell from its supports during a test (139).

Analytical and Monitoring Problems

Several sampling and analytical problems constrain emissions measurements. The concentrations of many pollutants are so low that they are at "detection limits"—i.e., they are lower than what current technologies are capable of measuring. Whether the expense of continuing to look for pollutants in such low concentrations is worthwhile is the subject of considerable debate and probably is not resolvable on technical grounds.

Another problem is the inherent variability in measurements. Even at the same facility and with the same technologies, results of different replicate runs have varied by a factor of 3 or more (157). This makes it difficult to compare results between replicate measurements (189). In addition, measurements of flow rate, which are used in calculating mass emissions (e.g., pounds emitted per hour), can vary by as much as 30 percent (76). Furthermore, some sampling methods developed for other situations may not be appropriate for MSW incinerators; for example, sulfuric acid may be difficult to measure with the standard EPA method, developed for sulfuric acid plants, because HCl acts like a sulfuric acid mist in the method and interferes with the measurement (135).

Monitoring With Indicator Parameters

The efficiency of a combustion system is often estimated by measuring, on a continuous basis, "surrogate" parameters that indicate whether the system is operating within a desired range of conditions. In contrast, actual combustion efficiency and emissions are rarely measured directly (65).

Carbon monoxide (CO) is one of the most common surrogate parameters. It is readily monitored on a continuous basis and its concentration reflects the completeness of oxidation. However, there is no established correlation between low CO levels and destruction and removal efficiency (112,129). For example, CO readings may rise or "spike" during short upsets without substantial increases in hydrocarbon or other organic emissions. For this reason, time-averaged CO readings are used to filter out the effect of spikes. Alternatively, low CO emissions may mask short-lived, low-temperature pathways that allow some dioxin and furan formation. However, CO readings over 100 ppm generally are considered to be a good indicator of incomplete combustion (65,112,129,154,189). Quantitative relationships tend to be unique to each facility.

Continuous monitoring of ambient air quality, as opposed to monitoring of specific emissions, occurs at some facilities in Europe and Japan (box 6-B). Several pollutants (e.g., CO, CO_2, SO_x, NO_x, total hydrocarbons, and HCl) and other parameters (e.g., opacity, oxygen, and temperature) also are subject to continuous emissions monitoring in other countries (105,106). Opacity, for example, is a common surrogate for particulates.

Risks From Air Emissions

Humans can be exposed to pollutants emitted from MSW incinerators by either direct pathways (e.g., inhalation) or indirect pathways (e.g., ingestion of contaminated food). Risk assessments typically use models and a set of conservative assumptions to predict potential exposure from these pathways. These exposure predictions, along with estimates of the number of exposed individuals and the carcinogenic or toxic potency of the pollutants, are used to estimate human cancer risks. Usually, a model presents a worst-case scenario that involves a "maximally-exposed individual"—e.g., someone exposed to high concentrations of a given pollutant over the course of a 70-year lifetime. This type of scenario is highly unlikely and thus is the source of controversy. Some people consider its conservatism

to be an appropriate safeguard, while others consider it to be unnecessary.

Risk assessments for different waste management methods are difficult to compare because of differences in the number and type of pollutants, potential pathways, potential effects, and facility designs and ages. Most risk assessments of MSW incineration do not address most of the organic chemicals known to be in emissions; however, not all that are unaddressed are necessarily risky, and proper risk assessments attempt to include all substances known to pose potential risks. They also usually do not address cumulative noncarcinogenic effects; cumulative effects of multiple facilities in a given area; and health risks from "criteria" pollutants as defined by the Clean Air Act, such as SO_2 and NO_x (at least in part because standards for these have already been set).

Few risk assessments have addressed populations that may experience the greatest exposure (e.g., incinerator workers, landfill operators, and children); the incremental effects given background levels or multiple sources (e.g., see ref. 83); or risks from synergistic or antagonistic reactions among different compounds (93). In general, risk assessments are not designed to evaluate ecological effects (e.g., increased CO_2 production, lake acidification, nutrient enrichment from deposition of NO_x in lakes and estuaries) or effects on equipment and buildings.

Nevertheless, risk assessments can play a role in decisionmaking, for example by examining the likely reduction in risks that might be associated with retrofitting a given facility. At least 24 States plan to use risk assessments on a case-specific basis to set regulations for various sources of carcinogens (177).

Importance of Different Pathways

In EPA's risk assessments for MSW incineration, direct pathways were defined to include only the inhalation of air emissions; quantitative cancer risks were estimated for four metals and six organic chemicals (table 6-4) (179). Indirect pathways, which were not assessed quantitatively, included ingestion of food (made from crops exposed to emissions), soil, surface water, and fish.

For **direct** exposure attributable to MSW incinerators, EPA concluded that chlorinated dioxins pose

Table 6-4—Contribution of Pollutants in MSW Incinerator Emissions to Estimates of Total Annual Cancer Incidence and Maximum Individual Lifetime Cancer Risk

Pollutant	Existing facilities		Projected facilities	
	Annual cancer incidence[a,b]	Maximum individual risk range[c,d]	Annual cancer incidence[a,b]	Maximum individual risk range[c,d]
Chlorinated dioxins	2-40	10^{-6}-10^{-3}	0.8-20	10^{-6}-10^{-4}
Chlorobenzenes	0.009-0.02	10^{-7}-10^{-6}	0.004-0.01	10^{-9}-10^{-7}
Chlorophenols	0.0001-0.0003	10^{-9}-10^{-8}	0.0001-0.0003	10^{-10}-10^{-9}
Formaldehyde	0.009	10^{-8}	0.02	10^{-8}-10^{-7}
Polychlorinated biphenyls	0.02	10^{-8}-10^{-5}	0.2	10^{-9}-10^{-6}
Polycyclic aromatic hydrocarbons	0.01-0.6	10^{-7}-10^{-5}	0.05-3.0	10^{-7}-10^{-5}
Arsenic	0.2	10^{-7}-10^{-4}	0.1	10^{-8}-10^{-7}
Beryllium	0.02	10^{-9}-10^{-6}	0.001	10^{-11}-10^{-8}
Cadmium	0.2	10^{-6}-10^{-4}	0.2	10^{-7}-10^{-6}
Chromium	0.2	10^{-7}-10^{-4}	0.1	10^{-8}-10^{-6}
Rounded total[e]	2-40	10^{-6}-10^{-3}	2-20	10^{-6}-10^{-4}

[a]Ranges reflect assumptions made regarding potential carcinogenicity of classes of organic compounds.
[b]Annual cancer incidence = average annual number of excess cancer cases in exposed populations.
[c]Ranges reflect differences in emissions and combustion technologies.
[d]Maximum individual risk = probability of contracting cancer following lifetime exposure at maximum modeled long-term ambient concentration. Probability is expressed as a negative exponent of 10; for example, a risk of one chance in 10,000 is expressed as 10^{-4}.
[e]Apparent errors in total are because of intentional rounding to one significant figure.

SOURCE: After U.S. Environmental Protection Agency, *Municipal Waste Combustion Study: Assessment of Health Risks Associated With Municipal Waste Combustion Emissions*, EPA/530-SW-87-02 (Washington, DC: September 1987).

the greatest cancer risk to humans, and that exposure to cadmium, arsenic, and chromium also pose significant potential risks. However, disagreement exists about the levels of cancer risks associated with these pollutants, particularly about the importance of dioxin and indirect pathways.

In particular, some observers contend that **indirect** exposure routes—especially bioaccumulation in the food chain and subsequent food ingestion—are more important pathways than inhalation (8,63,201,202,205). Indeed, ecological principles suggest that persistent substances such as dioxins should result in greater exposure over time because they tend to accumulate in the environment and in different organisms and to increase in concentration in successive levels of the food chain.

EPA did not present quantitative estimates of risks from the indirect pathways, so it is difficult to compare their importance relative to direct pathways. Nevertheless, EPA concluded that indirect exposure to emissions may be comparable to direct exposure for some pollutants. Among organic chemicals, for example, EPA considered dioxins to present possible health risks for every indirect pathway. Other investigators contend that deposi-

tion of dioxins and furans on agricultural lands may be a major pathway not only for people in that area, but also elsewhere because of the transportation of food products (202) (see "Dioxins and Furans" below).

Type and Age of Facilities

The type and age of the incineration facility can—but does not always—affect the potential risks from air emissions. Limited data on dioxin and particulate emissions from RDF facilities indicate that these facilities can achieve levels of emissions as low as new mass burn facilities (table 6-3). Assuming that all else is equal, differences in risks should not be significant.

Within a given type of facility, however, newer facilities provide much greater control than do older facilities because of better emission controls and combustion procedures. Various compliance tests indicate that new facilities usually meet their permit limits, often at levels far below the limits. This should not be surprising because new facilities usually are designed on the basis of what is technically achievable. For example, the Commerce, California, facility met all permit limits for NO_x, SO_x, carbon monoxide, total particulates, and metals, and had extremely low dioxin emissions (16), although it also had one incident where metal emissions were higher than expected. Similarly, Marion County, Oregon, met all of its limits except for NO_x, which exceeded its limit by 15 percent (183). The Bristol, Connecticut, facility met all 12 emissions limits (including mercury, lead, and dioxins and furans), usually by a factor of 10 or more (134).

Several States and countries and EPA have concluded that using a scrubber/filter system offers some emissions control advantages over an ESP-based system. For example, some risk assessments have predicted that scrubber/filter systems might reduce total cancer risk by one order of magnitude compared with an ESP system and by two orders of magnitude compared with other existing controls (119,179). The EPA Science Advisory Board also concluded that the scrubber/filter system was generally capable of achieving lower emissions (182) because it appears to remove particles (with attached pollutants) more efficiently, particularly smaller particles. Nonhealth risks also were expected to be greatly reduced by this system because it provides greater control of acid gases. Although new facilities equipped with 3- and 4-field ESPs are capable of achieving low total particulate emissions levels, facilities equipped with fabric filters are more likely to achieve lower levels (ref. 21; table 6-3).

Risks Associated With Specific Pollutants

Dioxins and Furans—Based on analyses of direct exposure via the inhalation pathway, EPA concluded that dioxins and furans in incinerator emissions pose cancer risks that are one to two orders of magnitude greater than does cadmium, the second most significant carcinogen in the pathway. EPA estimated that the upper risk limits were about 2 to 40 additional cancers per year in populations exposed to dioxin and furan emissions from all existing MSW incinerators, with an additional 2 to 20 excess cancers per year from proposed facilities. The maximum individual lifetime cancer risk was about one in 1,000 to 10,000 people (179).

These estimates have been disputed. EPA's Science Advisory Board considered them too high (182). Conversely, others contend that incremental lifetime cancer risks are much greater, perhaps by one to two orders of magnitude (26). Critics of this

latter estimate, however, contend that it is outdated because it is based on emissions from a relatively old facility and that risk estimates based on newer facilities would be much lower. This criticism is valid for new facilities because they clearly have better emissions control capabilities. However, it does not address older facilities that lack such capabilities or the issue of whether low emission levels from new facilities can be sustained for long periods.

Questions also exist regarding the indirect food chain pathways (201,202). Dioxins and furans are relatively stable and fat soluble, features that enable them to accumulate in organisms and increase in concentration at successive levels within food chains. Consequently, food intake may be more a significant pathway than inhalation. One assessment of dioxin and furan emissions from a proposed facility in Minnesota looked at three populations (i.e., urban, rural consuming locally grown food, and sports fishermen) (121). In all three cases, over 90 percent of the estimated incremental cancer risk was associated with ingestion of food. Another study of two counties in Pennsylvania estimated that the upper-bound incremental risks associated with the deposition of dioxin and furan emissions on agricultural lands and their uptake by cows and incorporation into milk were 0.15 to 1.5 cancer cases per year, several orders of magnitude greater than the risks from inhalation pathways. Because most of the milk is transported elsewhere, the risks would be spread beyond the area in question. Another study of incinerators proposed in Long Island and New York City also concluded that the majority of effects would be from long-distance transport and deposition of dioxins in milk-producing areas (63).

Other Sources, Ambient Conditions, Background Levels—Dioxins and furans can come from many sources other than MSW incinerators. In fact, some investigators claim that MSW incinerators are not important sources of dioxin emissions (154). However, other analysts contend the opposite (26). The World Health Organization took a somewhat intermediate position, concluding that inhalation of emissions from MSW incinerators contributed only a small fraction to the overall daily intake of dioxins and furans, but that the food chain pathway could be significant in some situations (205).

Few studies have examined whether dioxin emissions from MSW incinerators have a significant impact on surrounding ambient air or soil quality (and, potentially, human health). Very low levels of dioxins and furans (in the picogram/m^3 range) were detected away from one facility, with no clear pattern discerned between upwind and downwind stations. Furthermore, most of the detected compounds were of low or no toxicity (16). In this case, sampling and analytical techniques were not sophisticated enough to measure whether incremental changes in ground-level concentrations of dioxins and furans could be attributed to the incinerator.

Computer models were used in another study to predict dioxin emissions from one facility (83). The predicted emissions at the maximum point of impact were less than 4 percent of ambient concentrations measured within 1 to 2 miles of the facility before it opened. This study also concluded that current techniques were incapable of distinguishing dioxin emissions from MSW incinerators from background dioxin levels. These computer predictions need to be verified with actual measurements of emissions.

Metals—EPA considers several metals emitted from MSW incinerators to be possible human or animal carcinogens (i.e., antimony, arsenic, beryllium, cadmium, chromium, nickel) (179). Metals such as lead and mercury also have long been associated with noncancer risks. For example, lead is a neurotoxin.

Few studies have looked at the entire range of these metals in emissions or the relative importance of food chain pathways. In a study of risks associated with MSW combustion that focused on inhalation pathways, EPA estimated that emissions of arsenic, beryllium, cadmium, and chromium would be associated with up to 0.5 additional cancers each year from existing facilities and 0.4 additional cancers each year from proposed facilities (179). As with dioxins and furans, however, the importance of food chain pathways warrants more investigation. Noncancer risks also warrant more attention.

EPA estimated that ambient lead concentrations resulting from existing facilities would be between 20 and 60 percent of ambient air standards, and that ambient mercury concentrations would be between 1 and 40 percent. Thus, depending on the level of background concentrations and contributions from other sources, MSW facilities could contribute to violations of these standards. Of course, this could be true of other sources as well, and new MSW incinerators must undergo a "New Source Review" that includes evaluating potential effects on ambient air quality. One study of metals in emissions from several proposed facilities with a scrubber/filter system estimated that lead emissions would be lower than ambient background levels by a factor of around 100 (93). For mercury, the amount added to ground level concentrations would be at the lower end of the range of ambient air levels reported for rural areas.

Acid Gases—EPA examined potential corrosion of ferrous metals by acid gases, especially HCl. Using data on average emissions levels, EPA estimated that the majority of existing incinerators would exceed annual average ambient standards for ferrous metals corrosion. For proposed mass burn and RDF facilities with ESPs and dry scrubbers, EPA estimated that ambient HCl concentrations would be reduced by about 90 percent (179).

Regulatory Status

The Clean Air Act allows EPA to regulate MSW incinerators by developing numerical emissions limits for individual pollutants or by developing performance standards (i.e., specifying a range of acceptable technologies, generally termed Best Available Control Technology or BACT).

Currently, only a few Federal numerical emissions limits apply to MSW incinerators. Mercury is regulated under the hazardous air pollutants provision (Section 112), while particulate matter and opacity are regulated under the New Source Performance Standards provision (or NSPS, Section 111).[11] In addition, MSW incinerators are subject to national ambient air quality standards (Section 109); that is, emissions from an incinerator must not contribute to violations of ambient air standards for pollutants such as NO_x and carbon monoxide.

In general, the States administer the permitting process for individual incinerators. The process involves, for example, reviewing emissions from

---

[11]Existing facilities also can be required to retrofit when new NSPS regulations are promulgated.

new sources to ensure that they will not contribute to significant deterioration of air quality.

Most of EPA's regulatory efforts have involved defining BACT. In 1987, EPA issued guidance on BACT to those authorities (i.e., the States) that review and permit new sources of emissions (52 *Federal Register* 25399, July 7, 1987). The guidance indicated that BACT for new sources "should incorporate gas scrubbers, good combustion controls, and good particulate controls." EPA considers compliance with the guidance to have been excellent (25).

EPA is scheduled to propose more comprehensive regulations for new MSW incinerators in November 1989. These are likely to focus on technology-based standards.[12] EPA also expects to issue guidelines to States on retrofitting existing incinerators to bring them into compliance with the final regulations. Congressional proposals for measures to control air emissions from MSW incinerators have generally been more stringent than EPA's proposals.[13]

In 1989, EPA's Region 10 Office issued a recommendation regarding a permit for a new facility in Spokane, Washington, that, although denied by EPA Headquarters, has far-reaching implications (box 6-D; see ch. 1). The Region recommended that a permit for the new facility be issued only if **pre-combustion** controls such as curbside separation and recycling were included as part of the permit's BACT provisions. This would have been the first such linkage between recycling and incineration in a permit.

Some States have adopted their own BACT provisions. Scrubbers are required in many States (e.g., Connecticut, Florida, Indiana, Maine, Massachusetts, New Hampshire, New Jersey, New York, Oregon, Pennsylvania, Vermont, and Wisconsin), and similar requirements are being considered in California. Combustion and particulate controls also are required in a number of States, but specific requirements vary (table 6-5).

Some States have adopted minimum, uniform standards for operating conditions (e.g., temperature and residence time), continuous monitoring of surrogate parameters (e.g., carbon monoxide), and operator training at new facilities. However, maintaining uniform conditions often is difficult because of the heterogeneous nature of MSW. In addition, carbon monoxide emissions are not always indicative of other pollutant emissions. As a result, it is difficult to specify equivalent operating conditions or surrogate measurement parameters for all facilities.

One suggested approach for providing flexibility would be to have facility operators establish an "operating envelope"—a range of conditions that optimizes a given system's performance—by directly measuring conditions and emissions during the design and testing stages (154). The envelope would differ for each facility, but it could form the basis for facility-specific permit conditions necessary to meet any emissions standards. However, under current permitting procedures a facility must still demonstrate that it is using BACT, which could reduce this flexibility (56). A case also can be made that any emissions standards for MSW incinerators should be comparable to standards for industrial processes that have comparable emissions (e.g., fossil-fueled electricity generating plants, recycling facilities, and sewage treatment plants) (190).

Another approach would be to set minimum Federal emissions standards based on the highest removal efficiencies and lowest emissions levels observed during tests. It is unlikely that such standards can be met consistently. Test data are from relatively infrequent compliance tests, not day-to-day monitoring, and standards based on the best test results would be difficult for most facilities to achieve regularly. However, enforcement of minimum standards developed in this way might act as motivation to spur the development of more advanced technology (34). Representatives of the incinerator industry, however, argue that because

---

[12]EPA could regulate these sources by setting health-based standards under Section 112 or technology-based standards under the Section 111 NSPS provision. The latter approach is favored by groups such as the Natural Resources Defense Council and several States (see *New York v. Thomas*, CA DC, No. 84-1472, May 16, 1986).

[13]Legislation considered (but not passed) by the 100th and 101st Congresses would have defined BACT to include scrubbers, combustion controls, and particulate controls; emissions monitoring; operator training and certification requirements; and State planning for incineration that addresses reduction, recycling, and ash management. It also would have established numerical limits on dioxins, several metals, carbon monoxide, and other parameters.

Box 6-D—BACT, Incineration, and Recycling

In 1989, EPA's Region 10 office recommended that a permit for a new incinerator in Spokane, Washington, include source separation and recycling as part of its BACT provisions (54,97,188). Although EPA Headquarters denied the recommendation, this case is significant because EPA indicated that provisions for source separation and recycling might become a routine part of future permits for new incinerators (see ch. 1).

The potential inclusion of source separation and recycling as BACT provisions makes sense from a materials management perspective. If and when they are included as part of BACT, it will mark the first direct linkage between recycling and incineration in a permit. It also will directly address an issue of great public concern—the general relationship between recycling and incineration.

Many communities already have both a recycling program and an incinerator. Removing and recycling noncombustible materials such as glass and metals—roughly 15 percent of all MSW—can improve the operating efficiency of incinerators and reduce the levels of metals in emissions and ash. Beyond that 15 percent, however, the interplay between recycling and incineration is less clear.

Most incinerators are designed to produce a relatively constant output of heat, within a facility-specific range of conditions (e.g., fuel moisture and heat value) (figure 6-2). Paper and plastic materials have high Btu contents, and in some cases removing too much of them prior to incineration can reduce the heat content of the remaining MSW and cause the incinerator to operate less efficiently. Many incinerator operators try to combat this possibility by negotiating guarantees with the community they serve for delivery of a specified amount of MSW, most often through "flow control" agreements.

These kinds of problems might be avoided by designing the size of future incinerators to account for projected recycling rates and the potential effects of successful waste reduction efforts. If not done carefully, however, this could cause other problems. If a community sets recycling targets and then builds an incinerator with only enough capacity for the remaining MSW, then failure to meet the recycling targets might result in unexpected landfilling of some MSW. This could be one justification for designing larger-than-currently-needed facilities or for communities joining together to share management capacity.

---

plants cannot continuously achieve these levels, permit levels should be set somewhat above test levels to provide for an acceptable operating envelope (65).

Dioxin Limits

Several countries have limitations on dioxin emissions, and these have changed considerably in recent years. Much of the impetus for the changes comes from Sweden, where concerns about dioxins in the environment and in fish and dairy products led to a 1985 moratorium on new MSW incineration facilities while research was conducted (115). The moratorium was lifted in 1986, and temporary goals were established as the basis for granting permits.

The Swedish goal for emissions of dioxins from existing plants built before 1985 is 0.5 to 2.0 ng/Nm^3 (in Eadon Toxic Equivalents; see footnote 8) and 0.1 ng/Nm^3 for new plants; definitive standards will be set after a trial period. It is not clear whether the goals for new plants can be met on a sustained basis

under normal operating conditions, even by the best of current facilities. However, the goal has been achieved during tests at Swedish, German, and U.S. facilities (table 6-3); the lowest limits appear to occur at facilities with a dry scrubber/baghouse system in combination with careful combustion controls.

NO$_x$ and Acid Gas Limits

Several States have established limits for NO$_x$ emissions from individual incinerators, with limits ranging between 100 and 350 ppm (21,24). These limits generally were developed because of ambient air quality problems (e.g., with NO$_x$ levels themselves, acid deposition, or ozone). States such as California, Connecticut, New Jersey, and New York require that the use of BACT (e.g., Thermal DeNOx or combustion modification) for NO$_x$ control be evaluated for new facilities.

For HCl, about 10 States require either 90 percent removal or an emissions limit of 30 to 50 ppm (21).

For SO_2, some States require removal efficiencies of 70 to 80 percent or emissions limits of 30 to 100 ppm.

Particulate Limits

Limits on particulate emissions generally are based on what can be achieved with BACT. Several States (e.g., California, Connecticut, Michigan, and New York) consider the dry scrubber/fabric filter system to be BACT (178). However, new ESP-based systems appear to be just as effective. Whether dry scrubbers are more effective than wet scrubbers is unclear and more research on their long-term effectiveness is needed.

In any event, test results using scrubber/filter systems have served as the basis for new standards. The current U.S. standard for total particulates is 0.046 gr/dscf (table 6-5), but several States have set limits as low as 0.01 gr/dscf, which new plants have achieved during initial performance tests (table 6-3). Sweden set a total particulate limit of 0.008 gr/dscf (20 mg/Nm^3) on a monthly average (8).

Some States such as Oregon also distinguish between material collected on the air pollution controls (i.e., "front-half") and material emitted from the stack that later condenses into particles (i.e., "back-half"). Confusion can arise if this distinction is not made when measurements are reported, and there is a need to review and standardize sampling and reporting procedures. In addition, standards often are set in terms of pounds per hour (so that conditions relative to other sources can be calculated). However, stack emissions generally are measured in terms of gr/dscf or mg/Nm^3, and converting these measurements to pounds per hour requires data on flue gas flow rates (which can be in error by up to 30 percent), molecular weights, and operating temperatures (76).

Metals Limits

Few States have limits for metals, and those that have been developed tend to be based on data from older plants (127). Many environmentalists contend that limits for metals should be based on emission rates from state-of-the art facilities. In Sweden, the standard for mercury is 0.08 mg/Nm^3 on a monthly average (163), and it may be lowered to 0.03 mg/Nm^3 (8). Some industry representatives, however, contend that meeting emissions limits (other than ambient air standards) for particular metals is difficult because of the heterogeneous nature of MSW and the complex chemical reactions that occur within scrubbers and other pollution control devices (56).

Besides regulatory limits on emissions, one way to reduce metals in emissions might be to encourage municipalities and incinerator operators to separate noncombustibles or other items prior to combustion— that is, to implement the concept of "materials management" (ch. 1). The suggestion to include recycling in the BACT provisions for a proposed incinerator in Spokane, Washington, reflects this approach (box 6-D). Presorting MSW prior to incineration (see "Controlling Air Emissions") may help reduce metals in both emissions and ash, at least at older facilities; additional research is needed to explore this possibility.

Operator Training

West Germany and Japan often are cited as models for operator training, but the extent of training in these countries varies (box 6-B). Whether operator performance differs in relation to the type of training is unknown, but it is clear that lack of appropriate training (whether by schools or vendors) can cause more operational problems. In the United States, various companies and States require people to be licensed as operating engineers or to have special licenses to operate boilers. In 1989, the American Society of Mechanical Engineers proposed standards for the qualification and certification of operators (4). One member of the committee voted against the proposal, however, because it did not require enough training or cover enough employee types (23). EPA also is developing an operation and maintenance manual for small-scale facilities used in medical waste incineration (187).

Retrofitting

A major question to address is whether standards for new plants should be applied to older plants. Older incinerators can be retrofitted in ways that vary in expense and complexity—including increasing operator training, injecting lime into MSW or the furnace, changing air distribution systems, adding automatic computer controls, and adding scrubbers.

Several studies show that retrofitting can help reduce emissions. For example, the Canadian Na-

Table 6-5—Selected Emission Standards for MSW Incinerators[a]

	United States	California	Connecticut	Michigan	Japan	Sweden	West Germany
Solid particulate matter							
(gr/dscf)	0.046	0.01[b]	0.015	0.015	0.061[c]	0.008	0.012
(mg/m³)	113	25	37	37	150	20	30
Carbon monoxide (ppm)				113 (daily average)		80	
Hydrogen chloride		30 ppm (scrubbers required)	90% reduction	90% reduction	430 ppm 700 mg/m³	63 ppm 100 ng/m³	31 ppm 50 ng/m³
Sulfur dioxide (ppm)		30[d]	170[e] (0.32 lb/10⁶ Btu)	86	varies[f]		35 ppm 200 mg/Nm³
Dioxins (2,3,7,8-TCDD)[g]							
Existing plants (ng/m³)						0.5-2.0	
New plants (ng/m³)						0.1	
Total organics (mg/m³)							20
Mercury, cadmium, thallium (mg/m³), including vapors						0.8 (mercury)	0.2

[a]Gas correction factor = 12% CO_2 dry, except for Sweden (10% CO_2 dry) and West Germany (11% O_2 dry).
[b]California regulations permit more stringent limits. Two State guidelines are reported: 0.01 gr/dscf (25 mg/m³) for total solid particulates and 0.008 gr/dscf (20 mg/m³) for particles smaller than 2 microns.
[c]For continuous gas flows greater than 25,280 scfm (40,000 m³/h).
[d]Use of BACT required, but no technology specified.
[e]Use of dry gas scrubbers and baghouses expected to improve removal over ESPs alone.
[f]Based on formula related to stack height and plant location.
[g]TCDD = 2,3,7,8-tetrachlorodibenzo-p-dioxins; measurements in Eadon Toxic Equivalents.

SOURCE: U.S. Environmental Protection Agency, *Municipal Waste Combustion Study, Report to Congress*, EPA/530-SW-87-021a (Washington, DC: June 1987).

tional Incinerator Testing and Evaluation Program conducted pilot-scale experiments at a 17-year-old incinerator in Quebec City, primarily by changing some design features, adding computer-aided combustion controls, adjusting air distribution, and increasing residence time (107). Emissions of dioxins and particulate matter were significantly reduced under good design and operating conditions (by up to two orders of magnitude). Even under intentionally poor design and operating conditions, the retrofit facilities improved by one order of magnitude (figure 6-4). A facility at Hampton, Virginia, was retrofitted by modifying air distribution, improving operator training, and reducing the temperature of flue gases entering the ESP; subsequent tests showed that dioxin emissions were reduced by two orders of magnitude (117).

In Europe, scrubbers and, in some cases, fabric filters, are being added to some existing plants (8).

After six facilities were retrofitted with spray dry scrubbers, they were able to achieve removal efficiencies typical of new facilities with the same controls (40,41,42): HCl was reduced 87 to 98 percent; particulate matter dropped 99.8 percent; lead and cadmium fell 99 percent; and mercury fell 7 to 85 percent. In West Germany, new air quality regulations give all existing facilities 5 years to come into compliance (11).

The cost of retrofitting depends on the type of retrofitting and size of the facility, and the effect on individual owners obviously will depend on the financial status of the owners. The overall costs of retrofitting numerous facilities, however, are likely to be tens of millions of dollars. One study estimated the net annualized costs of meeting stricter emissions requirements that were in one bill proposed in Congress in 1988 (169). After accounting for likely actions under existing EPA regulations, the net

Figure 6-4—Dioxin Emissions at Quebec City Facility, Before and After Retrofitting

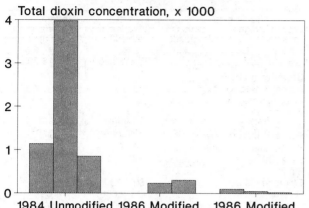

Total dioxin concentration, x 1000

1984 Unmodified   1986 Modified,   1986 Modified,
                    Poor conditions   Good conditions

NOTE: Total dioxin concentrations given in ng/Nm³, corrected to 12% CO_2. Poor and good refer to poor and good operating conditions, respectively, at facility after retrofitting.

SOURCE: R. Klicius, A. Finkelstein, and D.J. Hay, "The National Incinerator Testing and Evaluation Program (NITEP) Mass Burning Technology Assessment," Paper No. 87-94.5 presented at 80th Annual Meeting of APCA (New York, NY: June 21-26, 1987).

annualized cost of meeting the new requirements was estimated to be between $50 million and $450 million for all existing facilities.

ASH MANAGEMENT

General Management

Amounts

Ash is the noncombustible part of MSW. Much of it is an amorphous, glass-like material that includes minerals (e.g., from glass and food), metals (from cans, inks, and other products), unburned organic carbon, dirt, and grit. Two types of ash are generated during incineration. **Fly ash** is comprised of light particles that are carried off the grate by turbulence or that condense and form in the flue gas in the boiler system. **Bottom ash** is the relatively coarse uncombusted or partly combusted residue that accumulates on the grate.[14]

Ash from U.S. incinerators typically is 15 to 30 percent by wet weight and 5 to 15 percent by volume of the original MSW (65,80,180). In contrast, the portion of ash at Japanese facilities tends to be lower, probably because MSW is sorted into combustible and noncombustible portions (box 6-E). Pre-sorting MSW for non-combustibles lowered ash generation at some older U.S. incinerators by about half (159). The extent to which presorting would affect ash generation at other facilities would depend on the nature of the MSW, age and type of facility, and many other factors.

The amount of ash generated in the United States is about 2.8 to 5.5 million tons per year (46,70). This might increase two to five times depending on how many planned facilities are built. Fly ash typically amounts to about 5 to 15 percent of the total ash (80).

Ash Composition Prior to Management

The main components of ash are inert materials of low solubility (e.g., silicates, clay, sand, and fine ash) and inorganic substances. Several inorganic substances (e.g., aluminum, calcium, chlorine, iron, selenium, sodium, and zinc) are major elements in all ash particles and, along with carbon, can comprise over 10 percent by weight of the ash (44).

A broad range of trace metals and organic compounds also is found in fly and bottom ash (table 6-6). Data on ash composition are difficult to compare, however, because they reflect: 1) different types and sizes of facilities; 2) unknown sample sizes at each facility; 3) interlab variation in testing procedures (even using the same test); and 4) variable inputs into the ash itself (e.g., heterogeneous MSW). In addition, the presence of a substance in ash does not mean that it will enter the environment. Its fate depends on its solubility, how the ash is managed, and whether the ash is subject to conditions that cause leaching or inhalation and ingestion.

Metals tend to be distributed differently in fly and bottom ash. Most volatile metals (e.g., arsenic, mercury, lead, cadmium, and zinc) tend to be more concentrated or "enriched" in fly ash (151,180). Less volatile metals (e.g., aluminum, chromium, iron, nickel, and tin) typically are concentrated in bottom ash (150,151,192).

---

[14]Several other terms are associated with ash. **Clinker** is the large, fused noncombustible material that remains on the grate as part of bottom ash. **Superheater, boiler**, and **economizer** ash refers to ash that collects on different parts of the boiler system (figure 6-1) and that usually is handled as fly ash. **Combined** ash refers to mixing the bottom and fly ash waste streams together. **Scrubber residue** is fly ash that reacts with lime and often is collected after it forms a cake on particulate controls.

Table 6-6—Concentrations of Substances in MSW Bottom and Fly Ash

Substance	Fly ash	Bottom ash	Substance	Fly ash	Bottom ash
Inorganics (ppm)			Vanadium	22-166	53
Aluminum	5,300-176,000	5,400-53,400	Yttrium	2-380	
Antimony	139-760		Zinc	2,800-152,000	200-16,700
Arsenic*	15-750	1.3-24.6	**Organics** (ppb)		
Barium*	88-9,000	47-2,000	Acenaphthalene	ND-3,500	37-390
Beryllium	ND-4	ND-0.44	Alkanes	50,000	
Bismuth	36-100	ND	Anthracene	1-500	53
Boron	35-5,654	85	Benzanthrene	0-300	
Bromine	21-250		Benzo(k) fluoranthene	ND-470	ND-51
Cadmium*	5-2,210	1.1-46	Benzo(g,h,i) perylene	0-190	ND
Calcium	13,960-27,000	5,900-69,500	Benzo(a) pyrene	ND-400	ND-5
Cesium	2,100-12,000		Biphenyl	2-1,300	
Chloride	1,160-11,200		Chlorobenzenes	80-4,220	17
Chromium*	21-1,900	13-520	Chlorophenols	50.1-9,630	0
Cobalt	2.3-1,670	3-62	Chrysene	0-690	ND-37
Copper	187-2,380	80-10,700	Di-n-butyl Phthalate	ND	360
Gold	0.16-100		Dioxins		
Iron	900-87,000	1,000-133,500	2,3,7,8-TCDD	0.1-42	0.04-0.7
Lead*	200-26,600	110-5,300	Total PCDDs	5.23-10,883	ND-110
Lithium	7.9-34	7-19	Fluoranthene	0-6,500	110-230
Magnesium	2,150-21,000	880-10,100	Fluorene	0-100	ND-150
Manganese	171-8,500	50-3,100	Furans		
Mercury*	0.9-47	ND-1.9	2,3,7,8-TCDF	0.1-5.4	ND-10
Molybdenum	9.2-700	29	Total PCDFs	3.73-3,187	ND-65
Nickel	9.9-1,966	9-226	Naphthalene	270-9,300	570-580
Phosphorus	2,900-9,300	3,400-17,800	Phenanthrene	21-7,600	500-540
Potassium	11,000-99,000	920-14,500	Phthalates		
Selenium*	0.48-15.6	ND-2.5	Bis (2-EH)	85	2,100
Silicon	1,783-266,000	133-188,300	Butyl benzyl	ND	180
Silver*	ND-700	ND-38	Diethyl	6,300	
Sodium	9,780-49,500	1,800-33,300	PCBs	ND-250	ND-180
Strontium	98-1,100	81-240	Pyrene	0-5400	150-220
Tin	300-12,500	40-800			
Titanium	50-42,000	3,067-11,400			

*Regulated under the RCRA Extraction Procedure (EP) Toxicity Test (40 CFR 261.24).
ND = not detected.

SOURCE: U.S. Environmental Protection Agency, *Characterization of Municipal Waste Combustor Ashes and Leachates From Municipal Solid Waste Landfills, Monofills, and Codisposal Sites*, prepared by NUS Corporation for Office of Solid Waste and Emergency Response, EPA/530-SW-87-028A (Washington, DC: October 1987).

Organic chemicals also exhibit differential distribution. Dioxins and PCBs tend to be enriched in fly ash, while other chemicals such as polycyclic aromatic hydrocarbons and phthalates tend to be concentrated in bottom ash (180). Concentrations of dioxins and furans in fly ash exhibit a wide range, but they are significantly lower in ash from modern facilities than in ash from older incinerators (35,78,184,189).

MSW incinerator ash may contain higher concentrations of metals and organic chemicals than do ashes from other combustion processes. For example, one study compared concentrations of six heavy metals (i.e., cadmium, chromium, copper, lead, nickel, and zinc) in MSW bottom and fly ash with concentrations in coal ash (14). Except for nickel, average concentrations were greater in MSW ash.

Current Management Practices

Bottom ash typically is collected by "quenching" or cooling it with water in an ash pit and then moving it into a container or truck. Fly ash is discharged from the particulate control equipment into a quench tank or a container, where it can be saturated with water and then combined with bottom ash into a mixture that has the consistency of wet concrete. Using water helps retard emissions of dust during the handling process. Some people suggest that the lime from scrubbers might cause ash to set up like concrete and retard subsequent leaching (154,190),

Box 6-E—Ash Management in Japan

Japanese facilities typically generate only half (or less) of the amount of ash generated at U.S. facilities (95). Some of the difference may be related to higher moisture content of MSW in the United States (e.g., because of more yard wastes). A more important factor, however, is the common practice in Japan of separating out noncombustible materials. All municipalities in Japan decide which materials will be classified as combustibles for incineration and as noncombustibles for landfilling. Citizens are then required to sort their MSW into these categories.

Although ash management varies greatly, most often fly and bottom ash are combined. The combined ash usually is landfilled by itself or with the noncombustible materials that were separated prior to incineration. Ash is rarely landfilled with food wastes.

About 10 percent of ash undergoes some processing. Ten facilities are known to mix their ash with cement; one facility reuses ash in road pavement. A handful of facilities use vitrification (or melting) to treat the combined ash and produce a hard, glassy slag (94). At the Sohka facility, for example, vitrification reduces the volume of ash by two-thirds, which helps reduce subsequent transport and labor costs (125). The slag is landfilled alone in a lined facility. According to officials, short-term laboratory tests indicate that the concentrations of metals in leachate from the slag are low, but field tests have not been conducted.

The Takuma Co., Ltd., is building an advanced vitrification facility that will use electric arc melting techniques. Operating costs for electric arc melting are expected to be similar to the costs of current "surface" melting—about $100 per metric ton of ash (based on 1986 exchange rates). Although the electric arc process uses about eight times more electricity than the surface melting process, the costs of doing this are offset because the electric arc process uses about 40 times less natural gas (193). (However, a hidden cost in terms of global pollution is that increased electricity production results in higher emissions of carbon dioxide.)

Photo credit: Office of Technology Assessment

Almost all municipalities in Japan require their residents, including the American resident shown here, to separate their MSW into a combustible portion for incineration and a noncombustible portion for landfilling.

but others question the long-term physical stability of such material (28,43).

According to EPA, about 36 percent of all ash goes to monofills, 17 percent is co-disposed with MSW, and the fate of the remainder is unknown or not landfilled (180). The amount sent to monofills probably is an underestimate: one company estimates that it generates over 50 percent of all ash in the United States, and all of this ash is either monofilled or used as a final cover over closed MSW landfills (56). According to another survey, only about 2 percent of ash is reused outside of landfills (100).

Ash management in other countries varies greatly as well. In Japan, bottom and fly ash sometimes are combined, occasionally treated, and then landfilled alone or with the noncombustible fraction of MSW (box 6-E). A few Japanese facilities use "vitrification" to melt ash into an inert, glass-like substance (box 6-E).[15] Some European facilities do not mix fly and bottom ash (101), but others commonly do (58,96). In Sweden, bottom liners are not used at ash monofills; instead, a strategy of controlled dispersion of leachate, along with proper siting of monofills, proper drainage, and a final cover (of soil or stabilized ash) with vegetation, is used to control leaching (123). In most European countries, at least some ash is reused in roads and pavements, usually subject to some kind of guideline or standard (86).

Concentrations of Pollutants in Leachate

This section discusses: 1) factors affecting leaching, 2) concentrations in actual leachate, 3) types of tests used to predict leachate concentrations, 4) results of leachate tests, 5) comparability among tests and with actual leachate, and 6) risks.

Factors Affecting Leachability

Depending on their solubility, metals and metallic compounds in ash can be leached by aqueous solutions into surface water or groundwater. Solubility depends on many factors, including the mineral phase of the substance, equilibrium reactions (e.g., whether metals are sorbed onto other compounds), size of ash particles that metals sorb onto, liquid-to-solid ratio the particles encounter, and the pH and ionic strength of the leaching solution (43,44,60).

For example, lead and cadmium are present in fly and bottom ash in relatively high concentrations (table 6-6). The fractions of lead and cadmium that are soluble, however, usually are lower than the total concentrations; in extractions of bottom ash, the fractions often are less than 30 percent and sometimes less than 1 percent (44). Lead is relatively insoluble at a pH of 6 to about 11, cadmium at pH values of 7 and higher. Lead and cadmium also can be present in other, less soluble mineral phases (e.g., lead phosphate), and they can be trapped in aluminosilicates (45). The soluble fraction of lead, however, can leach in acid solutions with a pH of 5 and in alkaline solutions with a pH greater than 11 (i.e., it is amphoteric).

Leachate from a typical MSW landfill often is acidic because of the organic nature of MSW and because of byproducts from microbial activity that occurs within a landfill. When ash is co-disposed with MSW, these acidic conditions may leach some metals from the ash. However, the nature of the ash also may result in some buffering or neutralization of the acids. In particular, ash from incinerators with scrubbers may exhibit high buffering capacity because of the lime used in the scrubbers. However, more research is needed to evaluate this phenomenon. One study concluded that ash from incinerators without scrubbers reduced leachability of metals, while ash from incinerators with scrubbers reduced the leachability of some metals but increased the leachability of others (60). Another study concluded that the buffering capacity of lime from scrubbers is limited (150).

The concentrations of lead and cadmium in actual leachates under field conditions are hard to predict. EPA and the Coalition on Resource Recovery and the Environment are jointly sponsoring research on the composition of ash and associated leachates from monofills (130).

Concentrations in Actual Leachate

Several organic chemicals, including dioxins and furans, and many metals have been detected in samples of **actual** leachates at ash monofills (table 6-7). Small sample sizes and a lack of information on ash characteristics make it difficult to draw conclusions, particularly about what leaching might occur over the long-term (144).

The metal concentrations reported in table 6-7 are lower than Extraction Procedure (EP) Toxicity limits (with the exception of some cadmium samples), but higher in some cases than U.S. Drinking Water Standards (which are 100 times lower than the EP limits). At one Danish monofill, only 2 of 14 metals tested (chromium and copper) slightly exceeded Danish Drinking Water Standards (96). In contrast, concentrations of soluble salts (e.g., of calcium and potassium) tend to be high. One of the studies in table 6-7 also measured leachates at two co-disposal sites (180).[16] The reported concentrations of cadmium, lead, dioxins, and furans at the co-disposal sites were within the ranges reported at

---

[15]The American Society of Mechanical Engineers and the U.S. Bureau of Mines have proposed a study on the feasibility of using this technique in the United States (5).

[16]Laboratory extractions and toxicity tests also were performed.

Table 6-7—Range of Concentrations in Leachate at Ash Monofills

Substance	Concentration[a]	Drinking water standards		EP Tox Limit
		Denmark	United States	
Arsenic	0.005-0.218	0.05	0.05	5.0
Barium	1-2.48		1.0	100
Boron	<0.02-0.76	1		
Cadmium	<0.0001-0.044	0.005	0.001	0.1
Calcium	21-3200	200		
Chromium	<0.002-1.53	0.05	0.05	5.0
Copper	<0.005-24	0.1		
Iron	0.168-121			
Lead	<0.0005-2.92	0.05	0.05	5.0
Magnesium	0.09-41	30		
Manganese	0.103-22.4			
Mercury	<0.00005-0.008	0.001	0.002	0.2
Molybdenum	<0.03			
Nickel	<0.005-0.412	0.05		
Potassium	21.5-4300	10		
Selenium	0.0025-0.037		0.01	1.0
Silver	<0.001-0.07			
Sodium	200-7300	175		
Sulfate	310-4900	250		
Zinc	<0.01-0.32	5		
Benzaldehyde	ND-0.008			
Biphenyl	ND-0.051			
Dimethyl propane diol	ND-0.120			
Dioxins (ng/l)				
total	0.06-543			
2,3,7,8-TCDD	0.025-1.6			
Ethyl hexyl phthalate	ND-0.08			
Furans, total (ng/l)	0.04-280			
Hexa tiepane	ND-0.082			
PCBs (mg/ul)	<1			
Sulfonylbis sulfur	ND-0.011			
Thiolane	ND-0.400			

[a]Concentrations reported in ppm (=mg/l) except for PCBs, dioxins, and furans; ND = not detected. Data represent samples taken from range of monofill ages and operating conditions.

SOURCES: K.E. Forrester, "State-of-the-Art in Thermal Recycling Facility Ash Residue Handling, Reuse, Landfill Design and Management," unpublished manuscript (Danvers, MA: Wheelabrator Environmental Systems, Inc., January 1989); O. Hjelmar, "Leachate From Incinerator Ash Disposal Sites," paper presented at *International Workshop on Municipal Waste Incineration* (Montreal: Oct. 1-2, 1987); U.S. Environmental Protection Agency, *Characterization of Municipal Waste Combustor Ashes and Leachates From Municipal Solid Waste Landfills, Monofills, and Codisposal Sites*, prepared by NUS Corp. for Office of Solid Waste and Emergency Response, EPA/530-SW-87-028A (Washington, DC: October 1987).

four monofills (which represented a span of ages and operating conditions), although the highest sampled concentrations occurred at the monofills.

More recent studies on metals in leachate have been conducted at a combined ash monofill associated with a new incinerator in Shrewsbury, Massachusetts (60,61). At this site, concentrations of lead and cadmium in leachate and surface runoff are well below the EP limits and are either less than or only slightly higher than the Primary Drinking Water Standards.

The concentrations of dioxins and furans reported in table 6-7 are difficult to evaluate because there are no regulatory standards for comparison.

Some data are available on the concentrations of metals, dioxins, and furans in soil (with pH range of 4.7 to 6.0) around the Marion County, Oregon, "Woodburn" landfill (76). For example, the highest detected concentration of lead in the soil was 53 ppb; mercury and nickel were not detected. The highest values for the octa-homologue of dioxin was 0.112 ppb. The highest values tended to occur in the most acidic areas.

Tests for Predicting Leachate

Several methods are used to predict the leaching characteristics of ash under laboratory conditions. They vary in how well they represent different landfill conditions, as well as how they are conducted by different laboratories (137,138). An extensive review concluded that no currently available method can accurately predict concentrations of toxic substances in leachate (144).

The first three tests described below are "batch" tests, in which contact between the waste and an extraction fluid is maintained for a fixed time to increase the likelihood that all particles will contact the fluid. The last test is a "column" test, in which ash is placed in a column and the extraction fluid is allowed to flow through it.

The Extraction Procedure Toxicity Test (EP test) is the standard test used to determine whether wastes exhibit hazardous characteristics, based on the potential to leach metallic or organic compounds under acidic conditions similar to those that might be found at municipal landfills. The test consists of mixing the waste with deionized water and sufficient acetic acid to bring the pH to 5.0. The pH level is maintained around 5.0 and the mixture is agitated for 24 hours, after which the liquid portion is analyzed for 8 metals (i.e., arsenic, barium, cadmium, chromium, lead, mercury, selenium, and silver), 4 insecticides, and 2 herbicides—substances for which EPA has established Primary Drinking Water Standards. To determine whether a waste is hazardous, leachate concentrations are compared to standards that are based on 100 times the Drinking Water Standards to account for dilution and attenuation.[17]

The Toxicity Characteristic Leaching Procedure (TCLP test) modifies the EP procedure. It differs primarily in that a second extraction fluid is used for samples that are highly alkaline, and it analyzes 38 additional organic compounds. In 1986, EPA proposed a "Toxicity Characteristic" rule that included the TCLP (51 *Federal Register* 21468, June 13, 1986). EPA has not adopted this as a final rule, but has used it to evaluate the leaching potential of MSW ash. EPA concluded that TCLP and EP tests on the same sample show similar extractions for lead and cadmium, the two metals that most frequently exceed the EP limits (180). However, other investigators conclude that test results can differ depending on the type of fluid used in the TCLP test and how acetic acid is used in the EP test (56,144). Recently initiated research will compare different test results

to actual field leachates at ash monofills and at MSW landfills with ash disposal (130).

The Monofilled Waste Extraction Procedure (MWEP) (also known as the SW-924 test) uses distilled or deionized water to evaluate leaching when ash is disposed separately in a monofill (180). In this situation, acidity is determined by the characteristics of the ash itself, rather than the environment in which the ash might be buried. This may be a better predictor of lead and cadmium in leachate.

Lysimeter Tests are designed to simulate leaching in actual landfills, using an ash column and simulated rain or other extraction fluids as the leaching medium. Research efforts are underway to compare lysimeter tests to in-field conditions (49,130).

Leachate Test Results

Metals—Table 6-8 provides information compiled by the Environmental Defense Fund (EDF) on EP test results for fly, bottom, and combined ash. In general, these data indicate that metals are leachable under the acidic conditions of the EP test, and that fly ash samples almost always fail the test. Another review also concluded that nearly all tests of fly ash exceeded the EP limits (144).

The EDF analysis has been criticized (56). Critics claim the analysis: 1) used data collected by sampling and analytical procedures that did not follow regulations or test guidance; 2) failed to cite analytical or statistical procedures; and 3) used simple averaging on highly variable populations, with many facilities only represented by a few samples (e.g., 684 of 773 bottom ash samples for lead were from three facilities). EDF agreed that the data are limited, especially for facilities with small sample sizes. It also agreed that the EP test was not always appropriate (although it still is the test allowed under current regulations), and that caution should be exercized in drawing conclusions (36).

However, EDF also noted that the aggregate data still show that ash generally fails leachate tests and that **fly** ash usually would meet the characteristics under RCRA of a hazardous waste if it was handled by itself. For example, the data show that over 90

---

[17]Although waste generators are not required to use the EP test, they are required to determine whether the waste exhibits a hazardous characteristic (unless the waste is either exempt or already listed as hazardous).

percent of all fly ash samples exceed the EP limits for lead or cadmium or both (table 6-8). **Bottom** and **combined** ash would be considered hazardous in less than half of the cases. Only 36 percent of bottom ash samples and 39 percent of combined ash samples exceeded the limits for either lead or cadmium; most of the exceeded cases resulted from high concentrations of lead. In another EDF analysis of combined ash mixed with scrubber residues, two-thirds of the samples exceeded the EP limit when pH was lower than 5.5 and about 90 percent exceeded it when pH was greater than 12; none exceeded the limit at intermediate pH values (37).

In another review analysis, Resources for the Future (RFF) summarized results from several column leaching tests (144). In three studies on combined ash in contact with a neutral (distilled water) or slightly acidic extraction fluid, concentrations of cadmium and lead were well below EP limits. In one study using distilled water, only selenium from one ash sample exceeded the Federal Drinking Water Standards, which are lower than the EP test limits (62); in the MSW leachate test, metal concentrations were considerably higher, with cadmium, chromium, and lead exceeding the drinking water standards in some cases but always being below the EP limits. Other studies with ash that had higher levels of fly ash also had higher concentrations of cadmium and lead in leachate during column tests; in a few cases, EP limits were surpassed when fly ash alone was tested, especially during the initial portion of the test (96,144).

Even when only one facility is being considered, the same test data can be difficult to interpret. At the Marion County, Oregon, facility, for example, 18 samples were tested for eight metals, using the EP, TCLP, and deionized water tests (80,131,132). Seven metals were under the limit for all three tests, but lead exceeded the limit twice during the EP test (once by a factor of four) and once during the TCLP test. The vendor concluded that combined ash was not hazardous because the upper confidence limits (i.e., estimates to account for sampling variation) for all 18 samples were below the regulatory limits (131,132). In contrast, the State regulatory agency concluded that the results for lead were neither clearly above nor below the regulatory limit and that variability in sample composition and laboratory

Table 6-8—Summary of Extraction Procedure Toxicity Test Data for Lead and Cadmium from Ash

Type of ash	Lead	Cadmium	Either
Fly ash (23 facilities)			
# samples analyzed	185	97	185
# samples over EP limit	168	94	173
% samples over EP limit	91%	97%	94%
# facilities over EP limit[a]	20	21	22
Bottom ash (22 facilities)			
# samples analyzed	773	271	773
# samples over EP limit	276	5	278
% samples over EP limit	36%	2%	36%
# facilities over EP limit[a]	9	1	9
Combined ash (46 facilities)			
# samples analyzed	883	756	883
# samples over EP limit	345	90	354
% samples over EP limit	39%	12%	40%
# facilities over EP limit[a]	21	5	21

[a]Number of facilities for which mean of all available samples exceeds limits.
NOTE: Caution must be exercised in drawing conclusions about the overall rate at which samples exceed EP test limits (see text).
SOURCE: Environmental Defense Fund, "Summary of All Available EP Toxicity Testing Data on Incinerator Ash" (Washington, DC: February 1989).

procedures made it impossible to determine whether the ash exhibited hazardous characteristics (137).

Other studies have applied the EP or TCLP tests to ash from a FBC facility and to scrubber residues from European facilities. EP tests on bottom and fly ash samples from a Swedish FBC facility that burned only RDF indicated that concentrations of all metals tested (including lead and cadmium) in bottom and fly ash were below regulatory limits (122). It is not known whether the result for fly ash is a consequence of FBC incineration or differences in the composition of U.S. and Swedish wastes. In studies on incinerators with spray dry scrubbers, tests on five metals in the scrubber residues (which tend to have high metal concentrations) showed only one case involving lead in a highly alkaline residue that failed the TCLP (40).

Presorting of MSW to remove the noncombustible fraction has been shown to reduce the quantity of ash generated and the mass of metals in the ash (per ton of waste burned) (159). The results of EP tests on the ash were lower for lead, but higher for three metals (cadmium, silver, mercury) and unchanged for four others, in comparison with EP tests on ash from unsorted MSW.

Organic Chemicals—Leachate test results for organic chemicals are difficult to evaluate, because there are no regulatory limits that define allowable levels of these compounds in leachate (except for six pesticides regulated under the EP Test). EPA has proposed but not yet adopted limits for 38 organic compounds under the Toxicity Characteristic rule (51 *Federal Register* 21648, June 13, 1986).

Most available test data show little or no leaching of organic chemicals, especially dioxins and furans, from ash samples. In Canada, for example, tests using distilled water showed little or no mobility for dioxins and furans, polycyclic aromatic hydrocarbons, PCBs, and chlorinated benzenes (150,151). In contrast, the tests did show mobility for chlorophenols. These tests were not conducted under acidic conditions because most organic chemicals are more soluble at neutral or alkaline pH levels. Thus the tests do not necessarily indicate what might happen under landfill conditions where substances such as solvents are present. In addition, transport of such chemicals sorbed onto ultra-fine particles might be of concern (28).

Lysimeter tests in Sweden also showed no leaching of dioxins and furans (123). Similar tests conducted for EPA detected low concentrations of several organic chemicals in ash leachate (e.g., phenol, benzoic acid, and methyl naphthalene) (180).

Comparability Among Tests and With Actual Leachate

Caution is required when interpreting the results of leachate tests. Most observers consider the EP and TCLP tests to overestimate leaching potential, especially in monofills (100,137,138,153,154). Comparing leachate concentrations reported from the field (table 6-7) with test results (table 6-8) tends to confirm this. Both the EP and TCLP tests are intended to simulate leaching in landfills; the extraction fluid and waste stay in contact for longer periods and are mixed more thoroughly than in column tests, which makes the EP and TCLP tests relatively aggressive in extracting pollutants (138,144). Several problems also have been noted in the sampling and analytical procedures themselves: inconsistent procedures for obtaining representative samples from ash, which tends to be heterogeneous even within a given batch; variations in how pH is adjusted during the EP test; and variations among labs performing the same tests on identical samples (138,144).

The data from the field are limited and do not include results from long-term studies (e.g., more than 10 years) (144). As a result, the use of the EP test, even though it may overestimate leachate potential, can be considered a conservative way to classify ash, particularly because ash is not required to be placed in monofills; in addition, the EP test is the one now required by RCRA.

Whether better tests have been developed is uncertain. The MWEP and other distilled water tests may be better indicators of ash leaching in monofills. Such tests are required in Massachusetts, New Hampshire, and Vermont, and recommended in Minnesota. These tests may, however, sometimes underestimate leaching because rainwater tends to have lower pH values than distilled water. However, one modeling exercise concluded that the effect of rainwater should be low, especially for ash from an incinerator with a scrubber (60).

At least one State regulatory agency concluded that a more realistic extraction procedure would use real or synthetic rainwater (138). One ongoing study is comparing several existing extraction tests and some new ones (e.g., using CO_2-saturated deionized water and simulated acid rain) in comparison with field samples of leachate (130).

Risks From Ash

The potential risks associated with ash are the subject of great debate among regulators, industry, and the public (144). Several exposure pathways exist for pollutants in ash. One is the leaching of substances into groundwater, which can then be ingested in drinking water. Airborne and waterborne transport of ash during handling operations or from landfills also can lead to inhalation, ingestion in food crops, or dermal exposure.

Some observers suggest that the risks from airborne transport may be as important as the risks associated with emissions (see ''Metals'' below). Other observers contend that risks from ash management should be seen in perspective with risks from other sources, as well as with other MSW management methods such as recycling and landfilling

(6,56,60). In addition, they note that criteria such as the EP limits are conservative, particularly in terms of long-term dosages, to assure a wide margin of safety and account for individuals that have low tolerances to certain substances.

Results from leachate tests cannot be used quantitatively to predict potential health risks. However, rough indicators can be developed. For example, one toxicity index based on various physical and chemical conditions and pathways was used to compare different ash management scenarios at MSW landfills (56). Among the scenarios, MSW ash residues in monofills had the lowest relative risk ranking. However, quantitative risk assessments regarding ash do not exist.

Dioxins

In general, there is little information suggesting that dioxins and furans in ash pose significant risks. Sampling of field leachates has revealed low concentrations of dioxins and furans, generally in the parts-per-trillion (ppt) range. Together with leachate test results, this may indicate that dioxins and furans are relatively insoluble in water (150,151,181). The hydrophobic nature of dioxins, for example, suggests that they will tend to bind to ash and not to be leached by aqueous solutions into groundwater (166), unless microbial activity is sufficient to produce organic acids that can mobilize them (150). However, risk assessments still need to be conducted for the groundwater pathway to support this conclusion, and airborne and waterborne transport from landfills also need to be evaluated.

Metals

The metals of greatest concern in ash are lead and cadmium. Lead, for example, is a human neurotoxin, and some soluble lead salts and lead phosphate are carcinogenic to laboratory rats (174). As discussed above, concentrations of lead and cadmium in leachate extracted from most samples of fly ash and some samples of bottom and combined ash exceed EP limits. Distilled water extractions of fly ash,

designed to mimic disposal in a monofill, also have exceeded EP limits in a few tests (144).[18]

In contrast, most samples of actual field leachate from combined ash have not exceeded EP limits (table 6-7). In addition, lead and cadmium concentrations in ash from one new monofill have been shown to be less than or only slightly higher than Drinking Water Standards (60,61).

Some analysts suggest that **total** metal content should be used as a measure of ash toxicity (39). However, using the total content of lead, for example, is problematic because much of it is in insoluble forms or trapped in aluminosilicate material. In addition, total metal content may not account for how much of the metals actually move away from landfills and into groundwater.

However, total metal content may be more relevant for direct ingestion and inhalation pathways, in which solubility is not an important consideration (39). For example, potential exposure and risks associated with fugitive ash—i.e, during handling and disposal—at one ash monofill were considered as important as those associated with gas emissions (73).[19] Most of the incremental cancer risk was associated with ingestion and dermal absorption of arsenic. As a result, the vendor and municipality agreed to a plan to minimize fugitive emissions. In contrast, another analyst concluded that risks associated with ash dust were quite low (154).

Presorting MSW to remove metal or metal-containing products and materials could affect the risks associated with metals in ash. For example, most lead and cadmium in MSW comes from batteries and plastics (ch. 3). If the metal fraction could be separated and recycled prior to incineration, the amounts of these metals that are incorporated into incinerator emissions and ash should decrease. Some information from experiments at older facilities (see "Separation Prior to Collection or Combustion") indicates that presorting did lower concentrations of metals in subsequent ash. More

---

[18]A study of an old bottom ash landfill site, used from 1954 to 1973, indicated that lead concentrations in the soil were considerably above recommended levels and could lead to elevated blood levels in exposed children (162). However, other sources of lead were not analyzed, making it difficult to determine the relative importance of ash. In addition, design and operating conditions of new monofills differ considerably from this site.

[19]In comparison, lead concentrations in emissions from smelters and automobiles may be greater than in fugitive, dust-blown ash by a factor of 5 to 25 (153,154). This may depend, however, on the type of ash considered; fly ash particles are finer and more likely to be blown around, and finer particles tend to have higher metal concentrations.

research is needed to see how removal of various items affects the volume and toxicity of ash (144).

Ash Reuse and Treatment

Once MSW ash is collected, other management options besides landfilling exist. For example, **untreated** ash can be stabilized or solidified and then used in different ways—e.g., road construction, artificial reef construction, construction blocks, and landfill cover. Initial field research on the environmental effects of stabilized ash used in artificial reef construction looks promising (see "Artificial Reefs"). In addition, ferrous and nonferrous metals in the ash are recovered at some facilities by using screens, magnets, and other mechanical processes (67,80,100). Ash residues also can be **treated** chemically or thermally to decrease the likelihood of leaching.

Important questions remain unanswered, however, about the long-term effects of reused ash. EDF, for example, contends that long-term environmental testing needs to be conducted before full-scale ash reuse is allowed (38) because of questions about:

- the long-term physical integrity of stabilized ash products (e.g., will construction blocks used in buildings eventually crumble);
- the potential for occupational exposure (e.g., exposure to metals of workers sandblasting a building made of ash blocks); and
- the ability to take remedial action if problems occur, especially because reused ash products would be dispersed through commerce.

EDF also suggested that fly ash should be not be reused because of the high concentrations of metals and the failure of most fly ash samples to pass EP tests. Finally, EDF suggested that ash reuse should only proceed after regulations are developed to address these and other questions. Subjecting ash reuse to regulations that protect human health and the environment is consistent with OTA's conclusion that **all** MSW management methods should be regulated with these goals in mind (ch. 1).

Solidification and Reuse

Ash can be solidified by adding Portland cement or lime and dampening the mixture so that a concrete-like product forms. In theory, this immobilizes metals and inhibits leaching, allowing the blocks to be used for different purposes such as road aggregate and artificial reefs.

Road Aggregate—Reusing ash as a road aggregate was suggested decades ago. Bottom ash is used as road aggregate in several European countries (69,86,123,144), usually under some kind of guidelines. Denmark's rules for reusing ash residues in road construction, for example, require that the ash contain less than 25 percent fly ash and that reuse not occur less than 20 meters from drinking water wells (144). Over two dozen U.S. companies have expressed interest in using solidified ash in road beds or concrete construction (53).

Little research has been conducted, however, on the long-term fate of metals in road aggregate and on concentrations of leachate compared with other sources (e.g., surface runoff of oils, greases, and lead). Some initial research has been conducted in Tampa, Florida (198). In February 1987, a street was paved with an asphaltic concrete aggregate containing up to 15 percent incinerator ash treated with industrial reagents. The treated incinerator ash consistently passed EP toxicity tests; one sample of the asphaltic aggregate was tested and also passed. Runoff from the street was tested for 13 months (with an American Public Health Association method, not the EP toxicity method). Concentrations of 10 metals, including all 8 subject to EP limits, were below the Drinking Water Standards (except for lead in 1 of 16 samples). Three metals (iron, manganese, and sodium) exceeded the standards in some cases. These results are promising, but because test data are limited to about 1 year additional research is needed.

Artificial Reefs—Research at the State University of New York at Stony Brook is examining the feasibility of using stabilized incinerator ash, in the form of blocks manufactured from crushed combined ash and Portland cement, for artificial reef construction (145,146,147,148,149). Initial laboratory analyses revealed that the ash blocks contained significantly higher concentrations of lead, copper, zinc, cadmium, nickel, and chromium than ordinary cement blocks or Portland cement (149).

As a result, laboratory leaching studies were performed to determine the potential for releasing

Photo credit: Office of Technology Assessment

This pile of pelletized, solidified ash resulted from adding cement and dampening the mixture to form a concrete-like product. Solidified ash could be used for road and building construction, artificial reefs, or landfill cover. Important questions remain, however, about the long-term effects of reused ash.

pollutants in marine waters.[20] Concentrations of lead, cadmium, arsenic, and mercury were below RCRA limits. In addition, laboratory bioassays were performed on leachates from two samples of the stabilized combined ash (148). The activity of carbon-14 and chlorophyll-a pigments from diatoms was significantly reduced when the diatoms were exposed to a 10 percent concentration of the leachate. However, this concentration was considered unlikely to occur in most marine situations because of currents, although it might occur for short periods in small, enclosed embayments.

In April 1987, blocks were placed in two structures in the marine waters of Long Island Sound. After 1 year of submersion, the compressive strength of the ash blocks was unchanged and was well above the standard for marine disposal of stabilized prod-

ucts. In comparison, the strength of cement blocks declined by almost 30 percent in the same period.

Tests were conducted on the submerged blocks to see whether they retained metallic components. Of 13 metals tested, the only significant differences after 380 days of submersion were an increase in magnesium and a decrease in potassium. Metals such as lead, chromium, copper, and cadmium were retained within the block. The retention was attributed to the high alkalinity of the ash, the Portland cement additive, and alkalinity of the seawater—all of which favor formation of less soluble metal compounds and adsorption of metal ions (146).

The reef structures were colonized rapidly by hydroids, red and green algae, and bryozoans, which are common marine organisms, and they are visited commonly by different fish species. Initial monitor-

[20]A procedure with distilled water and filtered seawater was used.

ing found that the metal content of the hydroids growing on the ash blocks was not significantly different from those growing on cement blocks.

Treatment

Chemical treatment may lead to greater stabilization of ash and less leaching; research on this is being conducted, although results often are proprietary (144). One method involves passing ash through acidified water, with metals then extracted from the water. Others involve adding specific chemicals. Since 1987, for example, one company has been compacting combined ash and scrubber residues and adding lime (61). Tests after initial mixing show that the material has a particle size distribution similar to cement block aggregates, relatively low permeability, on the order of 10^{-6} cm/sec, and appears to retain metals in the block. After being allowed to cure for 7 to 28 days, permeability decreased to around 10^{-7} cm/sec. The company considered runoff over the treated ash to be of greater significance than leaching from the ash itself.

Vitrification is a thermal treatment method that involves melting ash into a solid residue. In Japan, for example, vitrification is used at about 4 out of almost 2,000 facilities (box 6-E). Little information is available regarding whether vitrification results in metals being volatilized and subsequently entrained in the flue gases.

Ash also can be combined with sewage sludge to help reduce leaching, at least under certain conditions. Lab and field studies indicate that microbial activity can result in the formation of lead carbonate, lead sulfide, and other salts, thereby reducing solubility (45,58,69). For example, bacteria present in sludge convert sulfate to sulfide, which combines with lead to produce lead sulfide, a relatively insoluble compound (45).

Regulatory Status

In 1980, EPA promulgated regulations that included a "household waste exclusion." This exclusion exempted MSW incinerator facilities that burned only **residential** MSW from being regulated as Subtitle C hazardous waste treatment facilities (144). Although the regulations did not specifically address ash residues, EPA generally applied the exclusion to include ash.

In 1984, Congress attempted to clarify and expand the exclusion. In particular, Section 3001(i) of the 1984 Hazardous and Solid Waste Act, which amended RCRA, extended the exclusion to **all waste-to-energy** facilities that burn any type of MSW and have a program to keep hazardous wastes out. However, Congress did not clarify whether **ash** from these facilities also was exempt from regulation as a hazardous waste.

As a result, confusion exists over whether ash should be managed as a hazardous waste if it fails the standard EP toxicity test. In 1985, EPA stated that if an ash exhibited hazardous characteristics on the basis of the test, then the facility producing the ash would not be exempt from having to manage it as hazardous (50 *Federal Register* 28735, July 15, 1985). However, EPA has not enforced this. In addition, few guidelines exist on the design and operating standards that Subtitle D facilities should meet for managing ash that is not considered hazardous. In 1987, EPA drafted some design and operating guidelines (186). However, EPA indicated in March 1988 that no guidelines on ash would be issued until the agency received directions from Congress (166). EPA's proposed criteria for Subtitle D landfills (ch. 7) do not address ash management in detail, although many of the provisions (e.g., location, closure and post-closure requirement, and financial assurance) presumably would apply to ash management facilities.

Failure to resolve these issues has created great uncertainty about what regulations are now required and what will be required in the future. In 1988, to obtain a legal clarification as to whether ash that fails the EP test is a hazardous waste, the Environmental Defense Fund (EDF) filed suits against the City of Chicago and Wheelabrator Technologies, Inc.[21] These cases are still in court. EDF also sent letters to other facility operators explaining its position on testing and ash management.

Most bills proposed in Congress during the 100th and 101st sessions would permit ash to be managed under Subtitle D, so long as procedures existed to ensure that landfill operators did not receive hazard-

---

[21]Civ. 88-0769, N.D. Ill., and Civ. 88-0560, S.D.N.Y., respectively.

ous wastes (other than hazardous household wastes, or hazardous wastes from "Very Small Quantity Generators," i.e., less than 100 kilograms per month). These proposed bills have tended to require that ash be managed by itself in a monofill with a single composite liner and leachate collection system, or be co-disposed with MSW in a landfill with a double liner and two leachate collection systems, in both cases with groundwater monitoring.[22] Most bills would allow ash to be reused if it passed specific tests to be established by EPA. Other proposed provisions include allowing alternate landfill designs in response to hydrologic and other conditions, if the designs provide similar protection as other required designs; allowing EPA to decide whether fly and bottom ash should be separated or not; allowing co-disposal with MSW only if the ash passes yet-to-be-developed tests; and requiring EPA to establish a framework for deciding when to remove certain items from MSW prior to incineration.

The provisions regarding management of ash under Subtitle D, in single-lined monofills or double-lined landfills, generally are favored by industry representatives and many solid waste management officials. One industry group, for example, suggested that disposal be allowed in monofills without testing and that co-disposal be allowed only if the ash passes an appropriate test (or is subsequently treated and passes the test) (101).

Similarly, Resources for the Future recommended that ash be managed in monofills that have a single liner, appropriate run-off controls, final cover, leachate collection, and groundwater monitoring (144). RFF also recommends moving toward managing ash on the basis of tests that can accurately predict the long-term toxicity of ash, but it concluded that such tests have not been developed yet. RFF also concluded that there is no strong justification to keep fly ash and bottom ash separate.

Some environmental groups oppose parts of this type of regulatory regime because few existing landfills have groundwater monitoring and leachate collection systems and because long-term exposures and risks from ash are uncertain. In general, they propose that ash be managed separately on the basis

of tests currently required under RCRA (i.e., if ash fails the EP test, then it should be managed as hazardous) and that greater attention be given to removing materials likely to contribute to ash toxicity (39). EDF also proposed that ash monofills be designed with two liners (an upper synthetic liner and a bottom composite liner) and two leachate collection systems, and that the monofill be covered after filling with a composite cap overlain by a vegetative cover (48). Some environmental groups also argue that bottom and fly ash should be not be combined (127); RFF concluded that allowing co-disposal of ash and MSW is generally a poor practice (144).

These issues, discussed in more detail in chapter 1, are further complicated by a recent EPA proposal to lower the maximum contaminant level (MCL) for lead in drinking water (53 *Federal Register* 31516, Aug. 18, 1988). The limit for lead in the EP test is based on multiplying the MCL by 100 to account for attenuation and dilution. EPA would have to decide whether or not to change this. If the 100-fold factor were retained, then much more ash would fail the EP test. Additional research is needed on attenuation factors for different substances and varying hydrologic conditions (144).

CHAPTER 6 REFERENCES

1. Alter, H., "The History of Refuse-Derived Fuels," *Resources and Conservation* 15:251-275, 1987.
2. Alternative Resources, Inc., "Coordinated Permits Application to Construct the Robbins Resource Recovery Facility," submitted to Illinois Environmental Protection Agency (Concord, MA: December 1988).
3. Alternative Sources of Energy, "Waste to Energy: The Exception to the Rule," *Alternative Sources of Energy*, pp. 10-11, January 1988.
4. American Society of Mechanical Engineers, "Proposed ASME Standard for the Qualification and Certification of Resource Recovery Facility Operators, QRO-1-19xx" Draft 5.1 (New York, NY: June 1989).
5. American Society of Mechanical Engineers, "Status Report, ASME/U.S. Bureau of Mines Investigative Program: Vitrification of Residue from Municipal Waste Combustion Facilities" (Washington, DC: May 30, 1989).

---

[22]Lined monofills are used at some facilities in several States (e.g., Florida, Massachusetts, New Hampshire, New Jersey, New York, and Oregon) (13,56,101).

6. Ames, B.N., "Six Common Errors Relating to Environmental Pollution," *Water* 27(4):20-222, Winter 1986.

7. Argonne National Laboratory, *Pyrolysis of Municipal Solid Waste, Annual Report, July 1985-June 1986*, ANL/CNSV-62 (Chicago, IL: 1987).

8. Aslander, O., "The Swedish Dioxine Moratorium," paper presented at *ASCE Dioxin Symposium* (New York, NY: Feb. 10, 1987).

9. Atanasio, P., "Public or Private Ownership of a Resource Recovery Project," unpublished manuscript, Dean Witter Capital Markets (1988).

10. Bellush, S.M., "The Effects of Tax Law on Resource Recovery/Solid Waste Financing," *Resource Recovery/Cogeneration World*, pp. 16-19, March-April 1988.

11. Biles, S., "A Review of Municipal and Hazardous Waste Management Practices and Facilities in Seven European Countries," paper prepared for German Marshall Fund of the United States (Washington, DC: February 1987).

12. Boley, G., Combustion Engineering, personal communication, August 1988.

13. Browning-Ferris Industries, "Letter from R.F. Goodstein, Washington Counsel, to W.J. Porter, Assistant Administrator, U.S. Environmental Protection Agency," Dec. 15, 1987.

14. Bridle, T.R., Cote, P.L., Constable, T.W., and Fraser, J.L., "Evaluation of Heavy Metal Leachability From Solid Wastes," *Water Sci. Technol.* 19:1029-1036, 1987.

15. California Assembly, *Integrated Solid Waste Management: Putting a Lid on Garbage Overload*, prepared by the Assembly Office of Research and the Assembly Natural Resources Committee (Sacramento, CA: April 1988).

16. Caponi, F.R., and Carry, C.W., "Overview of Air Quality Testing Programs at the Commerce Refuse-to-Energy Facility," Paper No. 88-24.8 presented at *81st Annual Meeting of Air Pollution Control Association* (Dallas, TX: June 19-24, 1988).

17. Chen, P.M., "Financing Resource Recovery Projects (1989)," paper presented at *Mayors Leadership Institute*, 1989.

18. Christrup, J., "Rising From the Ashes," *Greenpeace* 13(2):6-10, May-June 1988.

19. Churney, K.L., Ledrod, Jr., A.E., Bruce, S.S., and Domalski, E.S., *The Chlorine Content of Municipal Solid Waste From Baltimore County, MD and Brooklyn, NY*, National Bureau of Standards report NBSIR 85-3213 (Gaithersburg, MD: October 1985).

20. Clarke, M.J., "Issues, Options and Choices for Control of Emissions From Resource Recovery Plants," paper presented at *Sixth Annual Resource Recovery Conference* (Washington, DC: Mar. 26-27, 1987).

21. Clarke, M.J., "Improving Environmental Performance of MSW Incinerators," paper presented at *Industrial Gas Cleaning Institute Forum '88* (Washington, DC: Nov. 3-4, 1988).

22. Clarke, M.J., "Laboratory Research to Identify the Predominant Sources of Pollutant Precursors in Municipal Solid Waste and Impacts on Emissions, Ash and Leachate," paper presented at *New England Section Air Pollution Control Association Conference on Hazardous and Municipal Solid Waste Minimization* (Providence, RI: Feb. 7-8, 1989).

23. Clarke, M.J., "Disapproval of QRO-1-19xx Draft 5—April 1989," memorandum to D. Wizda, American Society of Mechanical Engineers (New York, NY: INFORM, June 2, 1989).

24. Clarke, M.J., "Technologies for Minimizing the Emission of NO_x From MSW Incinerators," Paper No. 89-167.4 presented at *82nd Annual Meeting, Air and Waste Management Association* (Anaheim, CA: June 26-30, 1989).

25. Clay, D., "Is New Legislation Needed on Incinerator Air Emissions?" *Waste Age*, pp. 40-46, June 1988.

26. Commoner, B., Webster, T., and Shapiro, K., *The Origin and Health Risks of PCDD and PCDF*, paper presented at *Conference on Solid Waste Management and Materials Policy* (New York, NY: Feb. 11-14, 1987).

27. Connett, P., and Webster, T., "Municipal Waste Incineration and Risk Analyses: The Need to Ask Larger Questions," unpublished manuscript (Canton, NY: St. Lawrence University, 1988).

28. Constable, T.W., Environment Canada, personal communication, Feb. 15, 1989.

29. Cook, R.J., Kalamazoo College, personal communication, July 20, 1988.

30. Cooper Engineers, Inc., *Air Emissions and Performance Testing of a Dry Scrubber (Quench Reactor), Dry Venturi and Fabric Filter System Operating on a Flue Gas From Combustion of Municipal Solid Waste in Japan*, report prepared for West County Agency of Contra Costa County, California (Richmond, CA: May 1985).

31. Council of State Governments and New York State Legislative Commission on Solid Waste Management, "Solid Waste Programs in the States," *J. Resource Management and Technology* 15(3):131-144, September 1987.

32. Cox, K.A., *The National Status of Municipal Solid Waste Activities: A Summary of Selected Surveys on State MSW Programs*, contract report prepared for

the U.S. Congress, Office of Technology Assessment (Takoma Park, MD: May 1988).

33. Darcey,, S., "Recovery Projects Grow Despite Recent Setbacks," *World Wastes* 32(6):24-25,55, June 1989.

34. Denison, R.A., Environmental Defense Fund, personal communication at Office of Technology Assessment "Workshop on Incineration/Waste-to-Energy Issues" (Washington, DC: June 28, 1988).

35. Denison, R.A., "Figure 3a, Dioxin/Furan Content of Fly Ash From Municipal Waste Incinerators, Expressed as 2,3,7,8-TCDD Toxic Equivalents. Summary of Data for All Samples, Grouped by Country, Linear Plot," copyright (Washington, DC: Environmental Defense Fund, 1988).

36. Denison, R.A., Environmental Defense Fund, personal communication, May 1989.

37. Denison, R.A., "Figure 1, Concentration of Lead in Leachates of Combined Fly Ash, Scrubber Residue, and Bottom Ash as a Function of Leachate pH," unpublished data (Washington, DC: Environmental Defense Fund, undated).

38. Denison, R.A., "Ash Utilization: An Idea Before Its Time?" unpublished manuscript (Washington, DC: Environmental Defense Fund, undated).

39. Denison, R.A., and Silbergeld, E.K., "Comprehensive Management of Municipal Solid Waste Incineration: Understanding the Risks," in Oak Ridge National Lab Office of Risk Analysis, ed., *Municipal Waste Incineration Risk Management* (Boca Raton, FL: CRC Press, 1989 in press).

40. Donnelly, J.R., and Jons, E., "By-product Disposal From MSW Incinerator Flue Gas Cleaning Systems," Paper No. 87-94A.3 presented at *80th Annual Meeting of Air Pollution Control Association* (New York, NY: June 21-26, 1987).

41. Donnelly, J.R., Quach, M.T., and Moller, J.T., "Joy/Niro SDA Systems for MSW Incineration, European Operating Results," Paper No. 87-26.8 presented at *80th Annual Meeting of Air Pollution Control Association* (New York, NY: June 21-26, 1987).

42. Donnelly, J.R., Quach, M.T., and Moller, J.T., "Joy/Niro MSW Incinerator FGC Systems, European Experience-An Update," Paper No. 88-98.5 presented at *81st Annual Meeting of Air Pollution Control Association* (Dallas, TX: June 19-24 1988).

43. Eighmy, T.T., University of New Hampshire, personal communication, Feb. 16, 1989.

44. Eighmy, T.T., Collins, M.R., DiPietro, J.V., and Guay, M.A., "Factors Affecting Inorganic Leaching Phenomena From Incineration Residues," paper presented at *Conference on Municipal Solid Waste Technology* (San Diego, CA: Jan. 30-Feb. 1, 1989).

45. Eighmy, T.T., Guay, M.A., et al., "Heavy Metal Immobilization During the Codisposal of Municipal Solid Waste Bottom Ash and Wastewater Sludges," Paper No. 88-26.10 presented at *81st Annual Meeting of Air Pollution Control Association* (Dallas, TX: June 19-24 1988).

46. Environmental Defense Fund, "Ash From Municipal Solid Waste Incineration Fact Sheet" (Washington, DC: undated).

47. Environmental Defense Fund, "Summary of All Available EP Toxicity Testing Data on Incinerator Ash" (Washington, DC: February 1989).

48. Environmental Defense Fund, "EDF Proposal for Design of MSW Incinerator Ash Monofills" (Washington, DC: Mar. 3, 1989).

49. Environmental Research Group, "Application for a Research Development and Demonstration Permit To: Waste Management Division, New Hampshire Department of Environmental Services," University of New Hampshire, Department of Civil Engineering (Durham, NH: May 10, 1988).

50. Environment Canada, Environmental Protection Service, "National Incinerator Testing and Evaluation (NITEP), P.E.I. Testing Program, Volume II," unpublished report prepared by Concord Scientific Corp. (Downsview, Ontario, Canada: June 1985).

51. Environment Canada, Environmental Protection Service, "The National Incinerator Testing and Evaluation Program: Two-stage Combustion (Prince Edward Island)," Report EPS 3/UP/1 (Ottawa, Canada: September 1985).

52. Environment Canada, "The National Incinerator Testing and Evaluation Program: Air Pollution Control Technology," Report EPS 3/UP/2 (Ottawa, Canada: September 1986).

53. Environment Reporter, "EPA to Develop Ash Mangement Strategy, Present it for SAB Review Within Two Months," *Environment Reporter* 18(53): 2548-2549, April 29, 1988.

54. Environment Reporter, "EPA Region X Calls for Recycling as Possible Incinerator Permit Condition," *Environment Reporter* 19(49):2565-2566, Apr. 7, 1989.

55. Feldman, R.D., Middleton, G.L., Jr., and Rescoe, M.E., "Needed: A Way to Privately Finance Refuse-to-Energy Plants; Found: Master Limited Partnerships," *Waste Age*, pp. 121-124, August 1987.

56. Ferraro, F.A., Wheelabrator Environmental Systems, Inc., letter to U.S. Congress, Office of Technology Assessment, Feb. 16-17, 1989.

57. Ferraro, F.A., and Parenteau, R.J., "Results of Emissions and Ash Testing at the Maine Energy Recovery Company Waste-to-Energy Plant," Paper

No. 88-21.7 presented at *81st Annual Meeting of Air Pollution Control Association* (Dallas, TX: June 19-24, 1988).

58. Fichtel, K., and Beck, W., "Leaching Behavior of Residues From Waste Incinerators, as Illustrated by the Grossmehring Residue Dump," translation, *MULL und ABFALL*, pp. 220-224, August 1984.

59. First, M.W., "Statement of Melvin W. First before the Municipal Solid Waste Task Force," Needham, Massachusetts, May 9, 1988.

60. Forrester, K.E., "Comparison of Municipal Solid Waste Leachate to MSW Ash Residue Leachate Using a Risk Algorithm," unpublished manuscript (Danvers, MA: Wheelabrator Environmental Systems, Inc., October 1988).

61. Forrester, K.E., "State-of-the-Art in Thermal Recycling Facility Ash Residue Handling, Reuse, Landfill Design and Management," unpublished manuscript (Danvers, MA: Wheelabrator Environmental Systems, Inc., January 1989).

62. Francis, C.W. and White, G.H., "Leaching of Toxic Metals From Incinerator Ashes," *J. Water Pollution Control Federation* 59(11):979-986, Nov. 1987.

63. Franke, B., "Review of the Environmental Impacts of the Solid Waste Incinerators Proposed for Long Island and New York City," prepared for *Newsday* (Takoma Park, MD: Institute for Energy and Environmental Research, November 1987).

64. Franklin Associates, Ltd., *Characterization of Municipal Solid Waste in the United States, 1960 to 2000 (Update 1988)*, Final Report prepared for U.S. Environmental Protection Agency (Prairie Village, KS: March 1988).

65. Gershman, Brickner & Bratton, Inc., *Performance, Constraints, and Costs of MSW Management Technologies*, contract prepared for U.S. Congress, Office of Technology Assessment (Falls Church, VA: Sept. 26, 1988).

66. Gildart, M., California Waste Management Board, personal communication, Mar. 22, 1989.

67. Goldberg, D., "Recycling Metal From MSW Incinerator Ash," *Recycling Today*, pp. 34-40, November 1988.

68. Goldfarb, T.D., "Evidence for Post-Furnace Formation of PCDDs and PCDFs—Implications for Control," *Chemosphere* in press.

69. Gortz, W., "Problems in Evaluating the Risk of Water Contamination by Solids From Incinerator Residues," translation, *Gewaesserschutz, Wasser* 99:144-169, 1987.

70. Governmental Advisory Associates, Inc., *1986 Resource Recovery Yearbook* (New York, NY: 1986).

71. Gregory, W., Smith Barney, personal communication at Office of Technology Assessment "Workshop on Incineration/Waste-to-Energy Issues" (Washington, DC: June 28, 1988).

72. Gregory, W.T., "Letter From W.T. Gregory, Managing Director, Smith Barney, to J. Kowalski, Office of Technology Assessment," Dec. 15, 1988.

73. Guldberg, P.H., and Eschenroeder, A.Q., "The Health Risks of Fugitive Ash Emissions From the Haverhill Resource Recovery Facility Ash Monofill," Paper No. 89-6.9 presented at *82nd Annual Meeting, Air and Waste Management Association* (Anaheim, CA: June 26-30, 1989).

74. Hagenmaier, H., Brunner, H., Haag, R., and Kraft, M., "Copper-catalyzed Dechlorination/Hydrogenation of Polychlorinated Dibenzo-*p*-dioxins, Polychlorinated Dibenzofurans and Other Chloroaromatic Compounds," *Environ. Sci. Technol.* 21(11):1085-1088, 1987.

75. Hagenmaier, H., Kraft, M., Brunner, H., and Haag, R., "Catalytic Effects of Fly Ash From Waste Incineration Facilities on the Formation and Decomposition of Polychlorinated Dibenzo-*p*-dioxins and Polychlorinated Dibenzofurans," *Environ. Sci. Technol.* 21(11):1080-1084, 1987.

76. Hahn, J.L., Ogden Projects, Inc., personal communication, August-September 1988.

77. Hahn, J.L., Ogden Projects, Inc., personal communication, Mar. 1, 1989.

78. Hahn, J.L. and Sofaer, D.S., "Variability of NO_x Emissions From Modern Mass-fired Resource Recovery Facilities," Paper No. 88-21.7 presented at *81st Annual Meeting of Air Pollution Control Association* (Dallas, TX: June 19-24, 1988).

79. Hahn, J.L., and Sofaer, D.S., "Environmental Test Results From the Stanislaus County, California Resource Recovery Facility," Paper No. 89-20.4 presented at *82nd Annual Meeting, Air and Waste Management Association* (Anaheim, CA: June 26-30, 1989).

80. Hahn, J.L., and Sussman, D.B., "Municipal Waste Combustion Ash: Testing Methods, Constituents and Potential Risks," *Resource Recovery* 2(5):16-18, December 1988.

81. Hahn, J.L., Von Dem Fange, H.P., Jordan, R.J., Finney, J.A., and Bahor, B., "Air Emissions Tests of a Deutsche Babcock Anlagen Dry Scrubber System at the Munich North Refuse-fired Power Plant," Paper No. 85-76B.1 presented at *78th Annual Meeting of Air Pollution Control Association* (Detroit, MI: June 16-21, 1985).

82. Hahn, J.L., Von Dem Fange, H.P., and Sofaer, D., "Recent Air Emissions Data From Ogden Martin Systems, Inc. Resource Recovery Facilities Which

Became Operational During 1988,'' Paper No. 89-109.1 presented at *82nd Annual Meeting, Air and Waste Management Association* (Anaheim, CA: June 26-30, 1989).

83. Hahn, J.L., Von Dem Fange, H.P., and Westerman, G., ''A Comparison of Ambient and Workplace Dioxin Levels From Testing In and Around Modern Resource Recovery Facilities With Predicted Ground Level Concentrations of Dioxins From Stack Emission Testing With Corresponding Workplace Health Risks,'' paper presented at *Dioxin '88, Eighth International Symposium on Chlorinated Dioxins and Related Compounds* (Umea, Sweden: Aug. 21-26, 1988).

84. Hahn, J.L., Von Dem Fange, H.P., Zurlinden, R.A., et al., ''Air Emissions Testing at the Wurzburg, West Germany Waste-to-Energy Facility,'' unpublished manuscript, June 1986.

85. Hamner, R.W., U.S. Environmental Protection Agency, Office of Water, letter to K. Kamlet, June 7, 1988.

86. Hartlen, J., ''Incinerator Ash Utilization in Some Countries in Europe,'' paper presented at *1988 Conference on Ash Utilization* (Philadelphia, PA: 1988).

87. Hasselriis, F., ''Technical Guidance Relative to Municipal Waste Incineration,'' report prepared for New York State Department of Environmental Conservation, Division of Air Task Force on Municipal Waste Incineration (Albany, NY: Aug. 18, 1985).

88. Hasselriis, F., ''What's In Our Garbage?'' *Waste Alternatives/Waste-to-Energy* 1(2):74-77, September 1988.

89. Hawley-Fedder, R.A., Parsons, M.L., and Karasek, F.W., ''Products Obtained During Combustion of Polymers Under Simulated Incinerator Conditions. I. Polyethylene,'' *Journal of Chromatography* 314:263-273, 1984.

90. Hawley-Fedder, R.A., Parsons, M.L., and Karasek, F.W., ''Products Obtained During Combustion of Polymers Under Simulated Incinerator Conditions. II. Polystyrene,'' *Journal of Chromatography* 315:201-210, 1984.

91. Hawley-Fedder, R.A., Parsons, M.L., and Karasek, F.W., ''Products Obtained During Combustion of Polymers Under Simulated Incinerator Conditions. III. Polyvinyl Chloride,'' *Journal of Chromatography* 315:211-221, 1984.

92. Hazardous Waste News, ''Study Finds Poor Neighborhoods Make Best Sites for Incinerators,'' *Hazardous Waste News* No. 81 (Princeton, NJ: Environmental Research Foundation, June 13, 1988).

93. Health Risk Associates, *Health Risk Assessment for the Brooklyn Navy Yard Resource Recovery Facility* (Berkeley, CA: November 1988).

94. Hershkowitz, A., and Salerni, E., *Garbage Management in Japan, Leading the Way* (New York: INFORM, 1987).

95. Hershkowitz, A., *International Experiences in Solid Waste Management*, contract prepared for U.S. Congress, Office of Technology Assessment (Elmsford, NY: Municipal Recycling Associates, October 1988).

96. Hjelmar, O., ''Leachate From Incinerator Ash Disposal Sites,'' paper presented at *International Workshop on Municipal Waste Incineration* (Montreal: Oct. 1-2, 1987).

97. Inside EPA, ''Environmentalists Launch Push to Get Mandated Recycling for Incinerators,'' *Inside EPA* 10(21):1,9-10, May 26, 1989.

98. Institute for Local Self-Reliance, *Garbage in Europe: Technologies, Economics, and Trends* (Washington, DC: May 1988).

99. Institute for Local Self-Reliance, ''Cities Cancel Incineration Plans, Herald Recycling Comeback,'' news release (Washington, DC: Aug. 5, 1988).

100. Institute of Resource Recovery, ''Management of Municipal Waste Combustion Ash'' (Washington, DC: undated).

101. Institute of Resource Recovery, ''Letter From J. Lyman, Director, to P. Prowitt, Staff Director, Senate Environment and Public Works Committee,'' Jan. 7, 1988.

102. Kamlet, K.S., and Sowrey, B.S., ''Off-Shore Incineration of Municipal Solid Wastes'' (Alexandria, VA: A.T. Kearney, June 1988).

103. Kamlet, K.S., and Sowrey, B.S., ''Ocean Incineration, a New Approach to Municipal Solid Waste Management'' (Alexandria, VA: A.T. Kearney, June 1988).

104. Kerr, R., New York State Department of Environmental Conservation, personal communication, September 1988.

105. Kiser, J.V.L., ''Continuous Emissions Monitoring: A Primer,'' *Waste Age*, pp. 64-68, May 1988.

106. Kiser, J.V.L., ''More on Continuous Emissions Monitoring,'' *Waste Age*, pp. 119-124, June 1988.

107. Klicius, R., Finkelstein, A., and Hay, D.J., ''The National Incinerator Testing and Evaluation Program (NITEP) Mass Burning Technology Assessment,'' Paper No. 87-94.5 presented at *80th Annual Meeting of Air Pollution Control Association* (New York, NY: June 21-26, 1987).

108. Kleinau, J.H., ''Fluid Bed Combustion: Lessons Learned,'' *Waste Age*, pp. 274,275,277,282,284, April 1988.

109. Komiya, O., letter to U.S. Congress, Office of Technology Assessment, Mitsubishi International

Corp. reference no. NYC/MCB 6446 (New York, NY: Dec. 21, 1988).

110. Komiya, O., Mitsubishi International Corp., personal communication, Feb. 17, 1989.

111. Lane, W.R., and Khosla, A., "Comparison of Baghouse and Electrostatic Precipitator Fine Particulate, Trace Element and Total Emissions," paper presented at *ASME-IEEE Joint Power Generation Conference* (Indianapolis, IN: Sept. 27, 1983).

112. Lauber, J.D., "An Overview of Toxic Emissions and Best Available Control Technology for Municipal Waste Incineration," paper presented at *ASCE Energy Division Specialty Conference "Energy 87"* (Atlantic City, NJ: Apr. 27-30, 1987).

113. Mader, P., Pyrolyse Kraftanlagen GmbH, Federal Republic of Germany, personal communication, October 1988.

114. Magee, R.S., "Plastics in Municipal Solid Waste Incineration: A Literature Study," prepared for the Society of Plastics Industry (Newark, NJ: Hazardous Substance Management Research Center, January 1989).

115. Magnusson, J., "Energy From Solid Waste— Conclusion From a Study by the National Energy Administration and the National Protection Board," paper presented at *An Environmentally Acceptable Solution to the Solid Waste Problem*, symposium sponsored by Swedish Trade Council and National Resources Recovery Association (Washington, DC: Mar. 23, 1988).

116. McCoy, R.W., Jr., Sweetnam, R.J., Jr., and Liker, M.A., "Resource Recovery as of December 31, 1987," Kidder, Peabody Equity Research Industry Comment (New York, NY: Kidder, Peabody & Co., Apr. 29, 1988).

117. McDonald, B., ESA, personal communication, Sept. 1988.

118. McInnes, R.G., and Kohl, N.H., "Heavy Metal Emissions From Resource Recovery Facilities," paper presented at *Sixth Annual New England Resource Recovery Conference & Exposition* (Manchester, NH: June 9-11, 1987).

119. Michigan Department of Natural Resources, "Staff Activity Report on Permit to Install a Resource Recovery System in Detroit, Michigan" (Lansing, MI: Air Quality Division, Apr. 9, 1986).

120. Michigan Department of Natural Resources, *European Study Tour, Composting and Recycling*, Report on trip conducted October 10-24, 1987 (Lansing, MI: 1987).

121. Minnesota Pollution Control Agency, *Supplemental Health Risk Assessment Technical Work Paper, Volume I: Polychlorinated Dioxins/Polychlorinated Furans, Winona County Resource Recovery Facility, Winona, Minnesota*, prepared by J.B. Stevens & Associates (April 1988).

122. Minott, D.H., "Operating Principles and Environmental Performance of Fluid-bed Energy Recovery Facilities," Paper No. 88-21.9 presented at *81st Annual Meeting of Air Pollution Control Association* (Dallas, TX: June 19-24, 1988).

123. Modig, S., "Swedish View of the Ash Issue," paper presented at *An Environmentally Acceptable Solution to the Solid Waste Problem*, symposium sponsored by Swedish Trade Council and National Resources Recovery Association (Washington, DC: Mar. 23, 1988).

124. Moody's Investors Service, "Resource Recovery: an Overview," *Moody's Municipal Issues* 4(3):1-16, September-October 1987.

125. Nakazato, K., Takuma Co., Ltd., personal communication, April 1988.

126. National Solid Waste Management Association, letter to U.S. Congress, Office of Technology Assessment (Washington, DC: February 1989).

127. Natural Resources Defense Council, Environmental Defense Fund, INFORM, et al., *A Solid Waste Blueprint for New York State* (New York, NY: March 1988).

128. Natusch, D.F.S., Wallace, J.R., and Evans, C.A., Jr., "Toxic Trace Elements: Preferential Concentration in Respirable Particles," *Science 183: 202-204, Jan. 18, 1974.*

129. New York State Energy and Research Development Authority, *Results of the Combustion and Emissions Research Project at the Vicon Incinerator Facility in Pittsfield, Massachusetts, Final Report (Volume I)*, Report 87-16 (Albany, NY: June 1987).

130. NUS Corp., "Final Work Plan," NUS Project No. 0081, submitted to U.S. Environmental Protection Agency and Coalition on Resource Recovery and the Environment (Pittsburg, PA: December 1988).

131. Ogden Projects, Inc., "Environmental Test Report, Marion County Solid Waste-to-Energy Facility Boilers 1 and 2," Report No. 118 (Emeryville, CA: Dec. 19, 1986).

132. Ogden Projects, Inc., "Environmental Test Report, Marion County Solid Waste-to-Energy Facility Boilers 1 and 2," Report No. 119 (Emeryville, CA: Dec. 22, 1986).

133. Ogden Projects, Inc., "Ogden Haverhill Associates' Responses to Information Requests by the Haverhill Board of Health, Set V" (Emeryville, CA: Nov. 10, 1987).

134. Ogden Projects, Inc., "Environmental Test Report, Bristol Resource Recovery Facility," Report No. 153 Revised (Emeryville, CA: Apr. 7, 1988).

135. Ogden Projects, Inc., "Hydrogen Chloride Interference in U.S. EPA Method 8," Technical Bulletin No. 01 (Emeryville, CA: June 17, 1988).

136. Olson, P., and Hedlund, K., "Impact of Tax Reform on Resource Recovery Projects," *Resource Recovery* 2:32-35, 1987.

137. Oregon Department of Environmental Quality, Laboratory Division, "Extraction Procedure Toxicity (EPtox) Characterization of Municipal Incinerator Ash From Ogden Martin, Brooks" (Portland, OR: May 1987).

138. Oregon Department of Environmental Quality, Laboratory Division, "Toxicity Characteristic Leaching Procedure (TCLP), Extraction Procedure Toxicity (EPtox), and Deionized Water Leaching Characteristics of Lead From Municipal Waste Incinerator Ash" (Portland, OR: July 1987).

139. Pasek, R.J., and Lindner, G.P., "Toxic Emission Sampling at the Commerce Refuse to Energy Facility," Paper No. 89-6.3 presented at *82nd Annual Meeting, Air and Waste Management Association* (Anaheim, CA: June 26-30, 1989).

140. Penner, S.S., Wiesenhahn, D.F., and Li, C.P., "Mass Burning of Municipal Wastes," *Ann. Rev. Energy* 12:415-444, 1987.

141. Peterson, P.R., Kaempf, E.R., and Mills, D.R., "Market Prospects for Refuse-to-Energy Development in California," undated manuscript.

142. Pollock, C., *Mining Urban Wastes: The Potential For Recycling*, Worldwatch Paper 76 (Washington, DC: Worldwatch Institute, April 1987).

143. Rappe, C., "Swedish View of the Dioxin Issue," paper presented at *An Environmentally Acceptable Solution to the Solid Waste Problem*, symposium sponsored by Swedish Trade Council and National Resources Recovery Association (Washington, DC: Mar. 23, 1988).

144. Resources for the Future, Center for Risk Management, *Management of Municipal Waste Combustor Ash* (Washington, DC: 1989).

145. Roethel, F.J., "Ash Disposal Solution is 2,000 Years Old," *Waste Age*, pp. 66-69, February 1987.

146. Roethel, F.J., and Breslin, V.T., "Unique Method of Ash Disposal Can Benefit Marine Life," *Solid Waste & Power* 2(5):42-48, October 1988.

147. Roethel, F.J., and Breslin, V.T., "Stabilized Incinerator Ash Tested in Construction of Artificial Reef," *Waste Management Research Report* 1(2):3-8, Spring 1989.

148. Roethel, F.J., Breslin, V.T., Schaeperkoetter, V., and Woodhead, P., "Stabilized Incineration Residue: A Possible Substrate for Artificial Reef Construction," undated manuscript.

149. Roethel, F.J., Schaeperkoetter, V., Gregg, R., and Park, K., *The Fixation of Incineration Residues, Final Report*, prepared for New York State Legislative Commission on the Water Resource Needs of Long Island (Stony Brook, NY: State University of New York, Marine Sciences Research Center, August 1986).

150. Sawell, S.E., Bridle, T.R., and Constable, T.W., "Leachability of Organic and Inorganic Contaminants in Ashes From Lime-based Air Pollution Control Devices on a Municipal Waste Incinerator," Paper No. 87-94A.4 presented at *80th Annual Meeting of Air Pollution Control Association* (New York, NY: June 21-26, 1987).

151. Sawell, S.E., and Constable, T.W., "NITEP Phase IIB: Assessment of Contaminant Leachability From the Residues of a Mass Burning Incinerator," volume VI of *National Incinerator Testing and Evaluation Program, The Combustion Characterization of Mass Burning Incinerator Technology, Quebec City* (Toronto, Canada: Environment Canada, August 1988).

152. Science Applications International Corp. and Meridian Corp., *Waste-to-Energy Compendium*, Revised 1988 edition, prepared for U.S. Department of Energy, Office of Conservation and Renewable Energy, Biofuels and Municipal Waste Technology Division (Alexandria, VA: December 1988).

153. Shaub, W.M., "Air Emissions Control and Ash Problems," background document for presentation at *Solid Waste Management Options for Texas Conference (Washington, DC: CORRE, May 19, 1988)*.

154. Shaub, W.M., "Incineration—Some Environmental Perspectives," paper submitted at Office of Technology Assessment Workshop on Incineration/Waste-to-Energy Issues (Washington, DC: June 28, 1988).

155. Shaub, W.M., "An Overview of What is Known About Dioxin and Furan Formation, Destruction, and Control During Incineration of MSW," paper presented at *Municipal Solid Waste Technology Conference* (San Diego, CA: Jan. 30-Feb. 1, 1989).

156. Shaub, W.M., Coalition on Resource Recovery and the Environment, personal communication, Feb. 15, 1989.

157. Siebert, P.C., Alston, D.R., Walsh, J.F., and Jones, K.H., "Statistical Properties of Available Worldwide MSW Combustion Dioxin/Furan Emissions," Paper No. 87.94.1 presented at *80th Annual Meeting of Air Pollution Control Association* (New York, NY: June 21-26, 1987).

158. Signal Environmental Systems, Inc., *CARB/DER Draft Dioxins/Furans Test Report-Additions, Revisions* (Hampton, NH: May 18, 1987).

159. Sommer, E.J., "Recycling Helps Improve Incinerator Operations," *Waste Alternatives/Waste-to-Energy* 1(2):66-71,78, September 1988.

160. Sommer, E.J., Kenny, G.R., Kearley, J.A., and Roos, C.E., "Emissions, Heavy Metals, Boiler Efficiency, and Disposal Capacity for Mass Burn Incineration With a Presorted MSW Fuel," Paper No. 88-21.2 presented at *81st Annual Meeting of Air Pollution Control Association* (Dallas, TX: June 20-24, 1988).

161. Steinzor, R.I., "EPA to Draft New Superfund Municipal Settlement Policy," paper presented at *Resource Recovery Conference* (Arlington, VA: Nov. 15-16, 1988).

162. Stern, A.H., Munshi, A.A., and Goodman, A.K., "Potential Exposure Levels and Health Effects of Neighborhood Exposure to a Municipal Incinerator Bottom Ash Landfill," *Archives of Environmental Health* 44(1):40-48, 1989.

163. Swedish Association of Public Cleansing and Solid Waste Management, *Solid Waste Management in Sweden* (Malmo, Sweden: February 1988).

164. Tanaka, M., Institute of Public Health, Tokyo, Japan, personal communication, April 1988.

165. Tattam, T., "Rating Project Bonds Is More Complex," *Waste Age*, pp. 119-124, Nov. 1987.

166. Thomas, L., "Testimony of Lee Thomas before the House Appropriations Subcommitte on HUD-Independent Agencies," Mar. 22, 1988.

167. Tomisawa, S., and Kaihara, Y., "NO_x Removal Pilot Test of Catalytic Reduction in Municipal Incinerator," paper presented at *4th International Recycling Congress*, Oct. 30-Nov. 1, 1984.

168. U.S. Conference of Mayors, "Resource Recovery Activities," *City Currents* 6(4):1-27, October 1987.

169. U.S. Congress, Congressional Research Service, "Municipal Waste Incineration: An Analysis of Section 306 of S. 1894," Report 88-402ENR (Washington, DC:, May 31, 1988).

170. U.S. Congress, Office of Technology Assessment, *New Electric Power Technologies*, OTA-E-246 (Washington, DC: U.S. Government Printing Office, July 1985).

171. U.S. Congress, Office of Technology Assessment, *Ocean Incineration: Its Role in Managing Hazardous Waste*, OTA-O-313 (Washington, DC: U.S. Government Printing Office, August 1986).

172. U.S. Congress, Office of Technology Assessment, *Issues in Medical Waste Management*, OTA-BP-O-49 (Washington, DC: U.S. Government Printing Office, October 1988).

173. U.S. Congress, Office of Technology Assessment, *Technologies for Reducing Dioxin in the Manufacture of Bleached Wood Pulp*, Background Paper, OTA-BP-O-54 (Washington, DC: U.S. Government Printing Office, May 1989).

174. U.S. Department of Health and Human Services, *The Nature and Extent of Lead Poisoning in Children in the United States: A Report to Congress* (Atlanta, GA: Public Health Service, Agency for Toxic Substances and Disease Registry, July 1988).

175. U.S. Environmental Protection Agency, *Municipal Waste Combustion Study, Report to Congress*, EPA/530-SW-87-021a (Washington, DC: June 1987).

176. U.S. Environmental Protection Agency, *Municipal Waste Combustion Study, Emission Data Base for Municipal Waste Combustors*, EPA/530-SW-87-021b (Washington, DC: June 1987).

177. U.S. Environmental Protection Agency, *Municipal Waste Combustion Study, Characterization of the Municipal Waste Combustion Industry*, EPA/530-SW-87- 021h (Washington, DC: June 1987).

178. U.S. Environmental Protection Agency, *Municipal Waste Combustion Study, Combustion Control of Organic Emissions*, draft (Washington, DC: June 1987).

179. U.S. Environmental Protection Agency, *Municipal Waste Combustion Study: Assessment of Health Risks Associated With Municipal Waste Combustion Emissions*, EPA/530-SW-87-02 (Washington, DC: September 1987).

180. U.S. Environmental Protection Agency, *Characterization of Municipal Waste Combustor Ashes and Leachates From Municipal Solid Waste Landfills, Monofills, and Codisposal Sites*, prepared by NUS Corp. for Office of Solid Waste and Emergency Response, EPA/530-SW-87-028A (Washington, DC: October 1987).

181. U.S. Environmental Protection Agency, "Letter From Lee M. Thomas, Administrator, to the Honorable John D. Dingell, Chairman, Committe on Energy and Commerce," Oct. 8, 1987.

182. U.S. Environmental Protection Agency, Science Advisory Board, "Evaluation of Scientific Issues Related to Municipal Waste Combustion," SAB-EETFC-88-25 (Washington, DC: April 1988).

183. U.S. Environmental Protection Agency, *Municipal Waste Combustion Multipollutant Study, Summary Report*, Office of Air Quality Planning and Standards, EMB Report No. 86-MIN-03A (Research Triangle Park, NC: September 1988).

184. U.S. Environmental Protection Agency, *Municipal Waste Combustion Multipollutant Study, Characterization Emission Test Report*, Office of Air Quality Planning and Standards, EMB Report No. 87-MIN-04 (Research Triangle Park, NC: September 1988).

185. U.S. Environmental Protection Agency, *Municipal Waste Combustion Multipollutant Study, Shutdown/Startup Emission Test Report*, Office of Air Quality Planning and Standards, EMB Report No. 87-MIN-04A (Research Triangle Park, NC: September 1988).
186. U.S. Environmental Protection Agency, *Draft Guidance: Municipal Waste Combustion Ash*, EPA/530-SW-88-006 (Washington, DC: 1988).
187. U.S. Environmental Protection Agency, *Operation and Maintenance of Hospital Medical Waste Incinerators*, Control Technology Center, EPA-450/3-89-002 (Research Triangle Park, NC: March 1989).
188. U.S. Environmental Protection Agency, 'Spokane Regional Waste to Energy Project PSD Appeal No. 88-12 (Spokane, Washington),'' Memorandum From G. O'Neal, Air and Toxics Division, to R.L. McCallum, Chief Judicial Officer, EPA Region X (Seattle, WA: 1989).
189. Visalli, J.R., "A Comparison of Dioxin, Furan and Combustion Gas Data From Test Programs at Three MSW Incinerators," *Journ. Air Pollution Control Assoc.* 37(12):1451-1463, Dec. 1987.
190. Visalli, J.R., New York State Energy Research and Development Authority, personal communication at Office of Technology Assessment "Workshop on Incineration/Waste-to-Energy Issues" (Washington, DC: June 28, 1988).
191. Visalli, J.R., New York State Energy Research and Development Authority, Letter to U.S. Congress, Office of Technology Assessment (Albany, NY: June 30, 1988).
192. Vogg, H., Metzger, M., and Stieglitz, L., "Recent Findings on the Formation and Decomposition of PCDD/PCDF in Solid Municipal Waste Incineration," unpublished manuscript dated 1987.
193. Wakamura, Y., "Processing of Residue for Re-use or Disposal," unpublished manuscript (Tokyo, Japan: Itoh Takuma Resource Systems, Inc., 1987).
194. Walter, D.K., "Energy From Municipal Waste Plants in the U.S.," U.S. Department of Energy, Biofuels and Municipal Waste Technology Division, database printout (Washington, DC: February 1988).
195. Waste Age, "Waste Age 1987 Refuse Incineration and Waste-to-Energy Listings," *Waste Age*, pp. 203-224, November 1987.
196. Waste Age, "Waste Age 1988 Refuse Incineration and Waste-to-Energy Listings," *Waste Age*, pp. 195-212, November 1988.
197. Waste Distillation Technology, Inc., *Evaluation and Test Program of a 50-Ton Per Day "Waste Distillator,"* submitted to U.S. Department of Energy, Office of Inventors Support Division (Irvington-on-Hudson, NY: June 1985).
198. Waste Management Energy Systems, Inc., "McKay Bay Refuse-to-Energy Facility, Tampa, Florida, McKaynite Asphalt Test Report" (Tampa, FL: December 1987).
199. Waste-to-Energy, "Project Growth Seen Slowing, Operating Services Continuing to Expand," *Waste-to-Energy Report*, pp. 1-2, Mar. 9, 1988.
200. Waste-to-Energy, "House Subcommittee Slates Markup of Luken Ash Bill for Thursday," *Waste-to-Energy Report*, p. 1, May 18, 1988.
201. Webster, T., and Connett, P., "Critical Factors in the Assessment of Food Chain Contamination by PCDD/PCDF From Incinerators," paper presented at *Dioxin '87* (Las Vegas, NV: Oct. 4-9, 1987).
202. Webster, T., and Connett, P., "Cumulative Impact of Incineration on Agriculture: A Screening Procedure for Calculating Population Risk," paper presented at *Dioxin '88, Eighth International Symposium on Chlorinated Dioxins and Related Compounds* (Umea, Sweden: Aug. 21-26, 1988).
203. Westergard, B., "Mercury From Hogdalen Incineration Plant in Stockholm, 1972-1985," *Waste Management & Research* 4:21, 1986.
204. Wheless, E., County Sanitation Districts of Los Angeles County, personal communication, August 1988.
205. World Health Organization, "PCDD and PCDF Emissions From Incinerators for Municipal Sewage Sludge and Solid Waste—Evaluation of Human Exposure," report on World Health Organization meeting, Naples, Mar. 17-21, 1986 (Copenhagen: Regional Office for Europe, 1987).
206. Yasuhara, A., and Morita, M., "Formation of Chlorinated Aromatic Hydrocarbons by Thermal Decomposition of Vinylidene Chloride Polymer," *Environ. Sci. Technol.* 22:646-650, 1988.

Chapter 7

Landfilling

CONTENTS

Boxes

Figures

Tables

Landfilling

INTRODUCTION

Landfilling refers to disposing of waste on land in a series of compacted layers and covering it, usually daily, with soil or other materials such as compost. Landfilling is the primary method of MSW management in the United States today. It will continue to be needed to manage nonrecyclable, noncombustible materials, as well as residuals from recycling and incineration.

MSW landfill capacity in the United States is declining, however, because old landfills are being closed and because siting new facilities is difficult. One reason landfills are increasingly difficult to site is because of public concerns stemming from past practices, when uncontrolled "open dumping" was more common and sanitary landfills had few pollution controls. Open dumping often resulted in unsanitary conditions, methane explosions, and releases of hazardous substances to groundwater and the atmosphere, and old municipal landfills make up twenty-two percent of the sites on the Superfund National Priorities List (which was established under the Comprehensive Environmental Response, Compensation, and Liability Act, or CERCLA).

To address these concerns, Congress directed EPA, under Subtitle D of the Resource Conservation and Recovery Act (RCRA), to develop landfill criteria that included a prohibition on open dumping; EPA issued the criteria in 1979. Landfills also are now subject to stricter State regulations and the specter of financial liability under CERCLA for cleanup of contaminated sites. As a result, many new landfills, though by no means all, have pollution controls (e.g., synthetic and clay liners, leachate and gas detection and collection systems, and final cover systems) and other engineering features designed to minimize and detect releases of potentially problematic substances. Whether these technologies are needed for all landfills is controversial. Some observers argue that the need for these technologies depends on the site-specific conditions that lead to the production and possible release of leachate and gas. In contrast, other groups argue that landfills should be uniformly required to have these advanced features, with some allowance for variations.

This chapter examines the numbers and capacity of landfills, behavior of MSW in a landfill, the extent and causes of environmental releases, and technologies for minimizing those releases.

NUMBER AND CAPACITY OF MSW LANDFILLS

Overall Trends

MSW generation in the United States has increased substantially during the last two decades. EPA estimates that over 130 million tons—about 80 percent of all MSW—were landfilled in 1986 (24). The actual total may even be greater than these estimates indicate because of definition and data difficulties (ch. 3). Landfilling is the predominant form of disposal in most other countries, including many in Europe (table 7-1). Nevertheless, Japan and some European countries (e.g., Sweden, Switzerland, Denmark) rely on landfilling to a much lesser extent than the United States.

At the same time that MSW generation is increasing, parts of the United States—particularly the Northeast and the Midwest—are in the midst of a landfill capacity crisis. In one survey, EPA indicated that about one-third of all existing landfills were expected to close by 1994 (44, 77). Moreover, EPA estimated that over 80 percent of the landfills **currently operating** in 1988 will close in the next 20 years (table 7-2). Some States or regions, such as New Jersey and Long Island, are facing critical landfill capacity problems. Other States, such as Delaware and Rhode Island, have managed to develop facilities to treat most or all of their MSW.

EPA's proposed requirements for landfill operators to provide financial assurance for cleanup (see "Proposed MSW Landfill Regulations") could

Photo credit: Office of Technology Assessment

A modern landfill design includes an integrated set of controls, such as liners, monitoring, leachate collection, and gas venting or collection. Liners installed along the bottom and sides of a landfill, as shown here, reduce leachate migration. Landfilled MSW usually is covered daily with soil or compost.

increase the rate at which landfills close. Once the regulations become effective, which is expected to be in 1991, any landfill that closes within 18 months after this date would not need to meet these requirements. Since the requirements could be costly to meet, this provision may be an impetus for many landfills to close before the 18-month period is over. In Wisconsin, for example, State officials estimate that up to 600 landfills, mostly small, rural ones, might close because of the regulations (19). In Nebraska, communities under 5,000 in size were previously exempted from meeting State landfill regulations (20, 54), so these types of facilities also are likely to close.

Closures of existing facilities do not necessarily predict future landfill capacity, however, because some new landfills are being sited and some existing ones are being expanded. It is particularly difficult to generalize about overall capacity because most problems and solutions occur at the city or county level and because information about capacity and numbers comes from extremely varied sources.

Capacity, as well as associated risks to human health and the environment, can be greatly affected by the practice at some landfills of accepting wastes other than MSW. Depending on the definition used, MSW accounts for an estimated 90 percent of all wastes sent to MSW landfills (77). The remainder is comprised of construction and demolition debris, nonhazardous industrial process wastes, sewage sludge, non-MSW incinerator ash, small quantity generator (SQG) hazardous waste, medical wastes, and miscellaneous wastes (77). According to an EPA survey in November 1986, about 28 percent of MSW landfills accept SQG hazardous wastes, 32 percent accept medical wastes, and about half accept sewage sludges, non-MSW incinerator ash, industrial process wastes, and asbestos-containing materials (73).

Table 7-1—Estimates of the Percentage (by weight) **of Post-Recycling MSW Landfilled in the United States, Japan, and Europe**[a]

Country	Percent landfilled	*Year*
Denmark	44	1985
France	54	1983
Greece	100	1983
Ireland	100	1985
Italy	85	1983
Japan	33	1987
Netherlands	56-61	1985
Sweden	35-49	1985,1987
Switzerland	22-25	1985
United Kingdom	90	1983
United States	90[a]	1986
West Germany	66-74	1985,1986

[a]These figures refer to landfilling *after* recycling (e.g., of source-separated glass, paper, metals) has occurred. For example, the United States landfills about 80 percent of all MSW, but about 90 percent of post-recycled MSW.

SOURCES: Franklin Associates, Ltd., *Characterization of Municipal Solid Waste in the United States, 1960 to 2000 (Update 1988),* final report prepared for U.S. Environmental Protection Agency (Prairie Village, KS: March 1988); A. Hershkowitz, "International Experiences in Solid Waste Management," contract prepared for U.S. Congress, Office of Technology Assessment (Elmsford, NY: Municipal Recycling Associates, October 1988); Institute for Local Self-Reliance (ILSR), *Garbage in Europe: Technologies, Economics, and Trends* (Washington, DC: 1988); C. Pollock, "Mining Urban Wastes: The Potential For Recycling," Worldwatch Paper 76 (Washington, DC: Worldwatch Institute, April 1987); Swedish Association of Public Cleansing and Solid Waste Management, *Solid Waste Management in Sweden* (Malmo, Sweden: February 1988).

Data on Numbers and Capacity

On a national scale, EPA estimated that 6,034 active MSW landfill facilities existed in 1986 (77).[1] EPA also indicated the rate at which it expects these facilities to close during the next 20 years (table 7-2).

Additional information about trends in landfill numbers and capacity is available from: 1) data in EPA's 1986 Census (62, 73); 2) State reports; and 3) conversations with State officials. Data from these sources are not always comparable because definitions often differ.

As reported by the above sources, though, landfill capacity problems appear to be most severe in the Northeast and parts of the Midwest:

Table 7-2—Projected Number of Municipal Landfills That Will Remain in Operation Over the Next 20 Years

Year	Number of landfills
1988	5,499[a]
1993	3,332
1998	2,720
2003	1,594
2008	1,234

[a]1988 figures reflect projected closings of 535 landfills during 1987.

SOURCE: U.S. Environmental Protection Agency, *Report to Congress: Solid Waste Disposal in the United States, Vol. II,* EPA/530-SW-88-011B (Washington, DC: Oct. 1988).

- 8 States had less than 5 years of remaining capacity (Connecticut, Kentucky, Massachusetts, New Jersey, Ohio, Pennsylvania, Virgina, West Virginia); and
- 15 States had between 5 and 10 years (Alabama, Colorado, Florida, Illinois, Indiana, Maine, Maryland, Minnesota, Mississippi, Missouri, Montana, New Hampshire, New York, Oklahoma, Vermont).[2]

Four states (Florida, Massachusetts, New Hampshire, and New Jersey) were expected to close almost all existing landfills within the next 10 years. Because it usually takes 5 or more years to permit and develop new facilities (ch. 8), any area with less than 10 years of expected landfill life can be considered to have capacity problems.

In New Jersey, for example, 7 of 10 major landfills that were open in early 1987 were expected to close by the end of 1989. New Jersey law prevents counties without landfill capacity from transporting MSW in-state to counties with remaining capacity; instead, counties lacking capacity must make other arrangements, such as transporting MSW out-of-state (67). As a result, the State as a whole has essentially no remaining capacity.

Even in the densely populated Northeast, however, it is difficult to generalize about capacity. For example, between 1980 and 1984 the Delaware Solid Waste Authority located three new landfills and expanded the State's available capacity to an

[1]EPA defined a facility as an MSW landfill if it received at least 50 percent household and/or commercial waste, was not a hazardous waste landfill, and had at least one active landfill unit (i.e., a disposal area within the facility that had the same liner type throughout). The average facility had 1.09 active units, 0.52 closed units, and 0.64 planned units. An earlier survey reported over 9,000 landfills, but that estimate included nonmunicipal landfills (39, 71).

[2]Rhode Island also was included in the latter category, but other data indicate that the State has an estimated 15 years of remaining capacity (63).

estimated 25 to 30 years (81). Rhode Island has an estimated 15 years of capacity, largely because of the Central Landfill (operated by the Rhode Island Solid Waste Management Corporation) that accepts 90 percent of the State's solid waste (63). Even New York had an estimated 9 years of remaining capacity as of 1987 (46).

In the Southwest, States such as Arizona and New Mexico do not appear to have an overall capacity crisis, possibly because of lower population densities and greater land availability (1, 65). In addition, groundwater aquifers in the Southwest tend to be located far below the surface where they are less likely to be contaminated by leachate from MSW landfills.

Great variation in capacity exists within States. Rural areas, for example, often do not have the same capacity problems as do urban areas. Within Illinois, the northwestern part of the State and the Chicago area face the most severe problems, while rural southern Illinois does not face capacity problems (79). Rural areas in Florida do not lack landfill capacity, but urban areas such as Pinellas County (St. Petersburg) and Dade County (Miami) are facing capacity problems (58).

Even these general rural and urban trends are variable. Some rural areas do face landfill shortages, and not all urban areas are unable to solve their capacity problems. In Ohio, landfill capacity in the more urban north was estimated as of 1988 to be between 8 and 21 years, while the rural southeast had only 3.5 years (48). Some large cities have succeeded in increasing their landfill capacity. Phoenix opened a new landfill that is expected to provide 50 years capacity (1). These facilities are not always near the cities, however. For example, in 1990 Portland will begin sending MSW to a new landfill in eastern Oregon that could meet the city's landfill needs for up to 20 years (34).

Data on Closings and Openings

Limited data are available on MSW landfill closings and openings. EPA estimated that 14,000 MSW landfills have closed around the country since 1978, 70 percent of those operating at the time (78). The number of closings, however, does not necessarily reflect net changes in available landfill capacity. For example, Pennsylvania lost 13 MSW landfills between July 1986 and November 1987. However, one new landfill was opened and two others were expanded, and statewide capacity increased from 4.2 years in May 1987 to 5.5 years by November 1987 (51). Unfortunately, most States collect data on numbers of closings, rather than capacity.

Many estimates about landfill numbers assume that current disposal rates will continue and that no new landfills will be sited in the future. It is true that new landfills are difficult to site. EPA estimated that only 10 percent of MSW landfills were under 5 years old, indicating that few had opened recently (77). However, in some cases the new facilities are larger than previous facilities, again illustrating the limitations of data based only on crude numbers.

Landfills are being sited or expanded in some States, even if the number of new sitings is declining. Delaware and Pennsylvania, as noted above, have sited new landfills and expanded old ones. In Missouri, four new landfills were permitted and five received permits to expand between July 1986 and late 1987 (17). In California, 4 new landfills were sited and 12 old ones were expanded between 1983 and 1988 (21). In Ohio, 2 new landfills were sited and 12 old ones expanded from 1985 through 1987 (48).

For some States (e.g., Missouri, California, and Pennsylvania), these developments can translate into a net increase in capacity. In addition, if new landfills are larger than the ones that close, then fewer new landfills would be required to replace lost capacity. This was the case in Missouri, where 90 percent of its increase was due to one new landfill in St. Louis county, and in Pennsylvania, where one new landfill accounted for 75 percent of the capacity increase.

Interstate Transportation of MSW

Proposals to use disposal sites in other States are frequent and often focus on areas that are either rural or that have existing disposal facilities. Although some States have tried to ban importation of MSW, such efforts frequently run afoul of the Interstate Commerce Clause (ch. 8).

Interstate transportation of MSW appears to have increased, particularly, but not only, in the Northeast. Little concrete information on interstate transportation is available, however. Anecdotal information obtained from State reports and conversations with State officials indicates that shipment of MSW to other States occurs from many areas, including, for example, Missouri, Ohio, Illinois, New York, New Jersey, and Wisconsin (17, 48,60,67). Missouri was estimated to transport one-third of its MSW out-of-state. In New Jersey, about 55 to 60 percent of the MSW produced in the State was exported out-of-state in 1988, primarily to Pennsylvania, but also to Ohio, West Virginia, Connecticut, New York, and Kentucky (67).

One factor that can influence interstate transportation is competition among landfill operators and haulers. In general, waste will flow in the direction of lower costs. For example, landfill capacity is adequate in Wisconsin, but even so some MSW is transported along the Milwaukee-Chicago corridor, possibly because it is less costly for haulers to transport MSW over longer distances to their own landfills than to dispose of MSW in a competitor's landfill (60).

DECOMPOSITION OF MSW IN LANDFILLS

About three-fourths of MSW by weight is organic waste (e.g., paper, yard waste, and food waste) and about one-fourth is inorganic (e.g., metals and glass) (ch. 3). Organic wastes are biodegradable and can decompose under proper landfill conditions to produce carbon dioxide, methane, organic acids, ammonia, water, and other chemicals. In contrast, inorganic wastes are not biodegradable and essentially remain unchanged over time.

Decomposition refers to the breakdown of organic materials into different compounds as a result of microbial activity. When organic wastes are put in a landfill, some **aerobic** decomposition occurs initially as aerobic bacteria (i.e., bacteria that function in the presence of oxygen) begin to break down the waste. They also quickly consume the available oxygen (64). **Anaerobic** decomposition (i.e., decomposition caused by bacteria that function without oxygen) then begins and is the dominant mode of decomposition (27).

Aerobic and anaerobic decomposition generate different byproducts. Aerobic bacteria break down the waste materials into organic acids and other chemicals, and the bacteria themselves produce carbon dioxide as a byproduct of their metabolism (64). Anaerobic bacteria, however, produce methane as a result of their metabolic activity (i.e., methanogenesis).

Decomposition can continue for many years, as long as some organic material is available for bacterial activity. The rate depends on many factors, including moisture content, pH, temperature, degree of compaction, and MSW age, composition, and size. When degradation occurs, the volume of the original MSW is reduced, in effect providing additional landfill capacity (see ''Recycling Landfill Space'' below). Decomposition also can cause subsidence of landfill caps and greater penetration by rain in some cases.

There is evidence, however, that decomposition rates of organic materials in landfills are so slow that the space-saving benefits may not be important (57, 85). In particular, decomposition under relatively dry conditions stops and materials can remain unaltered for decades (80). At some landfills, organic materials such as paper and food waste have not decomposed since their disposal 10 to 20 years ago. This is not necessarily surprising, since archaeologists have long known that perishable materials can last for centuries under the right conditions (85).

When decomposition does occur, the fate of the different byproducts depends on a number of factors. Liquids that percolate through the landfill (e.g., from rainfall, moisture in the waste itself, or the byproducts) can carry some chemicals through the soil and toward groundwater. This mixture is known as *leachate*. The organic acids formed during aerobic decomposition can increase the mobility, solubility, and sometimes the potential toxicity of metals in the leachate. In contrast, evidence suggests that under anaerobic conditions, metals are less soluble and instead may precipitate out as, for example, metallic sulfides (27,28).

The quantity of leachate generated depends on factors such as rainfall, temperature, humidity, surface runoff, and subsurface water migration, all of which affect the rate of anaerobic bacterial activity (27). The presence of leachate is the impetus for various pollution controls at landfills (e.g., liners and leachate collection systems) because decomposition of the organic materials without collection and control of the byproducts is undesirable.

In most cases, the carbon dioxide and methane generated by bacteria are eventually emitted to the atmosphere. These gases were previously considered relatively benign (except for the explosive threat of methane), but they now are considered as prime actors in the global warming phenomenon (87). All methods of dealing with organic wastes produce carbon dioxide, though, and landfills in the United States probably contribute a negligible amount of global carbon dioxide emissions. They may contribute between 2 and 6 percent of global methane emissions, however (see ''Atmospheric Emissions'' below). While the methane can be recovered for energy production, it often is not produced at a sufficiently high rate to make recovery economical. One idea to make recovery more viable and reduce atmospheric emissions is to enhance the rate of methane production (see ''Enhancing Decomposition Rates'').

Recycling Landfill Space

''Recycling'' landfills—reusing the same landfill space after a period of decomposition—has been suggested as a means of extending landfill lifetimes, allowing the repair of liners and leachate collection systems, and recovering materials of value (36, 80). One recycling operation in Collier County, Florida, already mines an MSW landfill and processes materials at a centralized facility (25). Screening is used to remove fine soil and humus and to recover ferrous metals.

The Delaware Solid Waste Authority plans to excavate—when degradation is essentially over, as measured by a decrease in methane production—an 8-acre cell containing about 140,000 tons of MSW deposited between 1980 and 1982. The excavated material will be screened for ferrous scrap, plastics, wood, textiles, aluminum, glass, and other materials; some of these could be burned (to exploit their Btu value), while others possibly could be recycled. The Authority intends to rebuild the liners and leachate collection systems so that the area can be reused, and to use the screened dirt as daily cover material.

Biodegradable Plastics

Biodegradable plastics are being promoted as a solution to litter problems and, to some extent, to landfill shortages. The reduction in volume associated with degradation into smaller pieces and dust-sized particles could be desirable, depending on its timing and impact on landfill subsidence and whether the extra capacity created is used to advantage. However, the types of products that could be made with biodegradable plastics comprise a relatively small portion of the MSW that enters landfills.

In addition, much is unknown about the performance, timing, and rate of degradation of biodegradable plastics (ch. 5).[3] Little is known about additives in plastic products; for example, depending on conditions, metal additives could be released in soluble forms and become part of leachate. In contrast, nondegradable plastics are basically inert when landfilled and probably are not significant contributors of byproducts.

Research is needed on subjects such as the conditions under which different components degrade, how rapidly they degrade, whether degradable plastics would have much effect on landfill capacity, and whether they would cause any environmental problems.

LANDFILLS AS SYSTEMS

Whether a landfill will eventually cause environmental problems depends on a host of factors—including the nature of the MSW, the rate of decomposition, site-specific hydrogeology, rainfall, distance to aquifers, types of liners and covers, runoff controls, and ability to collect leachate and gas. For example, some landfills that caused problems in the past clearly were sited inappropriately.

Many different engineering components or controls can be included in a landfill design, such as liners, monitoring systems, leachate collection systems, and gas venting or collection systems (figure 7-1; box 7-A describes a landfill in Japan that has many of these features). The necessity of various engineering controls can vary given the hydrogeological and other conditions at a site.

---

[3]**Photo**degradable plastics would not degrade in landfills because they would be buried and not exposed to light.

Figure 7-1—Diagram of Configuration of Selected Engineering Features at MSW Landfills

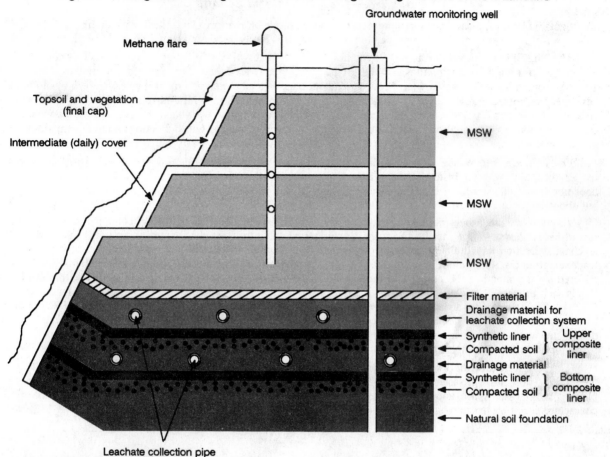

SOURCE: Office of Technology Assessment, 1989, after 52 *Federal Register* 20226, May 29, 1987.

Thus, to provide sufficient environmental protection a landfill must be designed as an engineered system and located where it will be least likely to cause contamination. For example, landfills should not be sited in areas with permeable soils, shallow groundwater, or wetlands. This approach enhances the prospects of collecting contaminants before they migrate to the surrounding environment.

This section discusses engineering control features from a technical standpoint. They are discussed separately below, but in practice they must be considered as integrated elements in a single system. The section also summarizes available information on the numbers of landfills that actually exhibit these features and discusses some additional design concepts that merit additional research.[4] A later section discusses EPA's proposed regulations for landfill design and operation.

Engineering Controls

Liners and Covers

Liners are installed along the bottom and sometimes the sides of a landfill to reduce the migration of leachate to groundwater beneath the site, as well as laterally. In addition, a "cover" or "cover system" can be placed over a landfill once it has closed to prevent the introduction of water into the landfill (and thus reduce leaching).

---

[4]The information on landfill features is drawn primarily from EPA's survey of landfill operators and owners (73). EPA combined data on the 70 percent of existing landfills that opened before 1980 and the 30 percent that opened since then.

Box 7-A—Japan's Santama Landfill

Santama landfill, located in Tokyo prefecture, is an example of a modern landfill. It came on line in 1984, and although it is not representative of most Japanese landfills, it is likely to be representative of many future designs.

The landfill is a joint venture among 25 municipalities and 2 towns. Funds for operating the facility come from taxing the contributing municipalities and charging a tipping fee twice a year. The site was identified in 1981, and although some public opposition was encountered, negotiations lead to an agreement that the facility would have advanced pollution controls. About 22 hectares will be used for landfilling, with a surrounding undeveloped green zone of 14 hectares. At the end of its useful life, expected to be about 13 years, the site will be capped and transformed into a sports facility. Details of post-closure monitoring and leachate collection and treatment plans are not known to OTA.

One unique aspect of the Santama facility is that, like many Japanese landfills, it does not accept organic wastes (paper, food, yard wastes). Instead, these wastes are collected by the municipalities and sent to incinerators. It also does not accept industrial waste. It does accept fly and bottom ash from the MSW incinerators (mostly untreated but about 10 percent processed by cementation).

Another unique aspect is its inclusion of many different engineering features: computerized weigh-in, record-keeping system for each truck, truck washing system, intricate liner system and "sandwich" process, leachate collection and drainage pipes, groundwater flow channels, secondary wastewater treatment plant for leachate, groundwater monitoring wells, and gas venting. The bottom liner system consists of 1 meter of thick clay covered by a synthetic rubber liner and then another 1 meter of clay. The filling of the landfill is based on a "sandwich process"—each 2-meter layer of MSW is covered with a 1 meter thick clay lining. The wastewater treatment facility provides activated sludge secondary treatment for the leachate. It removes an average of 92 percent of the biochemical oxygen demand (BOD), bringing post-treatment levels down to 8 to 10 ppm. The leachate is then disinfected with chlorine and sent to a sewage treatment plant in Tokyo. BOD is tested weekly at an on-site laboratory; cyanide, PCBs, nitrates, phosphorus, and seven metals are tested monthly.

The design is not without some problems and controversies. The landfill is located along a small stream, which dictates the need for a disaster prevention flood control system. One reviewer also suggests that the sandwich process may waste space and inhibit internal drainage (8). Data are not available on leachate volume and characteristics or on hydrological balance, so it is difficult to evaluate the effect of this feature.

About two-thirds of all landfills have some type of soil (including clay) beneath them, but the soil at these landfills was not necessarily engineered (i.e., compacted or remolded) to a particular design (table 7-3). Only 1 percent of landfills are estimated to have synthetic liners; the use of synthetic liners is expected to increase, but only to about 6 percent at planned landfills. Many other types of liners have also been used, including admix compositions (e.g., paving asphalt concrete), sprayed-liners (e.g., liquid rubber), and soil sealants (30).

One difference between clay and synthetic liners is permeability, the rate at which water and chemicals move through a liner. The permeability of clay liners to **water** ranges between 10^{-6} to 10^{-7} cm/sec, depending on clay content, compaction, and treatment (e.g., addition of lime). Synthetic liners are less permeable to water, with a range between 10^{-5} and

10^{-6} cm/sec. It is not clear whether one type is more or less permeable to organic chemicals (see "Synthetic Liners" below). Clay is more absorptive of chemicals (i.e., once a pollutant moves into clay, it tends to stay there) (30).

Both types of liners are subject to problems that can cause leachate to move through the liner more rapidly. Synthetic liners can sometimes be punctured or torn (e.g., in installation or in actual operation), while clay liners can crack. However, the frequency with which these problems occur is unknown.

Whether these differences and problems are significant depends on many factors, in particular the rate at which leachate is generated and how efficiently it is collected. A liner system cannot be judged in isolation; the leachate collection system and other design features must also be considered.

Table 7-3—Presence of Soil or Synthetic Membrane Liners at Closed, Active, and Planned MSW Landfill Units[a]

Type of liner	Percentage of landfill units with given type			Percentage used in combination with another type at active units
	Closed	Active	Planned	
In-situ soil	34	28	30	9
Engineered soil	35	39	36	15
Synthetic membrane	<1	1	6	<1
Other	8	7	8	2
None or unknown	39	40	35	—

[a]Totals add to more than 100 percent because some units have more than one type.

SOURCE: Adapted from U.S. Environmental Protection Agency, *Survey of State and Territorial Subtitle D Municipal Landfill Facilities*, draft final report, prepared by Westat, Inc., Oct. 13, 1987.

Synthetic Liners—Synthetic liners are thin sheets (i.e., 0.3 to 0.6 cm thick) composed of materials such as rubber, polyvinyl chloride, or various polyethylenes. Most synthetic liners are considered impermeable to water, especially when compared with natural soil liners.

The characteristics of a liner affect how it will react to different chemicals. For example, liners made of materials such as high-density polyethylene (HDPE) and vulcanized rubber have molecular arrangements that are crosslinked, an arrangement that resists swelling and dissolution by solvents of similar polarity (29).[5]

Some laboratory experiments suggest that volatile organic chemicals (e.g., trichloroethylene or TCE, toluene, and xylene) can migrate rapidly through synthetic liners (31). The amounts and directions of migration varied depending on characteristics of the chemicals (e.g., relative solubility), the liner (e.g., polymer content, thickness), temperature, and concentration of the chemicals on either side of the liner (31). In different tests conducted by EPA, most synthetic liners were eventually destroyed when exposed to methylene chloride in full strength concentrations (14, 68).

It is not known whether these results are representative of actual landfill conditions. In the laboratory experiments reported by Haxo and Lahey (31), the concentrations of organic chemicals in the solutions were relatively high, for example 1,100 ppm for TCE. In a landfill, synthetic liners probably encounter more dilute solutions in most cases. For example, although TCE is common in leachate, its average concentration in several MSW leachate samples was

generally less than 200 ppm (table 7-4); another study indicated an average of 38 ppm (but with a range of 1 to 1,460 ppm) (41).

Thus laboratory experiments with immersed liners involve TCE concentrations that may not represent field conditions, although they are within the upper limit of concentrations detected in some field samples. They do indicate, however, that additional research is needed on the frequency with which synthetic liners are exposed to high concentrations of volatile organic chemicals and on long-term performance of the liners under these conditions.

Seams for Flexible Membrane Liners—An important aspect of flexible membrane liners is the process by which the seams of the different liner segments are joined. Segments of a liner can be joined together in the factory by using solvent adhesives or dielectric methods, or in the field using various welding methods.

EPA has tested seam strength under conditions designed to simulate chemical and physical environments that might be encountered at hazardous waste facilities (43). Two types of strength generally are evaluated: peel strength (i.e., the ability of the seam to resist peeling apart of two liner segments) and shear strength (i.e., the ability of the liner material to resist lateral separation). Results indicate that shear and peel strength are not correlated, with peel strength being related to the strength of the bond and shear strength being related to properties of the liner material. The method used to create the seams causes differences in peel and shear strength. EPA concluded that existing data and manufacturers' recommendations on the chemical compatibility of

[5]Nonpolar molecules do not have a significant electrical charge.

Table 7-4—Median Concentrations of Substances Found in MSW Landfill Leachate, in Comparison With Existing Exposure Standards[a]

Substance[b]	Median concentration (ppm)	Type[a]	Value (ppm)	Substance[b]	Median concentration (ppm)	Type[a]	Value (ppm)
Inorganics:				Dichlorodifluoromethane (6)	237	T	7,000
Antimony (11)	4.52	T	0.01	1,1-Dichloroethane (34)	1,715	N	7
Arsenic (72)	0.042	N	0.05			C	0.58
Barium (60)	0.853	N	1.0	1,2-Dichloroethane (6)	1,841	T	5
Beryllium (6)	0.006	T	0.2	1,2-Dichloropropane (12)	66.7	W	5,700
Cadmium (46)	0.022	N	0.01	1,3-Dichloropropane (2)	24	C	0.19
Chromium (total) (97)	0.175	N	0.05	Diethyl phthalate (27)	118	T	30,000
Copper (68)	0.168	T	0.012	2,4-Dimethyl phenol (2)	19	W	2,120
		W	0.018	Dimethyl phthalate (2)	42.5	W	313,000
Cyanide (21)	0.063	T	0.7	Endrin (3)	16.8	T	0.2
Iron (120)	221	W	1,000	Ethyl benzene (41)	274	W	1,400
Lead (73)	0.162	N	0.05	bis (2-Ethylhexyl)			
Manganese (103)	9.59	W	0.05	phthalate (10)	184	T	70
Mercury (19)	0.002	N	0.002	Isophorone (19)	1,168	W	5,200
Nickel (98)	0.326	T	0.07	Lindane (2)	0.020	T	4
Nitrate (38)	1.88	W	10	Methylene chloride (68)	5,352	C	4.7
Selenium (18)	0.012	N	0.01	Methyl ethyl ketone (24)	4,151	W	2,000
Silver (19)	0.021	N	0.05	Naphthalene (23)	32.4	W	620
Thallium (11)	0.175	W	0.04	Nitrobenzene (3)	54.7	T	20
Zinc (114)	8.32	W	0.110	4-Nitrophenol (1)	17	W	150
				Pentachlorophenol (3)	173	T	1,000
Organics:				Phenol (45)	2,456	T	1,000
Acrolein (1)	270	W	21	1,1,2,2-Tetrachloroethane (1)	210	C	1.75
Benzene (35)	221	T	5	Tetrachloroethylene (18)	132	C	6.9
Bromomethane (1)	170	T	10	Toluene (69)	1,016	T	10,000
Carbon tetrachloride (2)	202	T	5	Toxaphene (1)	1	N	5
Chlorobenzene (12)	128	T	1,000	1,1,1-Trichloroethane (20)	887	N	200
Chloroform (8)	195	C	5.7			T	3,000
bis (Chloromethyl) ether (1)	250	C	0.0037	1,1,2-Trichloroethane (4)	378	C	6.1
p-Cresol (10)	2,394	T	2,000	Trichloroethylene (28)	187	N	5
2,4-D (7)	129	T	100			T	3.2
4,4-DDT (16)	0.103	C	0.1	Trichlorofluoromethane (10)	56.1	T	10,000
Di-n-butyl phthalate (5)	70.2	T	4,000	1,2,3-Trichloropropane (1)	230	T	20
1,2-Dichlorobenzene (8)	11.8	W	763	Vinyl chloride (10)	36.1	N	2
1,4-Dichlorobenzene (12)	13.2	T	75				

[a]Types of exposure standards:
 C=EPA Human Health Criteria, based on carcinogenicity
 N=National Interim Primary or Secondary Drinking Water Standard
 T=EPA Human Health Criteria, based on systemic toxicity
 W=Water Quality Criteria
[b]Number of samples in parentheses.

SOURCE: After U.S. Environmental Protection Agency, Office of Solid Waste, *Summary of Data on Municipal Solid Waste Landfill Leachate Characteristics, Criteria for Municipal Solid Waste Landfills (40 CFR Part 258)*, EPA/530-SW-88-038 (Washington, DC: July 1988).

liner materials provide an initial basis for evaluating expected liner performance in given chemical environments (43). However, EPA also concluded that tests of less than 6 months may be inadequate to determine the performance of some flexible membrane liners and that the 120-day immersion period specified in one standard test (known as EPA Method 9090) may need review to ensure that it is long enough to determine chemical compatibility.

Natural Soil—Soil, especially different types of clay, is commonly used to underlie MSW landfills (table 7-3). In some cases the materials are simply used in-situ. In other cases they are brought together and engineered (i.e., compacted or remolded) to increase strength and reduce permeability. As noted above, clay liners are more permeable to water than are synthetic liners. Engineered soil, however, is less permeable than uncompacted soil (52 *Federal Register* 12568, April 17, 1987).

The permeability of natural soil liners to organic chemicals such as solvents is variable and depends on many factors, including characteristics and concentrations of the chemicals, contents and degree of compaction of the clay, and type of engineering. The fate of chemicals also depends on whether they are adsorbed onto soil particles. EPA noted, in a proposed rulemaking for hazardous waste management systems, that compacted clay liners can adsorb much of the leachate, reducing the amount that reaches leachate collection systems (52 *Federal Register* 20224, May 29, 1987). Other researchers, however, contend that little is known about adsorptive capacity for chemicals such as solvents (8).

Soil liners also can become dessicated for various reasons. For example, some solvents that are insoluble in water (e.g., xylene and carbon tetrachloride) may cause water to migrate out of the soil. When dessication occurs, the soil may shrink. Subsequent cracking and channeling of the soil may form pathways through which liquids can flow (59).

Composite Liners—A composite liner is composed of an engineered soil layer overlain by a synthetic flexible membrane liner. This combination is uncommon (table 7-3). Such liners could provide higher protection than individual liners because each liner component has different resistance properties.

Cover Types—During the operating life of a landfill, cover is usually applied on a daily basis to control disease vectors and vermin, prevent odors and fires, and discourage scavenging (74). In general, about 6 inches of compacted earth is used. Currently, 45 States require that cover be applied daily. EPA's proposed landfill regulations also would require the application of daily cover (53 *Federal Register* 33314, Aug. 30, 1988). The type of soil used for daily cover does not appear to be critical (74); clay, silt, or a combination of the two with sand or gravel is generally considered adequate.

To close a landfill, a final cover usually is placed on top to reduce infiltration of water. The design of the cover considers various factors such as soil type, degree of compaction, surface slope, drainage, and water balance (77). For example, the top of the landfill can be sloped to increase runoff and reduce infiltration (64). The type of soil used also matters, because highly organic soils (e.g., peat) do not compact easily. EPA estimated that most active and planned units have or will have some type of earth cover (77); only 2 percent have or will have a synthetic membrane cover.

Leachate Collection and Removal Systems

Leachate collection and removal systems use pipes to collect the leachate that settles on top of a liner and prevent it from migrating into groundwater. A typical system consists of a series of perforated collection pipes (usually 4 to 6 inch PVC), drainage layers and blankets, header pipes, and sumps. The pipes are placed above the liner in drainage layers filled with sand or gravel (76). In landfills with double liners, the pipes are placed both above the top liner and between the top and bottom liners. In general, liners are designed with a slope so that leachate drains into a central collection point.

The efficiency of leachate collection systems depends on the rate of leachate generation, spacing of collection pipes, slope of liners, liner permeabilities, and presence of drainage blankets. EPA has used models to estimate leachate collection efficiencies. At rates of leachate generation considered typical of landfills (i.e., 10 to 100 gallons per acre per day), for example, EPA estimated that systems associated with composite liners would exhibit collection efficiencies approaching 100 percent, while systems associated with clay liners would exhibit much lower efficiencies (52 *Federal Register* 12571, April 17, 1987).

Only 11 percent of existing landfills have any type of leachate collection system (77) and available data do not allow a determination of how much leachate is actually subject to collection. In addition, the presence of a leachate collection system is not necessarily sufficient to prevent groundwater contamination. EPA has identified MSW landfills equipped with leachate collection systems that failed to prevent such contamination because of inadequate design and/or construction (76).

Once leachate is collected, it can be managed by recirculating it in the landfill, transporting it to a municipal sewage treatment plant, discharging it to a treatment plant through a sewer, and treating it on-site with biological treatment processes (77). Leachate recirculation is used at about 3 percent of MSW landfills. Other types of leachate management methods are used less frequently. According to EPA, the discharge of leachate to surface water is expected to decline in the future, while the use of recirculation and transportation to treatment plants is expected to increase.

Methane is of concern because of its explosive nature and potential to affect global temperatures. It can be collected for energy recovery, allowed to escape into the atmosphere through vents, or, as shown here, "flared" or burned as it is emitted from collection pipes.

Methane Production, Collection, and Use

Landfill gas is composed primarily of equal parts methane and carbon dioxide, with trace organic chemicals (e.g., benzene, trichloroethylene, vinyl chloride, methylene chloride) also present. Methane production begins once conditions in a landfill become anaerobic. Rates of methane production depend on moisture content of the landfill; concentrations of nutrients and bacteria; pH, age and volume of the degrading material; and the presence or absence of sewage sludge.

Methane can be collected and processed for energy recovery, allowed to escape into the atmos-

phere through vents, or "flared" (i.e., burned) as it is emitted from collection pipes. Several methods can be used to collect or vent methane: 1) a permeable trench can be installed at the landfill's edge to provide a pathway to vent gases; 2) a gravel trench with a semi-permeable liner can be built running from the top to the bottom of the landfill to provide a pathway for venting; 3) a system combining pipes with a gravel trench can be built; and 4) an active pumping system can be used to draw gas out of the landfill through wells. These systems are operated only in portions of landfills that have been closed temporarily or permanently with a cap (22), although they can be installed as the landfill is built and then later connected.

The recovery efficiency of individual collection systems varies, depending on the type and spacing of the recovery system and the type of landfill covering (i.e., its permeability to gas). According to EPA, active pumping systems are the most effective means for collecting landfill gas, while permeable trenches are the least effective (74). In active systems, perforated collection pipes are placed at depths usually of 30 to 100 feet. Compressors are used to create a vacuum within the pipes and draw the gas out of the landfill; an excessive vacuum, however, can draw atmospheric air into the landfill, resulting in an aerobic environment that changes the bacterial mix and leads to production of carbon dioxide rather than methane.

More than 1,500 MSW landfills deal with methane by venting, flaring, or collection and recovery. If methane emissions were collected completely and processed for energy recovery, they could account for up to 5 percent of all natural gas consumption or 1 percent of all energy demand in the United States (74). However, only about 123 landfills actually collect methane to recover energy (77). The collected gas can be purified to increase its Btu content (to values of 500 to 1,000 Btu per standard cubic foot) and then be used in boilers, space heaters, and turbines. Purification involves using chemical and physical processes (e.g., dehydration by triethylene glycol process, molecular sieves, and refrigeration) to remove particulate matter, water, carbon dioxide, and most trace elements (64, 74).

Ambient Environmental Monitoring

Most MSW landfills do not have equipment to monitor air, surface water, or groundwater for various pollutants (77). As of November 1986, only about 35 percent monitored groundwater, 15 percent monitored surface water, 7 percent monitored methane gas, and 3 percent monitored other air emissions. Among facilities that monitored groundwater, an average of 2.1 upgradient and 3.8 downgradient wells existed. Wells were sampled approximately three times annually, with about two samples taken per sampling period. On average these facilities had been monitoring groundwater for 5 years (73).

Ownership Status

EPA estimated as of 1986 that most MSW landfills (approximately 86 percent) were publicly owned: 29 percent by counties, 28 percent by cities, 3 percent by the Federal Government, 1 percent by State governments, and 25 percent by other governmental entities (77). The remaining 14 percent were privately owned. The majority of publicly owned facilities are small (i.e., receive less than 30 tons per day), while privately owned facilities are generally larger. One representative of private operators estimated that about 50 percent of total landfill **capacity** may be privately owned (55).

Data from the mid-1980s show that privately owned MSW landfills were designed more frequently with leachate collection systems than were publicly owned landfills (62 percent v. 35 percent for county-owned and 35 percent for city-owned). Privately owned landfills are also more likely to conduct groundwater monitoring (30 percent v. about 15 percent for county- and city-owned), and surface water monitoring (31 percent v. 24 percent for county and 13 percent for city) (44). It is not clear, however, whether this trend is the result of ownership or simply a response to more stringent State regulations that have been promulgated in recent years and that are applicable to all new landfills, regardless of ownership status.

Other System Designs

At least two different concepts regarding the design of landfills merit additional research. One concept involves enhancing the decomposition process by recycling leachate back into the landfill. The other involves confining waste in mounds that are built above the normal ground level.

Enhancing Decomposition Rates

Some researchers suggest that the decomposition process could be enhanced by collecting leachate and recycling it back into the organic material, an idea that has been examined in laboratory situations (28, 51, 80). Recycling leachate in some manner is used at a few MSW landfills today (see "Leachate Collection and Removal Systems" above).

One study at a Pennsylvania landfill concluded that recycling leachate resulted in more rapid decomposition, enhanced methane production, and increased stabilization (77). The Delaware Solid Waste Authority recently initiated a study to examine this idea on a larger scale under field conditions. It set up two 1-acre landfills cells for household MSW only; leachate is being collected and removed for external disposal from one cell, and recycled in the other cell. Decomposition rates will be measured after 5 years.

Experimental data indicate several potential benefits: 1) the time needed to decompose organic materials might be reduced from around 15 years to only a few years; 2) methane production could be maximized, making recovery more viable; 3) reusable space would become available more rapidly; 4) collected leachate would not have to be treated at wastewater treatment plants; and 5) metals might precipitate out within the landfill instead of being carried by leachate into groundwater.

However, the researchers also have noted several problems: 1) uncertainties exist about the ultimate reactivity or fate of chemical compounds created during the process; 2) regulatory proposals by EPA would ban addition of any liquids to landfills; and 3) these designs would require careful management (e.g., small landfill cells, proper design and location of leachate collection systems, and controlled rates of leachate recycling) to minimize potential off-site migration. In addition, if problems occur with the liner or leachate collection system, the chance of off-site migration would increase. For example, small tears in the liner can occur during construction or daily operation. EPA has noted that the increased volume of leachate may clog the leachate collection system (77). These potential problems suggest that enhanced decomposition be used only at sites that are not located near groundwater.

Above-Grade Containment Mounds

In general, MSW is now placed below ground level at landfills. One idea developed for hazardous waste treatment is to confine waste above-ground under a waterproof cover system to reduce leachate generation and make leachate collection easier (9,10). The design includes: 1) an above-ground storage mound, sloped to support the weight of the waste and the cover; 2) a liner system across the base to retard entry of water and subsequent percolation of leachate; 3) a drainage system consisting of stable aggregates and collection pipes installed over the lower liner; 4) a leachate collection system that is drained freely by gravity, with drainage exiting the mound above ground; and 5) a cover system consisting of a layer with gas collection equipment, a composite liner, a drainage layer, a topsoil layer, and permanent vegetative cover.

The possible advantages are that leachate would be removed immediately by gravitational drainage, sloped construction would reduce ponding of leachate on the liners, and repair may be easier. For example, if leakage became a problem because of a faulty cover system, it would become apparent soon after the fault develops, whereas leaking covers at below-ground landfills only become apparent as a result of groundwater contamination. Disadvantages include the potential for erosion of the topsoil layer and high costs (e.g., for excavating and transporting soil to the site to build the mound).

A few MSW landfills already incorporate parts of this design. For example, the Delaware Solid Waste Authority has one above-grade section with a 4-foot separation between the seasonally high groundwater level and the bottom of the liner (80). It is designed with two synthetic liners sandwiching a drainage layer and leachate collection. Another facility in Wisconsin has similar features (8). However, these have not been constructed with gravity-operated drains, so they do not incorporate all of the concept's features.

HEALTH AND ENVIRONMENTAL EFFECTS

This section reviews landfills on the Superfund National Priorities List, and discusses releases of toxic constituents and subsequent contamination of groundwater, surface water, and air. The information is derived in part from reviews conducted as EPA has worked to develop revised regulations under Subtitle D (72, 77).

Landfills on the Superfund List

According to EPA, 70 percent of existing MSW landfills began operation before 1980. Many of these older facilities were not designed with control features such as leachate collection systems or liners, and many accepted hazardous wastes. Moreover, many operating landfills continue to accept hazardous wastes. Small quantity generator wastes are exempted from the RCRA requirement to be managed at hazardous waste treatment facilities, and "household hazardous wastes" also are not subject to such regulation (ch. 3).

As a result, some older landfills accepted substantial amounts of hazardous waste. Some of these have been placed on the Superfund National Priorities List (NPL) due to their potential impacts on human health and the environment. In May 1986, 184 sites (22 percent) of the 850 sites proposed for the NPL were municipal landfills (77). One review of these sites indicated that only two of them did not involve co-disposal of MSW and hazardous wastes (41). Other observers, however, contend that MSW by itself, without any hazardous wastes, is sufficient to cause the types of problems associated with the municipal landfills on the NPL (see "Sources of Contamination" below).

The general lack of engineering controls at most existing landfills, combined with the fact that many landfills have accepted or continue to accept hazardous wastes or industrial nonhazardous wastes, suggests that additional municipal landfills may eventually require remedial action.

Releases of Potentially Toxic Substances

Releases of potentially toxic substances from MSW landfills occur primarily through three pathways: migration of leachate to groundwater, migration of leachate and runoff to surface water, and emissions of volatile gases to the atmosphere (figure 7-2). In addition, releases can occur through explosions caused by the buildup of explosive gases (e.g., methane). Current understanding of these release processes is incomplete. However, enough monitoring of MSW landfills has occurred to allow some conclusions to be drawn regarding the types of substances released to these environments and their subsequent impacts.

Violations of State environmental protection standards by MSW landfills have occurred at a number of sites—EPA reports almost 2,300 violations for groundwater, surface water, air, and subsurface methane (77). Most violations are detected through monitoring. However, since few MSW landfills conduct monitoring, these figures clearly represent a conservative estimate of actual violations. Although violations do not necessarily mean that impacts on human health or the environment have occurred, they do indicate a greater possibility of impacts now or in the future.

Groundwater Contamination

It is impossible to determine the actual risks posed by leachate from most landfills because groundwater monitoring data are rare. Only 25 percent of all MSW landfills monitored groundwater as of 1986 (77). This lack of monitoring is alarming because downgradient drinking water wells exist within 1 mile of an estimated 46 percent of all MSW landfills. Even given the relative lack of monitoring, over 100 potentially harmful substances have been identified in MSW landfill leachate (77).

Other data indicating that landfills can be a threat to groundwater quality come from case studies conducted by EPA at 163 landfills (primarily non-NPL landfills) (77). EPA identified 135 of these landfills that constitute a threat to human health or the environment because of their potential for groundwater contamination. Moreover, of the 184 MSW landfills on the NPL, 132 have had impacts on groundwater and 68 were listed solely because of groundwater contamination.

The extent to which substances of concern have migrated toward or into groundwater, and the range of potential risks associated with them, are critical unanswered issues. To estimate human health risks

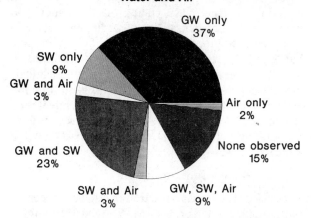

Figure 7-2—Observed Releases From NPL Landfills to Water and Air

GW only 37%

SW only 9%

GW and Air 3%

Air only 2%

None observed 15%

GW and SW 23%

SW and Air 3%

GW, SW, Air 9%

SOURCE: U.S. Environmental Protection Agency, *Report to Congress: Solid Waste Disposal in the United States, Vol. II*, EPA/530-SW-88-011B (Washington, DC: Oct. 1988).

posed by MSW landfills, EPA uses a model to predict the release, transport, fate, and impacts of eight pollutants (including vinyl chloride, tetrachloroethane, and methylene chloride) found in landfill leachate. Important variables that influence the magnitude of risks include distance to the nearest downgradient well, infiltration rate, landfill size, and aquifer characteristics (77). The model estimates, for example, that 5.5 percent of existing MSW landfills pose a lifetime cancer risk of 10^{-4} to 10^{-5} (i.e., one person out of every 10,000 to 100,000 people) and that 11.6 percent pose a risk of 10^{-5} to 10^{-7} (i.e., one person out of every 100,000 to 10 million people).

This model, however, has been criticized—both for **under**estimating risks and **over**estimating risks. One critic, for example, felt that using nationwide averages for some parameters masks important site-specific variability and leads to possible underestimates of risk (16). In contrast, another critic felt that the model used unreliable data that should not be extrapolated to national estimates because potential risks probably were overestimated (81). As of July 1989, EPA was revising its proposed landfill regulations in response to these types of public comments.

Microorganisms that can potentially spread disease also are present in landfills and have been detected in leachate and in the air (e.g., on dust particles) at landfills (49). They can originate from a number of sources, such as animal feces, human feces in diapers, sewage sludge, and even from materials such as glass, metal, plastic, paper, and yard wastes. Concentrations of pathogenic bacteria (e.g., fecal streptococci) vary substantially with time but tend to decrease rapidly after 3 to 6 months of operation, because they are destroyed by chemicals in the leachate (49). Viruses have not been found in leachate. Although only a few studies have been conducted, they have shown no adverse effects associated with microorganisms in MSW at landfills.[6]

Surface Water Contamination

Surface water contamination is related, at least in part, to the fact that few MSW landfills employ controls designed to prevent leachate and runoff from migrating out of the facility. Such contamination, for example, is known to have occurred at 73 (45 percent) of the 163 non-NPL landfills and at 79 (43 percent) of the 184 NPL landfills (77). The overall extent of surface water contamination associated with MSW landfills is impossible to determine, however, because of the general lack of monitoring.

The effect of leachate on organisms that live in surface water depends on the concentration of chemicals in the leachate and on the sensitivity of the organisms to those concentrations. Laboratory bioassays indicated that the toxicity of MSW leachate to rainbow trout living in surface water depended on where the leachate came from and how it was treated (12). Leachate taken directly from landfills was about 10 times more toxic than diluted leachate taken from drainage ditches surrounding landfills, although diluted leachate still caused some mortality. In contrast, leachate treated with physical or chemical methods was considered nontoxic. The experiments indicated that leachate toxicity was greater at low pH values but that it declined with time (also see ref. 35).

Ten cases of ecological damage (e.g., reduced diversity of bottom-dwelling aquatic communities) have been investigated that were related to contamination of surface water (77). Since ecological effects are rarely investigated, the extent of such damage probably is much greater than currently reported.

Atmospheric Emissions

MSW landfills generate several gases that pose risks to human health and the environment. The primary gases are methane and carbon dioxide, but numerous organic chemicals in gaseous forms are emitted as well (table 7-5). Of the 184 NPL landfills, less than 2 percent are listed for air emissions alone, but air emissions contributed to the decision to list the site in 17 percent of the cases (figure 7-2).

Methane emissions are of concern because of their explosive nature. EPA examined 29 cases in which damages occurred because of methane migration from landfills. In 23 of the cases, methane was detected away from the landfill at concentrations above the lower explosive level (77).[7] Explosions and fires occurred at 21 of the surveyed sites, resulting in a loss of life on five occasions.

More recently, methane emissions have received attention because of their potential to affect global temperatures. Current estimates of methane emissions from MSW landfills and other sources vary considerably and are highly uncertain. One study examined sources of atmospheric methane and estimated that the anaerobic decay of MSW in landfills around the world contributed between 30 million and 70 million tons annually (5). This could constitute about 5 to 20 percent of all methane released (13). The United States has been estimated to account for about one-third of biodegradable carbon content in the world (5); if this ratio is applicable to the amount of degradable MSW, then MSW landfills in the United States could contribute about 2 to 6 percent of global methane emissions (based on data in ref. 6). Moreover, since methane traps about 25 times more infrared energy than does carbon dioxide (56), from a climate perspective it

---

[6]According to the American Paper Institute (2), there is no evidence that disposable diapers add infectious material to landfill leachates or that handling such diapers is linked with viral diseases.

[7]Methane is explosive when its concentration is between 5 and 15 percent, by volume, in air at normal temperatures. Two Federal regulatory standards exist: an allowable concentration of 5 percent or less at a property boundary, and an allowable concentration of 1.25 percent or less at buildings both on and off the site (40 CFR 257.3-8(a)).

Table 7-5—Concentrations of Gaseous Constituents From MSW Landfills

Constituent	Range of concentration (ppm)	Median
Benzene	0-32	0.3
Carbon dioxide	342,000-470,000	350,000
Carbon tetrachloride	0.011	
1,2-Dichloroethane	19-59	
Ethyl benzene	0-91	1.5
Heptane	0-11	0.45
Hexane	0-31	0.8
Isopentane	0.05-4.5	2.0
Methane	440,000-587,000	500,000
Methyl-cyclohexane	0.017-19	3.6
Methyl-cyclopentane	0-12	2.8
Methylene chloride	0-118	0.83
Nonane	0-24	0.54
Perchloroethylene	0-186	0.03
Toluene	0-357	6.8
1,1,1-Trichloroethane	0-3.6	0.03
Trichloroethylene	0-44	0.12
Trichloromethane	0.61	
Vinyl chloride	0-10	2.2
Xylene	0-111	0.1
m-Xylene	1.7-76	4.1
0-Xylene	0-19	1.8

SOURCES: U.S. Environmental Protection Agency, *Report to Congress: Solid Waste Disposal in the United States, Vol. II*, EPA/530-SW-88-011B (Washington, DC: October 1988); J. Wood and M. Porter, "Hazardous Pollutants in Class II Landfills," *J. Air Pollution Control* 37(5):609-615, May 1987.

may be more desirable to flare methane and convert it to carbon dioxide, rather than merely vent it.[8]

Emissions of potentially carcinogenic organic chemicals (e.g., vinyl chloride and benzene) also have been detected at landfills. Evidence of this has been found in southern California at sites that do not accept non-MSW wastes (86), as well as at landfills in other States (e.g., Wisconsin and New Jersey) (42). EPA estimated that about 200,000 metric tons of non-methane volatile organic chemicals (VOCs) are emitted from landfills each year (53 *Federal Register* 33338, Aug. 30, 1988). However, EPA's estimates of VOC emissions have been criticized because there is no standard method for sampling air emissions, particularly VOCs, from landfills (84). The critique suggested that standard procedures need to be developed for collection of air samples, sample containment and analysis, and quality control. In one study in the San Francisco Bay area, VOCs were present in the gas at 47 of 60 landfills

(66). There was only minimal evidence of migration of the VOCs off-site into the ambient air, but problems in sampling procedures made it difficult to evaluate the ambient air data.

VOC emissions can affect ozone concentrations because many of these emissions are ozone precursors (26). It is unknown, however, to what extent emissions from landfills contribute to regional non-attainment of National Ambient Air Quality Standards for ozone.

In addition, mercury also has the potential to volatilize into the atmosphere. One Swedish study found that emissions of mercury from four landfills were one to two times higher than background levels (4). However, all four landfills had accepted large quantities of non-MSW, so it is difficult to use this data to evaluate the importance of mercury emissions from MSW landfills.

---

[8]Several legislative initiatives have tried to address this. One Senate bill proposed in 1988, for example, would have: 1) required Subtitle D facilities to be designed and operated to minimize methane emissions; 2) prohibited, as of Jan. 1, 1994, mass releases of methane (e.g., by venting wells); and 3) required EPA to determine the contribution of methane to global warming, the sources and sinks of methane, and methods of controlling methane emissions.

Sources of Contamination: MSW or Industrial Waste?

A well designed, constructed, and operated landfill might exhibit high rates of leachate and gas generation because it usually would be designed to decompose degradable MSW. However, such a landfill also should be designed to be highly efficient in collecting that leachate and gas. A landfill that exhibits these features and is sited properly thus should not be a major source of contamination of groundwater, surface water, or the air.

However, some old MSW landfills have been identified as sources of such contamination, indicating that they were not well designed or operated; as stated earlier, 184 such sites now are included on the NPL. The most common chemicals found at these landfills include halogenated and aromatic organic chemicals and metals (77). Approximately 72 percent of the landfills were associated with releases into groundwater, 44 percent experienced surface water contamination, and 17 percent experienced air emission problems (figure 7-2). At sites with surface water contamination, liquid waste was present at approximately 70 sites, sewage sludge at 45 sites, and pesticides at approximately 10 sites (77).

EPA considers industrial wastes disposed of at the 184 NPL landfills to be the most significant source of contamination, followed by sewage sludge and household hazardous wastes. One analysis of the landfills, for example, found that industrial wastes were co-disposed with MSW in all but two cases (41, 61). This finding has been used to support the contention that MSW landfills are not significant sources of releases of hazardous substances unless they have been used for disposal of industrial wastes.

However, there are other possible explanations. It is possible that MSW landfills that were not known to receive hazardous wastes were not allowed to be listed on the NPL, even if they had associated contamination problems. In particular, an EPA policy memo stated that MSW landfills without a clear record of accepting hazardous waste would not be listed on the NPL (37). This policy was later changed to allow the listing of MSW facilities that did not have a clear record of receiving hazardous waste (38), but whether such landfills will actually be listed is unknown.

Some researchers also suggest that substantial releases of hazardous substances will occur from MSW landfills even where no regulated hazardous wastes have been accepted (11, 83). Webster, in particular, hypothesizes that natural anaerobic processes in MSW landfills can convert nonhazardous waste (e.g., lignin in paper) into hazardous substances such as benzene and toluene (83). These compounds, which also are used to make ingredients in some common household products, are present in gas emissions from MSW landfills (table 7-5; also see ref. 35).

If correct, this hypothesis would have significant implications. If anaerobic processes do generate hazardous substances from MSW, then MSW landfills would not necessarily be safe repositories for MSW, particularly if the waste contains organic matter. Moreover, if these processes result in the formation and release of hazardous substances at levels comparable to industrial hazardous waste landfills, then it might not be appropriate to continue to allow MSW landfills to operate under less stringent standards than those imposed on Subtitle C landfills. In addition, if MSW could generate substantial amounts of hazardous substances, current Superfund apportionment policy, which is based on volume and toxicity, might force **municipal** Principal Responsible Parties to contribute a greater share to cleanup costs of sites where co-disposal of municipal and industrial waste has occurred. These costs could be enormous.

As might be expected, this hypothesis is controversial. Two independent reviews criticized both major premises, that organic substances found in MSW are degraded anaerobically into more toxic substances, and that this generation overshadows the contribution of toxic substances from industrial wastes (41,47). One critic believes that insufficient data were presented to support the premises and that lignin breaks down very slowly and is most effectively attacked by aerobic bacteria, rather than anaerobic bacteria (47). One study estimated that the total cancer risks from *all* chemicals in MSW leachate were one to two orders of magnitude lower than from chemicals in industrial leachate (11) (table 7-6); if true in general, these data would undermine the hypothesis.

Table 7-6—Estimated Cumulative Carcinogenic Potency for Organic Chemicals in MSW and Industrial Landfills

Type and name of landfill	Estimated carcinogenic potency ($\times 10^{-6}$)			
	All chemicals		Suspect carcinogens	
	Median	Mean	Median	Mean
Municipal:				
Lyon	303	1,270	296	1,260
Meeker	23	260	4	30
Rochester	210	1,150	112	573
Industrial:				
Love Canal	1,020	3,940	117	234
Kin-Buc	38,500	13,700	38,300	137,000
Mixed waste:				
La Bounty	1,160	22,900	110	689

SOURCE: K. Brown and K. Donnelly, "An Estimation of the Risk Associated With the Organic Constituents of Hazardous and Municipal Waste Landfill Leachates," *Hazardous Waste and Hazardous Materials* 5(1):1-30, 1988.

A review conducted for the National Solid Waste Management Association (NSWMA) pointed out contradictions between Webster's data and EPA's data on generation rates, with EPA's rates being substantially lower (41). The NSWMA review acknowledges that "microbiological degradation of MSW landfill contents does produce chemicals that are different than those originally present," but it also contends that concentrations of chemicals are almost always higher in leachates from industrial hazardous waste landfills than from MSW or mixed landfills. The central theme of the NSWMA report is that while the degradation of MSW may produce measurable quantities of hazardous substances, these quantities are small in comparison with those released from the disposal of industrial hazardous wastes in MSW landfills.

REGULATION OF MUNICIPAL LANDFILLS

Federal regulation of MSW landfills increased in 1979 with the promulgation of criteria for open dumps. These criteria, however, did not have a substantial impact on practices at MSW landfills. This prompted EPA to propose additional regulations in 1988 governing the design and operation of MSW landfills. Both the 1979 criteria and the 1988 proposal are discussed below.

Effect of 1979 Federal Criteria

The 1979 criteria for new and existing MSW landfills (listed in 40 CFR 257) were intended to provide greater protection from the adverse effects of landfills, but the criteria have had little impact. For example, the percentage of landfills that use engineering and/or design controls to prevent migration of leachate increased only slightly since 1979. Prior to 1980, only 11 percent of all landfills that began operation in the 1970s had leachate collection systems, while 18 percent of those that started after 1980 reported using such systems. Similarly, 67 percent of all landfills operating prior to 1980 had liners, while 75 percent that started after 1980 had liners. Moreover, the criteria have had almost no effect on the siting of new landfills in hydrologically sensitive areas (e.g., karst terrain or below the seasonal high water table) (77).[9]

Proposed MSW Landfill Regulations

In August 1988, EPA proposed new criteria to govern the design and operation of new and existing MSW landfills, as required by Section 4010 of RCRA (53 *Federal Register* 33313, Aug. 30, 1988). The proposed regulations include: location restrictions; facility design restrictions based on performance goals; operating criteria; groundwater monitoring requirements; corrective action requirements for groundwater contamination; financial assurance requirements for closure, post-closure,

---

[9]Karst terrain refers to an irregular limestone region with underground streams and caverns.

and known releases; closure standards; and post-closure standards.[10]

The proposed regulations reflect EPA's desire to reduce the costs to municipalities of meeting these requirements and to give States as much flexibility in implementing them as possible. EPA had several choices about the types of standards to propose:

- "performance" standards based on risk assessments, which would probably lead to high variability in landfill designs;
- "uniform" standards based on technical design considerations, with some allowance for variations, which would lead to little variability in designs; and
- "categorical" standards based on technical design considerations, with designs for different categories of site-specific conditions, which would lead to an intermediate level of variability.

EPA chose to propose risk-based performance standards for design (by outlining the range of risks allowed) and for closure procedures (by describing in narrative terms what is required). States would operate a permitting and regulatory program based on these standards.

The 1988 proposals received substantial public comments, including many criticisms of the risk-based performance approach. The Environmental Defense Fund, for example, called for uniform landfill standards (e.g., double liners, with an upper synthetic liner and a lower composite liner; double leachate collection systems; final cover of synthetic material), with a limited variance available if alternative design and operating practices at the site would prevent migration into groundwater or surface water at least as effectively as the uniform design standard (16). In contrast, the Association for State and Territorial Solid Waste Management Officials and the National Solid Waste Management Association called for a categorical approach that allows States and operators to choose designs based on site-specific conditions (e.g., rainfall and hydrogeology) (15). Other commenters have suggested that the regulations should not allow landfills to be located in areas such as flood plains or wetlands (8).

EPA currently is revising the proposed regulations in light of the public comments it received.

Application to Existing Landfills

The proposed regulations would regulate new and existing facilities differently. Facilities in existence when the regulations become effective would not be required to retrofit with liners, leachate collection systems, or other control features. Existing facilities would be required to provide financial assurance and perform closure, post-closure, and corrective actions. Until the regulations become effective, however, there would be considerable opportunity for existing landfills to close and avoid these potentially costly requirements.

The proposed regulations are designed to apply to all landfills that are in existence 18 months **after** the final rule has been promulgated and to all landfills constructed after that date. Facilities closed at the time the regulations become effective, however, would not be covered. Instead, EPA would encourage "each state to develop a long term regulatory strategy to deal with these closed facilities." **Consequently, there could be substantial incentive for many existing facilities, particularly those approaching the end of their lifespan, to close and avoid potentially expensive responsibilities such as corrective action and closure procedures.**

EPA's proposed regulations acknowlege that these closed facilities represent potential threats to human health and the environment and states that they "may be addressed under EPA's Superfund Program or by RCRA enforcement provisions for imminent hazards."

Even for facilities that close after the 18-month period, the proposed criteria set forth no minimum technical standards regarding how a landfill should be closed. Instead, landfill owners or operators are required to close "each landfill unit in a manner that minimizes the post-closure formation and release of leachate and explosive gases to air, groundwater or surface water to the extent necessary to protect human health and the environment." The lack of minimum technical requirements in the closure proposal would leave States with broad discretion in approving closure plans, while providing them with

---

[10]In general, the new EPA criteria would be equally applicable to both publicly and privately owned MSW landfills, although financial obligations would differ (see "Financial Assurance" below).

little guidance on what actions constitute adequate closure.

Risk-Based Design Criteria

EPA's proposed regulations do not necessarily require new landfills to install liners or leachate collection systems. Instead, the proposal would require each State to choose a "risk goal" based on the cancer risk associated with consuming contaminated groundwater, and then specify design standards intended to achieve that goal as each State sees fit. The range of acceptable lifetime risks set by EPA is 10^{-4} to 10^{-7} (i.e., one out of every 10,000 to 10 million people). If a State chose a high risk goal (i.e., to allow a relatively high risk of 10^{-4}), then it is possible that no liner or leachate collection system would be required.

According to the proposal, a State could choose a risk goal that applies to all landfills in the State or it could set risk goals on a site-specific basis, as long as the level of protection chosen by the State is within the range of allowable risks in the proposed regulations. That is, a State could choose to regulate each aquifer differently, in terms of allowable cancer risk, so long as the cancer risk from consuming contaminated drinking water is between 10^{-4} and 10^{-7}. The States also would have to solve the difficult task of determining which technical requirements will meet those standards; the proposed criteria did not indicate **how** design features such as liners, leachate collection systems, covers, and groundwater monitoring systems should be selected once a State determines the acceptable risk level.

This approach raises some important potential problems. For instance, the Nation lacks a consistent risk assessment methodology for States to use in evaluating landfills; there are also inherent uncertainties in risk assessments. In addition, it is debatable whether all States have the ability to quantitatively evaluate different control technologies in the context of potential risk reduction. There currently are no models or analytical methods for quantitatively evaluating which combinations of control technologies, under conditions of varying leachate quality and exposure pathways, will meet which standards. The availability of trained State employees capable of evaluating these models also is uncertain, and some critics question whether the

models themselves adequately mimic real conditions (7).

Ultimately, then, EPA's proposal as currently formulated could lead to an extremely diverse level of environmental protection provided at MSW landfills, even within an individual State. In addition, under these regulations it is likely that most planned landfills will lack features such as synthetic liners and groundwater monitoring systems (77).

Liner Specifications—The choice of landfill liners is not specified in the proposed regulations. This is significant because a number of different synthetic and natural liner materials can be used, each susceptible to different physical and chemical stresses. Because the requirement to install a liner would rest with the State and its determination of which control technologies are necessary to meet the specific risk goal at the point of compliance (POC), the determination of adequate liner types would also be made by the State. However, given the uncertainties associated with risk assessments and the added complication of trying to predict risk reductions associated with the installation of different liner types, another approach would be to specify approved liner types or systems to ensure a minimum level of protection nationwide.

Groundwater Monitoring—The proposed regulations are based in part on the notion that aquifers of lower resource value deserve less protection than those of higher resource value. This is consistent with EPA's Ground Water Protection Strategy, which calls for a sliding scale of protection for aquifers depending on their current status of contamination and use. Specifically, the proposed regulations would allow States to consider the "existing quality of the groundwater" in setting requirements for design of landfills. States also would have the flexibility to set alternative POCs beyond the landfill boundary where "the aquifer is of low quality and has little or no potential for future use." This would cause "contaminant concentrations to diminish (due to degradation, dispersion, and attenuation) over distance and, thus, potentially decrease the stringency of design criteria needed to meet the design goal." The use of alternative POCs would allow the costs of control systems to be mitigated by taking advantage of the dilution available in the aquifer.

The regulations also would set up a two-phase groundwater monitoring system. The first phase would monitor a limited number of substances, and if contamination was detected, the second phase would monitor for more substances. The frequency for initial groundwater monitoring would be set by the States depending on groundwater flow and the value of the resource.

An important feature of the proposed regulations is the availability of a waiver from groundwater monitoring when a facility can demonstrate that "there is no potential for migration of hazardous constituents from the landfill unit to the uppermost aquifer during the active life, closure, or post-closure periods." The intent of this provision is twofold: to ease the financial burdens on MSW landfill operators and to provide an incentive to site landfills in hydrogeologically preferred areas. However, use of this waiver probably would mean that States would have to rely on the uncertain predictive ability of current leachate migration models; where those models underpredict leaching of hazardous constituents, unmonitored releases to groundwater could occur.

These proposed provisions have been criticized by many observers. The groundwater monitoring requirements, and the requirement that States develop trigger levels, have been criticized as being too flexible and likely to lead to variable State standards (18). The Environmental Defense Fund, for example, considered the alternative POC provision to be a violation of RCRA (16). In contrast, the Small Business Administration felt the POC should be greater than proposed. Some groups also have objected to the requirements because they would be too costly and stringent, especially for small, municipally owned landfills.

Financial Assurance

The proposed regulations include a requirement for owners or operators of MSW landfills to demonstrate that they are capable of financing closure, post- closure care, and corrective action for known releases. The financial assurance criteria would **not** apply to landfills owned and operated by the States or the Federal Government, but they would still apply to local governments. This could impose large cleanup costs that would have to be borne entirely by local governments. This issue is discussed in more detail in chapter 1 (see option 2 under "Landfilling") and chapter 8.

Corrective Action for Air and Surface Water Emissions

The proposed regulations state that about 200,000 metric tons of non-methane volatile organic chemicals are emitted to the air from MSW landfills every year. As a result, the proposal states EPA's future intent to regulate these releases under other statutes—specifically, Clean Air Act Section 111(b) (for new landfills) and Section 111(d) (for existing landfills). Consequently, EPA would exclude these releases from the corrective action requirements in the landfill regulations. Whether future Clean Air Act regulations would require some corrective action for releases of VOCs is unclear, however. Similarly, the proposed landfill regulations include requirements to prevent the discharge of pollutants to surface waters, but would exclude releases to surface waters (as well as soil contamination) from the corrective action requirements.

CHAPTER 7 REFERENCES

1. Abbott, B., Arizona Department of Environmental Quality, personal communication, May 1988.
2. American Paper Institute, "Data on Disposable Diapers, Total U.S. and State of Washington" (New York, NY: January 1988).
3. BASF Corp., "CONTREP Base Sealing System," brochure on file at OTA (Mannheim, West Germany: 1988).
4. Bergvall, G., Karlsson, R., and Wallin, S., "Measurement of Mercury Vapor Emissions From Swedish Waste Landfills," in *ISWA 88: Proceedings of the Fifth International Solid Waste Conference, Volume 2* (San Diego, CA: Academic Press Limited, 1988), pp. 55-60.
5. Bingemer, H., and Crutzen, P., "The Production of Methane From Solid Wastes," *J. Geophysical Research* 92 (D2): 2181-2187, February 1987.
6. Bolle, H.J., Seiler, W., and Bolin, B., "Other Greenhouse Gases and Aerosols: Assessing Their Role for Atmospheric Radiative Transfer," *The Greenhouse Effect, Climate Change and Ecosystems*, B. Bolin et al. (eds.) (New York, NY: John Wiley & Sons, 1988), pp. 157-203.

7. Brown, K.W., "Letter to RCRA Docket Info Center (OS-305), U.S. EPA," Nov. 21, 1988.

8. Brown, K.W., Texas A&M University, personal communication, Feb. 13, 1989.

9. Brown, K.W., and Anderson, D.C., "Aboveground Disposal," *Standard Handbook of Hazardous Waste Treatment and Disposal*, H.M. Freeman (ed.) (New York, NY: McGraw-Hill, NY: 1988), pp. 10.85-10.91.

10. Brown, K.W., and Anderson, D.C., "Above Grade Storage of Waste," paper presented at *National Conference and Exhibition on Hazardous Waste and Environmental Emergencies* (Houston, TX: Mar. 12-14, 1984).

11. Brown, K., and Donnelly, K., "An Estimation of the Risk Associated With the Organic Constituents of Hazardous and Municipal Waste Landfill Leachates," *Hazardous Waste and Hazardous Materials* 5(1):1-30, 1988.

12. Cameron, R.D., and Koch, F.A., "Toxicity of Landfill Leachates," *Journal Water Pollution Control Federation* 52(4):760-769, April 1980.

13. Chandler, W.U., Barns, D.W., and Edmonds, J.A., "Atmospheric Methane Emissions: A Summary of Sources and Policy Issues," draft contract prepared for U.S. Congress, Office of Technology Assessment (Washington, DC: Battelle, Pacific Northwest Laboratories, Dec. 21, 1988).

14. Curran, M.A., and Frobel, R.K., "Strength and Durability of Flexible Membrane Liner Seams After Short-term Exposure to Selected Chemical Solutions," *Land Disposal of Hazardous Waste, Proceedings of Eleventh Annual Research Symposium*, EPA/600/9-85/013 (Cincinatti, OH: 1985), pp. 307-312.

15. Darcey, S., "New Draft of Subtitle D Regs Increases States' Discretion," *World Wastes*, pp. 24-26, March 1988.

16. Environmental Defense Fund, "Comments of the Environmental Defense Fund on the Solid Waste Disposal Facility Criteria," Docket No. F-88-CMLP-FFFFF (Washington, DC: Nov. 30, 1988).

17. Environmental Improvement and Energy Resources Authority, *Statewide Resource Recovery Feasibility and Planning Study*, Missouri Department of Natural Resources (Jefferson City, MO: December 1987).

18. Environment Reporter, "EPA Gets 250 Comments on Landfill Proposal; Design, Ground Water, Financial Sections Hit," *Env. Reporter* 19(33):1654-1656, Dec. 16, 1988.

19. Environment Reporter, "Up to 600 Wisconsin Rural Landfills Expected To Close Because of EPA Rule," *Env. Reporter* 19(48):2551-2552, Mar. 31, 1989.

20. Environment Reporter, "Unlicensed Garbage Dumps Tested To Check Effects on Ground Water," *Env. Reporter* 19(48):2556-2557, Mar. 31, 1989.

21. Eowan, G., California Waste Management Board, personal communication, May 1988.

22. Flanagan, K., "Methane Recovery Does More Than Provide Energy," *Solid Waste and Power* 2(4):30-33, August 1988.

23. Florida Department of Environmental Regulation, "Report on the Potential for Solid Waste Management Grants," May 1986.

24. Franklin Associates, Ltd., *Characterization of Municipal Solid Waste in the United States, 1960 to 2000 (Update 1988)*, final report prepared for U.S. Environmental Protection Agency (Prairie Village, KS: March 1988).

25. Gershman, Brickner & Bratton, Inc., *Performance, Constraints, and Costs of MSW Management Technologies*, contract report prepared for U.S. Congress, Office of Technology Assessment (Falls Church, VA: Sept. 26, 1988).

26. Haagen-Smit, A.J., Bradley, C.E., and Fox, M.M., "Ozone Formation in Photochemical Oxidation of Organic Substances," *Indust. Eng. Chem.* 45:2086, 1953.

27. Harper, S.R., and Pohland, F.G., "Design and Management Strategies for Minimizing Environmental Impact at Municipal Solid Waste Landfill Sites," paper presented at *1988 Joint CSCE-ASCE National Conference on Environmental Engineering* (Vancouver: July 13-15, 1988).

28. Harper, S.R., and Pohland, F.G., "Landfills: Lessening Environmental Impacts," *Civil Engineering* 58(11):66-69, November 1988.

29. Haxo, H., "Durability of Liner Materials for Hazardous Waste Disposal Facilities" (Oakland, CA: Matrecon, Inc., 1981).

30. Haxo, H., "Effects on Liner Materials of Long-term Exposure in Waste Environments," *Land Disposal of Hazardous Waste*, EPA-600/9-82-002 (Cincinnati, OH: U.S. Environmental Protection Agency, Municipal Environmental Research Laboratory, 1982), pp. 191-211.

31. Haxo, H.E., Jr., and Lahey, T.P., "Transport of Dissolved Organics From Dilute Aqueous Solutions Through Flexible Membrane Liners," *Hazardous Waste and Hazardous Materials* 5(4):275-294, 1988.

32. Hershkowitz, A., "International Experiences in Solid Waste Management," contract prepared for U.S. Congress, Office of Technology Assessment (Elmsford, NY: Municipal Recycling Associates, October 1988).

33. Institute for Local Self-Reliance, *Garbage in Europe: Technologies, Economics, and Trends* (Wash-

ington, DC: 1988).

34. Johnson, B., "Portland: First in the West To Send Waste Long Distance." *World Wastes* 31(10):21-32, October 1988.

35. Kinman, R.N., and Nutini, D.L., "Household Hazardous Waste in the Sanitary Landfill," *Chemical TIMES & TRENDS* 11:23-29 and 39-40, July 1988.

36. Knapp, D., and Sutton, C., *On the Recycling of Landfills* (Berkeley, CA: Materials World Publishing, 1981).

37. Longest, H., "Listing Municipal Landfills on the NPL," U.S. Environmental Protection Agency memorandum, Oct. 24, 1986.

38. Longest, H., "Listing Municipal Landfills on the NPL," U.S. Environmental Protection Agency memorandum, Aug. 21, 1987.

39. Maples, A., U.S. Environmental Protection Agency, personal communication, April 1988.

40. Mendieta, H., Texas Department of Health, personal communication, May 1988.

41. Meta Systems, Inc., "Municipal Solid Waste Landfilling: A Review of Environmental Effects" (Cambridge, MA: Oct. 4, 1988).

42. Minott, D., "Comparative Health Risk Assessment of Energy-Recovery and Landfill Facilities," presented at the *Conference on Solid Waste Management and Materials Policy* (New York, NY: January 1988).

43. Morrison, W.R., and Parkhill, L.D., *Evaluation of Flexible Membrane Liner Seams After Chemical Exposure and Simulated Weathering*, U.S. EPA Hazardous Waste Engineering Research Laboratory, EPA/600/S2-87/015 (Cincinnati, OH: April 1987).

44. National Solid Waste Management Association, "Landfill Capacity in the U.S.: How Much Do We Really Have" (Washington, DC: Oct. 18,1988).

45. New Jersey Department of Environmental Protection, *Solid Waste Management Plan, Draft Update: 1985-2000* (Trenton, NJ: July 15, 1985).

46. New York State Legislative Commission on Solid Waste Management, "Where Will the Garbage Go?" (Albany, NY: January 1987).

47. Noble, J., Tufts University, personal communication, Oct. 18, 1988.

48. Ohio Environmental Protection Agency, *Available Capacity for Solid Waste in Ohio*, Division of Solid and Hazardous Waste Management, Annual Report (Columbus, OH: July 1988).

49. Pahren, H., "Microorganisms in Municipal Solid Waste and Public Health Implications," *CRC Critical Reviews of Environmental Control* 17(3):187-228, 1987.

50. Pennsylvania Department of Environmental Resources, "Permitted and Operating MSW Landfills and Incinerators in Pennsylvania" (Harrisburg, PA: July 1986).

51. Pennsylvania Department of Environmental Resources, "Status of Existing and Proposed Facilities for the Processing and Disposal of Municipal Solid Waste in Pennsylvania" (Harrisburg, PA: November 1987).

52. Pohland, F.G., and Harper, S.R., "Critical Review and Summary of Leachate and Gas Production From Landfills," U.S. EPA, Hazardous Waste Engineering Research Laboratory, EPA/600/S2-86-073 (Cincinnati, OH: March 1987).

53. Pollock, C., "Mining Urban Wastes: The Potential For Recycling," Worldwatch Paper 76 (Washington, DC: Worldwatch Institute, April 1987).

54. Prindiville, S., "Testimony of Sheila M. Prindiville, Director, Solid Waste Program, National Solid Waste Management Association, before House Energy and Commerce Committee, Subcommittee on Transportation, Tourism and Hazardous Materials," June 5, 1987.

55. Prindiville, S., National Solid Waste Management Association, personal communication, November 1988.

56. Ramanathan, V., Cicerone, R.J., Singh, H.B., and Kiehl, J.T., "Trace Gas Trends and Their Potential Role in Climate Change," *J. of Geophysical Research* 90:5547-5566, 1985.

57. Rathje, W.L., Hughes, W.W., Archer, G., and Wilson, D.C., "Source Reduction and Landfill Myths," paper presented at *ASTSWMO National Solid Waste Forum on Integrated Municipal Waste Management* (Lake Buena Vista, FL: July 17-20, 1988).

58. Reese, J., Florida Department of Solid Waste, Bureau of Waste Planning and Regulation, personal communication, April 1988.

59. Reeves, D., "The Performance of Clay Liners for Hazardous Waste Landfills," Environmental Defense Fund In-House Report (Washington, DC: 1982).

60. Reindl, J., Wisconsin Department of Natural Resources, personal communication, May 1988.

61. Repa, E., "Lessons Learned From Past Disposal Practices," *Waste Age* 19(5): 86-90, May 1988.

62. Repa, E., "Landfill Capacity: How Much Really Remains" (Washington, DC: NSWMA, Oct. 1988).

63. Rhode Island Solid Waste Management Corp., *Statewide Resource Recovery System Development Plan* (Providence, RI: June 1987).

64. Robinson, W., *The Solid Waste Handbook* (New York, NY: John Wiley & Sons, 1987).

65. Silva, D., Science & Engineering Associates, Inc., personal communication, March 1988.

66. Siu, W., Levaggi, D.A., and Brennan, T.F., "Solid Waste Assessment Test Results From Landfills in the San Francisco Bay Area," paper 89-155.2 presented at *82nd Annual Meeting and Exhibition, Air & Waste Management Association* (Anaheim, CA: June 25-30, 1989).

67. Sondermeyer, G., New Jersey Department of Environmental Protection, personal communication, March 1988.

68. Sprague, R.T., and Boschuk, J., "Installation of HDPE Liners During Winter Months," Paper presented at *International Conference on Geomembranes* (Denver, CO: 1986).

69. Swedish Association of Public Cleansing and Solid Waste Management, *Solid Waste Management in Sweden* (Malmo, Sweden: February 1988).

70. Swindler, M., Indiana Department of Environmental Management, Office of Solid and Hazardous Waste Management, personal communication, April 1988;

71. U.S. Environmental Protection Agency, *Census of State and Territorial Subtitle D Non-Hazardous Waste Programs*, EPA/530-SW-86-039 (Washington, DC: October 1986).

72. U.S. Environmental Protection Agency, *Subtitle D Study, Phase I Report*, Office of Solid Waste and Emergency Response, EPA/530-SW-86-054 (Washington, DC: October 1986).

73. U.S. Environmental Protection Agency, *Survey of State and Territorial Subtitle D Municipal Landfill Facilities*, draft final report, prepared by Westat, Inc., Oct. 13, 1987.

74. U.S. Environmental Protection Agency, Office of Solid Waste, *Operating Criteria (Subpart C), "Criteria for Municipal Solid Waste Landfills" (40 CFR Part 258)*, EPA/530-SW-88-037 (Washington, DC: July 1988).

75. U.S. Environmental Protection Agency, Office of Solid Waste, *Summary of Data on Municipal Solid Waste Landfill Leachate Characteristics, "Criteria for Municipal Solid Waste Landfills" (40 CFR Part 258)*, EPA/530-SW-88-038 (Washington, DC: July 1988).

76. U.S. Environmental Protection Agency, Office of Solid Waste, *Design Criteria (Subpart D), "Criteria for Municipal Solid Waste Landfills" (40 CFR Part 258)*, EPA/530-SW-88-042 (Washington, DC: July 1988).

77. U.S. Environmental Protection Agency, *Report to Congress: Solid Waste Disposal in the United States, Vol. II*, EPA/530-SW-88-011B (Washington, DC: October 1988).

78. U.S. Environmental Protection Agency, Office of Solid Waste, *The Solid Waste Dilemma: An Agenda for Action*, EPA/530-SW-89-019 (Washington, DC: February 1989).

79. University of Illinois, "IEPA Report on Disposal Capacity," *Solid Waste Management Newsletter* 3(3):1, March 1989.

80. Vasuki, N.C., "Why Not Recycle the Landfill!" *Waste Age*, pp. 165-70, November 1988.

81. Vasuki, N.C., Delaware Solid Waste Authority, personal communication, Feb. 16, 1989.

82. Vonasek, J., "An Investigation of Solid Waste Management Methods, Formats and Charges in Florida," prepared for Government Refuse Collection and Disposal Association Mandatory Collection Committee (Tallahassee, FL: David M. Griffith & Associates, Ltd., Apr. 6, 1988).

83. Webster, I., "Municipal Solid Waste Landfills: Toxic Chemical Releases and the Role of Industrial Wastes in Those Releases," unpublished manuscript (Brea, CA: Unocal Corp., 1988).

84. Weston, R.F., Inc., "Air Sampling and Analysis of Organic and Inorganic Constituents at Various Solid Waste Facilities," report prepared for Delaware Solid Waste Authority (West Chester, PA: 1988 draft).

85. Wilson, D.C., "Ancient Trash, Modern Solid Wastes: An Archaeologist's Perspective on Reuse, Recycling, Waste, and Landfill Degradation," paper presented at *National Solid Waste Management Symposium* (Prescott, AZ: Apr. 10, 1989).

86. Wood, J., and Porter, M., "Hazardous Pollutants in Class II Landfills," *J. Air Pollution Control* 37(5):609-615, May 1987.

87. Woodwell, G.M., *The Role of Terrestrial Vegetation in the Global Carbon Cycle* (New York, NY: John Wiley & Sons, 1984).

Chapter 8

Government Planning
and Programs

CONTENTS

Chapter 8
Government Efforts: Planning and Programs

OVERVIEW

"Garbage costs to soar," "Bury and Burn forces collide with recyclers," "State urged to define, collect home toxins," "Town finds recycling works, worth the effort." These types of headlines, appearing with increased frequency in local newspapers all across the Nation, highlight the difficult challenges municipal solid waste (MSW) management poses for local and State governments. Many communities around the country are attempting to decrease reliance on landfilling by reducing the generation of the waste, increasing its reusability, expanding materials recovery and recycling, and/or building more incineration facilities. Determining the appropriate mix and feasibility of these prevention and management methods, however, can be a difficult task for State and local governments.

The management of MSW has traditionally been in the bailiwick of municipal and State governments. Although limited involvement by the Federal Government began in 1965 with the passage of the Solid Waste Disposal Act (see app. 8-A), the Federal role may be expanded as the national implications of increased MSW generation become more evident. In any case, the relationship among Federal, State, and local governments in the management of MSW continues to evolve and the most appropriate roles for each remain open issues.

The Resource Conservation and Recovery Act (RCRA), the major Federal statute regulating MSW, includes specific findings and objectives about MSW management (see app. 8-A).[1] Yet, RCRA does not include explicit findings, objectives, or goals which distinguish MSW prevention from management; the law also does not embody the materials management approach presented in this report (ch. 1). Although the Federal Government has had limited involvement in MSW activities to date, most observers now agree that a more clearly defined Federal role for MSW policy is needed. This task is a major focus of Congress' current RCRA reauthorization discussions.

Some Federal activity to pursue the materials and energy conservation objectives already stated in RCRA was undertaken in the 1970s. For example, the Bureau of Mines sponsored research on the technological and economic feasibility of recovering materials from MSW (94,121), the Department of Treasury investigated the effects of virgin materials tax subsidies on recycling (152), the Interstate Commerce Commission examined freight rates to determine their effects on the use of secondary materials (55), and the Environmental Protection Agency (EPA) established a program to transfer information about MSW to interested States, communities, and businesses (140). Energy recovery was encouraged by the Public Utility Regulatory Policies Act (PURPA) of 1978, which required utilities to purchase energy from waste-to-energy facilities at their "avoided cost" of its production, and the Department of Energy sponsored research on refuse-derived fuel and methane gas recovery techniques (127,138).

Most of this activity waned in the 1980s as concern over the energy crisis diminished and the Nation faced growing economic difficulties. At EPA, hazardous waste issues became the focal point. EPA's efforts to regulate existing MSW landfills and incinerators, as well as recycling facilities, remain limited to date. In 1979, EPA developed criteria to help improve landfill performance, but these are not enforceable regulations and are outdated. Although EPA proposed new regulations in 1988, their adequacy is debated (ch. 7). MSW incinerators also have received little regulatory attention; for example, ash has been left unregulated at the Federal level (ch. 6). Both Congress and EPA recently proposed applying more stringent regulations to MSW landfills and incinerators (chs. 6, 7).

---

[1]Statutes relevant to materials and energy recovery also include similar findings, for example, the National Materials and Minerals Policy, Research and Development Act of 1980 (Public Law 96-479), and the Public Utility Regulatory Policies Act of 1980 (Public Law 95-617).

Little information has been systematically collected on the status of State programs and activities, and information on local programs tends to be anecdotal. It is apparent, however, that State, county, and municipal governments use a wide range of approaches to address MSW issues. In particular, many State and local governments are developing programs to stimulate recycling and some are attempting to encourage waste reduction (chs. 4 and 5). States are also adopting stricter regulations for landfill disposal and incineration facilities to improve their environmental safety. Public involvement is critical to the success of any MSW management strategy, and a number of States and localities have developed noteworthy programs in public education and participation.

This chapter, rather than evaluating the limited efforts of the past, reviews the current status of governmental activities for MSW, highlights particularly noteworthy and innovative policy programs, and assesses a number of cross-cutting issues effecting the prospects for further development of MSW management programs. The information presented here is meant to be illustrative, but given the rapidly developing nature of government MSW activities it cannot be entirely complete or up-to-date.[2]

The focus is on State and local government activities, because this is where most MSW activity has taken place, and the relationship of Federal efforts to these programs. Details on specific Federal programs, some State and local efforts, and important private sector activities are also included throughout the report and are noted where appropriate.

The chapter is divided into four sections: 1) a brief overview of trends in MSW policymaking; 2) a discussion of MSW planning efforts by different levels of government; 3) an examination of other recent program developments for various MSW alternatives, with an emphasis on highlighting innovative approaches; and 4) an assessment of cross-cutting issues, such as siting and the need for public involvement.

THE MOVEMENT TOWARD COMPREHENSIVE MSW MANAGEMENT

The Evolving Nature of MSW Policymaking

The challenges facing State and local governments today in formulating effective MSW management policies have their roots in the evolution of MSW management over the past two decades. In the late 1960s, as the country became increasingly aware of the environmental impacts of past disposal practices and concern over air pollution sources grew, many communities began to phase out open dumps and open burning of MSW, as well as the burning of MSW in relatively uncontrolled incinerators. In the 1970s, attempts were made to improve land disposal through "sanitary landfill" practices and to experiment with new technologies to reclaim materials from waste and/or burn the remainder for energy recovery purposes (e.g., refuse-derived fuel technology).

In the 1980s, the limitations of these efforts became apparent as environmental concerns (e.g., groundwater contamination from existing landfill sites) became more apparent (ch. 7). A dilemma grew clear: just as permitted landfill space became increasingly scarce and expensive, especially in more densely populated areas, the lack of readily available alternatives became evident. Some alternatives, such as incineration, generate intense public opposition primarily because of concerns about potential environmental impacts and high costs. Other MSW alternatives, such as recycling, suffer from difficulties associated with market uncertainties.

In many areas, public pressure exists to investigate and support recycling at least as aggressively as landfilling and incineration when devising solid waste management systems, and also to address the

---

[2]A number of publications are available which surveyed State activities and innovative programs (see e.g., 54,86,150).

need for waste reduction activities.[3] Increasingly, communities and States are devising comprehensive or "integrated" MSW plans that consider a range of MSW options and then coordinate their use based on some presumed hierarchy. EPA, and many State and local governments, have explicitly adopted waste hierarchy and integrated waste management approaches for MSW, but the implications of such approaches do not appear to be generally well thought out.[4]

OTA finds a waste hierarchy can only be meaningfully applied to MSW when waste is managed on a materials management basis, that is, on a material by material basis, not generically as mixed MSW (ch. 1). A waste prevention and materials management approach is a more comprehensive approach to MSW than an integrated waste management approach. In any case, whatever approach a State or local government adopts, careful planning is key. Adequate resources, however, as well as sufficient authority or control over certain aspects of the MSW system, are not always available to local officials as they grapple to establish viable and publicly acceptable policies.

Yurtown and the Rest of the Nation

After nearly two decades of experimentation with MSW management alternatives, the Nation continues to landfill most of its waste—and approximately 40 percent of this waste goes to nonpermitted facilities (145). States and localities continue to search for new strategies to improve the management of the ever-growing amounts of MSW. As illustrated in the description of the experiences of the hypothetical town, Yurtown (box 8-A), localities across the Nation have continually adjusted their MSW management practices as Federal and State

governmental programs have changed and MSW management options have developed.[5]

The management options available to localities, however, have always been affected by State and Federal activities. For example, in the 1970s as Federal and State air pollution regulations became more stringent, many localities were prompted to move away from municipal incinerators and develop recycling programs and a greater reliance on landfilling for MSW. In the mid-1970s, when the energy crisis spurred the establishment of a Federal waste-to-energy program, communities were encouraged to apply for planning grants for MSW incinerators. The passage of PURPA in 1978 further supported the development of municipal incineration. Today, as more stringent State regulations are implemented for landfill operations, municipalities making MSW policy decisions are again faced with a climate of change (114).

Many factors combine to determine the most suitable variation of MSW management practices at any given location. These factors include: the degree and type of governmental regulations; the particular geological and environmental conditions of the area; and the level of public concern and the public's general disposition and attitudes toward MSW management. For instance, some communities are more receptive to voluntary versus mandatory recycling programs; some communities are opposed to the use of waste-to-energy facilities because of health and environmental concerns.

The tremendous variation in the demographics and topography of our Nation is clearly reflected in the types of waste management methods practiced. Even a brief review of available national data on State MSW programs indicates striking variation across the country (18).

---

[3]Numerous polls indicate that consumers strongly support the use of recyclables. For example, a Gallup poll found that over 50 percent of the respondents would change their purchasing habits to buy recyclable containers; a National Solid Waste Management Association survey found that over 40 percent of the respondents supported taxes on packaging and nonrecyclable materials to fund recycling programs; and a Schoen Asssociates poll found 91 percent of the respondents willing to pay a few cents more for recyclable or biodegradable products (87,98).

[4]Nearly all discussions about solid waste accept the premise that there is a hierarchy of management options that starts with "waste reduction," proceeds to recycling (and composting), incineration (and other treatment methods), and finally considers land disposal. In general, the hierarchy refers to an ordered set of preferences, based on supposed levels of human health and environmental risk. A hierarchy for management of hazardous waste is in fact widely employed today. Its application to MSW may be more problematic (ch. 1). Combining the hierarchy with an "integrated waste management approach" may have some utility, since both reduction and management can be used together, but in most applications an integrated waste management "hierarchy" for MSW is nonlinear. For example, EPA's discussion about integrated management states that "source reduction and recycling are the preferred options" (151). EPA's approach also considers incineration and landfilling as equally preferred options.

[5]Even though a typical town in our diverse nation is impossible to describe, a snapshot of a hypothetical town, Yurtown, illuminates the problems that are common to many real communities. Every event in the Yurtown snapshot occurred somewhere in the country during the past two decades.

Box 8-A—Yurtown: A Hypothetical Town

Yurtown is a middle to upper-middle class suburb of a medium-sized city (population 250,000) and has a population of about 50,000. The county, Mye County, has a population of nearly 1 million and generates about 2,000 tons a day of MSW. Like many areas in the country, Yurtown, its county, and State are grappling with a number of MSW management issues. Prior to 1968, open burning and dumps were the primary disposal method in Yurtown. Several open dumps operated in the rural parts of the township, usually sited in gravel pits or swamps. Some of the residents in the more rural areas of the township dumped their wastes in gullies and/or burned their garbage in "burn cans" (i.e., 50-gallon drums) on their property. Like most towns, Yurtown imposed few controls on these dumps. Consequently, hazardous wastes and other materials could be disposed of easily and smoke, odor, rodents, flies, blowing paper, and contaminated run-off were common.

In 1969, as Yurtown and the entire Nation became more conscious of environmental impacts from our society's activities, the State passed a law and established an air quality rule banning open burning. The State also directed the newly created State environmental protection agency to adopt standards, regulations, and variances regarding MSW. Under this authority, in 1970, the State agency adopted rules that required the closure of open dumps and placed operational controls on permitted facilities. In 1972, Federal guidelines for land disposal facilities were adopted and State requirements were revised accordingly. Most of the open burning at dumps ceased in Yurtown at this time, although many of the dumps continued to operate until newer sites could be located and permitted. As environmental consciousness became more prevalent, some community groups and neighborhoods in Yurtown organized recycling efforts. These were largely private citizen-sponsored activities, not town-supported efforts, although some funds from the State government were available.

By the mid-1970s, the energy crisis heightened concern over the use of resources. The Resource Conservation and Recovery Act passed by Congress in 1976 required the closing of all remaining open dumps and encouraged resource recovery of materials (through recycling) and energy (through incineration). Yurtown now had one of three permitted sanitary landfills in Mye County. The recycling programs were diminishing in size and impact, caused primarily by lower market values for the materials as a result of normal market fluctuations. At roughly this same time, the State and county expanded their involvement in MSW management. The State defined MSW goals (similar to those of RCRA), coordinated MSW management among local jurisdictions, and facilitated the development of waste facilities.

In the case of Yurtown, the county began to work with a major company to secure the construction of a resource recovery facility. The refuse-derived fuel plant (designed at 2,000 tons per day) was designed to handle all of the county's MSW and would require importing some MSW from surrounding areas. It cost over $50 million to build and its official start up was in 1978. The facility was designed to recover magnetic and non-magnetic metals and mixed glass for recycling and refuse-derived fuel (RDF) to be used by the local utility company. Some State and Federal funds supported the facility's construction and operation. The Public Utility Regulatory Policies Act (PURPA) of 1978 guaranteed the sale of any energy recovered by the facility to the local utility.

By the early 1980s, recycling efforts were almost nonexistent in Yurtown, the RDF facility was experiencing operating difficulties, and newly adopted State landfill regulations, combined with near-full capacity conditions, would ultimately lead to the closure of all but the Yurtown landfill in the county. The town and county were having difficulty finding suitable sites for new landfills, and a request for a permit to expand the Yurtown landfill was made to the State. The State now required county MSW plans to address certain goals for MSW management contained in the State's MSW plan. The State had authorized flow control for waste-to-energy facilities and had continued some support programs for "low technology waste management options." Many of these efforts and programs were discontinued, however, during the recession of 1982-83.

In 1984, the RDF facility closed. No new landfills had been sited in the county and by 1987, the Yurtown landfill was expected to reach capacity. A park had been built over one of the landfills and the waste management company that now owned and operated the Yurtown landfill was exploring the possibility of methane recovery at that site. Approximately 87 percent of the county's MSW was now being sent 90 miles away to another private landfill and disposal costs were increasing dramatically. At about this time, the county executive proposed to build a new mass burn incinerator, next door to the RDF facility, which would be a 2,000-ton-per-day facility and cost approximately $125 million to build. Again, a facility of this size would necessitate the importation of MSW from other jurisdictions.

The proposed plan for the incinerator and RDF facilities became a campaign issue and ultimately, given the concerns over the poor past performance of the RDF facility and concerns over the potential environmental effects of air emissions and ash from the proposed incinerator, the county executive was voted out of office and the proposal was shelved. The public was also concerned over possible groundwater contamination near old landfill sites and continued to oppose the siting of new landfills.

The State did grant the landfill in Yurtown an expansion permit. Nonetheless, about 90 percent of the county's waste is being transported to other areas for landfilling. Landfill costs have risen four-fold for Yurtown in the last decade and concerns over current MSW management practices have risen commensurately. A county survey found that about 80 percent of the citizens were willing to separate their waste as part of a recycling effort. A county recycling coordinator was hired in 1988 to develop a county recycling program. Meanwhile, Mye County continues to pursue siting a new landfill. One of the proposed sites is in Yurtown. The county is also reevaluating the necessity or desirability of an incineration facility for the area and how this management alternative could be coordinated with recycling and landfilling options.

For example, while some States report they have 5 years or less of permitted landfill capacity currently available, other States report no capacity problems at all (ch. 7) (16,17,145). Variation can also exist within a State, particularly between urban and rural areas. Among the States, four report recycling more than 15 percent of their MSW, while over half estimate that 5 percent or less of MSW is recycled (16,17).[6] Waste-to-energy facilities also are not an evenly distributed MSW management option. As of 1986, approximately 35 percent of the existing facilities were located in the Northeast, while only 7 percent were found in the Plains/Inter-Mountain and Pacific coast regions.

This variation in the types of MSW management options used in different regions of the United States reflects the difference in the nature and degree of problems associated with MSW. Naturally, this variation is also reflected in the types of policy programs articulated in these areas and has implications for any further policy development by the Federal Government. These diverse national MSW experiences underscore the importance of coordinating government efforts and carefully articulating a Federal involvement that recognizes regional variation.

MSW PLANNING

Local Planning

As noted, the primary responsibility for administering MSW management programs lies with local governments. Indeed, until recently MSW has been managed almost exclusively by local governments. As State governments have begun to take a more active role in MSW management, and the Federal Government is reconsidering its role, localities face ever more complicated conditions for MSW planning and management. Given that most implementation still continues at the local level, however, local MSW plans are a key part of MSW management efforts. Indeed, in some States their role may be most determinative of MSW policy actions.[7]

[6]The national recycling data from Franklin Associates are based on a materials flow calculation, while State data are likely to be calculated on different bases (such as within-State surveys of some sort). Thus the two types of estimates are not directly comparable.

[7]In this assessment, the term "local" includes both county and municipal levels of government. The split of responsibilities between these levels varies throughout the country. In some cases, counties are responsible for the operation of MSW facilities and municipalities are responsible for the collection and transportation of MSW; in other cases each level of government may have these responsibilities.

Considerable variation exists in local MSW plans. Although the details of local plans will not be discussed here, it is worth noting the major components of most plans before focusing on the important relationship between local and State governments in MSW planning. Local MSW planning is an ongoing, action-oriented process. Components of municipal plans may be required by county (or State) governments, and in turn county plans may have to meet State requirements. State plans to receive EPA approval must also meet requirements as defined by RCRA, but most States' planning processes are more comprehensive than that prescribed by the Federal requirements.

The local MSW planning process is likely to involve a number of studies: an engineering estimate of remaining solid waste capacity; a waste composition study; a recycling plan; an incineration feasibility study; analysis of ownership alternatives for MSW facilities; analysis of alternative pollution control equipment, facility size and stack height of incinerators; assessments of potential sites; possibly preliminary environmental and health assessments; and some assessment of public concerns over MSW alternatives. This information is then used by the local planning body (e.g., the county board, town council, or a designated planning board) to outline the best long-term and interim solutions to address the locality's MSW problems.

Typically, a local MSW plan will include some combination of management alternatives and goals for local reduction and recycling efforts. Interim solutions might include extending the permit of an existing landfill, which will be upgraded or closed when new management capacity is available. Long-term plans might include the development of transfer stations, a new landfill, an incineration facility, and/or a collection program for recyclable materials. Local plans involve some regional cooperation in the construction of new MSW facilities and/or arrangements for the use of facilities in other jurisdictions.

According to the U.S. Conference of Mayors, at least four concerns are uppermost in local officials'

minds as more regulatory, management, and planning requirements are imposed on localities. These are: 1) any liabilities these additional requirements might entail for the municipalities; 2) the adequacy of the local government infrastructures to meet or adapt to mandated requirements; 3) the impact on the localities' ability to site and finance needed MSW facilities; and 4) the effect on the continuity of existing MSW programs (71).

The critical equation for local officials to balance is achieving effective planning for MSW programs with limited resources while State and Federal requirements for MSW management increase. Given the continually evolving nature of MSW policies, incorporating flexibility into a waste prevention and materials management approach is critical to effective implementation.

Key factors in devising effective local MSW programs, according to participants at an OTA workshop,[8] include: 1) identifying resources (e.g., information exchanges, technical assistance on available options and other resources); 2) collecting site-specific data on waste quantities and composition to analyze appropriate MSW management options; 3) developing public outreach (e.g., public education and participation) to develop a common perspective and share responsibility for MSW problems in the community; 4) clarifying the regulatory regime (e.g., link planning to permitting; clarify definitions/policy directions); 5) devising funding strategies or sources for new programs; and 6) identifying implementation options (e.g., assess siting prospects, flow control issues, and market development).

How States and localities share in these activities for devising MSW programs varies. In some States, such as Rhode Island and Delaware, the State government assumes a primary and central role in MSW management and local levels of government are not highly involved. In other States, such as New Jersey and Missouri, the State's role is less pervasive and counties and/or municipalities have a more primary role in MSW management.[9] Sometimes planning appears to be uncoordinated. In most cases,

---

[8]This list is a composite developed by the State and local officials who participated in the OTA Workshop on State and Local MSW Programs, March 17-18, 1988. Examination of State and local programs confirms at least the importance of these factors.

[9]Other States that report primary authority for MSW management at a local level are Arkansas, Connecticut, Kentucky, New York, North Carolina, Utah, and Washington (16,17).

however, there is some cooperation between the levels of government within States, which can greatly improve MSW efforts. In some States, particularly those in New England where municipal governments are traditionally strong and active, the State and municipal governments may work together closely. Other State governments work more closely with the county level of government, as is the case for Michigan, South Carolina, Idaho, and several other States (16,17).

New Jersey and New York State exemplify situations in which the State government articulates goals, provides information, and establishes baseline regulations and directives to guide local MSW actions. In New Jersey, for example, a detailed planning process is outlined in the New Jersey Solid Waste Management Act Amendments of 1975 (Chapter 326), which sets rigid timetables and clear delegations of responsibility. The law is an attempt to move the State away from the past's uncoordinated and largely piecemeal approach to MSW management and build "a cooperative checks and balances strategy toward comprehensive long-term management" (117). The responsibilities are shared between the 21 counties, one special district, and the State. The counties and district assume primary responsibilities, including:

- 10-year Solid Waste Master Plan development;
- technology selection;
- site selection;
- permit application submission;
- project financing; and
- implementation.

The State's role is one of overseer and regulator. The New Jersey Department of Environmental Protection's functions include:

- State-level review coordination (including review and approval of county and district plans);
- plan amendment certification;
- permit application review;
- construction and operation permitting;
- compliance and enforcement monitoring; and
- State funding.

The State, after more than a decade of effort, believes that the long-term planning process has been successful and that it will reach its goal of self-sufficiency in MSW management (i.e., waste will not be shipped out of the State for disposal) by 1992. Long-term project development has been hindered, however, by problems siting facilities and the changing nature of landfill and resource recovery facility design. These have delayed specific technology selection and submission and review of permit applications (117).

In Missouri, local governments have full authority for MSW management. The State reviews and approves local MSW management plans, regulates permitted facilities, takes enforcement action against illegal dumps, and provides technical assistance. The Missouri Department of Natural Resources, based on studies and its assessment of MSW activities throughout the State, has identified the key social, environmental, technological, financial and market-related, and institutional factors which determine the success of a locality's materials recovery, composting and waste-to-energy projects (77). These types of factors are likely to be important to local planning in any State.

State Planning

In most States, primary responsibility for **overall** MSW planning lies with the State (16,17). A major focus of Subtitle D of RCRA was to encourage (not require) the development of State solid waste management plans covering MSW and other nonhazardous solid wastes to foster intergovernmental and public/private cooperation (App. 8-A). Federal technical and financial assistance was offered to States and localities as an incentive to develop the plans (Sections 4002-4003; Sections 4006-4008). Federal funding dwindled to zero in the early 1980s, however, and as a result some of the current State plans may not be formally EPA-approved. Most States continued the planning process for their own purposes and variation among State plans exists.

Given the voluntary nature of the State planning process and concern over the general effectiveness of past MSW management programs, some observers are critical of the State planning process (133). Congress could address this issue as part of the RCRA reauthorization by requiring that States submit plans and that the plans address certain MSW issues with national implications (ch. 1). Although RCRA lists some requirements that must be met if submitted plans are to be approved, some of these may no longer be relevant and new issues may warrant inclusion (ch. 1). For example, some topics for State plans to address include provisions for capacity assurance, a siting process, and reporting composition and generation data. Incentives, for example in the form of technical assistance, could be granted to a State if its plan was submitted and approved by EPA and/or funding decreases or other penalties could be imposed if a State did not submit a plan.[10] State solid waste plans thus could be important to national MSW prevention and materials management efforts (e.g., through their impact on increased interstate transportation of MSW, or their contribution to a national database for MSW and recovered materials).

In any case, most State MSW plans are just that, *plans*. That is, they are general statements of the direction the State anticipates focusing MSW management efforts within a time period, usually between 5 and 10 years. The level of specificity of the plans is usually not high, although they do represent an attempt at a comprehensive assessment of MSW management for the State. The plans usually contain an overview of the State's current MSW situation, including the amounts and composition of MSW, the use of various management methods, variation within the State, and any problem areas. In addition, the plans explain new objectives and programs and outline how existing efforts will be modified. How State efforts will be coordinated with municipal and possibly regional efforts may also be included.

One goal of most State solid waste management plans is "integrated waste management." Integrated waste management is basically the recognition that some combination of waste management methods (e.g., recycling, incineration, and landfilling) is necessary to ensure more efficient and environmentally sound MSW disposal. The waste prevention and materials management approach presented in chapter 1, although not explicitly embodied in any current State plan, is not inconsistent with an integrated approach. Indeed, the prevention and materials management strategy described by OTA

may clarify some of the distinctions and interrelationships now blurred in many of the existing plans' articulation of "integrated waste management." A prevention and materials management strategy could be required in State plans (ch. 1).

At least 12 States have legislation requiring recycling (or the opportunity for it). A larger number of States and localities have set goals for recycling a certain percentage of MSW. The range is from 15 to 50 percent, but usually the recycling goal is about 25 percent. Of course, how recycling is defined and which portions of the MSW stream are included in calculating the percentage affects the recycling rate figure. States may also project the amount of MSW to be managed by source reduction, incineration, and landfilling.[11] The State of Michigan, for example, has set an overall goal to reduce the use of MSW landfills by 70 percent and projects that it can reduce its waste by 5 percent, recycle 25 percent, reuse 5 percent, compost 6 percent, incinerate 40 percent to recover energy, and landfill 19 percent. Other States only set a goal for recycling; for instance, New Jersey has a recycling goal of 25 percent.

In 1986, EPA issued a report as part of its mandate from the Hazardous and Solid Waste Amendments (HSWA) of 1984 to survey and assess the adequacy of national Subtitle D activities (145). EPA reported that in 39 States and territories, 2 to 8 different agencies administer parts of the State's MSW program (usually solid waste and water-related agencies were listed). In the other 15 States and territories, only one State agency administered Subtitle D activities.[12] The number of agencies involved in State MSW management presents a challenge to efforts to achieve a more integrated waste management approach (145).

In most cases, State MSW plans have been revised recently or are in the process of changing. Indeed, State activities in general are in a state of flux. Almost every State in the country has several pieces of legislation related to MSW pending or recently passed. In some States the flurry of activity

---

[10]Federal involvement in encouraging the development of State solid waste planning began with the Solid Waste Disposal Act of 1965, which provided grants to States to develop statewide solid waste management plans and designate a single implementing agency. By 1975, all States had adopted some form of solid waste regulations, although tremendous variation existed among them (68).

[11]Source reduction, however, is defined differently by different States and often includes recycling. The definition may differ than that used by OTA.

[12]It should be noted that Subtitle D wastes are a larger universe than MSW as defined in this assessment. EPA believes that other State agencies may be administering parts of Subtitle D activities that were not reported since they are not generally recognized by these agencies as Subtitle D activities.

is almost too fast to follow; for example, in California close to 50 bills were pending in the legislature in early 1988 and others continue to be introduced. Administering agencies are also reorganizing and changing in response to the increased emphasis to MSW issues.

Despite the recent attention directed to recycling, most current State MSW activities are focused on landfill management. According to EPA, 41 percent of the estimated total number of hours spent on Subtitle D activities (which would include management of landfill operations) by States were spent on surveillance and enforcement activities. Permitting and licensing accounted for almost 28 percent, and technical assistance accounted for 9 percent. Planning, regulation, development, training, and research accounted for the remaining hours (145).[13] Respondents to EPA's survey indicated that surveillance and enforcement, followed by technical assistance, and permitting, and licensing, are the most important activities for improving overall Subtitle D program effectiveness (145). This assessment could change, however, as new programs are established to address recycling, source reduction, and other MSW issues.

There is tremendous variation in the staffing of MSW activities by States, with a reported range from zero to over 200 (16,17).[14] Utah reports the smallest staff—no professionals working on solid waste activities—while Pennsylvania reports the most, 212 professionals employed (16). EPA's census indicated that 10 or fewer persons were allocated to Subtitle D activities in 22 States and territories, 10 to 25 persons were allocated by 15 States and territories, and 25 or more persons were allocated by 10 States and territories (145). In many States, the staff allocations for MSW activities are increasing as MSW programs are dramatically expanded. Yet, as in many areas of public policy, staffing and funding resources rarely are commensurate with what is necessary to fully develop quality programs.

Photo credit: Office of Technology Assessment

Many States and communities have adopted slogans and logos to symbolize and promote their recycling efforts.

EPA provided Federal funds to help States fund Subtitle D programs from 1971 to 1981. Under this program, the Federal Government provided 25 percent if the States provided 75 percent. Federal grant money peaked in 1979, but dropped to zero in 1982 after the Reagan Administration's budget reductions (18). Since 1982, States have had to support Subtitle D activities essentially on their own. In 1981, the State provided 79 percent of the budget, while the Federal Government provided 21 percent; in 1984, the State provided 95 percent of the budget, and the Federal Government provided only 2 percent (some Federal funding did continue in water programs) (figure 8-1). EPA's survey indi-

---

[13]Data from the Association of State and Territorial Solid Waste Management Officials' survey generally support these findings (5,18).

[14]Discrepancies exist among the available estimates of the total number of people working full-time on Subtitle D issues. The most recent estimate is 1,098 full-time professionals (16). Based on information from 1984, EPA previously reported 858 full-time professionals and ASTSWMO reported 787 full-time equivalents (including clericals). The reliability of any of these estimates is questionable and the discrepancies may be due to the different number of States reporting, the definitions assumed by the respondents, the different years the surveys were taken, etc. Further, they may overestimate the number of persons working only on MSW, because they include all Subtitle D and all solid waste activities (18).

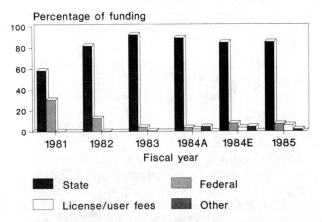

Figure 8-1—Sources of State Subtitle D Budgets, 1981-85

Percentage of funding

Legend:
- State (black)
- License/user fees (white)
- Federal (gray)
- Other (dark gray)

NOTES: "Other" includes district funding sources in Idaho and environmental license plate funds in California. Data for years 1981 to first 1984 column (labeled 1984A) are from ASTSWMO; data for second 1984 column (labeled 1984E) and 1985 are from EPA. Differences between ASTSWMO and EPA data in 1984 may be caused by differences in methodologies and number of States reporting.

SOURCES: Association of State and Territorial Solid Waste Management Officials (ASTSWMO), *National Solid Waste Survey* (Washington, DC: October 1984); U.S. Environmental Protection Agency, *Census of State and Territorial Subtitle D Non-Hazardous Waste Programs,* prepared by Westat, EPA/530-SW-86-039 (Washington, DC: October 1986).

cated that these trends continued for FY 1984 and FY 1985 (145).

License and user fees are increasingly important sources of funding for State MSW management (figure 8-1) (5,145). It remains to be seen, however, whether State funding will keep pace with the expanding scope of MSW activities. In the past, most States (28) have allocated less than $500,00 per year for Subtitle D activities; 13 States have budgeted between $500,000 and $1 million, while 7 have spent over $1 million (145,149).

Regional Planning and Cooperation Efforts

Some regional cooperation within or between States is planned or exists. Such cooperation is increasingly desirable given the siting difficulties, high costs, and capacity issues associated with planning and developing integrated MSW facilities. Regional efforts are particularly advantageous for local MSW management in some rural areas. For example, the Land-of-Sky Regional Council, a Council of Governments organization in North

Carolina, represents a four county region in western North Carolina. It includes the Regional Solid Waste Alternatives Committee, which is charged to spearhead solid waste projects in the region (including MSW management plans, feasibility studies for waste-to-energy plants, and waste composition studies) (80).

The Land-of-Sky Regional Council recently completed a nationwide survey of MSW activities of Regional Councils of Government and Development Districts. Thirty-seven States responded. In all regions of the country, "lack of landfill capacity" was identified as a significant concern (18,80). Differences in the nature of MSW concerns in different regions also were evident. In the Midwest, tipping fees and "intercounty and interstate transfer of waste" received more attention than in any other region. In the Southeast and Central regions, "problems with solid waste collection" and "illegal and open dumps" were identified as two issues of importance for MSW management (18,80). The critical MSW issues identified by regional governmental entities are the same as those identified by States and municipalities (133).

States also have begun to coordinate some efforts, in particular to support recycling efforts through an exchange of information and some coordination and facilitation of marketing secondary materials. The most formal regional recycling organization is in the Northeast: the Northeast Recycling Coalition (NERC) of the Eastern Regional Conference of the Council of State Governments. NERC, formed in 1988, consists of the recycling directors and representatives of the State legislatures of Connecticut, Delaware, Maine, Massachusetts, New Hampshire, New Jersey, New York, Pennsylvania, Rhode Island, and Vermont. The group meets quarterly, and publishes a newsletter to exchange information about State innovations and research (22).

One NERC project, "Developing a Regional Approach to Buying Recycled Paper Products," addresses matters such as definitions and percentages for the various types of recycled paper products, cooperative purchasing agreements among and within States, and standard vendor certification format and procedures. In addition, discussions at NERC meetings have addressed New York State's proposed packaging tax and similar legislation, research being conducted in each State, and areas in need of research (22). Independently, the Coalition of Northeastern Governors (CONEG) issued a policy statement about the reduction of packaging (11) (also see "Waste Prevention" below).

In the Midwest, a more informally organized regional effort exists. Every 3 to 6 months, recycling officials from the following States and one Canadian Province have been meeting: Arkansas, Illinois, Indiana, Iowa, Michigan, Minnesota, Missouri, New York, Ohio, Pennsylvania, Wisconsin, and Ontario, Canada. This regional effort has discussed plastic packaging and paper markets. The meetings help States exchange information and update the status of their activities. The group is seeking to expand their meetings into a national effort and are cooperating with the Association of State and Territorial Solid Waste Management Officials (ASTSWMO) to establish a Waste Reduction/Recycling Committee (10).

In the West, some effort to form an informal "compact" for recycling is being discussed. The States interested in such an activity are Alaska, California, Idaho, Oregon, and Washington (4). No government-level regional efforts in the Southwest and Southeast were identified. However, regional efforts between States are sometimes part of Council of Governments efforts. For example, county and municipal public works officials in Virginia, Maryland, and the District of Columbia meet to discuss how to attract recycling industries to their region. Their efforts have thus far focused on markets, cooperative purchasing of recycled products, and coordination to sell secondary materials (22,33).

SPECIFIC MSW PROGRAMS AND POLICY DEVELOPMENTS

Many State and local MSW programs are so recent in their development that there is little implementation history to evaluate. This chapter, however, presents examples of past as well as present MSW management experiences in an attempt to evaluate how the range of waste management and programs being adopted by particular States and localities are being implemented. For example, it is possible to examine some existing management alternatives and the plans for other programs, such as waste reduction. This section

looks at current policy and programs related to waste reduction efforts, recycling, resource recovery and landfill disposal use, and possible future trends. Special programs for particular problem wastes, such as household hazardous wastes, tires, and composting are noted.

Although this section focuses on State and local programs, it also reviews some Federal activities related to MSW management. EPA has the broadest Federal authority for regulating MSW activities (see "Environmental Protection Agency" below). Other Federal agencies also have key roles in particular aspects of MSW management (see discussions under "Waste Prevention," "Recycling," and "Incineration"). Even a cursory review of Federal activities shows the uneven and uncoordinated nature of past Federal MSW efforts. The need for a more comprehensive approach to MSW issues, by all levels of government, is clear.

Environmental Protection Agency

In 1988, EPA completed a major assessment of the adequacy of the current Subtitle D program for Congress (ch. 7), proposed new landfill guidelines, and established a special task force to examine broader MSW issues and outline an agenda for agency actions regarding MSW (147,149,151). Many of the specific actions recommended are described in chapter 1 and thus are mentioned only briefly in this chapter.

EPA's implementation of RCRA's solid waste provisions has been described as "tardy, fragmented, at times nonexistent, and consistently inconsistent" (66). This view is borne out by even a cursory examination of EPA's actions. According to Subtitle D of RCRA, Federal criteria for landfills form the basis of State regulations. However, the current Federal criteria are general and incomplete. For example, the Federal criteria do prohibit contamination of groundwater used for drinking water, but do not require any monitoring or specify corrective action requirements. Also, no Federal provisions related to closure, post-closure, or financial responsibility exist (40 CFR Part 257; ref. 149). The 1984 amendments to RCRA, the Hazardous and Solid Waste Amendments, required EPA to revise Federal criteria for solid waste landfills to ensure the protection of human health and the environment.

Chapter 7 discusses in greater detail the new proposed landfill criteria and the effect of the Federal criteria issued in 1979 (53 *Federal Register* 33314).

EPA has initiated some regulatory activity on air emissions from MSW incinerators, but generally it has been criticized for its slow pace. Based on emissions from new and existing MSW incinerators, EPA has documented risks to human health and the environment which warrant regulatory action (ch. 6). EPA and congressional approaches to regulating MSW incinerators differ, however, in significant ways (e.g., in emission limits) and contentious debate continues over how to regulate MSW incinerator ash (see ch. 6).

In 1976, RCRA required agencies to begin procurement of recycled products within 2 years. EPA was to establish procurement guidelines. Until recently, however, all three agencies with some Federal responsibilities for recycling—EPA, the Department of Commerce, and the Office of Policy Procurement (General Services Administration)— largely failed to encourage the Federal Government to use items containing the maximum amount of recovered materials as intended by RCRA (see ''Procurement'' below). The Department of Commerce, through the Office of Recycled Materials of the National Bureau of Standards, however, engaged in some activity (see ''Recycling'' below).

In 1980, in light of EPA's inactivity, Congress added specific deadlines requiring that procurement guidelines for certain materials be set by May 1, 1981, while guidelines for two other areas were due by September 30, 1982. The deadlines were missed again and the 1984 Amendments established a 1985 deadline for EPA to establish guidelines for paper products, tires, and two other materials. Four environmental groups (Environmental Defense Fund (EDF), Environmental Task Force, Coalition for Recyclable Waste, and the National Recycling Congress) sued EPA in 1987 to issue procurement guidelines and requested the Federal court to place EPA on an expedient schedule.[15] A consent decree

in the case required that these guidelines be finalized and also that EPA continue to explore additional product categories appropriate for guidelines.[16]

EPA, meanwhile, had issued only one final guideline addressing cement containing fly ash. In 1984, EPA proposed guidelines for recycled paper; in 1986, it presented a proposal for asphalt materials containing used tires; and in 1987, it proposed a guideline for re-refined lubricating oil. However, none of these proposals had been issued in final form. After the lawsuit was filed, however, EPA did issue the paper guideline in final form (52 *Federal Register* 37293).[17] In addition, EPA proposed an amendment to the paper guideline that would create minimum content standards (52 *Federal Register* 37335). Soon after, EPA also issued a proposed guideline for re-refined lubricating oil (52 *Federal Register* 48388). EPA issued final guidelines for purchase of paper on June 22, 1988; oil on June 30, 1988; tires on November 17, 1988; and insulation materials on February 17, 1989.

In 1989, EPA's MSW Task Force proposed a number of activities to increase waste reduction and recycling (chs. 1 and 4; ref. 151). In addition, the task force report suggests schedules for EPA's MSW activities.

MSW Prevention

Several Federal agencies have programs or statutory authorities that could be applied to help reduce the quantity or toxicity of MSW. These agencies include, for example, EPA, the Food and Drug Administration (FDA), and the Consumer Products Safety Commission (CPSC).

EPA had an active program investigating MSW reduction in the 1970s under the authorities of the Resource Recovery Act of 1970, which called for studying production and packaging practices to reduce waste generation (93). EPA created a waste reduction branch that studied, for example, beverage container deposits, milk packaging, and tires. Waste reduction options and activities were the subject of four EPA reports sent to Congress in the mid-1970s

[15]*Environmental Defense Fund, et al. v. EPA*, No. 87-3212 (D.D.C.).

[16]*Environmental Defense Fund v. Thomas*, No. 88-1003 (D.C. Cir.).

[17]In January 1988, EDF and the National Recycling Coalition filed a petition for review of the EPA's final paper guideline in Federal court in an attempt to address the substance of the guidelines (*Environmental Defense Fund and National Recycling Coalition v. Thomas*). For EDF's critique of the guidelines, see ref. 52.

(e.g., 141). Recently, EPA signaled its intent to reconsider MSW reduction (151). It took an initial step in this process by sponsoring a dialog on MSW reduction in 1988 (12).

The Food and Drug Administration also has authorities that could affect the composition of MSW. For example, FDA regulates food additives; some packaging materials; color additives in foods, drugs, and cosmetics; and various food constituents (132). FDA regulations require that food packaging either not be likely to become a component of food at all (i.e., no migration into the product) or be safe in a given application. Although FDA clears some materials, much of the responsibility for evaluating the health and environmental implications of new food packaging is given to the manufacturers of the packaging. These evaluations generally are based on extraction tests that indicate whether potentially toxic substances can be extracted from food packaging materials. Recently, the FDA announced that it would prepare an Environmental Impact Statement on the effects of its proposed action on the use of polyvinyl chloride in food containers (53 *Federal Register* 47264, Nov. 22, 1988).

The Consumer Products Safety Commission has authority for all consumer products except foods and drugs, pesticides, tobacco and tobacco products, motor vehicles, aircraft and aircraft equipment, and boats and boat accessories.[18] CPSC can require labeling or packaging as control measures against accidental or improper use of hazardous substances. The CPSC also can ban products. In 1978, for instance, the commission banned consumer use of any paint that contains lead or lead compounds in concentrations exceeding 0.06 percent. The commission's approach since 1981, however, has been toward voluntary standards developed in cooperation with industry (19a).

Several ongoing CPSC projects within the Chemical Hazards program are relevant to MSW prevention, even though their focus is harm from usage rather than from disposal. For example, one project

is evaluating products containing methylene chloride, perchloroethylene (dry-cleaning fluid), paradichlorobenzene (room air fresheners and deodorizers), and 1,1,1 trichloroethane (a solvent).

Although few other countries have directly addressed waste prevention, West Germany has made strides to reduce MSW toxicity and quantity (box 8-B). For instance, the Federal Environmental Agency has studied ways for individual consumers to reduce waste generation rates (48), as has the City of Hamburg (43). The greatest value of these studies may lie in drawing attention to the possibility of MSW reduction (48). West Germany also awards an "Environmental Angel" logo (figure 8-2) to products considered beneficial on the basis of environmentally related criteria; over 2,200 products in 50 categories have received the award in the last 10 years (box 8-B). Canada is instituting a similar program, using a maple leaf and dove logo, and Japan and Norway are considering such programs (28,160).

State governments generally recognize the value of MSW prevention, but it has been difficult to translate this into clearly focused programs. Few States provide the types of positive incentives to manufacturers or consumers that OTA discusses in chapter 1 (e.g., information clearinghouses, grants, procurement, and awards). Most waste reduction programs proposed in State plans are broad and they often focus on recycling. OTA, however, considers recycling as a separate alternative from waste reduction (see chs. 1 and 4).[19]

Some States consider recycling together with reduction because recycling decreases the amount of MSW that needs landfilling. The Rhode Island Source Reduction Task Force, a leader among State groups involved in reduction efforts, devotes some attention in the State's reduction program to increased recyclability and use of recycled material (106). New York's solid waste plan sets a goal of 8 to 10 percent weight reduction by 1997 and lists six initiatives for potential legislation; three of these,

---

[18]CPSC acts under the authority the Consumer Product Safety Act of 1970 (Public Law 92-573). Action under the Act requires a finding of unreasonable risk of injury or illness. Under the Federal Hazardous Substances Act, CPSC can find that a substance will cause substantial personal injury or illness as a result of any customary use or foreseeable handling or use.

[19]Although OTA treats recycling and reduction separately, there may be some merit in a logistical sense for States to link the two. For example, one State official argues that reduction efforts are unlikely to receive financial commitments from State legislators unless they are linked with recycling programs that yield measurable results in a relatively quick period (49).

Box 8-B—Federal Republic of Germany: Section 14 and the Environmental Angel

West Germany has one of the most advanced approaches to MSW management of the industrialized nations. For instance, Section 14 of the 1986 Waste Avoidance, Utilization, and Disposal Act gives the government statutory authority to ban problem products. The act covers all products, not just packaging and containers, and focuses on materials that increase the amount or toxicity of MSW. When the government determines that a product contributes unnecessarily to MSW generation or contains toxic substances that hinder MSW management, the act requires one of three responses:

1) *Labeling*—the specified products can only be marketed if they have labels showing how to deal with the product after use (e.g., return to manufacturer or separate for municipal collection). This is intended to provide an incentive to industries to change product designs.

2) *Mandatory return*—the specified products can only be marketed if distributors offer the possibility of return or if they include a deposit on the products to encourage return. This gives manufacturers and distributors responsibility for waste management of products they market.

3) *Restrictions on circulation*—if restricted use or appropriate management of resulting waste cannot be guaranteed, then a product can be banned. These regulations can only be implemented after the government has first sought voluntary agreements with the industries involved. The ultimate effect of the regulations may be to act as a signal to industry.

Implementation of Section 14

Actions taken under Section 14 include: 1) proposals by the Environment Agency that list substances and products of concern; 2) a voluntary agreement regarding household batteries; and 3) regulations for plastic beverage containers. Negotiations are proceeding on other plastic products and tinfoil caps for bottles. Discussions with the plastics industry about the effects of plastics on automobile recycling efforts are also ongoing.

The Environment Agency's Proposals

Thus far, proposals have been developed for various products or substances for which regulations might be issued if voluntary agreements cannot be reached with manufacturers. As of April 1989, the list included lead-acid batteries, tires, waste paper, drugs, ferrous scrap from households, scrap from electronic equipment, used tapes from typewriters and printers, toner cartridges from copiers, plastics containing fluorinated and chlorinated hydrocarbons, refrigeration liquid from household refrigerators, tinfoil bottle caps, plastic and metal foil from food packaging, fluorescent lamps, PCBs in household appliances, small PCB-containing capacitors (e.g., from fluorescent lamp starters), motor oil and oil filters and containers, and pesticide residues and containers (48). In 1988, the Agency proposed **mandatory return** for starters for electrical equipment and cars, fluorescent tubes, household batteries, and thermometers, and it drafted a regulation on halogen-containing solvents (48).

A Voluntary Agreement on Household Batteries

In 1987, a voluntary agreement on household batteries was reached between the government, the Association of Electronic and Electrotechnical Industries, and involved trade organizations (48). Manufacturers and importers agreed to reduce the level of mercury in alkali-manganese batteries from 0.5 to 0.15 percent by weight by 1988, with an option to reduce the level to 0.10 percent by 1990 and to less than 0.10 percent by 1993. Manufacturers also agreed to accept used alkaline/manganese batteries with mercury concentrations above agreed limits, nickel/cadmium batteries, mercury oxide batteries, and button-shaped batteries (e.g., from watch-makers and camera shops). If the percentage of returned batteries is deemed insufficient, the government could impose a mandatory deposit on the sale of new household batteries. One complicating factor is a guideline being prepared by the European Community on the mercury content of batteries. If the guideline is less stringent than Germany's voluntary agreement, it is not clear how it would affect implementation of the voluntary agreement.

Mandatory Deposit of Plastic Beverage Containers

Before the 1970s, about 90 percent of Germany's beer, wine, and soft drinks were packaged in refillable bottles. This percentage declined in the 1970s as plastic and metal single-use containers became more popular. In 1977, the government and the beverage industries reached a voluntary agreement to stabilize the use of refillable and single-use containers, but the proportion of single-use containers continued to grow, reaching about 25 percent in 1986. The government is concerned that the refillable system might collapse economically if the percentage of refillable bottles drops much lower, and that this might increase MSW generation by about 20 percent.

Consequently, in November 1986 the government began to negotiate with the beverage industry to stabilize the use of refillable beverage containers. Government proposals involved specific percentages for different refillable bottles, increased recycling of throw-aways, and mandatory labeling. The beverage industry offered instead to reduce the types of bottle shapes and carriers (to make the existing deposit/return system work more easily), include some labeling information, and work on innovative packaging designs. In response, the government again proposed quantitative goals for different refillables and indicated that it would consider regulations on labeling, deposits, and obligations to accept returned containers if a voluntary agreement could not be achieved.

In late 1987, Coca-Cola announced the pending introduction of a new single-use container made of PET plastic. The beverage industry announced at the same time that it would build a recycling system to accept between 40 and 70 percent of these bottles. This added a new dimension to the negotiations. In spring of 1988, after no agreement had been reached, the government proposed regulations on plastic beverage bottles—the first time that Section 14's regulatory authority was to be used in this context. In December 1988, the government adopted the regulations, which required: 1) a deposit on plastic beverage containers with capacity between 0.2 and 3 liters; 2) all retailers, distributors, and bottlers to accept returned plastic beverage containers; and 3) labeling. The deposit is higher than the deposit on refillable glass bottles. The regulation became effective on March 1, 1989, although Coca-Cola had announced in January 1989 that it would not use the nonrefillable bottle. The regulation provides a one-year phase-in period for plastic beverage containers that had already been introduced.

The Environmental Angel

Prior to the 1986 act, the Environmental Agency had developed a special product label, the Environmental Angel, to highlight environmentally sound products. The logo, a blue angel in the middle of a blue circle (figure 8-2), is awarded to products that contain fewer toxic substances or are more recyclable than similar products. Over 2,200 products have received awards during the last 10 years, including water-soluble paints and floor coverings without asbestos. The label's main purpose is to give consumers information about environmentally improved products and provide a publicity incentive to manufacturers. A list of the products that can use the Environmental Angel logo and their manufacturers is published by the Environment Agency (20).

however, are more related to recycling than reduction (89).[20]

States and local communities have taken several approaches to developing MSW reduction efforts: packaging review boards, packaging taxes, bans on products, education of consumers, and toxics reduction legislation. Most have focused on implementing taxes or bans on particular components of MSW, usually packaging or plastic products, but potentially toxic substances are beginning to receive greater legislative attention. In addition, the governors of States in the Northeast have initiated a region-wide reduction task force to address these issues, and several States have initiated education programs.

Washington State was the first to establish an office of waste reduction, which also includes recycling activities. The Unit of Waste Reduction and Recycling of the State Department of Ecology, at least to date, focuses most of its activities on increasing public awareness, although some localities such as Seattle are adopting bans or taxes on nonrecyclable products. As with most State and local waste reduction efforts, however, waste reduction is not clearly distinguished from recycling, and recycling programs have received most of the attention thus far. Rhode Island has an innovative reduction program, primarily focused on education. It established a source reduction task force in 1986 to develop a research program, educational efforts, information-gathering forums, technical assistance to commercial establishments, and legislative initiatives (107).

Thus far, most State and local efforts to encourage post-consumer MSW reduction have consisted mainly of proposed bans of plastics or certain types of packaging and proposed packaging or product taxes. Some of these measures have passed; most are pending. Their main message and impact may ultimately be to encourage industry and society as a whole to consider the disposal implications of

---

[20]Fee on non-recyclable packaging, deposits on tires, price preference for recycled paper products.

Figure 8-2—West Germany's "Environmental Angel" Logo

umweltfreundlich

weil

Jury Umweltzeichen

SOURCE: Deutsches Institut für Gutesicherung und Kennzeichnung, "Verzeichnis der Produkte und Zeichenanwender sowie der jeweiligen Produktanforderungen" (Bonn: June 1988)

products as they are made. The best way to encourage waste prevention may not be direct regulation by any level of government, but rather indirectly through education programs and incentives for industry and the public that focus on the importance of changing the nature of the Nation's waste stream (ch. 1).

Packaging Review Boards

The first packaging review board was established in Minnesota in 1973, when a law passed giving the Minnesota Pollution Control Agency authority to review new and modified packages sold at retail outlets (12,93). Although challenged, the courts eventually ruled that the law did not violate the interstate commerce clause, but also that the agency could only issue guidelines, not regulations. Minnesota also passed the Excess Packaging Act in 1977, which established a State board to review all new packaging in the State. Guidelines on packaging

were not issued until 1980, and they apparently have had little effect, apparently because of perceived industry resistance and some administrative difficulties (12). Iowa passed a law modeled after the Minnesota statute, and it may soon have its first test case. Several other States also have proposed legislation to establish packaging review boards or study packaging issues.

Packaging Tax Proposals

Packaging taxes are also being proposed with increased frequency. In New York State, a Waste Reduction Packaging Tax of $0.03 was to be levied on non-food or fast-food packaging (i.e., deposit bottles and other food packaging are not included). According to the proposal, however, a packaging review board could apply a tax credit of $0.01 if the package is made of recyclable material, or if the product itself is recyclable. Also, the package could be exempted from the tax if it qualifies for both credits. The money collected from the tax would form the "Solid Waste Management Fund," to be used for activities such as remedial action at municipal landfill closure projects, grants for recycling, and technical assistance grants.

At least four other States have proposed packaging taxes similar to the proposed New York State legislation or tax incentives to encourage the use of degradable packaging. These include Iowa, Maine, Massachusetts, and Minnesota. The proposed taxes range from $0.01 to $0.05 per package and would be applied to either manufacturers or distributors.

The packaging tax concept has not been fully analyzed, particularly the relationship between the disposal costs of a package, the suggested tax rates, and MSW generation rates. Another problem is that the tax rate may be too low to induce change across the multitude of packaged products that industries sell. If manufacturers rather than retailers or consumers are charged the tax (to increase the likelihood of influencing packaging design), they can maintain their profit margins by passing the tax along in the price of products or they can decide that paying the tax is preferable to changing product design. Moreover, unless some special labeling is required on the packages that are subject to such a tax, most consumers will never know they are paying the tax. For high-priced items, the tax may be such a small portion of the cost that, even if known, it will be of no consequence to the consumer. Thus, the tangible outcome of these taxing bills is likely to be revenue generation rather than changes in MSW generation.

Alternatives to packaging taxes and product bans are appearing. Recently, for example, a project to foster recycling of HDPE and PET plastics involving public-private sector cooperation was announced between the State of Illinois and the DuPont Co. The initial project, entirely funded by DuPont, will evaluate the viability of using reprocessed scrap plastics in highway construction and maintenance (99) (ch. 5).

Product Bans

Bans on the use of plastics in food packaging have begun appearing across the country.[21] This legislation is attempting to address concerns about: 1) the Earth's ozone layer and the potential for types of polystyrene made with certain chlorofluorocarbons (CFCs) to harm it (box 4-E in ch. 4); 2) solid waste, including the tendency for polystyrene/styrofoam to be nondegradable and nonrecyclable, as well as resistant to compacting (thereby requiring more scarce landfill capacity) (ch. 5); and 3) litter.

At least 16 States have legislation pending that would ban or prohibit the use of some plastic materials or polystyrene, or require the use of biodegradable materials. It is not clear how many of these proposals will actually pass into law. Examples, including examples of local efforts, include:

- Suffolk County, New York, passed a law on March 29, 1988, scheduled to take effect July 1, 1989, requiring that all retail food establishments within the county only sell food packed in biodegradable packaging. The law also bans the use of polyethylene grocery sacks and polystyrene or polyvinyl chloride in eating utensils and food containers sold or provided within the county by retail food establishments. The law was stayed by the New York Supreme Court in 1989 until its potential environmental impact is studied.[22]
- Rockland County, New York, and the City of New York have similar legislation pending that

would ban the use of polystyrene foam food packaging.
- Minneapolis and St. Paul, Minnesota, passed legislation in 1989 that could ban the use of nonrecyclable plastic food packaging.
- Berkeley, California, in 1988 had one vote on a proposed ordinance to ban polystyrene foam food packaging. Another vote was pending and required for the ordinance to take effect. The City's Solid Waste Management Commission did ask fast-food restaurants to reduce nonbiodegradable packaging by 50 percent.
- Maine was the first State to pass a law prohibiting the use of polystyrene foam food packaging made with ozone-depleting CFCs, specifically CFC-11 or CFC-12. Minnesota and Rhode Island recently passed similar laws.
- Minnesota had a law that prohibited the use of plastic milk bottles but it was repealed. In 1987, however, the State enacted a law banning plastic beverage containers.
- One proposed law to control packaging in Missouri would ban the sale of multi-resin plastic containers. Connecticut has banned the plastic-aluminum beverage container.
- Disposal of yard wastes in landfills has been banned in Minnesota, effective in the 1990s.
- At least three States have had legislation introduced attempting to ban the use of disposable diapers. New Jersey and Rhode Island considered legislation to ban plastic tampon applicators.

Many of the proposed bans on polystyrene or other nondegradable plastic products require the substitution of degradable products. In particular, some proposed laws require State agencies to procure "ozone safe" and/or degradable food packaging. Legislation has been introduced in New Jersey that would prohibit the sale or distribution of any packaging made of "thermoplastic synthetic polymeric material or any other petroleum-based, non-biodegradable material." In Florida, as of January 1, 1990, plastic shopping bags used by retailers will have to degrade within in 120 days.[23]

---

[21]Other types of bans are also appearing in some legislative proposals. For example, a law proposed in Connecticut would ban the use of lead and cadmium as stabilizers, pigments, inks, or glazes in packaging.

[22]*Society of the Plastics Industry, Inc., et al.* v. *The County of Suffolk, et al.,* No. 88/11262, New York State Supreme Court.

[23]Technical information on degradable plastics is presented in ch. 5.

Two problems associated with these bans are that they do not consider whether the replacements will be improvements, and they rarely consider the economic implications to retail stores. For example, polystyrene is used in many single-use products. The costs of banning polystyrene foam cups include not only the costs of replacements, but also the labor and energy needed to wash or reuse cups, and the costs of washing equipment; on the other hand, new service jobs might be created, disposal costs might be lowered, and other packaging manufacturers would benefit by having their products purchased. However, polystyrene foam cups probably constitute less than 0.1 percent of all MSW by weight; their replacements could be heavier, single-use, plastic-coated paper cups, as opposed to reusable washable cups. Also, plastic-coated paper cups cost more, and increasing their production would require additional investments in manufacturing equipment (1).

Another example of the trade-offs to be considered is seen in switching from plastic to paper bags. Switching from plastic to paper bags could increase waste generation because paper bags actually take up more landfill space than plastic bags, and paper often does not degrade rapidly in landfills (ch. 7). The relatively low use of energy for plastics production, although nonrenewable fossil fuels are used, is another issue (ch. 5).

Product bans in general might be more effective if they focused on toxicity reduction—removing toxic products or chemicals from use to lower the toxic content of MSW.

Toxics Reduction Legislation and Propositions

States have responded to concerns about household hazardous wastes by providing information and funds to develop local household hazardous waste collection programs. On a broader scale, States also have developed various activities oriented toward the issue of toxicity in general. In 1986, for example, voters in California approved Proposition 65, which shifts the burden of proof in toxicity determination by saying, essentially, that a manufacturer must prove that a substance released into the environment or included in a product is **not** toxic.

Other action includes lobbying by local grassroots and statewide environmental organizations to pass versions of a model toxic use reduction bill authored by the National Toxics Campaign and the Massachusetts Public Interest Research Group (2). The intent of this type of legislation is to help industry reassess and reduce the use and production of toxic substances, by requiring toxics-use reduction plans and by offering grants, education, and information. Revenue would be raised through a tax provision. The bill has been introduced and debated in Massachusetts and other States, and sponsors planned to re-introduce it in a number of States in 1989 (2).

Education

Rhode Island has adopted a strong educational approach at all levels, from grade to graduate school, which is focused on both consumers and industry (107). The State's Department of Environmental Management has published books on waste management, including waste reduction, and has held workshops on the topic. A task force is charged with providing technical assistance to commercial establishments, including guidance documents, training and certification of waste auditors, and design and specification of equipment and services. The New York State Department of Economic Development established a secondary materials program in 1989 that will serve as a clearinghouse for information about waste reduction techniques available to commercial and industrial firms.

Regional Efforts

In 1988, the Coalition of Northeastern Governors (CONEG), which includes nine States, issued a policy statement on the reduction of packaging (11). The statement called for working with the packaging industry to reduce the volume of disposable packaging, increase the recyclability of packaging products that cannot be reduced, increase the use of more environmentally benign packaging material, and increase the recycled material content of packaging. CONEG also established a task force on source reduction to identify voluntary and other measures that could be carried out by and within the region. The task force includes four working groups that focus on different product categories (i.e., convenience food, consumer electronics, hardware, and automotive goods). Recommendations, expected by September 1989 (11a), are likely to address guidelines (i.e., definitions, goals, standards, timetables) for "preferred" product packaging; voluntary efforts by industry; education; and criteria to evaluate legislation that incorporates the use of incentives and disincentives.

Recycling

Although some Federal authority exists to encourage recycling, it has not been exercised in a concerted, consistent, or coherent manner. In general, States and communities have been left to devise their own programs. Indeed, recycling is an increasingly popular management option for communities and States across the country. Many of these programs focus on the collection of recyclable materials. Comparable efforts to increase the demand for recycled materials have not been coordinated with efforts encouraging separation and collection, however.

Government efforts to increase recycling must take into account the market conditions of materials, their dynamic nature, and the effects of programs on existing recycling activities and markets (ch. 5) (66). For example, a glut of used newsprint paper in the Northeast in 1989 was in part attributed to the increased supply of used newsprint collected by new recycling programs in Northeast States. To expand the market for recycled newsprint, Connecticut passed legislation in 1989 that requires newspaper publishers to phase in increased use of recycled newsprint, and several other States (e.g., California and Wisconsin) have introduced similar legislation. In Florida, effective January 1, 1989, newsprint users began paying a waste disposal fee of $0.10 per ton of all nonrecycled newsprint. If by October 1, 1992, newsprint is recycled at a rate of 50 percent or more, the fee will be rescinded; if the rate is not achieved the fee will be increased, but credits to publishers using recycled newsprint will also be available. Some experts suggest that a sufficiently high consumption tax might be more effective in altering a publisher's newsprint purchasing decisions (155).

Beverage Deposit Laws and Recycling Laws

Nine States have mandatory deposit laws for beverage containers: Connecticut, Delaware (applies to glass only), Iowa, Maine, Massachusetts, Michigan, New York, Oregon, and Vermont. California and Florida have different types of mandatory programs (discussed below) and Florida's law applies to additional types of containers and products. Mandatory recycling programs, other programs to encourage recycling, and deposit laws vary considerably from State to State. At least a dozen States have passed legislation encouraging or requiring localities to implement community recycling programs.[24] Rhode Island, New Jersey, and Connecticut were the first States to adopt mandatory source separation programs. Laws enacted more recently by such States as Florida, Maryland, and Pennsylvania more explicitly recognize a need for a comprehensive approach to recycling. Although some European countries have adopted beverage container deposit systems, they are geographically much smaller than the United States and factors affecting the feasibility of such systems differ (box 6-C).

These State laws attempt to encourage cooperation between the existing recycling industry and counties and municipalities and allow the flexibility needed to design programs to meet specific State goals. State programs to stimulate recycling can include financial incentives, technical assistance, information dissemination and research, procurement requirements, recycling goals, and mandatory local collection of materials for recycling.[25] In the past, most MSW recycling collection programs have been based and managed at the local level.

Some States, such as Oregon and New York, have both mandatory deposit programs and community recycling programs. The two systems are not necessarily incompatible, but the combination can be inefficient and less cost-effective than a mandatory local collection of materials for recycling (chs. 1 and 2). Mandatory recycling laws vary with respect to: requiring mandatory source separation or primarily using drop-off centers; local, regional or State implementation; and whether other mechanisms such as grants, funding, or educational programs are included. Variation also exists in the types of mandatory deposit legislation adopted; for example, the types of beverage containers included, the amount and nature of the deposit system can vary.

[24]Connecticut, Florida, Hawaii, Illinois, Maryland, Massachusetts, Minnesota, New Jersey, New York, Oregon, Pennsylvania, Rhode Island, Washington, and Wisconsin.

[25]"Mandatory" can mean the State mandates all details of local recycling programs, but usually means the collection of some materials is mandated and some flexibility remains with the locality to determine which materials are collected, by which methods, etc.

In some States with deposit legislation—e.g., Connecticut, Massachusetts, and New York— curbside collection programs also are being adopted. In areas where either recycling programs existed first and then mandatory deposit/redemption legislation came into effect (e.g., California), or deposit legislation existed first and then mandatory recycling laws were enacted (e.g., New York), neither program appears to have been hindered in the amount of material collected (15,40,42,63,78,92,133). However, when both approaches operate concurrently, recycling revenues to the public sector may decrease because aluminum is the highest value material collected and presumably a beverage container law would largely eliminate its collection with other recyclables (ch. 2; ref. 37). A recent report concluded, in part based on its analysis of the States of Vermont and New York, that comprehensive materials recovery programs are more efficient and cost-effective if beverage containers are included in them (37).[26]

In the past, the intent of most State deposit laws was to deter littering rather than encourage recycling (ch. 1) (130).[27] Ohio and some other States enacted litter control legislation that does not involve a mandatory deposit system. Although some research indicates that aggressive litter control programs can be highly successful (56), other studies show that litter programs are not as effective as deposit legislation in controlling litter and that they do not address the nonlitter objectives of deposit legislation, such as increasing recycling of beverage containers (110,130). In general, beverage container deposit systems capture between 70 and 90 percent of the targeted containers and are particularly effective in reducing litter (7). Several States with deposit systems report that roadside litter decreased 15 to 50 percent, and beverage container litter decreased by as much as 80 percent (47,110).

The impact of deposit legislation on MSW, however, is less certain and difficult to calculate. Critics of mandatory deposit legislation point out that it has a relatively small impact on MSW disposal problems, given that beverage containers are a small, albeit highly visible, portion of the waste

---

Box 8-C—Beverage Container Deposit Systems in Europe

Deposit systems on beverage containers exist in several European countries (8,95), with the focus of activity being in Scandinavia and West Germany.

In Sweden, a deposit system exists for most glass bottles, including wine, beer, and carbonated soft drinks (74,122). About 98 to 99 percent of the beer and soft drink bottles and 75 percent of the wine bottles are returned. Sweden also has a deposit system on aluminum cans, and over 75 percent of such cans are recovered; the system is run and financed by the can companies, breweries, and retailers. A deposit system for PET bottles was tested on one island and may be introduced throughout the country. The Swedish National Environmental Protection Board has proposed a target return rate of 90 percent for both aluminum cans and PET bottles.

Norway also has a deposit system on glass bottles, although imported bottles are exempted (8). In contrast to Sweden, Norway places a high tax on aluminum beverage containers and they are not used at a high rate.

Denmark does not have a deposit system on glass or aluminum containers, but in 1984 it placed a tax on aluminum beverage containers and required all beverage containers to be refillable (8). As a result, most beverage containers are now made of glass and about 50 percent were recycled in 1985 (53). This action has been criticized by other European countries as restricting international trade, because many of Denmark's plastic and aluminum beverage containers are imported from other countries (8).

Switzerland has a deposit system on glass beverage containers, and the rate of return appears to be high. In contrast to Denmark and Norway, it has not placed a deposit or high tax on aluminum beverage containers, and the market share for these containers is increasing.

In September 1988, the West German government adopted regulations for a mandatory deposit system on plastic beverage bottles (see box 8-B).

---

[26]Whether directly or indirectly, the consumer will bear costs associated with either system or the combination of them. Which system is most cost-effective is a separate issue, but one that effects the ultimate cost to consumers.

[27]Proposals for a national manadatory deposit system of some type for beverage containers appear before Congress annually. They are designed to address a variety of issues, including litter control and energy conservation.

stream (ch.3).[28] New York State estimates that adoption of their Returnable Beverage Container Law has reduced MSW by 5 percent by weight or 8 percent by volume (47,89). Curbside programs to collect recyclables, on the other hand, cover a broader portion of MSW (e.g., newspapers and nonbeverage containers) and have the potential to achieve greater diversion of materials from landfills.

Where in the collection and processing systems costs are borne is critical to consider. In a comprehensive curbside collection program, collection costs are high, but necessary (and become part of a government infrastructure). In contrast, a deposit container system has a "free" collection system, but the retail handling and wholesale processing operations do not generate net revenues (even with unredeemed deposits). Thus, one recurring concern about deposit systems is increased costs to consumers, retailers, the beverage industry, and the government. The extent of such increases is disputed (72,96,108), but it appears that the benefits and costs of deposit systems are relatively balanced (84,96,110). Studies show a net gain of jobs, plus some energy and resource savings, from deposit systems, but that the rate of price increases for beverages in nonrefillable containers is above normal inflation. Costs for converting to a system for returnable/refillable containers can be high for the beverage industry, but they are at least partially recovered within a few years (84,110).

Laws to Encourage or Mandate Recycling

Typical features of recent State recycling laws include:

- A numerical recycling target ranging between 15 to 50 percent, but usually about 25 percent. These recycling goals generally are not set based on knowledge of the waste stream or actual projections of the recycling potential for particular materials.
- Provisions on segregation of materials. There is a trend toward mandatory source separation of selected MSW components. Sometimes commercial and institutional sources of MSW, as well as residences, are covered by the law.

- Designation of the materials to be recycled or delegation of a local authority to designate them.
- Requirements for local government to develop a recycling plan.
- Funding mechanisms. These include such mechanisms as a surcharge on the tipping fee at landfills to fund grants for local planning and development of recycling programs, or financial incentives to encourage new recycling operations.

In addition, States can attempt to stimulate recycling markets through procurement programs and/or by providing tax incentives. In general, mandatory programs are preferred on the east coast, while the voluntary programs work best on the west coast. Among the States that have received attention for their recycling programs are Oregon, Rhode Island, New Jersey, California, and Florida.

In 1972, Oregon passed a beverage container deposit law that reportedly recovers over 90 percent of all soda and beer containers sold and brings a 7-percent reduction of the total waste stream to be landfilled (84). In 1983, Oregon passed the Opportunity to Recycle law, which requires municipalities of over 4,000 to provide convenient drop-off centers and at least monthly curbside collection of recyclables. Household participation is voluntary; localities are required to fund, administer, and report their recycling plans to the State. Public education is an important part of the program. In 1982, only 14 multi-material curbside recycling programs existed. Since the law's passage the number of programs has grown to over 110 programs, even though the requirement applied to only 70 cities. Oregon now estimates that it recycles 18 to 22 percent of its waste stream.

Rhode Island's Solid Waste Management Act Amendments of 1986-87 is the Nation's first mandatory State source separation program. The State has a target goal of recycling 15 percent of its MSW by 1992. A new materials recovery facility is being built as part of the program. The recycling efforts are part of a comprehensive waste management program that also includes the establishment of three waste-to-energy facilities and possibly a landfill.

---

[28]Beverage containers constitute 6 to 11 percent of all MSW on a national basis; beverage containers covered by most deposit legislation are a smaller portion, approximately 5 percent, of MSW because some types of containers are not included (e.g., wine, liquor, and milk containers).

Another State recycling program receiving attention is New Jersey's Mandatory Recycling Act of 1987. This law requires localities to reach a recycling rate of 25 percent by 1989. Each county designs its own program by designating three materials (from a list of materials provided by the State) that households will be required to separate, in addition to leaves. The programs are supported by a landfill tax of $1.50/ton that should provide counties with $8 million to begin their programs.

In 1987, California enacted a redemption law for beverage containers that requires the establishment of "convenience" buy-back centers for recycling. However, the financial stability of the convenience centers, administrative burdens associated with implementing the program, and other difficulties are creating concern over the viability of this approach.

A processing fee is the mechanism driving the California program and is its most unique feature. If recycling is not high enough, distributors must pay a processing fee; this keeps market prices high so recyclers can stay in business. It also gives the State some control over the markets. Unlike Florida and most States with beverage deposit laws, California does not require a deposit by consumers. Instead, consumers are paid a redemption of $0.01 for returning containers.[29] Convenience is seen as key to the law's success, and the establishment of 2,400 redemption collection centers was required.

Recycling rates have increased only slightly since the California law took effect. This may be caused by the slow start-up of the program or its cumbersome administrative nature. Many local officials express skepticism over the law, in particular that it is inefficient to team the processing fee with an emphasis on convenience—although all acknowledge they benefit from the inflated scrap values. Some officials also maintain that if the same State resources spent on administering the beverage container law were spent on curbside collection, more recycling would occur. Some officials actually predict that the law will "collapse under its own weight" within a few years. Still, the processing fee continues to attract attention from other State and Federal officials (15,40,42,63,92).

In 1988, Florida adopted a deposit-fee system that affects all types of containers, not just beverage containers. The law attempts to distribute the rising cost of solid waste disposal and emphasize the virtues of recycling in a State where a high water table prohibits landfilling in many areas and where siting incineration facilities has been difficult. As of October 1, 1992, a disposal fee of one cent will be levied on any container (i.e., glass, plastic, plastic-coated paper, aluminum, and other metals) sold at retail which is not recycled at a 50 percent rate in Florida. The fee will increase to two cents if the 50 percent target is not met by October 1, 1995. The goals of the law are to discourage single-use disposable items and build a statewide infrastructure for recycling.

The inclusive scope of materials covered by the Florida law is generally viewed as an asset, but it is too soon to judge how effectively this program will be implemented. Florida's new law is one of the most recent and ambitious efforts to manage MSW. Localities are required to reduce landfilling by 30 percent by 1993, mostly by recycling. If a locality does not meet the goal, funding can be suspended by the State; most municipalities are expected to establish mandatory residential recycling programs. Taxes and fees on a variety of products and materials will be used to encourage recycling.

Variety of Local Programs

In a survey, the Council of State Governments found that 25 States responding to a question on recycling identified 6,461 local recycling programs (16,18). The western States reported the most, with 3,378 recycling programs in Oregon and California alone. Alaska reported approximately 100 programs. In the Midwest, 1,710 programs were identified; the Northeast reported 1,148, the Plains States identified 118, and only 7 programs were reported in the South. Some of these programs may be private (e.g., sponsored by the Boy Scouts, civic groups, or others groups), although most are assumed to be local government programs. Because it is not clear how the respondents were defining "recycling program," it is not known for sure how many of these efforts are public versus private in nature.

---

[29]Curbside collection program operators can also receive the $0.01 redemption.

Local recycling programs can vary. What mix of characteristics is "best" will depend on the locality (see ch. 2 for cost comparisons between methods). In many States, recycling associations provide guides, hold conferences, and distribute information to local communities to promote recycling. In addition, organizations such as the National Association of Towns and Townships issue guides to help communities establish recycling programs (85). Two basic characteristics of recycling programs are whether they are mandatory or voluntary and how recyclables are collected (separated or commingled). Other factors such as the frequency and efficiency of collection, or location of collection centers (if drop-off centers are used), and public education programs also affect the effectiveness of recycling programs. In general, mandatory recycling programs generate higher participation rates than voluntary programs with the same frequency of collection (18,150).

Variation in participation also occurs when more than one material is collected. For example, in Minneapolis, Minnesota, only about 50 percent of all participants recycle all the collected materials, 25 percent recycle paper and one other item, and the other 25 percent recycle only paper. In Austin, Texas, less than 50 percent of the participants recycle bottles and cans in addition to paper. Even in Montclair, New Jersey, where recycling is mandatory, only 75 percent of the participants recycle all the materials required. Not surprisingly, newspaper makes up about 75 percent of the material collected; glass contributes 15 to 25 percent and metal 5 to 10 percent (46). It is important to note that participation rates, however, are different than materials recovery rates.

Collection of recyclables can happen in at least three different ways: household source separation of individual materials or commingled materials and curbside collection; household collection of mixed wastes with processing at a centralized facility; and drop-off centers. Some systems combine two or all three of these options. In general, weekly curbside collection of source-separated material is most effective, generates the most (and least contaminated) material, and achieves higher participation rates. Curbside collection is often impractical in rural areas and drop-off centers (and the buy-back variation of this) are more common.

Photo credit: M. Wagner

Some community programs for collecting recyclable materials distribute special recycling bins to citizens. Filled with separated materials, the bins are put out at the curbside for pickup on specified days.

A study completed by The Minnesota Project, a nonprofit rural community development organization, found that in seven innovative programs in rural communities, drop-boxes and drop-off recycling centers have been successful (83). In rural Wayne County, New York, however, private haulers are cooperating with local officials to initiate curbside collection of some recyclables (thus far, newspaper, corrugated cardboard, and tin cans) to supplement the drop-off collection program.

The striking contrast between the coasts illustrates the Nation's great variation in MSW management programs. For example, most communities in the San Francisco Bay area of California favor voluntary, curbside recycling programs and strongly support source separation. Many are expanding their programs to include community composting and commercial recycling. Indeed, the desirability of the "three C's of recycling" are repeatedly referred to by these local officials: 1) a curbside program; 2) a compost program; and 3) a commercial/industrial program. These programs are not yet common in the Northeast.

Even within California, however, there is variation among recycling programs. For example, the City of San Francisco sees its primary purpose as coordinating and encouraging the numerous (over 20) private recycling efforts in the city and county. It estimates that approximately 25 percent of its waste stream is recycled. The City of San Jose, in contrast, is more directly involved in recycling. It operates the largest curbside program in the country, servicing 180,000 residents, recycling 100 tons/day, and reportedly diverting about 35 percent of its waste stream.

The incentive for recycling in California is not, for the most part, lack of landfill space or high landfill cost. In fact, some waste officials there look to the higher disposal costs of Seattle, Washington, the Northeast, and elsewhere with a bit of envy, believing it would allow them to justify further expansion of their recycling operations (15,40,40a,42,63,78,92,133). Strong markets are a key advantage for California, which relies primarily on overseas markets. Profit is not a driving force for these programs and an important factor contributing to support for them is that new waste-to-energy or other combustion facilities are not being sited in California. This is primarily because of concerns over air pollution potential and strong public opposition. Using intensive recycling to prolong the life of landfills is the main MSW management rationale.

In the United States, most communities with curbside collection designate no more than three materials to be separated. Typically, localities separate newspapers, other waste paper, glass and cans, and sometimes plastics. Sometimes grass clippings and leaves are collected separately for composting. Materials for recycling are collected in various types of bins and containers, usually provided by the community, and collected on specially designated days (weekly, biweekly, or monthly). In Japan, a few communities have households separate their MSW into seven or more categories. Most **community** programs, however, have households separate MSW into only two categories, combustible and noncombustible, for municipal collection; recyclable materials are separated for collection by the **private** sector.

Some communities, regions, and States have developed materials recovery facilities (MRFs) for commingled recyclables (ch. 5). The State of Delaware manages all waste disposal through the Delaware Solid Waste Authority (DSWA) and does so on a mixed waste basis. Mixed waste is brought to the State's largest facility in northern Delaware, a centralized processing facility. A landfill and waste-to-energy facility are also located at this site. The facility has had some difficulty marketing recovered materials because of contamination, a problem that is not uncommon with this type of centralized processing (ch. 5). The compost material produced is also too contaminated to be marketed for many uses, but it can be used for landfill cover (156).

The costs of collecting different materials from MSW for recycling vary depending on their weight, volume, and other factors (chs. 2 and 5). The collection of newspapers (given their weight and volume) and plastics (given their volume) are the most expensive materials to collect for recycling. Materials collected directly from households are usually less contaminated and of higher market value than those recovered through centralized processing facilities.

Financial Incentives

Federal and State financial incentives to stimulate recycling activities, as well as increase the markets for recycled materials, have been limited. The following sections describe past efforts and note some recent initiatives. Although this discussion is primarily descriptive, some effort is made to determine the potential for programs, especially at the Federal level, to increase the use of secondary materials.[30]

Federal financial incentives for recycling are essentially nonexistent. An investment tax credit for recycling equipment to promote energy conservation was available from 1978 to 1983 under the Energy Act of 1978. Although many businesses took advantage of this credit, with total value reaching $143 million (27), it is difficult to prove that the investments would not have occurred absent the credit.

To date, this was the only direct Federal initiative to provide incentives for market development,

---

[30]The majority of this discussion is based on ref. 36.

despite the fact that RCRA directed the Department of Commerce to undertake market development efforts.[31] However, the Tax Reform Act of 1986 did remove some disincentives to recycling in an attempt to equalize the tax system. The act repealed some preferential tax treatment for the timber industry and modified oil depletion allowances.

Approximately 16 States use financial incentives to encourage recycling (16). These incentives include subsidies, grants, low interest loans, and/or preferential tax treatments. Most States with such programs are located east of the Mississippi River. The next section focuses on tax incentives, one of the most prevalent (such provisions exist in at least 11 States), but also problematic, types of financial incentive programs.

Tax Incentives—Three main types of tax incentives are available for recycling activities: investment tax credits, sales tax exemptions, and property tax exemptions. Examples of these incentives are noted in tables 8-1 and 8-2. As shown in table 8-3, there is considerable variation in the types of programs adopted by States, both in the types of incentives offered and their areas of application.

Investment tax credits (ITCs) allow businesses to subtract a portion of the cost of qualifying capital purchases from their Federal or State tax liability, thus reducing the net after-tax cost of capital. The most recent Federal experience with ITCs was in the early 1980s, after Congress passed the Economic Recovery Tax Act (ERTA) in 1981.[32] The purpose of this ITC was to stimulate economic activity through increased investment. Thus, the real target of the ITC was not the investment alone, but the general economic growth that the increased investment would generate through the "multiplier effect." One of ERTA's effects was to cut the cost of borrowing for capital equipment roughly in half (36).

The impact of ERTA's ITC provisions was uneven across the economy, because the Deficit Reduction Act of 1982 eliminated ERTA's tax subsidies for certain investments and retained them for others. In any case, the correlation between the reduction in the net cost of capital and business investment was not strong, leading to the conclusion that tax consequences are not the only consideration in business decisions. The House Committee on Ways and Means surveyed evidence on business response to ERTA and concluded (36):

> Proponents of the massive tax benefits for depreciable property have theorized that these benefits would stimulate investment in such property, which in turn would pull the entire economy into more rapid growth. The committee perceives that nothing of this kind has happened.

Among the States, pioneering tax incentive programs of Oregon and Wisconsin are examples of investment tax mechanisms and sales and property tax mechanisms, respectively. Oregon has three tax investment programs, two with purposes broader than recycling (the business energy tax credit and the pollution control facility tax credit), and one dedicated exclusively to the reclaiming of plastics (the plastics recycling tax credit).

The Oregon Department of Energy administers the Business Energy Tax Credit, which allows companies to write off, over a 5-year period, 35 percent of the cost of any equipment used solely for recycling. Garbage haulers and supermarkets have been the primary recipients of the tax credits to date. In 1985, the legislature renewed the law until December 31, 1990. The program is popular with legislators and businesses. The effect on the State treasury, however, is not known (although it clearly amounts to a revenue expenditure for the State) (36).

Oregon's Pollution Control Facility Tax credit was made available to recycling facilities or materials recovery facilities in 1973. The Oregon Department of Environmental Quality, which administers the program, has no limit on the individual project or total annual project costs. The credit is 50 percent of the certified costs, which may be taken over 10 years or the life of the facility if it is shorter than 10 years, and it can be applied against corporate, individual income, property taxes for nonprofit organizations. Pollution control facility tax credits have been used by firms that process a variety of materials, such as tires, asphalt, yard debris and wood wastes, gravel,

---

[31]The Department of Commerce, through the National Bureau of Standards, undertook numerous studies of recycling markets, costs, and technologies (138). However, no direct action to stimulate markets was taken as a consequence.

[32]Public Law 97-34.

Table 8-1—State Tax Incentives (Active and Proposed)

State	Investment tax credit	Property tax exemption	Sales tax exemption	Other
California				Consumption tax credit
Illinois			X	
Indiana		X		
Kentucky		X		
Massachusetts[a]	X			
New Jersey	X		X	
New York[a]	X			
North Carolina		X		Income tax deductions
Oklahoma	X			
Oregon	X (3 programs)			
Pennsylvania	X			
Wisconsin		X	X	

[a]Proposed incentives.

SOURCE: Franklin Associates, Ltd., *Economic Incentives and Disincentives for Recycling Municipal Solid Waste,* contract report prepared for U.S. Congress, Office of Technology Assessment (Prairie Village, KS: December 1988).

waste paper, plastics, batteries, and glass. Examples of certified projects include a $23.8 million battery recycling plant and a $13.3 million for a facility for old newsprint deinking.

The Department of Environmental Quality also administers Oregon's Plastic Recycling Tax Credit, which began in 1986. This income tax credit applies to machinery and equipment that uses at least 50 percent recycled post-consumer or industrial plastic from Oregon and is manufactured into a product there. The credit of 50 percent of allocatable costs taken over 5 years can apply to 100 percent of costs (or less, if the facility is not only dedicated to recycling plastics) (36).

Wisconsin uses both a sales tax exemption and a property tax exemption as financial incentives to encourage recycling.[33] Nonprofit organizations, including some recycling facilities, can avoid sales taxes in some States but few States offer sales tax exemptions specifically for recycling, such as Wisconsin does. In Wisconsin, collectors, processors, and manufacturers using secondary materials are exempt from paying the 5 percent sales tax on equipment or on the recyclables themselves. Recyclers can also benefit from the property tax exemption in Wisconsin.

Wisconsin's Department of Revenue determines whether a piece of equipment qualifies, and some

litigation has resulted over the Department's interpretation of the tax code. This type of problem can occur where tax incentive programs are administered by the Department of Revenue because the first concern of tax officials is revenue losses, not promoting the program's intent. Another difficulty with property tax exemptions is that reduced property taxes through statewide legislation often hurts local governments. The overall effect of both the sales exemption and property tax exemption on recycling in Wisconsin is reported as minimal (36).

The purpose of recycling tax incentives is different than that of ERTA; recycling tax incentives are not intended to promote the general economy but to increase capital in firms using recycled materials, boost productivity, and thus increase greater demand for recycled material inputs, and divert solid waste from landfills. The reduction in the cost of capital would also theoretically reduce the cost of production, which could then be passed on as a reduction in the price of the final product. Tax incentives cost a State a certain amount of money in foregone revenues and administrative costs, but this should be offset by increased economic activity and increased recovery of materials from solid waste. **The extent of these benefits, however, has not been documented in operational programs. Most States do not know the impact the incentives have had on**

---

[33]This is because recyclers are classified as manufacturers in Wisconsin for purposes of property taxes, and are thereby eligible for these benefits available to all manufacturers. Statutes expressly grant these two tax exemptions to both encourage waste reduction and recovery and to provide tax equity with other manufacturing (103).

Table 8-2—State Investment Tax Credits

State	Eligibility	Amount	Comment
Massachusetts	Research and development on recycled and recyclable materials in manufacturing.	50% of R&D costs (100% if performed by institution of higher learning).	Available to corporations manufacturing plastic and paper consumer products.
	Tangible property used in manufacturing.	10% of cost in year of acquisition.	
New Jersey	Recycling equipment used in transportation, processing, or manufacturing.	50% spread over 5 years; may be carried over.	Available to corporations only.
New York (proposed)	Recycling equipment used solely for processing secondary materials.	50%; may be carried over for 4 years.	Includes deduction for construction or improvement of recycling facilities.
Oklahoma	Installation, purchase, and construction of facilities.	20%	Hazardous wastes only.
Oregon (3 programs): Business Energy Tax Credit	Equipment used solely for recycling.	35% (10% in each of first 2 years; 5% each of next 3 years). May be carried over for 3 years.	Certification simple, quick. Major state program used by MSW recycling activities. Due to sunset after 1990.
Pollution Control Facility Tax Credit	Equipment, land, and buildings used for recycling.	50% spread over 10 years (5% a year). May be carried over for 3 years.	Credit will be reduced to 25% in 1989. Due to sunset after 1990.
Plastics Recycling Tax Credit	Machinery and equipment used solely for reclaiming plastic and making it into a product.	50% spread over 5 years (10% a year). May be carried over for 5 years.	Applies to capital investment made from January 1, 1988, to January 1, 1989.
Pennsylvania (proposed)	Machinery and equipment used to process and manufacture products from post-consumer waste materials.	50% of equipment cost credit shall not exceed 20% in any year or 50% of total tax liability.	Does not apply to secondary waste material or demolition waste.

SOURCE: Franklin Associates, Ltd., *Economic Incentives and Disincentives for Recycling Municipal Solid Waste*, contract report prepared for U.S. Congress, Office of Technology Assessment (Prairie Village, KS: December 1988).

Table 8-3—State Tax Incentives and Areas of Application

State	Supply-side incentives: For recycling operations			Demand-side incentives: To manufacturers/users of recycled materials
	Equipment	Buildings	Land	
California[a]				CTC
Illinois				STE
Indiana	PTE	PTE	PTE	PTE
Kentucky	PTE			—[c]
Massachusetts[a]				ITC
New Jersey	ITC			ITC
New York[a]	ITC	ITD		
North Carolina	PTE, ITD	ITD	ITD	—[c]
Oregon:				
Business Energy Tax Credit	ITC			
Pollution Control Facility Tax Credit	ITC	ITC	ITC	
Plastics Recycling Tax Credit				ITC
Pennsylvania	ITC			
Wisconsin	STE, PTE[d]			STE, PTE

[a]Proposed incentives.
[b]Includes collection and/or processing operations.
[c]Some users of recycled materials may qualify as recycling operations.
[d]Some processors qualify as a result of court ruling.
Abbreviations: ITC=investment tax credit; PTE=property tax exemption; STE=sales tax exemption; CTC=consumption tax credit; ITD=income tax deduction.
SOURCE: Franklin Associates, Ltd., *Economic Incentives and Disincentives for Recycling Municipal Solid Waste*, contract report prepared for U.S. Congress, Office of Technology Assessment (Prairie Village, KS: December 1988).

their treasuries or if they have significantly increased the amount of material recycled (35,36).

In most cases, tax incentives do not appear to be major influences on business investment decisions and they do not necessarily lead to increased recovery of materials from wastes (35,36). Historical trends in manufacturing industries using secondary materials indicate that recent capital investments have been relatively limited. For example, most glass container manufacturers, steel mills, and paper mills are operating with facilities older than 10 years. No new glass container plants have been built in the last 10 or 15 years in the United States, and the actual number of operating glass plants has declined over the last several years as competition from plastics has increased.

These long-term trends suggest that the lack of investment in recycling industries is unlikely to be reversed by the small change in the cost of investment that could be brought about by an ITC. Of course, definitive estimates of investment behavior would require a case by case evaluation of individual plants. If an ITC were available, it would obviously become a factor in investment decisions. However, industry representatives indicate that such tax incentives would not be a deciding factor (36). Other factors, such as labor costs and proximity to markets, are more critical determinants of investment decisions.

Even if recycling ITCs were successful in expanding capacity to manufacture products from secondary materials, however, the capacity will not be used unless there is a demand for the final product. In sum, without increases in the demand for products made from recycled inputs, there is little reason to believe that supply-side tax incentives for the purchase of capital equipment will result in the increased use of recycled materials.

In addition, no evidence suggests that sales or property tax exemptions are a determining factor in a company's decisions for expansion or startup (36). In Illinois, and probably elsewhere, a general limit on the amount of influence any tax incentive will have is the fact that tax liabilities for most companies are quite low, generally less than 1 percent of gross sales. Every business manager interviewed by Franklin Associates reported that this amount is not significant enough to effect their business decisions. Further, nonprofit organizations, which many recovery operations are, have no State tax obligations.

Consumption Tax Credits—Consumption credits act as an incentive by reducing the cost of the targeted material to the manufacturer. In particular, they reduce tax liability by an amount proportional to the quantity of targeted material used. For such a tax-based "throughput subsidy" to be effective, two assumptions must hold:

1. taxes paid by the target industry must be high enough that credits for purchasing a favored material can actually affect the material's net after-credit price; and

2. the primary factor in buyers' choice between competing materials must be price, so that a difference no larger than possible through the tax code will cause them to change their buying habits.

Subsidies can be granted to manufacturers who reprocess newsprint, glass bottles, and other wastes, as a way of reducing the cost of the wastes they buy. They can also be granted to firms that purchase recycled finished goods such as newsprint, bottles, and other goods as inputs into their own productive process. The goal of these subsidies is to reduce the cost of recycled inputs relative to virgin inputs.

Consumption tax credits have not yet been applied anywhere, but they are considered by some analysts to be a potentially effective stimulant for secondary materials markets (35,36). Also called "secondary materials use credits," this mechanism allows companies using secondary materials in manufacturing to apply a portion of the price paid for those materials as a credit against owed income tax. Even if effective, however, the use of consumptive tax credits could require a long-term, State-financed subsidy to users of secondary materials to maintain the desired market conditions (36).

A bill proposed in California during the 1985-86 session (Assembly Bill No. 1109), would have given consumption tax credits to users of recovered glass, paper, oil, and plastics from the State and used in the State. The bill would have allowed a tax credit against a company's State income tax, based on an amount calculated as a percent of the amount paid for qualifying secondary materials.[34] The bill was not enacted, reportedly because of an inability to develop a suitable funding mechanism, and subsequent versions have also failed.[35]

The potential effect of consumption tax credits can be difficult to estimate. For example, newsprint can be produced from old newspaper (ONP) or virgin wood pulp, or both. A consumption credit applied to ONP would theoretically lower its price as a raw material in newsprint production relative to the price of virgin wood pulp. This would theoretically increase the use of ONP to make newsprint. Because the raw material is less expensive, the price of the finished newsprint could be reduced, and thus more could be sold. However, historical data for the newsprint industry indicate that movements in the price of waste paper are not reflected in price movements for finished newsprint. In fact, the price of ONP has declined dramatically over the long run relative to the price of the newsprint made from it (table 8-4). These data call into question any program based on the assumption that a reduction in the price of an input would lead directly to a reduction in the price of output.

Because it appears that consumption credits are not likely to offset prices in all instances, a great deal of attention need not be given to the second condition for success—that buyers will choose recycled products if prices are reduced. Nevertheless, evidence suggests that this condition is not likely to hold in all cases either. For example, consumer perceptions that recycled inputs produce inferior quality products, whether true or not, can subvert the goal of such credits. Furthermore, industries such as newspaper publishing are vertically integrated and have substantial investment in, or longstanding ties to, virgin sources of inputs.

The experience with newsprint suggests that resistance to production with a particular input may be caused by factors other than price. Table 8-5 supports this conclusion for the paper industry as a whole. Over a 16-year period, the utilization ratio of recycled paper in total paper production has fluctuated over a range of only about 1 percentage point, despite a long-term trend toward lower recycled input prices. The recent change, shown in the table, cannot be attributed to the relative price relationship.

---

[34]The percents for the four qualifying secondary materials are: 15 percent for glass; 10 percent for paper; 22 percent for used oil; and 22 percent for plastics (36).

[35]It was re-introduced in 1988 as the Recycling Tax Fairness Act (Senate Bill No. 188).

Table 8-4—Relative Prices of Old Newspaper (Old News No. 1) and Newsprint from 1970 to 1986, Compared With 1967 Prices[a]

Year	Old news No. 1[b]	Newsprint[c]	U.S. consumer prices-urban (CPIU)	Ratio of old news to newsprint[d]	Ratio of newsprint to CPIU[d]
1970	108.1	107.6	116.3	1.005	0.925
1971	103.1	112.2	121.3	0.919	0.925
1972	119.2	116.7	125.3	1.021	0.931
1973	137.2	122.2	133.1	1.123	0.918
1974	201.6	151.2	147.7	1.333	1.024
1975	111.8	184.0	161.2	0.608	1.141
1976	199.5	198.2	170.5	1.007	1.162
1977	209.6	215.5	181.5	0.973	1.187
1978	200.5	226.3	195.4	0.886	1.158
1979	151.8	250.2	217.4	0.607	1.151
1980	167.4	279.3	246.8	0.599	1.132
1981	95.7	308.0	272.4	0.311	1.138
1982	72.1	315.8	289.1	0.228	1.092
1983	N/A	303.0	298.4	—	1.015
1984	193.1	323.1	311.1	0.598	1.039
1985	150.0	332.5	322.2	0.451	1.032
1986	137.1	326.1	328.5	0.420	0.993

[a]The price in 1967 is set equal to 100, and then the prices in other years are compared with this value (i.e., Price Index = 100).
[b]Price index for postconsumer newspapers purchased by paper mills.
[c]Price index for rolls of newsprint paper purchased from paper mills.
[d]Column 4 = (column 1/column 2); column 5 = (column 2/column3); — means that calculation could not be made.
N/A = Not available.

SOURCE: Compiled by Franklin Associates, Ltd., *Economic Incentives and Disincentives for Recycling Municipal Solid Waste*, contract report prepared for U.S. Congress, Office of Technology Assessment (Prairie Village, KS: December 1988).

Table 8-5—Price Indices of Wood Pulp and Waste Paper Compared With 1967 Prices, and Recyclable Paper Utilization Ratio, From 1970 to 1986[a]

Year	Waste paper	Ratio of waste paper wood pulp	Recycled paper to wood pulp	Utilization ratio
1970	125.0	109.6	1.141	0.228
1971	112.1	112.1	1.000	0.228
1972	133.6	111.5	1.198	0.225
1973	197.4	128.3	1.539	0.235
1974	265.5	217.8	1.219	0.236
1975	110.2	283.3	0.389	0.230
1976	184.9	286.0	0.647	0.233
1977	187.2	281.1	0.666	0.234
1978	191.2	266.5	0.717	0.237
1979	206.6	314.6	0.657	0.238
1980	208.7	380.3	0.549	0.234
1981	175.7	397.1	0.442	0.233
1982	122.8[b]	397.0	0.309	0.237
1983	201.2[b]	346.9	0.580	0.234
1984	240.1	397.6	0.604	0.241
1985	148.8	346.6	0.429	0.238
1986	172.8	358.8	0.482	0.247
1987	219.8	422.5	0.520	0.250

[a]The price in 1967 is set equal to 100, and then the prices in other years are compared with this value (i.e., Price Index = 100).
[b]July to December average.

SOURCE: Compiled by Franklin Associates, Ltd., *Economic Incentives and Disincentives for Recycling Municipal Solid Waste*, contract report prepared for U.S. Congress, Office of Technology Assessment (Prairie Village, KS: December 1988).

This implies that programs that seek to increase the use of recycled inputs by further reducing the relative price of such inputs (whether through the tax system or in any other way) are not likely to meet much success, at least not in the short term.

Although data from other industries are not as easy to analyze, no indication is found that low recovered material prices will increase recycling. For example, since 1970 the prices of glass cullet have doubled, or tripled in some instances, while the consumption has actually risen. The same is true for aluminum. For steel scrap, prices were deeply depressed for many years with no widespread switches in the industry from virgin to recycled inputs occurring. What does seem to occur is that the basic demand for these materials determines the price, not the converse. The demand is created by complex economic and noneconomic factors, of which the price of the recycled input is a small part.

Research and Development Tax Credits—For a tax credit for research and development (R&D) expenditures to be successful, it must meet the same criteria as any other investment tax credit. That is, it must actually increase R&D expenditures above their previous level or it must reduce the cost of previously planned R&D. The cost saving must be passed on to consumers, and sales must increase as a result.

At the Federal level, ERTA provided a 25 percent tax credit for R&D expenditures that exceeded average R&D expenditures in a base period, usually the three previous tax years. One study concluded that "there was no evidence . . . which supported a strong conclusion about the impact of R&D specific tax incentives on R&D spending" (Piekarz, 1983, cited in ref. 36).

One reason for this apparent lack of effectiveness of R&D tax incentives is that R&D costs are only a small proportion of the total costs involved in bringing a new product to market. Also, many firms cannot benefit from tax incentives because of low or nonexistent tax liability. Overall, firms that took advantage of the 1981 ERTA credit could only use 59 percent of it in the first year, with the rest being carried forward (36).

In short, it is unlikely that a tax credit for R&D for recycling will be a cost-effective method to increase the amount of solid waste recycled. Taxpayer dollars might be spent more effectively on direct subsidies to R&D organizations, such as universities, with a requirement that discoveries enter the public domain if not actually put into production within a specified time. This would foster increased recycling by discouraging licensing or other arrangements that permit the licensee to hold a discovery for a lengthy period of time before deciding whether to use it.

Subsidies, Grants, and Loans—Direct appropriated subsidies are an alternative to tax subsidies. Such subsidies have advantages over tax credits in several important respects. First, the appropriation of a direct subsidy is for a fixed dollar amount, so that the cost of the subsidy program is known and can be controlled. Furthermore, the subsidy appropriation must be reconsidered annually, allowing restructuring and adjustment to reflect changing conditions.

Second, direct subsidies are not administered by the Internal Revenue Service, but by other government agencies that are more likely to have experience with the recycling industries targeted for assistance. Also, the granting agencies are subject to oversight by congressional committees with responsibilities and expertise relevant to the original goals of the subsidy. Under these conditions, a direct subsidy can be carefully targeted to achieve the desired effects.

Third, direct subsidies can provide benefits more quickly to firms in need than can tax credits, which may take many months or years to be realized. These benefits are available even to firms with no tax liability; such firms would not be able to take advantage of tax credits. Finally, the effects of direct subsidies can be more easily determined than those associated with a more diffuse tax subsidy program.

Of course, direct subsidies also have some associated problems. Direct subsidies will increase the Federal budget deficit if new revenue sources are not specified. Large direct subsidies, although more likely to be effective than small ones, tend to make the recipients dependent on them—if the subsidy is suddenly terminated, these firms may face serious threats to their continued operation.

Finally, as with the tax incentives, the question of equity among competitors will arise when deciding among subsidy recipients.[36] There can be no doubt that the historical use of subsidies at the local level has played a key role in keeping many recycling operations in business, especially during difficult times. However, no direct subsidies to the demand-side of the recycling system are known, nor are any broad subsidies at the Federal level to recycling industries known. To date, the debate about whether direct subsidies are preferable to tax incentives has not been resolved (36).

Direct subsidies, sometimes funded through user fees collected as part of tipping fees at landfills, may be of a substantial enough size to more strongly influence business decisions than tax incentives. For example, in Illinois, the Solid Waste Management Act designates the Department of Energy and Natural Resources to implement State programs to provide alternatives to traditional landfill disposal. The programs are to be funded by a surcharge placed on landfill tipping fees, which is expected to raise $10 million annually for solid waste planning, recycling, and resource recovery programs.

Although the constitutionality of the fees was successfully challenged on the grounds that exemption of certain wastes and a "pass through" exemption (for landfill owners with nonnegotiable contracts but not for haulers with similar agreements) were not defensible, the fees schedule was upheld. The case is being appealed by the Illinois Environmental Protection Agency.[37] In August 1988, the State of Illinois enacted legislation to correct the defects in how the fee was imposed. Other States (e.g., Massachusetts, New Jersey) and localities also charge such fees to generate revenue to fund solid waste management activities.

Grants, direct loans, and loan guarantees are non-tax types of financial incentives that can be funded by revenues generated by user fees. These programs are not revenue expenditures for the State and/or local government and can be of sufficient size to directly influence business decisions with respect to recycling. In New York State, for example, the Department of Economic Development (in part as a response to the State Solid Waste Management Plan) established a Secondary Materials Program that not only provides technical assistance, but also financial assistance in the form of grants and loans to qualifying companies. The purpose of the program is to stimulate private sector investment in recycling capacity, and projects funded by either the grant or loan program must document increased recycling and energy savings resulting from the project (88). Grants up to $50,000 or 80 percent of the total study cost (whichever is less) can be awarded to firms to evaluate the feasibility of recycling projects. In addition, loans up to $250,000 per applicant will be available to eligible companies to finance the acquisition, alteration, repair, or improvement of buildings or equipment used for recycling (88).

Several States award direct grants or loans to eligible recycling businesses. The Minnesota Waste Management Board can award grants for the establishment of eligible recycling operations. In Illinois, the Development Finance Authority Direct Loan fund provides subordinated, fixed asset loans based on a fixed rate of interest for 7- to 25-year periods, depending on the depreciable assets purchased.[38] The loans average about $150,000 for creditworthy businesses that could not acquire conventional financing (51). The New Jersey Office of Recycling provides low-interest, 10 year direct loans to recycling businesses, which range from $50,000 to $500,000 for the acquisition of fixed assets.

Loan guarantees for various percentages of loans may cover fixed assets or working capital and be offered by the State. New Jersey offers loan guarantees from 30 to 90 percent for up to 10 years for working capital ($600,000 maximum) and fixed asset ($1 million maximum) loans to creditworthy firms. Other types of non-tax financial incentives offered in some States, which could be used to encourage recycling businesses, are venture capital financing (e.g., Massachusetts) and industrial revenue bonds (e.g., Pennsylvania).

---

[36]Any subsidy, whether in the form of a direct cash payment or a tax incentive, entails the provision of benefits to some groups and not to others. Because tax-based subsidies cannot be targeted as specifically as direct subsidies, they are much more likely to create inequities among competing groups of taxpayers and among taxpayers within the same industry.

[37]See for example, *E & E Hauling, Inc. Browning Ferris Industries of Illinois, Inc., Land and Lakes Co., and Haulaway, Inc. v. Illinois Environmental Protection Agency* (No. 87 CH 1262, Circuit Court of Cook County, Illinois County Department, Chancery Division, State of Illinois).

[38]Fixed assets might include equipment, land, or building purchases. Direct loans could also be used for working capital, for example for inventory purchases. Direct loans are also usually low interest (i.e., below prime rate) and may have an extended repayment term. See ref. 51.

Other types of non-financial assistance for recycling businesses offered by States include technical assistance (e.g., management training, site selection assistance, export assistance, regulatory compliance assistance, direct business consulting); business incubators (i.e., providing space, office services, consulting services and financial services at reduced fees or included in the rent in a multi-tenant facility); and categorical assistance (based on categories of business) (see ref. 51).

Procurement

To function, all governments and businesses must purchase materials and services; these are usually procured by awarding contracts. The most common method of awarding government contracts is by low bid. It is not uncommon, however, for noneconomic factors to be considered, such as special arrangements to Buy American or encourage affirmative action. Similarly, at least 23 States and the Federal Government have enacted legislation encouraging the purchase of secondary materials and items containing recycled materials.[39]

More than half of the States with procurement programs include more than paper in the materials to be preferentially procured (58). Items eligible for recycled materials procurement programs, in addition to paper, include tires, re-refined lubricating oil, construction materials such as glassphalt, and potentially items such as asphalt, HDPE drainage pipes, plastic floor mats, and polyester carpeting.

The potential of this market is large—Federal, State, and local government purchases of goods and services account for about 20 percent of the gross national product (GNP), amounting to expenditures of $865 billion in 1986 (135a).[40] However, the amount of a product procured by the government will not necessarily have a significant effect on the overall market for the product or on MSW management. For example, one reason for the minimal impact of government procurement programs on paper recycling is that the government consumes only 1 to 2 percent of the Nation's total paper (36).

Many State and Federal procurement provisions have not yet been implemented, or have not achieved their intent to provide viable markets for secondary materials. EPA's failure to issue procurement guidelines was discussed above (see ''Environmental Protection Agency''). The Department of Commerce, specifically the Office of Recycled Materials of the National Bureau of Standards (ORM/NBS), was at least initially the most active agency in attempting to fulfill the procurement requirements set under RCRA. ORM/NBS produced reports on State procurement efforts and on test method development and specification guidelines for numerous materials (136,137). The methods and standards developed by the ORM/NBS have been adopted by the recycling industry. Yet most of this activity occurred nearly a decade ago. Further, demonstration projects and other activities were not vigorously pursued.

A variety of reasons have been suggested for this lack of success, including unclear or no guidelines, inexact specifications, uncompetitive costs, and a generally negative societal attitude toward recycled materials (134). Two particularly critical barriers to implementing procurement guidelines are 1) conflicting definitions and percentages of recycled content, which hinder mass production; and 2) the lack of knowledge of where to buy recycled products (155).

Nonetheless, despite problems achieving specific quantitative results, procurement policies can act as stimulants and demonstrate government leadership in materials and energy conservation. One major advantage of procurement programs is their visibility and educational value. They can be used to demonstrate the successful use of recycled products. Widespread use of consistent guidelines by both government and business could provide economic stimulus for market development and expansion.

One noteworthy development is the initiation of ''buy-recycled'' programs by State and local governments (155). For example, Massachusetts, Oregon, Pennsylvania, and Washington, and Suffolk

---

[39]These include Alaska, Connecticut, California, Florida, Iowa, Illinois, Maine, Maryland, Massachusetts, Michigan, Minnesota, Missouri, New Hampshire, New Jersey, New York, Ohio, Oregon, Pennsylvania, Rhode Island, Texas, Vermont, Washington, and Wisconsin. For a comparison of State procurement laws see refs. 3 and 105.

[40]It should be emphasized, however, that 20 percent of the GNP does not directly translate into that percentage of product consumption. In fact, no national statistics document percentages that high (155).

County, New York have such programs. NERC also has supported the development of "buy-recycled" plans.

Paper Procurement—Most targeted procurement programs focus on paper, primarily recycled printing and writing paper. Despite these programs, however, the supply of such paper made from "waste paper" has not increased significantly.[41] Although total U.S. shipments of printing and writing papers increased from 15.5 million tons in 1980 to 19.6 million tons in 1986 (a 26 percent increase), the amount of high-grade deinking recycled paper consumed in the manufacture of printing and writing paper increased from only 303,000 tons in 1980 to 342,000 tons in 1986, about a 13 percent increase.

This actually represents a slight reduction in the utilization rate (i.e., waste paper consumed/paper production) of high-grade deinking recycled paper from 1.95 to 1.74 percent. The amount of pulp substitutes consumed in the manufacture of printing and writing papers increased from 502,000 tons in 1980 to 910,000 tons in 1986, for an increase in the utilization rate of 3.2 to 4.6 percent. Therefore, constrained supply may present a barrier to increased consumption of recycled printing and writing paper.

Many factors might be contributing to the relatively small increase in recycled printing and writing paper production:

- capital investment required to build a recycled paper mill is high;
- government procurement programs do not provide adequate incentive because they are small and do not assure a long-term market;
- costs at smaller, non-integrated recycled paper mills are higher than at big, integrated virgin paper mills because economies of scale have not been realized, making it difficult to compete in the highly competitive non-specialty paper product market;
- consolidation in the paper industry has resulted in purchases of recycled paper mills by larger companies that subsequently resorted to the use of virgin raw materials and closed the deinking facilities required to use post-consumer waste paper;

- increased exports of waste paper have reduced the domestic supply and increased the price significantly;
- use of waste paper in producing printing paper requires more energy, labor, and materials than use of virgin pulp;
- a great deal of competition exists for the supply of clean waste paper from domestic mills producing tissue, paperboard, and other paper products; and
- the use of waste paper in paper products other than printing papers may be more efficient from a raw materials viewpoint—the yield (weight of finished product/weight of raw material) in paperboard is 85 percent, compared with 65 percent in printing paper.

On the demand side, barriers to increase paper recycling via government procurement programs exist in the procurement process itself. Purchasing officials are often reluctant to use price preferences because of a desire to restrict "unnecessary" expenses and maximize the purchasing value of public funds (161). Other arguments include:

- scientific tests to verify the recycled content of particular lots of paper are not economically available, providing no legal means of supporting a bid choice if contested;
- government orders are sometimes too small to qualify for direct mill runs, which often can supply paper at lower cost and allow for easier verification of recycled content;
- fewer responses to purchasing requests for recycled paper might be likely, reducing both competition and purchasing options considerably;
- the amount of paper procured by the government is too small to have an effect on MSW; and
- purchasing officials receive complaints about the quality of recycled paper (although it appears that high-quality recycled papers are more readily available and at more competitive prices than previously, an image of the inferior quality of recycled paper still persists).

These problems are not insurmountable. In some States, notably California, New York, and Maryland, procurement programs for secondary materials have

---

[41]The General Accounting Office is scheduled to release a report in 1989 on implementation of the paper guideline.

provided a market for recycled paper. The mechanisms most commonly used for recycled paper procurement are minimum content standards, price preferences, and set asides. Minimum content standards define the procuring agency's idea of "recycled" paper. Separate standards are often set for each type, or grade, of paper purchased to allow for technological constraints. A minimum content standard may include requirements for post-consumer waste as well as any type of waste paper in general. Price preferences allow the procuring agency to subvert the usual legal requirement to award contracts to the lowest qualified bidder. Most commonly, preferences range from 5 to 10 percent for paper, thus allowing the purchase of recycled paper at a price up to 10 percent above that of competing paper without the specified waste paper content. Set-aside programs allocate a specified amount of paper purchases to recycled paper, without consideration of price.

New York's procurement program has a 10 percent price preference for paper with a recycled content of at least 40 percent. During the period 1981 to 1987, paper certified by the State as recycled accounted for 40 percent of the paper purchased by the State government. This percentage fluctuated, with no discernible trend, reaching a high of 59 percent in 1985 and a low of 24 percent in 1987. A preference of $77,403 was paid in 1987 for the recycled paper, amounting to 0.9 percent of the total value of paper purchases. The types of recycled paper products purchased under the preference program in 1987 included offset sheet and rolls (43 percent), paper towels (38 percent), scratch pads (18 percent), and text and cover paper (1 percent).[42] In addition to certified recycled paper obtained under the recycled paper procurement program, the State purchased tissue, corrugated and chipboard boxes, napkins, fiber drums, and refuse sacks, all commonly made of recycled fiber, that amounted to about 30 percent of total paper purchases (45).

California has a 5 percent price preference for paper with a recycled content of 50 percent, including 10 percent post-consumer waste. During the period 1977 to 1987, 14.4 percent of California's paper expenditures was for recycled paper (57). The preference paid to procure this paper amounted to $505,000, or only 0.2 percent of the total value of paper purchases. In fiscal year 1986-87, California's recycled paper purchases amounted to 25 percent of total State paper purchases, the highest proportion of recycled paper attained thus far. Even so, the preferences granted amounted to only 0.35 percent. The types of recycled paper bought in that year included bond paper (52 percent), copier paper (22 percent), envelopes (22 percent), lunch boxes (3 percent), and chipboard (1 percent).[43]

Maryland has a set-aside program for recycled paper that specified graduated increases in recycled paper purchases up to 40 percent of total paper purchases by 1985, the eighth year of the program. By 1986, Maryland had spent more than $19 million to purchase recycled paper products, defined as containing 80 percent recycled paper, including 80 percent post-consumer waste (57,58,153,154). Maryland's program focuses on bond paper.

Clearly, this review of various Federal and State financial incentives indicates that careful evaluation of the potential effect of incentives to encourage recycling is necessary before program commitments are made. Indeed, the dynamic nature of secondary materials markets makes it imperative that recycling be a carefully planned and implemented MSW management option.

Incineration

OTA estimates that about 10 to 15 percent of the Nation's MSW is managed through incineration. The status of regulation of air emissions and management of ash residues from MSW incineration is discussed in chapters 1 and 6. The discussion in this chapter is limited to the general context in which this policy debate is taking place.

Local officials were first encouraged to develop waste-to-energy incineration facilities by the Department of Energy and EPA, which in the mid-1970s promoted incineration as part of the Nation's strategy to be energy self-sufficient. The Department of Energy (DOE) was given authority to provide Federal funds to encourage the developing

---

[42]Offset papers, bond paper, copier paper, envelopes, and text and cover paper are considered printing and writing paper, while toilet paper, paper towels, and facial tissues are considered tissue papers.

[43]Previous years' purchases included tissue, paper towels, corregated, and other non-printing and writing papers.

waste-to-energy industry (i.e., incineration facilities that recover energy). A comprehensive waste-to-energy program, however, never developed. DOE issued several internal drafts of a Comprehensive Waste-To-Energy Plan, but the document was not published or submitted to Congress (66). Nonetheless, DOE continues to sponsor some related research efforts (139).

Price support regulations, in accordance with the Energy Security Act, were issued in 1980 but withdrawn in 1982. The funding for loan guarantees and price supports for waste-to-energy facilities was virtually eliminated at this same time (66). However, Federal support for waste-to-energy facilities continues through the Public Utility Regulatory Policies Act. PURPA guarantees a market for the electricity generated by waste-to-energy facilities (chs. 5 and 6). Utilities are not generally enthusiastic about the requirement to make "avoided cost" purchases of energy from MSW facilities, and although the program is under review it to date has served to create an artificial market for these sources.

Many early combustion facilities suffered mechanical and technical difficulties, thus creating a climate of skepticism about the reliability of this management option. Today, the industry believes it has acquired the technical expertise necessary to run successful facilities (116). The public, however, remains concerned about the high capital costs associated with incineration, site selection, air emissions, and ash management.

Siting incineration facilities is a slow process that can take 5 years or more. In addition, several more years may pass before a facility is operational. For example, in New Jersey the Department of Environmental Protection estimates that it may take a year or more to complete its comprehensive permit process; construction is estimated to require an additional 2 to 3 years (117). The financing and management costs associated with incineration can also be formidable (ch. 2). Some localities have

canceled or postponed proposed waste-to-energy facilities (including Austin, Texas; Seattle, Washington; Philadelphia, Pennsylvania; and Alachua County, Florida). In March 1989, Tulsa, Oklahoma adopted an ordinance that increases trash collection rates for households and businesses to help finance the city's waste-to-energy facility. The facility has experienced annual shortfalls of $6.3 million since 1986, largely caused by lower than projected natural gas prices and because the facility is operating at only 65 percent capacity (31).

In the current highly uncertain regulatory climate for MSW incineration, municipalities need reliable information on incineration technologies, cost estimate scenarios, and realistic assessments of their potential liabilities if they are to plan and evaluate proposals for incineration projects. The National League of Cities published a guide to answer questions many municipalities face when contemplating an incineration project, and some other information resources are available (86a). Guidance from the Federal Government to clarify the regulation of incineration is strongly needed, however, to facilitate local planning.

Compatibility With Recycling

As incineration and landfilling become more costly, recycling may become more cost competitive with these options. Some observers are concerned, however, that "flow control ordinances," designed to ensure sufficient refuse for efficient incinerator operation, and related factors make these two options basically incompatible.[44] Flow control ordinances, in which a municipality grants an exclusive contract for the collection and/or disposal of waste to an incinerator (or other waste facility), have been upheld as "a reasonable and foreseeable exercise of [State] powers."[45] That is, flow control ordinances under certain circumstances have been upheld by the Supreme Court, and are not a violation of antitrust laws even though they can displace competition.

---

[44]Most localities do guarantee a certain flow of MSW to facilities, the so-called "put or pay" or "flow control" contracts. If a facility is not sized to adjust for the amount of MSW a community will recycle, and an ambitious recycling program reduces the volume of waste available to the facility, the locality may have to contract with other communities for that amount of MSW. Flow control ordinances of some sort exist in every region of the country (80).

[45]*Hybud Equipment Corp.* v. *City of Akron*, Ohio 742 F.2d 949 (1984), 471 U.S. 1004; see also *Town of Hallie, et al. (Wisconsin)* v. *City of Eau Claire (Wisconsin)* 700 F.2d 376 (1983), 467 U.S. 1240; *Central Iowa Refuse Systems, Inc.* v. *Des Moines Metropolitan Solid Waste Agency, et al.* 715 F.2d 419 (1983), 471 U.S. 1003; and *J. Filiberto Sanitation, Inc.* v. *State of New Jersey Department of Environmental Protection and Board of Public Utilities*; Hunterdon County Municipal Utilities Authority 857 F.2d 913 (3rd Cir. 1988).

Although some experts argue that incineration deters recycling, others disagree, saying that recycling and incineration are compatible management options (ch. 6). Section 4003(d) of RCRA states that the sizing of waste-to-energy facilities should take recycling and resource recovery activities into account. In some cases, States are taking an active role to help ensure that recycling and incineration are compatible. This is essential if States are to successfully implement a waste prevention and materials management approach to MSW.

In New Jersey, the State's mandatory recycling law targets 25 percent of MSW for recycling. In Essex County, New Jersey, the State funded a study to examine how comprehensive recycling might effect the design and operation of the county's proposed waste-to-energy project. The study estimated that removing significant quantities of recyclables could increase the heat content of the remaining waste and reduce the quantity of ash produced. In addition, capital costs could be reduced by approximately $22 million by reducing the size of the facility 15 percent. Ground was recently broken for the 2,250-ton-per-day facility. According to the New Jersey Department of Environmental Conservation, most of the State's planned waste-to-energy projects have been scaled down to be consistent with the State's 25 percent recycling goal. Scaling facilities to meet recycling goals underscores the critical role of recycling in integrated MSW management systems.

Failure to consider the reduction in waste caused by recycling can bring unexpected problems. In Warren County, New Jersey, for instance, a 400-ton-per-day facility is under construction. It will be the first large-scale waste-to-energy facility to open in New Jersey; a new landfill was also permitted nearby. But Warren County, in meeting its 25 percent recycling goal and given the anticipated growth of its communities, may have a shortfall of refuse for its facility by 1990. It has, therefore, contracted with Hunderdon County for 100 tons per day. It also decided not to require newspaper recycling, and has instead targeted glass and aluminum containers, and plastic beverage bottles for recycling. The newspaper will then flow to the

waste-to-energy facility. This compromise brought mixed reactions from citizens and public officials.

This situation and similar ones around the country illustrate the difficulty of achieving a delicate balance between incineration and recycling management options. Recently in Spokane, Washington, the County Board of Health issued a permit that requires 35 percent of Spokane's MSW to be recycled by 1998, but supporters of the incineration project believe that the new county recycling requirement may make the incinerator economically unfeasible because there would not be enough MSW to burn.[46]

In contrast, the County Commissioner of Marion County maintains that Oregon's ambitious recycling goals are not having a negative impact on operation of the county's waste-to-energy facility (133). New York State has a regulatory requirement that a community applying for a permit to build an MSW management facility include a comprehensive recycling analysis in the preliminary application.

The ultimate effect of provisions to ensure the compatibility of recycling and incineration is not yet clear. State and local planning and development of incineration facilities requires as careful consideration as the development of any other MSW alternative.

Landfill Disposal

Many areas around the country are facing shortages in permitted landfill capacity (ch. 7). Continued reliance on landfilling is a source of concern as a number of potential problems become increasingly apparent: capacity issues (as landfills unable to meet permit requirements close); costs (as tipping fees increase to cover costs or control use); siting difficulties for new landfills; and concerns over ground and surface water and air emissions. In addition to efforts to upgrade existing landfills and site new landfills with better environmental designs (ch. 7), many States are also attempting to clean up existing landfills. This can be expensive. For example, in Wisconsin it is estimated that a six-fold increase in the State's tipping fee could be needed to cover expected pollution problems at licensed landfills during the next 30 years.

---

[46]In 1989, EPA Region 10 (which includes Washington State) included the front-end source separation of recyclables in the permit as a Best Available Control Technology (BACT) requirement. Although EPA Headquarters denied the permit, the attempt has potentially far-reaching implications (chs. 1 and 6).

The current Federal criteria regulating landfills became effective in late 1979 and apply to both new and existing MSW landfills. In August 1988, EPA proposed regulations for the design and operation of new and existing MSW landfill facilities (ch. 7). Currently, 38 States require groundwater monitoring, but only 14 States require corrective action for groundwater contamination. Final cover at closure is required in 49 States and 42 States have requirements for post-closure care (this varies, however, from 1 to 5 years to 20 years), and 20 States require some financial assurance.

EPA has concluded that while a few States have comprehensive regulations, the majority have inadequacies in one or more provisions (149,149a). For example, few States include location standards for landfill sites in their regulations.[47] Almost 60 percent of all MSW landfills have permits or approved plans (yet 50 percent of **all** Subtitle D facilities are operating without a State permit). Enforcement efforts in general also need improvement, even though most of the States' activities (as noted above) are spent on surveillance/enforcement and permitting.[48] Inadequacies with State regulations indicate that Federal criteria may need to be more complete, and the proposed regulations include provisions for corrective actions, performance standards, closure and post-closure requirements, and financial assurance. As Federal requirements are developed, the relationship to State permitting and enforcement programs needs to be clarified. State variation in standards also means that the degree to which landfills are located, designed, and operated in an environmentally sound manner is highly dependent on where in the country they are located.

Although landfill ownership varies among States, on a national level most MSW landfills tend to be owned and operated by public entities (ch. 7) (16,18,145).[49] Overall, 86 percent of all the landfills are publicly owned, 57 percent of these by local governments (149a). In some States (e.g., Indiana, Kentucky, Michigan, Minnesota, Missouri, Ohio,

Pennsylvania, and West Virginia), however, the distribution of ownership among public and private entities is relatively even.

Details of landfill technologies and related issues of performance are discussed in chapter 7. As in many areas of MSW management, contrasts between different regions of the country, particularly between the west and east coasts, are apparent. For example, methane gas recovery at landfills began in California at the Los Angeles Sanitation District in the early 1970s. Most sites recovering methane gas remain in the West, but recovery operations are opening with increased frequency east of the Mississippi (78).[50] Some of the recovery operations in California are associated with sites that are now closing as new regulations take effect or adapting to changing circumstances.

One example is the landfill in Mountainview, California, which has a successful methane gas recovery project. The landfill project started in 1970 and today is nearly completed. Mountainview wanted a park in a swampy, wrecking area which is the landfill site, but to bring in fill would have been too costly. Nearby San Francisco wanted a transfer station and additional disposal capacity; Mountainview built the landfill to secure the money for a park and eventually a park was developed over closed areas of the landfill. In addition, an amphitheater, a golf course, park, and saltwater lake have been created. The methane gas recovery project was established largely as a response to flares of methane gas escaping from the landfill caused by cigarette smoking on the amphitheater grounds.

In some areas of the country, particularly rural areas of the Midwest and in the generally arid Southwest, municipalities and States are generally concerned over their ability (and in some cases need) to meet any new Federal requirements for landfills. Even in these areas where the goal is to upgrade landfills to better protect groundwater or for other purposes, lack of financial resources seriously con-

---

[47]That is, only 12 States include location standards for wetlands, 3 States have such standards for seismic impact zones, and 6 States have them for subsidence-prone areas.

[48]EPA estimates that approximately $200 and 8 labor hours per facility per year are spent on average by States agencies for Subtitle D activities. It is not surprising, then, that about 75 percent of all MSW landfills are inspected only once a year.

[49]The actual volume of waste disposed of in these facilities may be a much smaller percentage of the waste. For example, in Wisconsin 95 percent of the landfills are owned by public entities, but they manage only 28 percent of the waste (103).

[50]Details about the recovery of methane gas are discussed in ch. 7.

strains these activities and the development of any management alternatives. These concerns need to be addressed at the Federal level. Clearly, programs cannot be implemented at the State and local level without resources, and the funding of any new MSW regulations and provisions needs to be considered at the time of their adoption.

Special Programs

The potential for certain elements of MSW to pose greater risks than the rest of the waste stream or require special handling has caused some States and localities to establish special programs for these MSW components. Such programs are being adopted for household hazardous wastes (including waste oil and batteries), tires, and yard wastes. Concerns over the possible harmful effects from improper disposal of these wastes are associated with both landfilling (i.e., releases of harmful substances to groundwater or the air) and combustion technologies (i.e., contributing to hazardous air emissions or ash toxicity).[51] Again, this discussion only highlights the general nature of some of these special programs.

Household Hazardous Waste

Household hazardous waste (HHW) is now exempt from Federal regulations for disposal that are applicable to other types of hazardous wastes (RCRA, Section 3001).[52] About 1 percent or less of MSW is believed to be hazardous, but the potential impact of these wastes on leachate and emissions from waste management facilities continues to fuel interest in household hazardous waste programs (ch. 3) (see e.g., 146,39).

EPA completed the only comprehensive study of HHW in 1986, which is already dated given how rapidly the number and nature of these programs is changing (144). The EPA survey found that participation in HHW programs has been low, often less than 1 percent. The quantities collected, however, typically range from 20 to 40 pounds per household (apparently representing several years accumulation of wastes). Unit costs for these collection programs can be very high, up to $18,000 per ton. A program with high participation may cost $2/pound of HHW

Photo credit: Office of Technology Assessment

Special management programs for household hazardous wastes are increasing throughout the country. The information distributed as part of the programs can be a very effective way of educating people about alternatives to toxic products.

collected, while a program with low participation may cost over $9/pound (144).

The relatively high economic cost of collecting HHW raises some questions, given that other sources of toxic pollution such as small quantity industrial generators may dwarf the HHW contribution to potential environmental and health risks (60,79) (ch. 3). Small quantity generators (SQGs) may be included in HHW programs and at least one study, for Seattle/King County, Washington, found that about the same amount of HHW and SQG waste was sent to the area landfill as was sent off-site from larger industrial sources (39). In addition, the separate collection of HHW is not always necessarily consistent with a materials management ap-

---

[51]The effects of household hazardous wastes on municipal wastewater and its treatment also are a concern if they are disposed of into a sewer system.

[52]This means that it is not necessary to obtain a permit to store HHW. Liability under CERCLA (''Superfund''), however, may be incurred by a municipality transporting or disposing of HHW at a site (21).

proach to MSW (ch. 1).[53] In any case, support for HHW programs continues because of the educational value of these efforts, especially in terms of promoting the use of alternative, less toxic products (24,144).

At least one HHW collection program has been held in each of 42 States between 1981 and 1987; in total, there are at least 849 ongoing HHW programs (23,24).[54] Half of the States have laws and/or regulations addressing HHW. Often, however, localities hold these programs with or without State or Federal funding (18,24). This, in part, may be why many HHW programs are short-lived or sporadically held. Nonetheless, particularly in areas highly dependent on groundwater, HHW programs tend to persist and appear to be expanding.

Some areas are establishing regional and permanent facilities for HHW management. These facilities are intended to boost participation rates and distribute the cost of HHW collection among communities. Public education is also key to the success of HHW programs. As of 1988, there were 27 permanent HHW collection programs in the country, sometimes at transfer stations (figure 8-3). For example, San Bernardino County, California, has two permanent HHW centers that are open on a daily basis. Each facility has a specially designed storage unit for the wastes. Wastes are accepted, categorized (open and unidentified wastes are not accepted), properly packaged, and entered on a log sheet. Wastes are then shipped off site for disposal (usually in drums to hazardous waste landfills). The program is funded by the State with some matching funds from the county's surcharge at landfills (38,81,82,91,111).

One of the oldest and largest State HHW programs is in Florida (62,73,146). Florida, with its high water table and porous soil, is dependent on groundwater and vulnerable to groundwater contamination. The county-based "Amnesty Days" program is funded by the State through the Water Quality Assurance Trust Fund and is supervised by the Department of Environmental Regulation. A variety of approaches have been used in the 3 1/2-year-old program, but educational efforts are generally combined with collection. Usually a "trans-

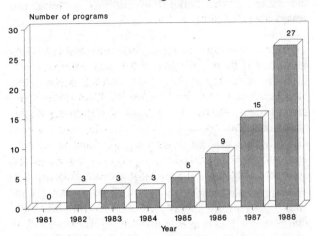

Figure 8-3—Permanent Household Hazardous Waste Collection Programs By Year

SOURCE: Dana Duxbury & Associates, personal communication, February 1989.

fer station on wheels," tractor rigs equipped for the collection process, are used. Unlike some HHW programs, the "Amnesty Days" collections will accept hazardous waste (and pesticides) from small businesses, farmers, and State agencies as well as households. Rhode Island has a similar State-managed regional collection program (50). Other States, such as California and Washington State provide guidelines but no direct funding.

Perhaps the most effective framework for HHW programs is a statewide, State-managed collection program with adequate funding (73). If no funds are available, at a minimum State guidelines or regulations are considered desirable (73). A State excise tax (essentially a user fee) is one funding option for HHW programs. Connecticut, Massachusetts, New Hampshire, and Vermont, among other States, have matching grant programs to help fund local HHW efforts. For example, in Connecticut matching grants of 50 percent are available for HHW collection days. Other types of funding available are EPA grants, State Superfund monies, and State bonding (73,100). Local governments may use a variety of approaches to fund or subsidize HHW programs, such as establishing surcharges (e.g., refuse collection surcharge, water bill surcharge, or tipping fee sur-

---

[53]For example, some toxic residues in glass containers might be destroyed during recycling processes, in which case the collection of this type of HHW in a separate program may not be desirable from a materials use perspective.

[54]In contrast to the proliferation of HHW programs today, in 1981 there were only two programs in one State.

charge), stipulating the establishment of an HHW program when granting a site permit to an appropriate firm, and/or using subsidies or general tax revenues (100,101).

States can also provide technical assistance to localities for HHW programs and evaluate the impacts of existing programs. Indeed, some State statutes require the evaluation of pilot HHW program efforts. Areas of concern for improving HHW programs that could be addressed by the Federal Government include clarifying the liability of collection program sponsors, improving technical assistance, funding public information efforts, and addressing labelling and disposal restriction issues (e.g., providing clearer guidelines for use and disposal; requiring consideration of HHW in MSW plans). Industry cooperation, by both manufacturers and waste management companies, will facilitate any of these efforts for proper disposal of HHW.

In some States and/or localities, more specialized programs to handle pesticides, paints, used oil, and batteries have been established.[55] "Pesticide Days" are held with increased frequency around the country, but pesticides are also often accepted at HHW collection programs (6,41). Some communities will collect used oil at their recycling centers (e.g., Davis, California); several communities also collect used oil through curbside collection programs (e.g., Palo Alto, California) (44,148). Liability concerns have limited efforts to establish permanent collection sites in some areas, but collection directly from households may avoid classification of the oil as hazardous.

Batteries are also collected by some targeted programs. For example, the New Hampshire/Vermont Solid Waste Project, a consortium of 26 municipalities in the two States, began a program to collect household batteries in 1987. The batteries are collected through retail stores that sell dry cell batteries for flashlights, radios, cameras, and hearing aids.[56] Consumers are encouraged to return batteries through public education efforts, and batteries are collected by local civic groups and stored in 55 gallon drums in a secure location until the next local HHW collection is held.[57] In New York City, the Environmental Action Coalition (EAC) began in 1988 to collect button cell batteries from apartment buildings participating in its recycling programs. The EAC estimates that as many as 10,000 button cell batteries may be disposed of daily in the city.[58]

Tires

Tires are a prevalent MSW problem for States and localities because they create serious problems for landfills. They tend to float to the surface; sometimes they ignite underground and cause severe fires. Aboveground stockpiles are fire and health hazards (e.g., mosquitoes, which can transmit diseases, breed when water collects in the tires). Chipping tires and landfilling them or chipping and burning them have been expensive alternatives to landfilling whole tires.[59] The Department of Energy estimates that 168 million of the 200 to 250 million tires disposed of each year are landfilled or placed in junk yards. At least 34 stockpiles of 100,000 tires or more have been identified and are within 150 miles of major metropolitan areas.

Some States impose deposits on tires to help finance recycling and research on appropriate disposal methods (e.g., Wisconsin imposes a $2 deposit). Other States have adopted a fee (e.g., Florida and Oregon) or are proposing to adopt a fee (e.g., New York State) on new tires and to use the money to help municipalities remediate existing tire piles, provide grants and/or loans to businesses adopting new technologies for tire recycling, and/or support research on new methods for managing discarded tires. Fee systems typically require that tire retailers accept discarded tires from consumers purchasing new tires. At least three States have a used tire recycling program.

---

[55]These items are also often collected in high volumes in HHW programs, and they do require special handling.

[56]Lead-acid batteries are also a concern, but no known program for their collection was identified. Private recycling of these batteries has been affected by liability concerns and, until recently, depressed prices for lead in secondary market (ch. 5).

[57]The Southwest Missouri State University Household Hazardous Waste Project is establishing a mechanism to facilitate battery collection in retail stores by providing self-mailer boxes (123) (ch. 5).

[58]Liability concerns over the processing of the batteries for recovery and recycling are not resolved. See refs. 91 and 123.

[59]Ch. 5 discusses technologies and related concerns associated with tire disposal.

Yard Wastes

Several States (e.g., California, Massachusetts, Minnesota, New Jersey, Oregon, Washington, and Wisconsin) have programs and/or regulations to encourage or even mandate composting (10a,107a). In 1988, New Jersey banned disposal of leaves in landfills (September through December) and mandated composting (76).[60] Minnesota and Wisconsin banned landfill disposal of all yard wastes effective in 1993 (46). At least three States (i.e., California, Massachusetts, New Jersey) have preferential procurement policies regarding compost. The New Jersey State Department of Transportation, however, has said it cannot give preferential treatment to compost until specifications are developed (76). Minnesota has a policy of using compost, and Montana has exempted compost from the State sales tax (107a).

Some States offer technical or financial assistance to foster composting (10a). New Jersey, Wisconsin, and other States provide manuals on composting for community-level operations. In New Jersey, leaf composting operations are eligible for State recycling grants and, because siting in general is so difficult, the State will approve the siting of such operations on public lands (10a,120a). The 1987 Massachusetts Solid Waste Act provides $7 million for municipal yard waste composting programs (109). Minnesota's Waste Management Board has provided funding for various studies and projects, and Florida has provided financial assistance for feasibility studies (107a). Delaware played a major role in developing the mixed MSW composting facility in Wilmington.

Many localities operate yard and leaf waste composting operations or contract with private operations (ch. 5). For example, Urban Ore, a nonprofit recycling business in Berkeley, California, produced commercial grade compost for 3 years. The program ended because of political reasons, not its effectiveness (63). However, the city may renew its composting efforts because studies indicate that 35 percent of the MSW volume accepted by the landfill is brush and yard debris from small and independent haulers.

Two private firms in Portland, Oregon, cooperate with the Metropolitan Service District (Metro) to compost the area's yard waste. Metro provides technical assistance to the firms, marketing assistance to processors, and a public education program to promote composting. At least 25 percent of the area's yard waste is now composted and officials expect this will double within 5 years (157). In Davis, California, leaves are collected in plastic bags by the municipality, which grinds them and makes non-commercial grade compost. Unlike some communities with similar programs, it has been able to give away compost the town does not use. These few examples indicate that compost programs, if carefully planned and executed, can preserve landfill space and produce usable compost (also see ch. 5).

CROSS-CUTTING CHALLENGES

As the responsibilities for MSW management are increasingly shared among local, State, and Federal Governments, a high level of coordination and clear designation of responsibilities becomes critical. Requirements and program initiatives cannot be enacted by higher levels of government without considering available resources and activities at lower levels of government. Further, planning efforts are severely handicapped if the regulation of various management alternatives, and indeed the entire Federal MSW program, is in a constant state of flux or is ambiguous.

Several problems exemplify contentious issues and illustrate the need for coordinated and cooperative intergovernmental efforts. Concerns over the potential for increased interstate shipment of MSW are often sparked by the problem of insufficient capacity within jurisdictions. Issues of siting and public participation are related to the problem of a lack of public confidence in newly proposed MSW policies.

Self-Sufficiency and Interstate Transportation Issues

To plan an effective MSW strategy, the responsible political jurisdiction needs to be able to predict the approximate amount of MSW to be handled and provide sufficient capacity. Currently, however,

---

[60]However, sufficient permitted capacity to compost all the leaves collected does not exist. As a result, New Jersey promulgated an emergency rule that simplified the permitting process for small operations and allowed larger facilities to obtain temporary operating certificates.

many communities and States are experiencing an MSW capacity shortfall, at least until new facilities are operational. This often leads to a greater shipment of waste between political jurisdictions. As a result, some States and communities are experiencing unexpected and dramatic increases in the amount of waste received from other areas at their facilities (ch. 7), which generates concern over the effect on their own future capacity and on other, revenue-raising activities (e.g., tourism).

In response to interstate imports, some States have attempted to ban the importation of MSW. However, given that siting MSW facilities may take 5 or more years, it is likely that at least in the short term, some communities will continue to need to ship some waste to areas with existing capacity. Therefore, the concerns of jurisdictions with existing capacity need to be addressed.

The Commerce Clause of the Constitution grants Congress the power to regulate all commerce; the "dormant commerce clause" is essentially a restatement of this power that makes explicit that State lines cannot be made barriers to the free flow of commerce (19).[61] The *City of Philadelphia* v. *New Jersey* case is the landmark decision regarding the question of whether a State may regulate the shipment of MSW into its jurisdiction.[62] In 1973, New Jersey enacted a waste control law clearly aimed at prohibiting the shipment of "unusable" MSW into the State for landfill disposal, but allowing shipment of MSW materials with some potential economic value (e.g., through reprocessing, heat recovery, recycling, or as animal feed).[63] Philadelphia sued New Jersey over the statute, claiming it was an encumbrance to interstate commerce, and the U.S. Supreme Court held that the

New Jersey law was indeed in violation of the Commerce Clause. The New Jersey statute was not preempted by any existing Federal law; it was considered a "protectionist" measure rather than a law "directed to legitimate local concerns, with effects on interstate commerce that are only incidental."[64] Some municipal bans on MSW importation also have been challenged as violations of the Commerce Clause, but the case law is not entirely consistent.[65]

Federal courts and at least one State appellate court have addressed the "market participation" exception to the Commerce Clause (as articulated by the Supreme Court) with respect to landfills.[66] If the State is acting as a "market participant," that is, it owns, operates, or transacts business itself, then it may chose to conduct business with whom it wishes (e.g., refuse to accept out-of-State shipments of MSW) without violating the Commerce Clause.[67] The Commerce Clause is interpreted as prohibiting a governmental unit from "hoarding" all landfill facilities for its citizens, when the sites are viewed as natural resources. Restrictions are permissible under certain conditions if facilities are viewed as complex activities rather than natural resources (e.g., when private operators are allowed to compete with publicly operated landfills) (67).

Thus Delaware, which established the Delaware Solid Waste Authority to manage **all** of the State's MSW, can restrict the influx of any out-of-State waste.[68] Maine passed legislation that requires future solid waste facilities to be State-owned, the apparent intent being greater control over siting and interstate shipments of wastes. It appears that a **locality** would also be able to restrict the flow of

---

[61]U.S. Constitution, Article I, Section 8, Clause 3; *Southern Pacific Co.* v. *Arizona*, 325 U.S. 761 (1945).

[62]*City of Philadelphia* v. *New Jersey*, 437 U.S. 617 (1978); 98 S. Ct. 2531.

[63]Waste Control Act, N.J. Admin. Code 7:1-4.2 (Supp. 1977). See refs. 19, 70, and 128.

[64]The Court rejected New Jersey's argument that MSW was "valueless." See refs. 19, 70, 128.

[65]See *Monroe-Livingston Sanitary Landfill, Inc.* v. *Town of Caledonia,* 51 N.Y. 2d 679; *Dutchess Sanitation Serv., Inc.* v. *Town of Plattekill* 51 N.Y. 2d 670; 435 N.Y.S.2d 966 (1980). In addition, attempts by municipalities to control MSW disposal through their zoning power have also been challenged successfully if they discriminate on the basis of the source of the MSW (see refs. 70, 128).

[66]See *Hughes* v. *Alexandria Scrap Corp.* 426 U.S. 794 (1976); also *Reeves, Inc.* v. *Stake* 477 U.S. 429 (1980) and *White* v. *Massachusetts Council of Construction Employees* 460 U.S. 204 (1983).

[67]See, e.g., *LeFrancois* v. *Rhode Island* 669 F. Supp. 1204 (D.R.I. 1987); *Shayne Brothers* v. *District of Columbia* 592 F. Supp. 1128 (D.D.C. 1984); and *County Commissioners of Charles County* v. *Stevens* 299 Md. 203 (1984). These cases generally find that when States or municipalities operate landfill services as market participants they may under certain conditions be able to restrict their services to wastes from only their jurisdictions without violating the Commerce Clause of the Constitution.

[68]Delaware Solid Waste Authority, 7 Delaware Code, Chapter 64; also, *Hughes* v. *Alexandria Scrap Corporation*, 426 U.S. 794 (1976). See ref. 128.

waste if it was a "market participant," that is it owned or operated a facility.[69]

The Federal Government could address the issue of self-sufficiency and interstate transportation by requiring or encouraging State solid waste plans to address capacity and how it will be provided (see ch. 1 for additional discussion). Some legislation has been proposed or discussed in Congress to establish Federal requirements regarding interstate transportation of MSW, as well as the exportation of MSW to foreign countries. One proposal, for example, would allow a State to ban imports from other States if it had an EPA-certified solid waste plan and a process for developing sufficient capacity to handle its own MSW. A reliable system to collect data on existing, planned, and future capacity also is needed and could be included in requirements for approval of State plans.

An alternative approach would be to provide mechanisms for cooperation in interstate MSW transportation (ch. 1). For example, interstate compacts have been used to deal with issues such as low-level radioactive waste disposal, navigation and flood control, water pollution control, community development, and crime prevention (66). In fact, provisions exist in RCRA (Sections 4002(a) and 4006(c)) to encourage interstate regional planning to facilitate MSW management. These provisions, which have not been implemented, could provide a basis for allowing States to enter into agreements on MSW issues such as transportation of wastes, disposal fees, or development of new management facilities. Instead of erecting a barrier, this would allow some wastes to move unimpeded across State lines, but in an orderly manner.[70]

Restoring Public Confidence

Siting

Siting new MSW management facilities— whether landfills, incinerators, or recycling facilities— has become increasingly difficult in some areas. Some State MSW plans, which in part address the development of adequate capacity, have failed to be implemented because new facilities to meet the goals of the plan could not be sited. Given that additional capacity shortages are expected as landfill closings increase when the new EPA landfill regulations take effect (ch. 7), the problem of siting facilities in a timely way is a growing concern.

Informal discussions by OTA with State and local officials and developers of various types of waste management facilities throughout the country revealed that **most facilities have taken at least 5 to 8 years to site**. Realistically, any locality needing additional disposal capacity within a shorter period of time will probably have to make interim arrangements for MSW disposal, such as expanding the capacity of existing facilities and/or entering into agreements with jurisdictions or facilities nearby that have sufficient capacity to accept additional wastes. Again, escalating costs will result.

Public opposition is the primary cause for the lengthiness of the siting process. The opposition is in part related to the "NIMBY" (not in my backyard) syndrome, which seems to affect a broad range of activities. The primary cause of the opposition, however, stems from a lack of confidence in the safety of a proposed facility and the uncertainties associated with its regulation and reliable operation. Residents also have concerns about potential negative effects on local property values.

Nonetheless, some new management facilities of all types have been sited in recent years (box 8-D). An extensive body of literature exists on the difficulties of siting facilities (particularly hazardous waste facilities) and evaluating various approaches to siting. In general, the key factors to foster public acceptance of a facility identified by such studies (69, 97, 131) are the:

- **credibility** of the siting process (i.e., the scientific assessments and political judgments of a site's suitability are trusted by the public);

---

[69]*Evergreen Waste Systems, Inc.* v. *Metroplitan Service District* 820 F2d 951 (1987).

[70]One bill proposed in the 100th Congress (H.R. 3515) would not prohibit interstate transport of MSW, but would require that a written agreement exist between a party transporting MSW across a State line and the facility accepting the waste, and that other specified conditions be met as well. Bills restricting interstate transportation continue to be proposed in Congress (e.g., H.R. 2099, 101st Cong., 1st sess.), although it is not clear whether Congress will enact any such measures (75).

- **equity** issues (i.e., assurances to the host community that health and environmental risks will not be unfairly borne on its residents); and
- **public participation** (i.e., involving the public in selecting, evaluating, and locating facilities).

Successful siting is most likely if there is early, substantive, and continual public participation, positive local-State relations, and sincere efforts to mitigate risks (e.g., through additional controls, frequent monitoring and inspection, and rigorous enforcement).

Involving the public and building trust can add a significant amount of time and expense to the siting process. Yet, allowing the public only limited opportunities for participation (e.g., public hearings on an already government-selected site) can fuel opposition to waste management alternatives and also add delays and high costs to a project.

A comparison of the political processes in Japan and the United States provides some guidance on how to improve this critical component of policymaking. In Japan, public acceptance for new facilities is gained primarily by meeting public demands for advanced pollution controls. That is, political and social acceptability (rather than environmental, health, economic, or technical factors) are critical in determining which methods a community adopts. In addition, a community swimming pool or greenhouses, heated by steam recovered from the waste-to-energy facility, may be provided to the host community as part of the facility. This process, although generally successful, has resulted in escalating expectations by the public, longer negotiations, and substantial extra costs (in some cases up to 50 percent, some of which are borne by the national government). In the United States, similar approaches may prove necessary to gain public confidence in our entire approach to MSW management.

Effective siting is most likely when two basic premises are recognized—siting is a continual negotiations process and it must take place with public support (125,126).[71] One study, which reviewed 120 proposed MSW incineration projects and analyzed 20 as representative of the national situation, found that 35 percent completely aban-

Photo credit: M. Wagner

The famous "Not In My Backyard" or NIMBY situation applies not only to incinerators and landfills, but also to facilities for processing recyclable materials. It stems from past experiences with poorly performing facilities, concerns over potential risks, and failure to involve the public adequately in decisionmaking.

doned plans for the facility, 15 percent are in "serious difficulty" proceeding, 25 percent are proceeding toward contract signing and are not at more than double the expected time at this stage, and 25 percent are under construction or operational (13).

In this study, the investigators found that it was not the technology, concerns over air degradation, or other concerns which caused a site or project to be abandoned, but rather "insufficient public appreciation of the need to find a waste disposal alternative." The researchers found that public education programs needed to begin before the site was announced and needed to include detailed explanations about the need for the facility.

Political and personal economic considerations can affect citizens living near a site. Sometimes indecision by local officials can fuel opposition to a proposed site; citizen advisory committees without sufficient public education efforts can also be associated with siting difficulties. In addition, if homeowner equity is the major personal asset of local citizens, opposition is likely to be high.

---

[71]See also refs. 64 and 124. For discussions of how procedural improvements in the siting process could increase the likelihood of siting, see ref. 9.

> ### Box 8-D—Examples of Successful Local and State Siting Experiences
>
> The Palm Beach County (Florida) Solid Waste Authority considers involvement of the Citizens Advisory Council (CAC) key to the successful siting of its resource recovery facility. The CAC assisted in defining the details of the $320 million bond issue, reviewing elements of the project before contract signing occurred, and continues to serve as a ''watchdog'' for the project. The authority, in an attempt to gain public confidence, went beyond regulatory requirements and attempted to address public concerns throughout the planning and implementation of the project. Although the siting process for the resource recovery facility did take 7 years and possibly entailed some additional expenditures, public support was established for the project and the county's MSW efforts (115).
>
> Approximately 5 years were required to site the waste-to-energy facility in Marion County, Oregon. In total, however, 12 years were spent to develop a relatively long-term MSW solution for the county. The County Board of Commissioners, after meeting resistance to siting a new landfill, established a citizens group (the Solid Waste Advisory Council) in 1979 to study MSW options. The citizens advisory group recommended at the end of 2 years that a waste-to-energy facility be built. The board concurred and selected a prospective vendor. Soon, however, public pressure mounted again. A public relations firm was hired, and another citizens group was formed (the Citizens' Committee to Solve Marion County's Garbage Crisis). Eventually, a petition filed in opposition to the waste-to-energy facility was defeated and the plant opened in 1986 (34).
>
> In Wisconsin, the Department of Natural Resources (DNR) is responsible for the technical and environmental regulatory review of landfill sites, and the State Waste Facility Siting Board has the power to arbitrate an agreement between a municipality and a landfill developer as long as the agreement meets the regulatory requirements set by the DNR.[1] The DNR includes in its technical and environmental review criteria such as: an evaluation of the need for the facility; location criteria; environmental criteria (e.g., soil type); design criteria (e.g., liner and cap design); construction documentation; proof of financial responsibility for closure and long-term care; site licensing; and periodic inspections. The negotiated agreement can address landfill design, operation and closure issues, and alleviating economic impacts on the local area—but, again, State requirements must be met.
>
> Of the 103 facilities that have been subject to the law, in 30 cases no negotiation process was sought; for the 73 which entered into the process, 26 reached a negotiated agreement, 41 are still in the process, 5 have withdrawn, and one is being brought to arbitration (102). The State of Wisconsin acknowledges that its siting process is ''complex, comprehensive and time consuming''—taking 3 to 5 years to complete, but it is also successful (102,112). One State official concludes that it is, ''The interplay of planning, state licensing and enforcement and the negotiation/arbitration of local approvals [which] makes the siting of new environmentally safe facilities possible'' (112).
>
> Another key to the siting program's success is the local approval process, which allows local units of government to establish reasonable controls on the facility and provides an opportunity for any adverse social and economic impacts to be mitigated through the negotiation process. Apparently, economic compensation to host communities and sometimes directly to property owners has been important to a number of agreements. In general, the negotiations proceed in good faith and result in resolution because of the specter of arbitration by the State, which could result in a less favorable outcome.
>
> ---
>
> [1]For more discussion of the Wisconsin siting process, see ref. 112.

Although OTA did not attempt an exhaustive review of all siting experiences, it recognizes siting as a central problem for MSW managers. As discussed in box 8-D, several examples of successful State and local siting experiences can help identify what types of siting policies are likely to be most effective. In Palm Beach County, Florida, for example, local officials were able to implement a multi-faceted MSW program consisting of recycling, a refuse-derived fuel (RDF) resource recovery facility, and landfilling. A different approach, also successful, occurred in Marion County, Oregon, for a waste-to-energy facility. Wisconsin is often identified as having an innovative siting program for landfills that incorporates the use of a negotiation/arbitration process.

As this discussion indicates, public support is crucial to success. This means public involvement, through education and participation, must occur early and throughout the planning, siting, and development of MSW management options. Sporadic involvement of the public, an unwillingness (or the appearance of inflexibility) to address public concerns, and a lack of consideration of all available management alternatives, can jeopardize successful siting. This may add time and additional expense to MSW projects, but it will encourage necessary public support.

Public Education and Participation

The importance of consumer education of the next generation of consumers—our children—can not be understated. As the public grows more aware of the environmental consequences of its lifestyles (e.g., purchasing decisions), its understanding of waste reduction, recycling, and other management alternatives broadens. In addition, concern for the interconnectedness of environmental problems increases. Public education, public participation, and public acceptance of MSW management alternatives are inextricably intertwined. One effort will not have meaningful results without the others.

A number of States and localities have created education programs as part of their MSW activities. For example, in California, particularly in the San Francisco Bay area, the importance of public education is widely recognized and is a key component in local recycling programs. This includes not only pamphlets and materials distributed to residents about the recycling program, but also a recycling curriculum guide for teachers. In Ohio, the Department of Education requires all Ohio schools to include environmental education in the curriculum, and the Department of Natural Resources' Division of Litter Prevention and Recycling developed a comprehensive solid waste, recycling, and litter prevention curriculum guide. It developed the guide because a review of current health, science, and social studies texts in the schools revealed that solid waste issues generally were not included. The solid waste curriculum guide is indexed to allow activities to be selected for lessons in mathematics, English, science, and social studies (158).

Most State and local education programs assume that the use of materials and the prevention and

management of MSW should be included in the curriculum of all school-age children. The logic is that if the importance of sound waste management and the ethics of waste reduction and recycling are taught beginning in elementary school, by the time a child reaches adulthood practices such as materials separation will be part of one's lifestyle. In Japan, as well as in a number of other countries, lessons on recycling and other waste management issues are taught to all school-age children.

One example of a successful recycling information center is in Portland, Oregon. The Metropolitan Service District in Portland operates a Recycling Information Center that responded to nearly 30,000 calls in 1988. The Center began as a volunteer organization initially supported by a grant from the U.S. Office of Environmental Education (part of the Department of Health, Education, and Welfare) and donations. To date, however, the Federal Government has not been extensively involved in supporting any educational programs for MSW. Suggestions have been made that the Federal Government establish an organization similar to the Clean Japan Center to serve as an information source and clearinghouse for citizens and the private sector (66). Again, although some States and localities have established information centers, most have a more narrow focus than the Clean Japan Center.

Views of Appropriate Federal Roles

OTA released a study on materials in MSW 10 years ago, *Materials and Energy From Municipal Waste,* and many conclusions regarding key issues, findings, and the "current" Federal role appear strikingly similar to those in this report—at least at first glance (130). Little has changed in the Federal Government's role in MSW in the last 10 years. Concerns over appropriate methods of "resource recovery," the marketability of recovered materials, institutional barriers to recycling, inequities in the governmental incentives for resource recovery and recycling, and the desirability of source separation,

The links between the extraction of virgin resources and the mounds of waste that we discard must be made more apparent to the next generation than they are to most Americans today. States and localities usually cite education—particularly at the grade school level—as a key factor in their recycling programs.

are all topics in the decade-old OTA assessment.[72] Yet new concerns have also arisen, such as the need for waste reduction efforts, and the technologies for resource (both energy and materials) recovery and recycling have changed. In the 1979 report, an entire chapter analyzed proposals for beverage container deposit legislation. In 1989, implications of newly adopted mandatory source separation recycling programs warrant detailed examination. Further, the rationale for source separation has been broadened beyond recycling (ch. 1).

Although the list of appropriate Federal activities suggested 10 years ago is not very different from that discussed in this assessment, the motivation for action may have changed. As more stringent landfill requirements have been adopted, available MSW capacity has declined dramatically. This was not a serious concern in 1979, although the potential environmental problems associated with improper landfilling methods were and prompted adoption of stricter regulations.[73]

Whether the pressure for new, more adequate MSW capacity and other conditions present today will motivate Federal action remains to be seen. As the 1979 OTA assessment concluded:

Ultimately, the widespread adoption of resource recovery and recycling may depend not so much on the objective analysis of small actions taken together or separately, but on Federal action to create a climate in which the recovery, recycling, and reuse of discarded wastes becomes a valued way of life for all Americans.

Federal attention to MSW disposal and management problems lapsed during the last decade, primarily because of the Nation's preoccupation with hazardous waste problems. As municipalities struggle to devise appropriate mixes of MSW management options for their communities, and States become more directly involved in MSW management, the issue of the appropriate role for the Federal Government resurfaces. State by State, locality by locality, MSW policy development is hampered by limited resources. This results in inconsistent MSW programs and regulations. Consequently, the need for greater Federal involvement is once again being emphasized. As in other areas of environmental policy where a strong rationale for Federal involvement is clear, inconsistencies can lead to a confusing regulatory climate (hampering business decisionmaking) and even encourage the movement of waste from more regulated to less regulated jurisdictions (ch. 7).

State and local officials generally agree that there should be greater Federal involvement in MSW management. Specifically, the following tasks, compiled from a roundtable discussion at an OTA workshop (133), are frequently included in "wish lists" for an expanded Federal role in MSW management:

- establishing a national clearinghouse for information (e.g., developing a database, standardizing terms and definitions, compiling bibliographies);
- providing Federal incentives for recycling (e.g., stimulating markets, mandating product disposal charges, encouraging design for recyclability of products);
- undertaking research and development (e.g., ash disposal methods, determine health effects of management options, improve recycling processes, provide incentives for private research and development);
- providing technical assistance (e.g., provide training to State officials, develop performance-based standards for options, assist States in methods of waste reduction);
- establishing packaging and product regulations/guidelines to reduce waste/toxicity (e.g., require labeling, ban toxic constituents);
- establishing workable Federal procurement standards; and
- finalizing regulations for landfilling and incineration facilities.

These tasks for further Federal involvement are not unlike those frequently voiced by other public and private interests as well.

---

[72]Usage of the term "resource recovery" has changed somewhat. In the 1979 OTA report, resource recovery activities referred mainly to the use of technologies for burning the combustible portion of MSW or converting it (through RDF processes) and recovering energy. At that time recovery of materials for recycling or composting was less available commercially. In this assessment, materials recovery is distinguished from energy recovery, and resource recovery can refer to either or both types of recovery activities.

[73]In addition to environmental concerns, wise and efficient use of materials, the preservation of virgin materials, energy conservation, and improving the balance of trade by reducing our dependence on imported natural resources were goals noted in the 1979 assessment.

As indicated in appendix 8-A, authority for many, but not all, of these activities already exists in RCRA. The current reauthorization of RCRA is an opportunity to address these issues and further define the Federal role in MSW. The establishment of a more effective system to reduce the generation of MSW and better manage what is produced is directly dependent on how well Congress meets the challenge of defining Federal involvement in MSW management.

The effective management of MSW will require not only intergovernmental changes in responsibilities and changes in Federal, State, and especially local budgets for MSW management, but also changes in people's lifestyles. If this is to happen, governments will have to proceed now with programs that will restore public confidence. Involving the public in meaningful ways—i.e., without allowing citizens only the power to object—in the MSW planning and facility siting processes will be key to ensuring the public trust necessary to re-direct past MSW management efforts and adopt lifestyle changes that generate less waste.

APPENDIX 8-A: FEDERAL STATUTORY AUTHORITY

Solid Waste Disposal Act and Resource Recovery Act

Congress first established a Federal role in solid waste issues by passing the Solid Waste Disposal Act of 1965.[74] As was typical at this time for other environmental policy areas, the law merely authorized Federal research in the area and set up a program of grants to the States for similar research. The Resource Recovery Act of 1970 amended this law and strengthened the Federal role.[75] It was not until the Resource Conservation and Recovery Act (RCRA) of 1976 that Federal involvement was significantly expanded (see next section).

Prior to the mid-1960s, fewer than half of the municipalities with populations greater than 2,500 had programs for solid waste disposal (68). Waste management regulations that did exist were primarily general health and safety ordinances applied to waste disposal sites. State activities were for the most part limited to formally delegating authority to municipalities for solid waste management, prohibitions against dumping of wastes on public property, and anti-litter programs. A few States, however, did have some solid waste activities, usually as part of their public health program (68).

The Solid Waste Disposal Act of 1965, in addition to initiating the Federal role in MSW policy, encouraged greater State involvement while affirming primary reliance on local management. The Department of Health, Education, and Welfare was authorized to provide technical and financial assistance to State and local governments. In addition, grants were available to States that developed statewide solid waste management plans and designated a single implementing agency (Section 206). By 1975, all States had adopted some form of solid waste regulations, although there was tremendous variation among them.

The Resource Recovery Act of 1970 amended the Solid Waste Disposal Act to authorize a Federal grant program for the "demonstration, construction, and application of solid waste management and resource recovery systems" (Section 101) and established Federal authority for the promulgation of guidelines for "solid waste collection, transport, separation, recovery, and disposal systems" (Section 104(b)). The funding of such solid waste activities increased after the creation of the Environmental Protection Agency (EPA) in 1970. EPA, for example, funded eight resource recovery projects under the program established by the 1970 Act. Shortly after this time, however, EPA activity decreased as other environmental issues received higher priority (68).

Resource Conservation and Recovery Act (RCRA) of 1976[76]

Passage of RCRA in 1976 was a clear movement toward more direct Federal involvement in solid waste management. The intent of RCRA was to improve waste management by discouraging landfill disposal. This was done by shifting the burden of costs more directly to users, and by encouraging development of resource recovery

---

[74]Public Law 89-272.

[75]Public Law 91-512.

[76]Public Law 94-580 (1976). RCRA's statutory definition of solid waste was quite broad, and included "garbage, refuse, and other discarded solid materials, including solid-waste materials resulting from industrial, commercial, and agricultural operations, and from community activities . . ." (42 U.S.C. §3251-3259 (1970). Later, the definition was expanded to include sludges of various types and ". . . other discarded material, including solid, liquid, semisolid, or contained gaseous material resulting from industrial, commercial, mining, and agricultural operations, and from community activities" (42 U.S.C. Section 6903(27) (1977)). This assessment, however, does not examine all of these types of waste (ch. 1). Solid waste management was also broadly defined by the act to include "the collection, source separation, storage, transportation, transfer, processing, treatment, and disposal of solid waste" (42 U.S.C. Section 6903(28)).

technologies and use of the materials or energy recovered (66).

RCRA distinguishes between hazardous (Subtitle C) and nonhazardous (Subtitle D, including MSW) wastes. Since its passage, most activities by the Federal Government have focused on hazardous waste issues. RCRA did establish an office of solid waste within EPA, mandated regulations on solid waste disposal, and established procedures for State development of solid waste management plans. Yet most responsibility for overseeing the management of solid wastes remains with the States, as Congress expressly avoided preemption of State regulations in this area.

Subtitle D (Subchapter IV, RCRA) includes objectives that encourage methods of MSW management that are "environmentally sound and [will] maximize the utilization of valuable resources including energy and materials which are recoverable from solid waste and to encourage resource conservation" (Section 4001). These objectives are consistent with the findings presented in RCRA's initial section (Section 1002) about solid waste, the environment and human health, and materials and energy. Similar findings relevant to MSW management are included in other statutes, such as the Mineral Lands and Mining Act (MLMA) and the Public Utility Regulatory Policies Act (PURPA).[77]

Despite these types of findings and objectives, what is **not** stated in the act is of great interest. **It is noteworthy that RCRA does not contain a statement of national policy for MSW.** Indeed, the lack of national goals for MSW possibly has contributed to the general lack of Federal leadership in this area. Such a policy may not have been stated because Congress has been careful to respect the traditional roles of local and State governments.

In addition, **although it is frequently assumed that a hierarchy of preferred MSW management options is stated in RCRA, no such hierarchy is explicitly outlined in the statute.** The section on findings (Section 1002(b)(8)), for example, only notes a need for alternatives to landfills. With the statute's general emphasis on resource recovery, recycling and waste-to-energy incinerators seem to be viewed as equally desirable. **MSW prevention is not clearly stated as a policy or as the preferred option within a hierarchical approach.**[78] Finally, contrary to what often may be assumed, **RCRA does not explicitly state a policy of minimizing environmental and health risks associated with MSW management practices.** Again, however, the sections on

findings (Section 1002(b)) and objectives (Section 4001) note the danger to human health and the environment from inadequate MSW management and state an objective of environmentally sound MSW management.

A major focus of Subtitle D was to encourage the development of State solid waste management plans (addressing both MSW and nonhazardous wastes) and foster intergovernmental (Federal, State, and local) and public/private cooperation. Federal technical and financial assistance were offered to States and localities as incentives for the development of plans (Sections 4002-4003, Sections 4006-4008). Another major focus of Subtitle D is the improvement of landfills. EPA was authorized to promulgate regulations containing criteria for classifying types of sanitary landfills (Section 4004), to facilitate in the closing or upgrading of existing open dumps (Section 4005), and to provide some assistance for these activities to rural communities (Section 4009).

RCRA also contains a substantial research, development, demonstration, and information subtitle (Subchapter VIII). This subtitle, in addition to establishing broad research authorities for EPA, "alone or after consultation with the Secretary of Energy" (Section 8001), identifies a number of special studies to be supported, such as glass and plastic, tires, waste composition, "small-scale and low technology," and "front-end source separation" (Section 8002). The act established the Resource Conservation Committee, composed of the EPA Administrator, the Secretary of Commerce, the Secretary of Labor, the Chairman of the Council on Environmental Quality, the Secretary of Treasury, the Secretary of Interior, the Secretary of Energy, the Chairman of the Counsel of Economic Advisors, and a representative of the Office of Management and Budget (Section 8002(j)). The committee was to investigate "all aspects of the economic, social, and environmental consequences of resource conservation," including the "appropriateness and feasibility" of product charges or product bans, and the effect of existing policies (e.g., subsidies and other economic incentives) on resource conservation (104).

In addition, Section 8003 identifies a comprehensive list of topics for which the EPA is to "develop, collect, evaluate and coordinate information." This includes information on methods to reduce the amount of solid waste generated, the availability of markets for energy and materials recovered, methods and costs of solid waste collection and management, and research and development projects for solid waste management (Section 8003(a)). A central reference library was to be established

---

[77]Public Law 96-479 and Public Law 95-617, respectively.

[78]RCRA's policy statement about reducing the generation of waste applies only to hazardous wastes (Section 1002(a)(6)), although MSW reduction is included in the findings as an area necessitating Federal action.

and maintained to house this information and other relevant data on performance and cost-effectiveness records for various solid waste management and resource conservation technologies and systems (Section 8003(b)). Full-scale demonstration facilities and grants for resource recovery systems and "improved solid waste disposal facilities" programs were also established (Sections 8004-8006).

Procurement guidelines are to be prepared by EPA, after consultation with the Administrator of General Services, the Secretary of Commerce (acting through the Bureau of Standards), and the Public Printer (RCRA, Subchapter IV). The guidelines should designate items produced with recovered materials that must be procured by Federal agencies (in accordance with the provisions of the Section), recommend practices for the procurement and certification of such items, and provide information on the availability, relative price, and performance of such items (Section 6002(e)). EPA was required to prepare final guidelines for paper and three other product categories, including tires, by 1985. In addition, each procuring Federal agency is required to establish an affirmative procurement program (Section 6002(i)).

In addition to EPA, the other Federal agency given major responsibilities under RCRA is the Department of Commerce. Four special areas of responsibilities under RCRA (Subchapter V, Sections 5001-5005) are delineated for the Secretary of Commerce: 1) to develop accurate specifications for recovered materials; 2) to stimulate and develop markets for recovered materials; 3) to evaluate and promote proven energy and materials recovery technologies; and 4) to establish a forum for the exchange of technical and economic data relating to resource recovery facilities.

Even this brief summary of RCRA indicates that it established broad authority for Federal involvement in the development of MSW policies. RCRA already includes provisions to address many of the areas frequently identified today in need of Federal attention (ch. 1). Yet Congress did not grant EPA any authority to **require** State implementation of any Federal standards relating to MSW management.[79] This, as noted above, preserved the primacy of State and local responsibilities for MSW management. Federal activity in MSW management has indeed remained limited, as clearly illustrated in the lack of funding of Subtitle D activities since 1981.

Hazardous and Solid Waste Amendments of 1984[80]

The Hazardous and Solid Waste Amendments (HSWA) of 1984 represent a broadening of the Federal involvement in MSW management, although their major focus is on refining hazardous waste management under RCRA. HSWA does add one additional method for EPA to encourage compliance of State solid waste plans with federal guidelines. EPA can use its enforcement powers under the hazardous waste provisions of RCRA if a State fails to implement permit programs for solid waste facilities receiving hazardous wastes from small quantity generators (SQGs) and/or household hazardous wastes (HHW) (Section 4005(c); see also Section 3001(d)).

HSWA also gives EPA the authority, if necessary, to directly manage portions of a State's solid waste management plan. Successful implementation, however, still depends on State and local planning and enforcement efforts. In addition, EPA is directed to survey solid waste management facilities across the Nation and evaluate whether current guidelines and standards are adequate to protect the environment and human health. It is also directed to promulgate revisions of the landfill guidelines and those for landfills receiving HHW and SQG hazardous wastes (Section 4009a) (143,144,145,147,149a). HSWA also clarified the open dumping ban and reemphasized the procurement program.

Current RCRA Reauthorization Efforts

Congress is focusing its attention during the current reauthorization process for RCRA on Subtitle D of the law and is revisiting the issue of the appropriate Federal role in MSW management. There is agreement that the Federal role in this policy area needs to be expanded, yet it is unlikely that a Federal role comparable to that established in other environmental areas (e.g., hazardous waste management) will be defined for MSW management.

The Chairman of the Senate Subcommittee on Hazardous and Toxic Substances of the Committee on Environment and Public Works introduced the Waste Minimization and Control Act of 1989 (S. 1113; also see S. 1112) and held hearings throughout the year on MSW issues. The Chairman of the House of Representatives Subcommittee on Transportation, Tourism and Hazardous Materials of the Energy and Commerce Committee also held hearings and is expected to introduce a RCRA reauthorization bill in 1989. Separate legislation also has been

---

[79]Several methods exist, however, for EPA to encourage compliance. For example, if a State does not develop or implement a management plan, it will not receive financial or technical assistance (Section 4007). Also, EPA may seek injunctive relief if disposal practices present "an imminent and substantial endangerment to health or the environment" (Section 7003). Citizen suits can also be used to encourage compliance (Section 7002).

[80]Public Law 98-616.

introduced to address specific aspects of MSW issues (e.g., the disposal of incinerator ash residues, interstate transportation restrictions, etc.).

Other Relevant Statutes and Authority

Public Utility Regulatory Policies Act and Other Energy Laws—The Public Utility Regulatory Policies Act (PURPA, Section 210)[81] of 1978 requires the Federal Energy Regulatory Commission (FERC) to guarantee a market for electricity generated by qualified small power producers, which includes most waste-to-energy incineration facilities (chs. 5 and 6). FERC is mandated to issue rules requiring electric utilities to purchase electricity from qualified cogenerators and small power producers. A qualified facility must: 1) produce electric energy "solely by the use, as a primary energy source, of biomass, waste, renewable resources, or any combination thereof"; 2) produce no more than 80 megawatts of power; 3) have the total annual input of oil, coal, and natural gas not exceed 25 percent in Btu value of the fuel; and 4) have equity ownership of a small power producer by a utility exceed 50 percent (Section 201; 16 U.S.C. Section 824a-3). PURPA also provides some exemptions from Federal and State requirements, such as those relating to financial arrangements for power sources and the Federal Power Act (Section 201(e)).

The intent of PURPA was to encourage cogeneration and small power energy production and thus decrease the Nation's dependence on fossil fuel and foreign sources of energy, and diversify energy production. Concern has been raised that FERC regulations issued in 1980 to implement PURPA essentially created a subsidy system for such sources of power. This is because the 1980 regulations allow States to set rates exceeding or falling below the avoided cost of purchasing the qualified facility's energy production.[82] These "incentive rates" can be used to encourage certain technologies, such as waste-to-energy incineration. In April 1988 FERC invalidated New York State's law which set the purchase rate above the utility's full avoided cost.[83] At least 20 other States have similar laws or regulations which could be preempted. The claim is that these laws could encourage

the production of energy from "inefficient" sources, which was not the intent of PURPA; the counter-claim is that utilities are generally opposed to small power generators and this FERC decision reflects a "pro-utility" perspective (26). In any case, the New York Public Service Commission is contesting FERC's order in court and in Congress.

A number of other past energy and conservation statutes encouraged the use of resource recovery, either of energy or secondary materials. The Energy Security Act[84] of 1980 has a purpose of reducing the dependence of the Nation on imported oil. This in part entailed financial support of waste-to-energy facilities by providing the Secretary of Energy authority to grant construction loans and guarantee them, provide price support loans and guarantee them, and establish an accelerated research, development, and demonstration program (Section 237). The Non-Nuclear Research and Development Act[85] of 1974 was amended by the Department of Energy Act[86] of 1978 (Civilian Applications) to give the Department of Energy (DOE) general authority to award grants, contracts, price supports, and loan guarantees for municipal waste reprocessing demonstration projects (Section 20). In addition, the Department of Energy Act of 1978 amended the Energy Security Act to accelerate further the research, development, and demonstration program for waste-to-energy and to evaluate existing facilities for performance and costs.

The act which created DOE, the Department of Energy Organization Act[87] of 1977, includes as a goal the development and commercialization of recycling as part of a general emphasis on energy conservation. The National Energy Conservation Policy Act[88] went further to encourage the use of recovered or recycled materials in industrial operations by requiring DOE to set targets for the use of secondary materials for the metals, paper, textile, and rubber industries, and to create incentives for industries to work with the government to achieve these goals.

Other Relevant Statutes—Several other environmental statutes contain authority relevant to MSW

---

[81]Public Law 95-617.

[82]The "avoided cost" is calculated based on what a utility would have paid to produce or purchase the energy itself rather than from a qualifying facility.

[83]*Orange and Rockland* v. *New York Public Service Commission,* Docket No. EL87-53.

[84]Public Law 96-294. Biomass, which the Act encourages the use of by all economically and environmentally sound ways, is defined in the Act to include MSW and industrial waste.

[85]Public Law 95-238.

[86]Public Law 95-238.

[87]Public Law 95-91.

[88]Public Law 95-619.

management or its reduction. These include the Clean Air Act, the Comprehensive Environmental Response, Compensation and Liability Act (CERCLA, often referred to as "Superfund"), and the Toxic Substances Control Act. In addition, the Internal Revenue Service (IRS) has some relevant authority effecting MSW activities. The Consumer Product Safety Commission and the Food and Drug Administration have authorities relevant to product or packaging changes that might result from waste reduction efforts (see "Waste Prevention" in text).

The only current standards promulgated under the Clean Air Act[89] that apply specifically to MSW incinerators are those for particulate emissions (ch. 6). In June 1987, EPA sent guidance to its regional offices that permits for new and modified facilities should be issued based on a dry scrubber and fabric filter, or electrostatic precipitator, as the best available control technology (BACT) for sulfur dioxide and particulate matter, and combustion controls as BACT for carbon monoxide (ch. 6).[90]

EPA is scheduled to propose new regulations for MSW incinerators by November 1989 (ch. 6). At that time, EPA also expects to issue guidelines for States to regulate the retrofitting of existing incinerators to bring them into compliance with new emission limits. Current congressional proposals for controlling air emissions are generally viewed as more stringent than EPA's proposals (29,30). Some environmental groups, such as the Environmental Defense Fund and the Natural Resources Defense Council, generally favor the more stringent congressional proposals. Some local and State officials, such as the U.S. Conference of Mayors and the Northeast States for Coordinated Air Use Management, and industry interests favor the EPA proposal (29,30).

CERCLA[91] directly affects localities whose MSW landfills are identified by EPA as Superfund sites (chs. 1,7). Under the liability provisions of CERCLA, all responsible parties (i.e., all parties disposing of waste at a site) can be required to pay proportional shares of remediation costs. In the past, EPA usually only required private industrial parties to cover the costs of remedial actions and compensation from MSW landfills. Recently, EPA convened a Municipal Settlement Task Force to determine how local governments involved with Super-

fund sites will be handled. Local officials, for example the National League of Cities, argue that EPA should continue to consider the public and private sectors differently. In contrast, industry interests argue that local governments should be treated and prosecuted in the same way as corporate defendants (119,120). Indeed, it appears that there is no basis in Superfund to treat local governments differently from other responsible parties. However, the potential for creating a financial crisis for some municipalities by imposing this interpretation is a legitimate source of concern to local governments.

Some observers suggest that the Toxic Substances Control Act[92] (TSCA) is a potential tool for EPA to prevent or minimize toxic substances in products which ultimately become part of the MSW stream. Clearly, TSCA does contain appropriate legal authority, because it provides authority to regulate any part of a chemical's life cycle from production, distribution, use, and disposal (Section 4(a)(1)(A)(i); also Sections 5 and 6). To do so, however, requires determination of "unreasonable risk of injury to health or the environment" (Section 4(a)(2). A major problem for regulating under TSCA is that "unreasonable risk" is not defined. This requires a tremendous amount of data, and the resulting case-by-case approach leads to an extremely slow regulatory process. Thus TSCA is not likely to be an efficient way to prevent or minimize toxic substances in MSW. Rather, approaches that attempt more directly to affect the design of products (considering their waste implications) may be more effective for this purpose (chs. 1 and 4).

At least two sections of the Internal Revenue Code are directly related to MSW (chs. 5 and 6).[93] First, the Internal Revenue Service's (IRS) definition of solid waste is based on that of the Solid Waste Disposal Act of 1965, with the additional condition that the material have no market value.[94] Therefore, if anyone is willing to purchase the material at any price, it is not solid waste according to the IRS definition (66). Second, Section 103 of the Internal Revenue Code allows tax-exempt industrial development bonds to be issued by political subdivisions to private corporations to finance the construction of solid waste disposal facilities and any waste disposal function of a facility. However, once the material is in saleable form it is no longer solid waste and bond revenues can not be

---

[89]Public Law 95-95.

[90]EPA believes that a combination of an acid gas scrubber, controlled combustion conditions, and a particulate matter collection device can also reduce dioxins, furans, other organic chemicals, and metals to acceptable levels (ch. 6).

[91]Public Law 96-510.

[92]Public Law 94-469.

[93]In 1982, the Energy Tax Act (Public Law 95-618) provided a credit for "recycling equipment," but this has been repealed.

[94]Treas. Reg. Section 1.103-108(2)(ii)(b); Rev. Rul. 72-190, 75-184, and 76- 222.

applied to it. At least 65 percent of the materials processed are required by the IRS to be "solid waste."

Exercising existing Federal regulatory authority could have the effect of internalizing production costs associated with environmental pollution in a way favorable to the use of secondary materials. Because the use of primary materials is sometimes more polluting in manufacturing processes than the use of secondary materials, further regulation and enforcement of pollution standards could indirectly increase the demand for secondary materials (ch. 5).

For example, under the Clean Water Act[95] EPA has set effluent guidelines and standards for industries in the pulp, paper, and paperboard point source category (including subcategories for primary and secondary material industries). Initially, the rulemaking focused on establishing effluent limitations based on "best practicable control technology currently available" (BPT), "best available technology economically achievable" (BAT), and "new source performance standards" (NSPS) for conventional pollutants such as biochemical oxygen demand (BOD), total suspended solids, and pH.[96] To address toxic and nonconventional pollutants as well, BPT and BAT control and treatment options have been adopted for some sources in the pulp, paper, and paperboard industry category directly discharging into navigable waters. Requirements for all toxic pollutants have not been established to date (142). If regulations for additional toxic and nonconventional pollutants were promulgated—and these regulations applied to more subcategories of the industry—it is likely that they would have a greater economic impact.

CHAPTER 8 REFERENCES

1. Alexander, J.H., James River Corp., personal communication, Feb. , 1989.
2. Allen, D., National Toxics Prevention Fund, personal communication, March 1989.
3. American Paper Institute, "State and Local Procurement of Recycled Products" (Washington, DC: Sept. 20, 1989).
4. Anderson, R., Washington State Senate, personal communication, May 20, 1988.
5. Association of State and Territorial Solid Waste Management Officials, *National Solid Waste Survey* (Washington, DC: 1984).
6. Auerbach, J., "Pesticides," *Summary of the Second National Conference on Household Hazardous Waste Management* (Boston, MA: Tufts University, Center for Environmental Management, 1987), pp. 112-114.
7. Belasen, A.T., *The New York State Returnable Beverage Container Law—Economic Effects, Industry Adaptations, and Guidelines for Improved Environmental Policy*, Rockefeller Institute Working Papers No. 31 (Albany: State University of New York, Spring 1988).
8. Biles, S., "A Review of Municipal and Hazardous Waste Management Practices and Facilities in Seven European Countries," working paper prepared for German Marshall Fund of the United States (Washington, DC: February 1987).
9. Broiles, S., "Incineration: A Suggested Approach to Overcome California's Inability to Permit Urban Resource Recovery Facilities," *Risk Analysis* 8(3):357-366, 1988.
10. Buckner, D., Illinois Department of Natural Resources, personal communication, July 7, 1988.
10a. Cal Recovery Systems, Inc., *Composting Technologies, Costs, Programs, and Markets*, contract report prepared for U.S. Congress, Office of Technology Assessment (Richmond, CA: January 1989).
11. Coalition of Northeastern Governors, "CONEG Policy, Source Reduction and Packaging" (Washington, DC: September 1988).
11a. Coalition of Northeastern Governors, "Interim Report of the CONEG Source Reduction Task Force, Executive Summary" (Washington, DC: April 1989).
12. Conservation Foundation, "Summary of Design for Disposal Dialogue," meeting held June 14, 1988 (Washington, DC: Sept. 9, 1988).
13. Chertoff, L., and Buxbaum, D., "Chapter 3, Public Perceptions and Community Relations," *The Solid Waste Handbook* (New York, NY: Wiley-Interscience, 1986).
14. Clay, D., "Is New Legislation Needed on Incineratory Air Emissions?" *Waste Age*, pp. 40-46, June 1988.
15. Cotter, D., West Coast Salvage and Recycling Co., personal communication, March 1988.

---

[95]Public Law 95-217. Section 208 of the Clean Water Act provides for areawide waste treatment management and funding provided under such programs has been used for some solid waste management activities.

[96]40 CFR Part 430, Subparts A-U. In 1977, performance standards for existing sources were proposed and efforts were directed toward establishing "best conventional pollutant control technology" and BAT effluent limitations, along with pretreatment standards for existing and new sources, to result in reasonable progress toward the discharge elimination goal of the law (40 CFR Part 128; see Clean Water Act Sections 101, 304, and 306). In setting effluent limitation guidelines, the Act includes a provision requiring EPA to consider, among other factors, "non-water quality environmental impact[s]" when determining control measures. This would include effects on solid waste generation (e.g., sludge).

16. Council of State Governments and the New York State Legislative Commission on Solid Waste Management, "Solid Waste Programs in the States," *Journal of Resource Management and Technology* 15(3):132-144, September 1987.

17. Council of State Governments, "1987 Municipal Solid Waste Questionnaires" (New York, NY: 1987).

18. Cox, K.A., *The National Status of Municipal Solid Waste Activities: A Summary of Selected Surveys on State MSW Programs*, contract report prepared for the U.S. Congress, Office of Technology Assessment (Takoma Park, MD: 1988).

19. Curlin, J., "Can a State Limit, Regulate, or Prohibit the Importation of Solid Waste From Another State?" unpublished memorandum (Washington, DC: 1988).

19a. Dawson, C., "Safe Products Through Cooperation," *Chemical TIMES & TRENDS* 11(1):35-37, January 1988.

20. Deutsches Institut für Gutesicherung und Kennzeichnung, "Verzeichnis der Produkte und Zeichenanwender sowie der jeweiligen Produktanforderungen" (Bonn, Federal Republic of Germany: June 1988).

21. Dougherty, J., "Household Hazardous Waste Program Liability," *Summary of the Second National Conference on Household Hazardous Waste Management* (Boston, MA: Tufts University, Center for Environmental Management, 1987), pp. 25-27.

22. Dresser, S., Council of State Governments, untitled paper presented at Office of Technology Assessment "Workshop on State and Local MSW Programs" (Washington, DC: Mar. 17-18, 1988).

23. Duxbury, D., "Household Hazardous Waste: State Laws, Regulations, and Guidelines Regarding Household Hazardous Wastes," *Summary of the Second National Conference on Household Hazardous Waste Management* (Boston, MA: Tufts University, Center for Environmental Management, 1987), pp. 20-24.

24. Duxbury, D., Dana Duxbury & Associates, personal communication, March 1988.

25. Duxbury, D., Dana Duxbury & Associates, personal communication, February 1989.

26. Electric Utility Weekly, "FERC Strikes Down New York Law Setting 6-Cent Floor for 'QFs'," *Electric Utility Weekly*, pp. 1 and 9-11, April 1988.

27. Environmental Defense Fund, *Coming Full Circle: Successful Recycling Today* (New York, NY: 1988).

28. Environment, "Environmentally Friendly Products," *Environment* 31(2):23, 1989.

29. Environment Reporter, "Bill To Impose Stringent Emission Limits on Municipal Incinerators Criticized by EPA," *Environment Reporter* 18(11):767-768, July 10, 1987.

30. Environment Reporter, "EPA Decides To Regulate Air Emissions From Municipal Solid Waste Incinerators," *Environment Reporter* 18(11):768-769, July 10, 1987.

31. Environment Reporter, "Tulsa, Okla., Trash Collection Rates Increased," *Environment Reporter* 19(48):2557, Mar. 31, 1989.

32. Ferrey, S., "A Liability Crisis Cities Can't Throw Away," *The Los Angeles Times*, Part II: Oct. 20, 1986.

33. Foerter, D., Council of State Governments, personal communication, 1988.

34. Franke, R., "Establishing a Solid Waste Management Program," paper presented at Office of Technology Assessment "Workshop on State and Local MSW Programs" (Washington, DC: Mar. 17-18, 1988).

35. Franklin Associates, Ltd., *Feasibility of Tax Incentives for Purchases of Recycling Equipment or Recycled Products, Final Report*, prepared for Illinois Department of Energy and Natural Resources, ILENR/RE-EA-87/06 (Prairie Village, KS: May 1987).

36. Franklin Associates, Ltd., *Economic Incentives and Disincentives for Recycling Municipal Solid Waste*, contract report prepared for U.S. Congress, Office of Technology Assessment (Prairie Village, KS: December 1988).

37. Franklin Associates, Ltd., *The Role of Beverage Containers in Recycling and Solid Waste Management: A Perspective for the 1990s*, final report prepared for Anheuser-Busch Companies, Inc. (Prairie Village, KS: April 1989).

38. Gage, K., "Permanent Site," *Summary of the Second National Conference on Household Hazardous Waste Management* (Boston, MA: Tufts University, Center for Environmental Management, 1987), pp. 73-75.

39. Galvin, D., "Why Worry About Household Hazardous Waste?" *Summary of the Second National Conference on Household Hazardous Waste Management* (Boston, MA: Tufts University, Center for Environmental Management, 1987), pp. 20-24.

40. Garbarino, J., Marin Sanitary Service, San Rafael, CA, personal communication, March 1988.

40a. Geisler, J., City of Davis, CA, personal communication, March 1988.

41. Gelinas, J., "Pesticides," *Summary of the Second National Conference on Household Hazardous Waste Management* (Boston, MA: Tufts Univer-

sity, Center for Environmental Management, 1987), pp. 115-117.

42. Gertman, R., City of San Jose Office of Environmental Management/Solid Waste Program, personal communication, March 1988.

43. Gewiese, A., Bilitewski, B., and Okeke, M., "Abfallvermeidung—ein Modellversuch in Hamburg-Harburg im Jahre 1987," *Mull und Abfall*, pp. 104-120 (Berlin: Erich Schmidt Verlag, March 1989).

44. Gilson, D., "Waste Oil," *Summary of the Second National Conference on Household Hazardous Waste Management* (Boston, MA: Tufts University, Center for Environmental Management, 1987), pp. 103-105.

45. Gleason, J., New York State Office of Procurement, personal communication, June 1988.

46. Glenn, J., "Special Report: Curbside Strategies; Junior, Take Out the Recyclables," *Biocycle* 29(5):26-31, May/June 1988.

47. Golub, N.M., Strachan, J.R., Berle, P.A.A., et al., *Final Report of the Temporary State Commission on Returnable Beverage Containers* (Albany, NY: Mar. 27, 1985).

48. Goosmann, G., Director, Federal Environment Agency, Federal Republic of Germany, personal communication, Apr. 14, 1989.

49. Guttman, E., Rhode Island Solid Waste Management Corp., personal communication, Feb. 20, 1989.

50. Harvey, F., "State-Sponsored Collection Programs," *Summary of the Second National Conference on Household Hazardous Waste Management* (Boston, MA: Tufts University, Center for Environmental Management, 1987), pp. 37-40.

51. Hemphill, T., "State Economic Development Incentives," *Resource Recycling* 7(2):36-37,54-56, May/June 1988.

52. Herz, M., "Federal Procurement of Recycled Products," paper presented at *Fourth Annual Conference on Solid Waste Management and Materials Policy* (New York, NY: Jan. 28, 1988).

53. Institute for Local Self-Reliance, *Garbage in Europe: Technologies, Economics, and Trends* (Washington, DC: May 1988).

54. Institute for Local Self-Reliance, *Beyond 25 Percent: Materials Recovery Comes of Age* (Washington, DC: April 1989).

55. Interstate Commerce Commission, "Investigation of Freight Rates for the Transportation of Recyclables or Recycled Commodities," *Ex Parte 319* (Washington, DC: February 1977).

56. Journal of Resource Management and Technology, "Special Issue: Second Penn Workshop on Litter Management and Recycling," *Journal of Resource Management and Technology* 15(2&3):41-114, December 1986.

57. Keller, R., Maryland Energy Office, personal communication, March 1988.

58. Keller, R., and VandenBerg, N., "State and Local Procurement of Recycled Products: Programs Defined by Legislation as of 8/87," unpublished manuscript, March 1988.

59. King, L., "Public Concerns in Siting of [sic] a Waste Facility and the Permitting Process From the Citizens' Point of View," paper presented at Office of Technology Assessment "Workshop on State and Local MSW Programs" (Washington, DC: Mar. 17-18, 1988).

60. Kinman, R., and Nutini, D., "Household Hazardous Waste in the Sanitary Landfill," *Chemical Times and Trends* 11(3):23-29, July 1988.

61. Kiser, J., "Waste-To-Energy and Recycling: A Compatible Solution," *Waste Alternatives*, pp. 18-21, June 1988.

62. Kleman, J., "State Collection Programs—Florida," *Summary of the First National Conference on Household Hazardous Waste Management* (Boston, MA: Tufts University, Center for Environmental Management, 1986), pp. 27-28.

63. Knapp, D., Urban Ore, and VanDeventer, M., Materials World, personal communication, Mar. 7, 1988.

64. Konheim, C., "Incineration: Risk Communication in the Real World," *Risk Analysis* 8(3):367-373, 1988.

65. Konheim, C., untitled paper presented at Office of Technology Assessment "Workshop on State and Local MSW Programs" (Washington, DC: Mar. 17-18, 1988).

66. Kovacs, W.L., "The Coming Era of Conservation and Industrial Utilization of Recyclable Materials," *Ecology Law Quarterly* 15:537-625, 1988.

67. Kovacs, W.L., and Anderson, A., "States As Market Participants in Solid Waste Disposal Services," *Environmental Law* 18(4):779-816, 1988.

68. Kovacs, W., and Klucsik, J., "The New Federal Role in Solid Waste Management: The Resource Conservation and Recovery Act of 1976," *Columbia Journal of Environmental Law* 3:205-265, 1977.

69. Kraft, M., and Kraut, R., "The Impact of Citizen Participation on Hazardous Waste Policy Implementation: The Case of Clermont County, Ohio," *Policy Studies Journal* 14(1):52-61, 1985.

70. Lanza, D., "Municipal Solid Waste Regulation: An Ineffective Solution to a National Problem,"

Fordham Urban Law Journal 10:215-245, 1982.

71. Lederer, J., U.S. Conference of Mayors, "Mayors' Question: How Many Experts Are There That Can Give Me Advice? Answer: How Big a Conference Room Are We Talking About?" paper presented at Office of Technology Assessment "Workshop on State and Local MSW Programs" (Washington, DC: Mar. 17-18, 1988).

72. Lesser, W., and Madhavan, A., "Economic Impacts of a National Deposit Law: Cost Estimates and Policy Questions," *Journ. Consumer Affairs* 21(1):122-140, Summer 1987.

73. Lewis, L., "State Matching Grants Program, Connecticut," *Summary of the Second National Conference on Household Hazardous Waste Management* (Boston, MA: Tufts University, Center for Environmental Management, 1987), p. 30.

74. Lindhqvist, T., "The Deposit System—Swedish Experiences Concerning Present and Proposed Systems," paper for *ECE Seminar on Economic Implications of Low-waste Technology* (The Hague, Netherlands: Oct. 16-19, 1989).

75. Luken, T., Opening Remarks at Hearing on MSW Crisis, Subcommittee on Transportation, Tourism and Hazardous Materials of the Committee on Energy and Commerce, U.S. House of Representatives, Washington, DC, June 22, 1989.

76. McShane, E., New Jersey Department of Environmental Protection, personal communication, December 1988.

77. Markus, L., "Recycling: Institutional Constraints and Innovative Approaches—The Missouri Experience," paper presented at Office of Technology Assessment "Workshop on State and Local MSW Programs" (Washington, DC: Mar. 17-18, 1988).

78. Marshall, B., and Powell, D., Laidlaw, personal communication, March 1988.

79. Mattheis, A., "Collecting Household Toxics—Is It Worth the Effort?" *Waste Age*, pp. 76-90, February 1987.

80. Maurer, S., Land-of-Sky Regional Council, untitled paper presented at Office of Technology Assessment "Workshop on State and Local MSW Programs" (Washington, DC: Mar. 17-18, 1988).

81. Meiorin, E., "Regional Programs," *Summary of the Second National Conference on Household Hazardous Waste Management* (Boston, MA: Tufts University, Center for Environmental Management, 1987), pp. 51-63.

82. Merry, W., "Collection Programs at a Landfill," *Summary of the Second National Conference on Household Hazardous Waste Management* (Boston, MA: Tufts University, Center for Environmental Management, 1987), pp. 66-72.

83. Minnesota Project, *Case Studies in Rural Solid Waste Recycling*, prepared for the Ford Foundation (Minneapolis, MN: 1987).

84. Moore, W.K., and Scott, D.L., "Beverage Container Deposit Laws: A Survey of the Issues and Results," *Journ. Consumer Affairs* 17(1):57-80, Summer 1983.

85. National Association of Towns and Townships, *Why Waste a Second Chance: A Small Town Guide to Recycling* (Washington, DC: National Center for Small Communities, 1989).

86. National Conference of State Legislatures, "Solid Waste Management" (Denver, CO: April 1989).

86a. National League of Cities, *Local Officials Guide; Municipal Incinerators: 50 Questions Every Local Government Should Ask* (Washington, DC: National League of Cities, 1988).

87. National Solid Waste Management Association, "Public Attitudes Toward Garbage Disposal," Special Report (Washington, DC: 1988).

88. New York State Department of Economic Development, "Program Information," Energy Conservation Series (Albany, NY: 1989).

89. New York State Department of Environmental Conservation, *New York State Solid Waste Management Plan, 1987-88 Update* (Albany: March 1988).

90. Orttung, J., "Use of A Permanent Facility at a Transfer Station," *Summary of the First National Conference on Household Hazardous Waste Management* (Boston, MA: Tufts University, Center for Environmental Management, 1986), pp. 25-26.

91. Orttung, J., "Batteries," *Summary of the Second National Conference on Household Hazardous Waste Management* (Boston, MA: Tufts University, Center for Environmental Management, 1987), pp. 101-102.

92. Perlmutter, A., City and County of San Francisco, CA, personal communication, March 1988.

93. Peterson, C., "A Waste Reduction Boom ... In The Seventies!" *Waste Age*, pp. 100-106, Feb. 1989.

94. Phillips, T.A., "An Economic Evaluation of a Process to Separate Raw Urban Refuse Into Its Metal, Mineral and Energy Components," IC 8732 (Washington, DC: Bureau of Mines, 1977).

95. Pollock, C., *Mining Urban Wastes: The Potential for Recycling*, Worldwatch Paper 76 (Washington, DC: April 1987).

96. Porter, R.C., "Michigan's Experience With Mandatory Deposits on Beverage Containers," *Land Economics* 59(2):177-194, May 1983.

97. Portney, K., "The Potential of the Theory of Compensation for Mitigating Public Opposition to Hazardous Waste Treatment Facility Siting: Some

Evidence From Five Massachusetts Communities," *Policy Studies Journal* 14(1):81-89, 1985.

98. Powell, J., "The Public Wants Recycling," *Resource Recycling* 7(6):32,42, November/December 1988.

99. Powell, J., "Packaging Under Attack: The Waste War," *Resource Recycling* 8(2):26-27, May/June 1989.

100. Purin, G., "Financing Programs and Reducing Costs," *Summary of the First National Conference on Household Hazardous Waste Management* (Boston, MA: Tufts University, Center for Environmental Management, 1986), pp.38-47.

101. Purin, G., "Overview of Future Funding Options," *Summary of the Second National Conference on Household Hazardous Waste Management* (Boston, MA: Tufts University, Center for Environmental Management, 1987), p. 126.

102. Reindl, J., Wisconsin Department of Natural Resources, personal communication, March 1988.

103. Reindl, J., Wisconsin Department of Natural Resources, personal communication, Feb. 12, 1989.

104. Resource Conservation Committee, *Choices for Conservation; Final Report to the President and Congress*, Solid Waste Information, SW-779 (Cincinnati, OH: U.S. Environmental Protection Agency, July 1979).

105. Resource Recovery Report, "Compilation of State Statutes Regarding Procurement of Items Containing Recycled Materials" (Washington, DC: 1989).

106. Rhode Island Solid Waste Management Corp., "Source Reduction Task Force Report" (Providence, RI: November 1987).

107. Rhode Island Solid Waste Management Corp., *Comprehensive Solid Waste Management Plan*, draft report (Providence, RI: December 1988).

107a. Ron Albrecht Associates, Inc., *Composting Technologies, Costs, Programs and Markets*, contract report prepared for U.S. Congress, Office of Technology Assessment (Annapolis, MD: December 1988).

108. Rose, D., "National Beverage Container Deposit Legislation: A Cost-Benefit Analysis," *J. Environmental Systems* 12(1):71-84, 1982-83.

109. Roy, N., Massachusetts Department of Environmental Quality and Engineering, personal communication, November 1988.

110. Rozett, J.M., "Resolving the "Bottle Bill" Controversy: The Role of Policy Analysis in Decision Making," Rockefeller Institute of Government, New York Case Studies in Public Management No. 14 (Albany, NY: State University of New York, November 1984).

111. Schafer, S., "Pilot/Permanent Site," *Summary of the Second National Conference on Household Hazardous Waste Management* (Boston, MA: Tufts University, Center for Environmental Management, 1987), pp. 76-80.

112. Schuff, R., "Solid Waste Landfill Siting in Wisconsin: An Effective Process," unpublished manuscript (Madison, WI: Wisconsin Department of Natural Resources, 1986).

113. Science Applications International Corp., "New Jersey Household Hazardous Waste Study," submitted to the New Jersey Hazardous Waste Advisory Council (Trenton, NJ: Nov. 16, 1987).

114. Seldman, N., "Technology and Society: How Shall We Put Out the Trash?" draft (Washington, DC: Institute for Local Self-Reliance, 1988).

115. Snow, D., "County's Creativity Cures Waste Crisis," *Waste Alternatives*, 1(3):6-12), December 1988.

116. Sokol, D., "What We Have Learned, Where We Are Headed; An Industry Leader Speaks to the Past Weaknesses and Current Strengths of Refuse-to-Energy System Contractors," *Waste Age*, pp. 81-90, June 1988.

117. Sondermeyer, G., New Jersey Department of Environmental Protection, personal communication, March, 1988.

118. Steinzor, R., "Municipal Incinerators: Recent Regulatory and Legislative Developments," paper presented at *First Resource Recovery Technology Conference* (Arlington, VA: Nov. 12-13, 1987).

119. Steinzor, R., "EPA to Draft New Superfund Municipal Settlement Policy," paper prepared at *Second Annual Resource Recovery Conference* (Arlington, VA: Nov. 15-16, 1988).

120. Steinzor, R., "Comments of the National League of Cities and the Governmental Refuse Collection and Disposal Association on EPA's Proposed Revisions to the Superfund National Contingency Plan" (Washington, DC: Spiegel & McDiarmid, Mar. 23, 1989).

120a. Strom, P.F., and Finstein, M.S., *Leaf Composting Manual for New Jersey Municipalities* (New Brunswick, NJ: Rutgers University, revised edition, October 1986).

121. Sullivan, P.M., Stanczyk, M.H., and Spendlove, M.J., "Resource Recovery From Raw Urban Refuse," RI 7760 (Washington, DC: Bureau of Mines, 1973).

122. Swedish Association of Public Cleansing and Solid Waste Management, *Solid Waste Management in Sweden* (Sweden: Malmo, February 1988).

123. Taylor, K., Hurd, D. and Rohan, B., "Recycling in the 1980s: Batteries Not Included," *Resource*

Recycling 7(2):26-27,58-60, May/June 1988.

124. Trimble, L., "What Do Citizens Want in Siting of Waste Management Facilities?" *Risk Analysis* 8(3):375-377, 1988.

125. Trumbell, T., "Siting Waste-to-Energy Facilities: Putting Citizen Concerns First," paper presented at *Renewable Energy Conference* (Palo Alto, CA: Waste Management Communications, June 9, 1988).

126. Trumbell, T., "Using Citizens to Site Solid Waste Facilities," *Public Works* 119(9):66-67, August 1988.

127. United Kingdom Department of Energy and U.S. Department of Energy, *Energy From Landfill Gas*, Proceedings of a Conference Jointly Sponsored by the U.K. Department of Energy and the U.S. Department of Energy, Solihull, United Kingdom, October 1986 (United Kingdom: Harwell Reprographic Section, 1986).

128. U.S. Congress, Congressional Research Service, "State and Local Bans on the Import of Solid Waste: Constitutional Issues," Report No. 86-943A (Washington, DC: 1986).

129. U.S. Congress, House of Representatives, Hearing on MSW Crisis, Subcommittee on Transportation, Tourism and Hazardous Materials of the Committee on Energy and Commerce, U.S. House of Representatives (Washington, DC: June 22, 1989).

130. U.S. Congress, Office of Technology Assessment, *Materials and Energy From Municipal Waste*, OTA-M-93 (Springfield, VA: National Technical Information Service, July 1979).

131. U.S. Congress, Office of Technology Assessment, *Wastes in Marine Environments*, OTA-O-334 (Washington, DC: U.S. Government Printing Office, April 1987).

132. U.S. Congress, Office of Technology Assessment, *Identifying and Regulating Carcinogens—* Background Paper, OTA-BP-H-42 (Washington, DC: U.S. Government Printing Office, November 1987).

133. U.S. Congress, Office of Technology Assessment, Workshop on State and Local MSW Programs (Washington, DC: Mar. 17-18, 1988).

134. U.S. Congress, Office of Technology Assessment, Workshop on Markets for Recycled Materials (Washington, DC: June 8, 1988).

135. U.S. Congress, Office of Technology Assessment, Workshop on MSW Reduction (Washington, DC: July 14-15, 1988).

135a. U.S. Council of Economic Advisers, *Economic Report of the President* (Washington, DC: U.S. Government Printing Office, 1987).

136. U.S. Department of Commerce, National Bureau of Standards, Office of Recycled Materials, *Procurement Policies Containing Recovered Material: A Summary of Activities in 7 States* (Washington, DC: July 1981).

137. U.S. Department of Commerce, National Bureau of Standards, Office of Recycled Materials, *The National Bureau of Standards Office of Recycled Materials; 1976-1982*, NBS Special Publication 662 (Washington, DC: 1983).

138. U.S. Department of Energy, *Energy From Municipal Waste: State-of-the-Art and Emerging Technologies—Workshop Proceedings*, Argonne National Laboratory, Contract W-31-109-Emg-38 (Chicago, IL: Nov. 28-30, 1983).

139. U.S. Department of Energy, "Municipal Waste-to-Energy Research," unpublished manuscript (Washington, DC: 1988).

140. U.S. Environmental Protection Agency, *Resource Recovery and Waste Reduction; Third Report to Congress* (Washington, DC: National Technical Information Service, 1975).

141. U.S. Environmental Protection Agency, *Resource Recovery and Waste Reduction, Fourth Report to Congress* (Washington, DC: National Technical Information Service, 1977).

142. U.S. Environmental Protection Agency, *Development Document for Effluent Limitations Guidelines and Standards for the Pulp, Paper, and Paperboard and the Builders' Paper and Board Mills; Point Source Categories*, EPA 440/1-82/025 (Washington, DC: October 1982).

143. U.S. Environmental Protection Agency, *Summary of Data on Industrial Non-Hazardous Waste Disposal Practices*, prepared by Science Applications International Corp., EPA Contract No. 68-01-7050 (Washington, DC: December 1985).

144. U.S. Environmental Protection Agency, *A Survey of Household Hazardous Wastes and Related Collection Programs*, EPA/530-SW-86-038 (Washington, DC: 1986).

145. U.S. Environmental Protection Agency, *Census of State and Territorial Subtitle D Non-Hazardous Waste Programs*, prepared by Westat, EPA/530-SW-86-039 (Washington, DC: October 1986).

146. U.S. Environmental Protection Agency, *Characterization of Household Hazardous Waste From Marin County, California, and New Orleans, Louisiana*, Environmental Systems Monitoring Laboratory (Las Vegas, NV: August 1987).

147. U.S. Environmental Protection Agency, *Report to Congress, EPA Activities and Accomplishments Under the Resource Conservation and Recovery Act: Fourth Quarter Fiscal Year 1986 Through*

Fiscal Year 1987, EPA/530-SW-88-007 (Washington, DC: December 1987).

148. U.S. Environmental Protection Agency, "Review of Curbside Used Oil Recycling Programs in the United States," contract submitted by Versar, Inc. (Washington, DC: April 1988).

149. U.S. Environmental Protection Agency, Office of Solid Waste, "Updated Review of Selected Provisions of State Solid Waste Regulations, Draft, Background Document" (Washington, DC: July 1988).

149a. U.S. Environmental Protection Agency, *Report to Congress: Solid Waste Disposal in the United States, Vol. I*, EPA/530-SW-88-011 (Washington, DC: October 1988).

150. U.S. Environmental Protection Agency, "Recycling Works! State and Local Solutions to Solid Waste Management Probelems," Office of Solid Waste (Washington, DC: January 1989).

151. U.S. Environmental Protection Agency, *The Solid Waste Dilemma: An Agenda for Action*, Office of Solid Waste, EPA/530-SW-89-019 (Washington, DC: February 1989).

152. U.S. Treasury Department, "Federal Tax Policy and Recycling of Solid Waste Materials," Office of Tax Analysis (Washington, DC: February 1979).

153. VandenBerg, N., "Recycled Materials Procurement: Part 1," *Resource Recycling* 5(5):14-15,38-39, September/October 1986.

154. VandenBerg, N., "Recycled Materials Procurement: Part 2," *Resource Recycling* 5(6):12-15,36, November/December 1986.

155. VandenBerg, N., Council on the Environment of New York City, personal communication, Feb. 8, 1989.

156. Vasuki, N., Delaware Solid Waste Authority, personal communication, January 1988.

157. Watson, T., "Yard Waste Composting—Portland's Success Story," *Resource Recycling* 7(2):18-19,52, May/June 1988.

158. Wiard, M., Ohio Department of Natural Resources, personal communication, February 1989.

159. Wilson, D., and Rathje, W., "Quantities and Composition of Household Hazardous Wastes: Report on a Multi-Community, Multi-Disciplinary Project," paper prepared for *Third National Conference on Household Hazardous Waste Management* (Boston, MA: Nov. 2-4, 1988).

160. Worldwatch Institute, "Environmental Seal of Approval," *World Watch* 2(3):6-7, May/June 1989.

161. Zemansky, S., "Procurement: The Great Purchasing Mythstery," *Government Executive*, pp. 25-30, July 1981.

Appendixes

Additive—a substance added to plastic resins that imparts physical properties to meet specific applications and improve processing.

Ash—the noncombustible solid byproducts of incineration processes.

Avoided cost—costs a utility may pay for electric power purchased from a waste-to-energy facility, based on how much it would have cost the utility to generate the power itself; or, costs not incurred because of diversion of waste from a landfill (e.g., disposal, environmental, and opportunity costs).

Baghouse (or fabric filter)—emission control device; an array of cylindrical bags used to trap solid particles and dust.

Beneficiation—initial processing of a raw material to remove contaminants.

Biodegradable plastic—a plastic that can be broken down by microorganisms such as bacteria and fungi; as generally used, the term does not necessarily mean complete degradation into carbon dioxide and water.

Bottom ash—relatively coarse uncombusted or partly combusted residue of incineration that accumulates on the grate of a furnace.

Buy-back—a facility that pays individuals for recyclable materials and further processes them for market.

Capacity utilization—ratio of quantity of production to total capacity of production facilities.

Capture rate—tonnage of recyclables collected, divided by total tonnage of MSW generated by participating households or commercial establishments.

Codisposal—disposal in one area of two or more types of solid waste, for example unprocessed MSW and incinerator ash in a landfill.

Cogeneration—production of both electricity and steam at one facility, from same primary fuel source.

Collection—gathering of MSW for subsequent management (i.e., landfilling, incineration, or recycling).

Combined ash—mixture of bottom ash and fly ash.

Combustion—see incineration.

Commerce Clause—a constitutional clause granting Congress the power to regulate all commerce; the "dormant commerce clause" makes it explicit that State lines cannot be made barriers to the free flow of commerce.

Commingled recyclables—recyclable materials separated from mixed MSW at point of generation; further separation into individual components occurs at collection vehicle or centralized processing facility.

Composite liner—a liner system composed of an engineered soil layer overlain by a synthetic flexible membrane liner.

Composting—biological decomposition of solid organic materials (e.g., yard waste, paper) by microorganisms (mainly bacteria and fungi); "compost" is the humus- or soil-like product.

Cullet—crushed waste glass.

Curbside collection—collection at individual households or commercial buildings by municipal or private haulers, for subsequent transport to management facility.

Demand-limited materials—secondary materials for which buyers are relatively scarce even though supplies may be available.

Dioxins—a family of chlorinated chemicals, some of which are toxic to animals under certain exposure and dosage conditions.

Drop-off—transport of individual MSW materials (e.g., newspaper, cans, bottles) by individuals to specified area, for subsequent processing and transport to recycling facility.

Dry injection—injection of a dry reagent such as lime powder into an incinerator boiler or the original MSW, to aid in control of acid gases.

Economies of scale—increases in production capacity that reduce the average cost per ton of output.

Electrostatic precipitator (ESP)—emission control device that electrically charges particles, which are drawn to oppositely-charged plates; particles fall from the plates and are collected for management.

Energy recovery—retrieval of energy from MSW by converting heat from incineration or methane gas from landfills.

Fabric filter—see baghouse.

Fixed costs—costs that do not vary with level of output of a production facility (e.g., administrative costs, building rent, mortgage payments).

Flaring—burning of methane emitted from collection pipes at a landfill.

Flint glass—clear glass.

Flow control ordinances—ordinances that require delivery of collected MSW to specific management facilities.

Fly ash—particles that are carried off an incinerator grate by turbulence or volatilized material that condenses in the flue gas into particles.

Furnish—the pulp used as raw material in a paper mill.

Glassphalt—an asphalt product that uses crushed glass as a partial substitute for aggregate in the mix.

Heavy metals—metals of high atomic weight and density, such as mercury, lead, and cadmium, that are toxic to living organisms.

Home scrap—waste produced and reused inside a production facility.

Household hazardous waste—products used at residences that are discarded in MSW and that contain substances already regulated under RCRA as an industrial hazardous waste.

Incineration—burning of fuel under controlled conditions, ideally converting all carbon to carbon dioxide and all hydrogen to water.

Integrated waste management—coordinated use of a hierarchy of management methods, including waste prevention; OTA does not use the term because prevention is fundamentally different than management.

Investment tax credit—a tax credit that allows businesses to subtract a portion of the cost of qualifying capital purchases from their Federal or State tax liability, thus reducing the net after-tax cost of capital.

Landfilling—disposing of solid waste on land in a series of compacted layers and covering it, usually daily, with soil or other materials.

Leachate—contaminated water emanating from a landfill.

Leachate collection and removal system—pipes used to collect leachate that settles on a liner and prevent it from migrating into groundwater.

Liner—a protective layer, made of soil or synthetic materials, installed along the bottom or sides of a landfill to reduce migration of leachate into groundwater beneath the site or laterally away from the site.

Loan guarantee—government-funded insurance that protects lenders against the failure of a project to pay back the principal and interest on a loan.

Low-interest loans—government subsidy that allows loans for specific purposes to be offered at below market interest rates.

Mass burn—incineration without prior sorting or processing of MSW, in a one-chamber combustion system under conditions of excess air; built on-site.

Materials management—an MSW management approach that would: 1) coordinate product manufacturing with different management methods (e.g., design products for recyclability); and 2) manage MSW on a material-by-material basis, by diverting discarded materials to most appropriate management method based on their physical and chemical characteristics.

Materials recovery—retrieval of materials from MSW.

Materials recovery facility (MRF)—facility for separating recyclables from mixed waste or for separating commingled recyclables.

Mixed MSW—trash that is not sorted into categories of materials.

Modular—incineration without prior sorting or processing of MSW, in relatively small two-chamber combustion system; usually fabricated elsewhere and then delivered to incineration site.

Monofill—a sanitary landfill for one type of waste only.

Municipal solid waste (MSW)—solid waste generated at residences, commercial establishments, and institutions; as used here, MSW excludes construction or demolition debris and automobile scrap.

Nonferrous metals—metals other than iron and steel that are found in MSW.

Old scrap—waste generated by the product's final consumer.

Open dumping—disposing waste in an open, uncovered area that lacks pollution controls and associated design features.

Opportunity cost—the cost of foregoing alternative uses of a resource.

Paper converting operations—manufacturing facilities that transform paper into products such as envelopes or boxes.

Participation rate—portion of a population participating in a recycling program.

Photodegradable plastic—a plastic that will break down in the presence of ultraviolet (UV) light.

Post-consumer waste—waste generated by the product's final consumer.

Pre-consumer waste—waste generated in processing materials or manufacturing them into final products.

Prevention/reduction—activities by manufacturers (e.g., modifying products) and consumers (e.g., modifying purchasing decisions) that reduce toxicity or quantity of products before they are purchased.

Primary material—a commercial material produced from virgin materials.

Processing—preparing individual or mixed MSW materials for subsequent management, using processes such as baling, magnetic removal, shredding.

Procurement—the purchase of materials and services, usually, in the case of government procurement, through awarding contracts to low bidders.

Product fee—a tax or fee on materials or products that can be designed to add the cost of their disposal to the purchase price.

Prompt industrial scrap—waste produced in an intermediate stage of processing and returned to the basic production facility for reuse.

Pyrolysis—chemical decomposition of a substance by heat in the absence of oxygen.

Quantity reduction—changing the design of a product so that less MSW is generated when the product or its residuals are discarded, or so that the product is more durable or repairable.

Recycling—collecting components of MSW and processing them into forms in which they can be reused as raw materials for new products.

Recycling/recovery/diversion rate—the tonnage of recyclables collected and processed into new products, divided by total tonnage of MSW generated.

Refuse-derived fuel (RDF)—fuel produced from MSW that has undergone processing; fuel can be in shredded, fluff, or densified pellet forms.

Resource recovery—retrieval of materials or energy from MSW, for purposes of recycling or reuse; the term "waste-to-energy" is used here for incinerators that recover energy.

Reuse—taking a component of MSW and, possibly with some slight modification (e.g., cleaning, repair), using it again for its original purpose (e.g., refillable beverage bottles).

Sanitary landfill—a specially designed and operated landfilling facility that meets local, State, and Federal regulations and permit requirements.

Scrubber—emission control device that adds alkaline reagents to react with and neutralize acid gases; resultant products are then collected for management.

Secondary material—a commercial material recovered from the waste stream for reprocessing and remanufacturing.

Sensitivity analysis—an analysis that compares changes in a dependent variable resulting from incremental changes in independent variables.

Solid waste—defined in RCRA as "garbage, refuse, sludge from a waste treatment plant, water supply treatment plant, or air pollution control facility and other discarded material, including solid, liquid, semi-solid, or contained gaseous material resulting from industrial, commercial, mining, and agricultural operations, and from community activities. . ."

Solid waste management—planning and implementation of systems to handle solid waste.

Source separation—separation at a household or commercial establishment of MSW into different recyclable components.

Source-separated recyclables—recyclable materials separated from each other and from mixed waste at the point of generation.

Subsidy—direct or indirect payment from government to businesses, citizens, or institutions to encourage a desired activity.

Supply-limited materials—secondary materials that are not collected in sufficient amounts or are too highly contaminated for current manufacturing processes.

Tipping fee—price charged for delivering MSW to landfill, incinerator, or recycling facility; usually expressed in dollars per ton.

Toxicity reduction—eliminating or reducing (including using benign substitutes) substances in products that pose risks when the products are discarded as MSW.

Transfer station—facility at which MSW is transferred from collection vehicles to larger trucks or rail cars for longer distance transport.

Virgin material—material extracted from nature in its raw form.

Waste-to-energy facility (WTE)—MSW incinerator that converts heat from combustion into energy (i.e., steam or electricity).

Waste paper utilization rate—ratio of waste paper consumption to total production of paper and paperboard.

White goods—large, metal household appliances (e.g., stoves, dryers, refrigerators, etc.).

Appendix B

Acronyms and Abbreviations

AA	—Aluminum Association
ANPA	—American Newspaper Publishers Association
API	—American Paper Institute
ASME	—American Society of Mechanical Engineers
ASTM	—American Society for Testing and Materials
ASTSWMO	—Association of State and Territorial Solid Waste Management Officials
BACT	—Best Available Control Technology
Btu	—British thermal unit
CERCLA	—Comprehensive Environmental Response, Compensation, and Liability Act (Superfund)
CFC	—chlorofluorocarbon
CJC	—Clean Japan Center
CO	—carbon monoxide
CONEG	—Coalition of Northeastern Governors
CPRR	—Center for Plastics Recycling Research
CPSC	—Consumer Products Safety Commission
DOE	—Department of Energy
DSWA	—Delaware Solid Waste Authority
EAC	—Environmental Action Coalition
EAF	—electric arc furnace
EDF	—Environmental Defense Fund
EP	—Extraction Procedure
EPA	—Environmental Protection Agency
ERDA	—Energy Research and Development Authority
ERTA	—Economic Recovery Tax Act
ESP	—electrostatic precipitator
ESRG	—Energy Systems Research Group
FBC	—fluidized bed combustion
FDA	—Food and Drug Administration
FERC	—Federal Energy Regulatory Commission
GPI	—Glass Packaging Institute
GSA	—General Services Administration
HDPE	—high-density polyethylene
HHW	—household hazardous wastes
HSWA	—Hazardous and Solid Waste Amendments
ISRI	—Institute of Scrap Recycling Industries
ITC	—investment tax credit

LDPE	—low-density polyethylene
OTA	—Office of Technology Assessment
MCL	—maximum contaminant level
MHI	—Mitsubishi Heavy Industries
MRF	—materials recovery facility
MSW	—municipal solid waste
MWEP	—Monofilled Waste Extraction Procedure
NAPIM	—National Association of Printing Ink Manufacturers
NECRInc	—New England Container Recovery, Inc.
NEMA	—National Electrical Manufacturers Association
NERC	—Northeast Recycling Coalition
NIMBY	—Not In My Backyard
NO_x	—nitrogen oxide
NPL	—National Priorities List
NSDA	—National Soft Drink Association
NSPS	—New Source Performance Standards
NSWMA	—National Solid Waste Management Association
OCC	—old corrugated containers
OECD	—Organization for Economic Cooperation and Development
ONP	—old newspapers
PCB	—polychlorinated biphenyls
PE	—polyethylene
PET	—polyethylene terephthalate
PS	—polystyrene
PURPA	—Public Utilities Regulatory Policy Act
PVC	—polyvinyl chloride
RCRA	—Resource Conservation and Recovery Act
RDF	—refuse-derived fuel
RFF	—Resources for the Future
SCR	—selective catalytic reduction
SQG	—small quantity generator
TDF	—tire-derived fuel
TCLP	—Toxicity Characteristic Leaching Procedure
TSCA	—Toxic Substances Control Act
UBC	—used beverage container
UV	—ultraviolet
VOC	—volatile organic chemical
WTE	—waste-to-energy

Contractors

Principal contractors
Allen Hershkowitz
Cal Recovery Systems, Inc.
Chris Elfring, *Editor*
Energy Systems Research Group
Franklin Associates, Ltd.
Gershman, Brickner & Bratton, Inc.
Ron Albrecht Associates, Inc.

In-house contractors
Rhonda Bitterli
Kathryn Cox
Ingeborg Stehr
Eric Washburn

OTA Services

Special thanks for internal support at OTA are due to the:
- Information Center
- Publishing Office
- Service Center

Reviewers and Other Contributors

Many individuals and organizations contributed valuable information, guidance, and substantive reviews of draft material. In addition to the advisory panel members and contractors, OTA wishes to extend its gratitude to the following for their help (and apologizes to any contributors inadvertently omitted from this list):

Judd Alexander, James River Corp.
David Allen, National Toxics Campaign
Harvey Alter, U.S. Chamber of Commerce
Mary Amini, General Foods
A.L. Andrady, Research Triangle Institute
William Apgar, Pennsylvania Dept. Environmental Protection
Rob Arner, Versar Inc.
Raymond Balfour, Rayovac Corp.
Thomas Ballestero, Univ. New Hampshire
Jerome Balter, Public Interest Law Center
Donald Barnes, Science Advisory Board
John Bastey, Maine Dept. Environmental Protection
Victor Bell, Rhode Island Dept. Environmental Management
Robert Bennett, Univ. Toledo
Andrea Bilson, Food Marketing Institute
Richard Bishop, Richard Bishop Consulting, Ltd.

Gary Boley, Combustion Engineering, Inc.
Melissa Bouzianis, Belland
Gretchen Brewer, Earth Circle
K.W. Brown, Texas A&M
Raymond Brown, Bureau of Mines
Steve Brown, Council of State Governments
William Brown, Waste Management
Dietrich Brune, Kernforschungszentrum Karlsruhe, Federal Republic of Germany
David Buckner, Illinois Dept. Energy and Natural Resources
John Burke, James River Corp.
Kerry Callahan, Assoc. State and Territorial Solid Waste Management Officials
Allegra Cangelosi, Coalition of Northeastern Governors
Charles Carson, U.S. Steel
Ron Catlett, Dow Consumer Products, Inc.
Christine Chapman, Washington Dept. of Ecology
Marjorie Clarke, INFORM
Fred Clinton, Michigan Dept. Natural Resources
Thomas Constable, Environment Canada
Richard Cook, Kalamazoo College
Leroy Cooper, California Dept. General Services
Kim Copperthite, Dept. of Commerce
Dan Cotter, West Coast Salvage and Recycling Co.
Tom Couling, Minnesota Waste Management Board
J.B. Cox, Department of Commerce
Michael Curry, CTZ Inc.
Herschel Cutler, Institute of Scrap Recycling Industries
Steve Cutler, Cutler Salvage
Ervin Dan, Polysar
Drew Davis, National Soft Drink Association
Truett DeGeare, Environmental Protection Agency
Maarten de Kadt, INFORM
Richard Denison, Environmental Defense Fund
Bruce DeWoolfson, ENVIPCO
Robert Deyle, Univ. Oklahoma
Luis Diaz, Cal Recovery
John Dickenson, Aluminum Association
Glenn DiGiovanni, Malcolm Pirnie
Daryl Ditz, Cornell Univ.
Bill Doane, U.S. Dept. Agriculture
Michael Downs, Oregon Dept. Environmental Quality
Shelley Dresser-Gagnon, Council of State Governments
Taylor Eighmy, Univ. New Hampshire
Robert Ennis, Plastigone
George Eowan, California Waste Management Board
Rolf Faste, Stanford Univ.

Harry Fatkin, Polaroid Corp.
Trisha Ferrand, Ferrand Associates
Francis Ferraro, Wheelabrator Environmental Systems
Melvin Finstein, Rutgers University
Mike Flynn, Environmental Protection Agency
Jack Force, MRE Corp.
Domenic Forcella, National Governors' Association
Keith Forester, Wheelabrator Environmental Systems
Ed Fox, Procter & Gamble Co.
Bernd Franke, Institut für Energie und Umweltforschung, Federal Republic of Germany
Randall Franke, Marion County Board of Commissioners
Henry Frankel, Rutgers Univ.
Marjorie Franklin, Franklin Associates
Lewis Freeman, Society of the Plastics Industry
Jack Friedline, Phoenix Dept. of Sanitation
Bob Friedman, OTA
Charlotte Frola, Combustion Engineering, Inc.
Eugene Gabrielli, The Ecology Companies, Inc.
Wes Gaskin, Container Recovery Corp.
Dave Gatton, U.S. Conference of Mayors
Helmut Geipel, Bundesministerium für Forschung und Technologie, Federal Republic of Germany
John Geisler, City of Davis, California
Richard Gertmann, R.W. Beck and Associates
Lois Gibbs, Citizens' Clearinghouse
Jane Gilbert, Arthur D. Little
Martha Gildart, California Waste Management Board
Joseph Gilson, Camden County Office Solid Waste Management
John Gleason, New York State Procurement Division
Alan Gloxin, Diamond Bathurst
John Gold, North Shore Recycled Fibers
Marc Goldberg, Safer, Inc.
Ted Goldfarb, State University of New York, Stony Brook
Nora Goldstein, Biocycle
Richard Goodstein, Browning-Ferris Industries
William Gooden, Haverhill/Natick Paperboard Corp.
Georg Goosmann, Environment Agency, Federal Republic of Germany
Mike Gough, Resources for the Future
Robert Graulich, Oxford Energy Company
Sharon Green, Conservation Foundation
Jonathan Greenberg, Browning-Ferris Industries
Joseph Greenblott, Technical Resources, Inc.
Warren Gregory, Smith-Barney
Jim Grove, Miami Paper Corp.
James Guillet, Univ. Toronto
Erica Guttman, Rhode Island Solid Waste Management Corp.
Hiroyuki Hatano, Kyoto University, Japan
Tom Hemphill, New Jersey Recycling Office
Roy Herndon, Florida State Univ.

Lanny Hickman, Governmental Refuse Collection and Disposal Association
William Hinkley, Florida Dept. Environmental Regulation
Taka Hiraishi, Environment Agency, Japan
Joel Hirschhorn, OTA
Buzz Hoffmann, Food and Drug Administration
Ken Hunnibell, Rhode Island School of Design
Carl Hursh, Pennsylvania Dept. Environmental Resources
Rinzo Iijima, Plastic Waste Management Institute, Japan
Peter Ince, Forest Products Lab
David Jeanes, Iron & Steel Institute
Jerry Johnson, Polystyrene Packaging Council
Lanny Johnson, Mackormick and Putziger
Yuji Kaihara, Mitsubishi Heavy Industries, Ltd., Japan
Ken Kamlet, A.T. Kearney, Inc.
Richard Kashmanian, Environmental Protection Agency
Rosamond Katz, General Accounting Office
Tom Keith, Palm Beach County
Janet Keller, Rhode Island Dept. Environmental Management
Michael Kelley, Department of Commerce
Richard Keller, Maryland Energy Office
Robert Kerr, New York Dept. Environmental Conservation
Linda King, Citizen's Clearinghouse
Ed Klein, Environmental Protection Agency
Raymond Klicius, Environment Canada
Bruce Kline, Pentapco, Inc.
John Klungness, Forest Products Lab
Dan Knapp, Urban Ore
Katsuhiko Kobayashi, Mitsubishi Heavy Industries, Ltd., Japan
Carol Kocheisen, National League of Cities
Richard Koelling, New York State Dept. Environmental Conservation
Mel Koenigs, General Accounting Office
O. Komiya, Mitsubishi Heavy Industries
Carolyn Konheim, Konheim and Konheim
Hiroshi Kubota, Mitsubishi Heavy Industries, Ltd.
Robert Lamb, McGuire Woods Battle & Booth
Ruth Lampi, Coalition for Recyclable Waste
David Larrabee, Dept. of Commerce
Connie Leach, Vermont Dept. Environmental Conservation
Gerry Lederer, U.S. Conference of Mayors
Debra Levin, Intitute of Scrap Recycling Industries
Thomas Lindhqvist, Univ. Lund, Sweden
Glenn Lovin, Resource Recovery Institute
Rod Lowman, Council for Solid Waste Solutions
Michael Lynch, Illinois Tool Works
John MacLean, Homans McGraw
Lou Magdits, Exide Battery Corporation

Lynne Markus, Missouri Dept. Natural Resources
Bruce Marshall, Laidlaw Gas Recovery Systems
Wayne Martin, DuPont
Mark Matlock, Archer Daniels Midland
Cassandra Maurer, Land-of-Sky Regional Council
Jim McCarthy, Congressional Research Service
Frank McManus, Resource Recovery Report
Eve McNiff, Council on Environment of New York City
Ellen McShane, New Jersey Dept. Environmental
  Protection
Hector Mendieta, Texas Dept. Health
Ken Mentzer, Mineral Insulation Manufacturers
  Association
Barry Meyer, Aluminum Association
Jack Milgrom, Walden Research
Chaz Miller, Glass Packaging Institute
Ron Miller, New York Dept. Environmental
  Conservation
David Minott, Alternative Resources, Inc.
Susan Mooney, Environmental Protection Agency
Bill Moore, Waste Management
John Murphy, Chemical Specialties Manufacturers Assoc.
Kazuhiro Nakane, Plastic Waste Management Institute,
  Japan
Kunihiro Nakazato, Takuma Co., Ltd., Japan
Bob Neuman, Ogilvy & Mather Public Affairs
Fred Nicholson, National Electrical Manufacturers Assoc.
Norman Nosenchuck, New York Dept. Environmental
  Conservation
Thomas Obermeier, ITU-Ingenieurgemeinschaft, Federal
  Republic of Germany
George Oechsle, Atlantic Coast Paperboard
Hidenobu Ogasawara, Clean Japan Center, Japan
Kiyomi Ogawa, Clean Japan Center, Japan
Kirsten Oldenburg, OTA
Greg Olson, National Institute of Standards and
  Technology
Paul O'Neill, General Accounting Office
Theodore O'Neill, Cape May County Municipal Utilities
  Authority
William O'Toole, Recovery Sciences
Barbara Paley, National Assoc. of Counties
Jim Palmer, GNB Inc.
Al Pederson, AMG Resources Corp.
Amy Perlmutter, City and County of San Francisco
Amy Perry, Mass PIRG
Bruce Piasecki, Clarkson Univ.
Suellen Pirages, National Solid Waste Management
  Assoc.
Pat Plunkert, Bureau of Mines
Cynthia Pollock Shea, Worldwatch Institute
Donald Powell, Laidlaw Waste Systems, Inc.
Jerry Powell, Resource Recycling

Sheila Prindiville, National Solid Waste Management
  Assoc.
Ellen Rajewski, General Accounting Office
Sidney Rankin, Rutgers Univ.
William Rathje, Univ. Arizona
Pat Raymond, Environmental & Energy Study Institute
Merilyn Reeves, League of Women Voters
John Reindl, Wisconsin Dept. Natural Resources
Paul Relis, Gildea Resource Center
Dick Richards, Science Applications International Corp.
Jenifer Robison, OTA
Margaret Rogers, Society of the Plastics Industry
Natalie Roy, Massachusetts Div. Environmental Quality
  & Engineering
John Ruston, Environmental Defense Fund
Dennis Sabourin, Wellman Trading Corp.
Gene Salerni, Schillinger, Salerni and Boyd, Inc.
Amy Sapowith, Renew America
Steve Sawell, Environment Canada
Moira Schoen, Environmental Protection Agency
Hans-Dieter Schulz, Munich Planning Board, Federal
  Republic of Germany
Jim Sears, Marion Co. Dept. Solid Waste
Richard Sedgley, McGuire Woods Battle & Booth
Nancy Seidman, Northeast States for Coordinated Air
  Use Management
Jere Sellers, Franklin Associates, Ltd.
Terry Serie, American Paper Institute
Walter Shaub, Coalition on Resource Recovery and the
  Environment
Mary Shiel, New Jersey Dept. Environmental Protection
Duane Siler, Institute of Scrap Recycling Industries
Don Silva, Science and Engineering Associates
Bill Sim, American Recovery Corp.
Ed Skernolis, Waste Management
Kurt Smalberg, Steel Can Recycling Institute
Allan Smith, Health Risk Associates
Garrett Smith, Ogden Martin Systems, Inc.
Gary Sondermeyer, New Jersey Dept. Environmental
  Protection
David Sorenson, Can Manufacturers Inst.
Gifford Stack, National Soft Drink Association
Gary Stanley, Dept. of Commerce
John Stark, Rubber Research Elastomerics, Inc.
Marie Steinwachs, Southwest Missouri State Univ.
Rena Steinzor, Speigel and McDiarmid
Andrew Stephens, Eaglebrook Plastics, Inc.
Tom Stinsen, Industrial Power Technology
Dennis Stone, California Dept. Conservation
Peter Strom, Rutgers Univ.
David Sussman, Ogden Martin Systems, Inc.
Akira Takimura, Environment Agency, Japan
Masaru Tanaka, Institute of Public Health, Japan
Terry Telzrow, Eveready Battery Co.

Patrick Toner, Society of the Plastics Industry
Roger Tuttle, Earthlife Sales Co.
Alyce Ujihara, Resources for the Future
Nancy VandenBerg, Markets for Recycled Products
May VanDeventer, Materials World
N.C. Vasuki, Delaware Solid Waste Authority
Jim Vilendre, Oregon Department of Environmental
    Quality
Joe Visalli, New York State Energy Research and
    Development Authority
Donald Walter, Dept. of Energy
Richard Wand, P.H. Gladtfelter
David Ward, Hershman Recycling
Ian Webster, Unocal Corp.
Thomas Webster, Center for Biology of Natural Systems
Bruce Wedddle, Environmental Protection Agency

Nancy Weissman, Philadelphia Recycling Office
Ed Wheless, County Sanitation Districts of Los Angeles
    County
Mary Wiard, Ohio Dept. Natural Resources
Douglas Wilson, Univ. Arizona
Jeanne Wirka, Environmental Action Foundation
Dan Witkowsky, Bureau of Mines
Liz Wood, Gershman, Brickner and Bratton, Inc.
William Woodbury, Bureau of Mines
Richard Wool, Univ. Illinois
Shelby Yastrow, McDonald's Corp.
Shizuo Yasuda, Mitsubishi Heavy Industries, Ltd., Japan
Iraj Zandi, Univ. Pennsylvania
Elliott Zimmerman, Illinois Dept. Dept. Energy and
    Natural Resources

Index

Index

Superintendent of Documents Publication Order Form

Charge your order.
It's easy!

Order Processing Code:

＊6584

☐ **YES,** please send me the following indicated publications:

Facing America's Trash: What Next for Municipal Solid Waste? (400 pages in length)
GPO stock number 052-003-01168-9; price $16.00.

1. The total cost of my order is $_____ (International customers please add an additional 25%.) All prices include regular domestic postage and handling and are good through 2/90. After this date, please call Order and Information Desk at 202–783–3238 to verify prices.

Please Type or Print

2.

_____
(Company or personal name)

_____
(Additional address/attention line)

_____
(Street address)

_____
(City, State, ZIP Code)

(___)_____
(Daytime phone including area code)

3. **Please choose method of payment:**

☐ Check payable to the Superintendent of Documents

☐ GPO Deposit Account ☐☐☐☐☐☐–☐

☐ VISA, CHOICE or MasterCard Account

☐☐☐☐☐☐☐☐☐☐☐☐☐☐☐☐☐☐☐☐

☐☐☐☐ _____
(Credit card expiration date) *Thank you for your order!*

_____
(Signature)   10/89

4. **Mail To:** Superintendent of Documents, Government Printing Office, Washington, D.C. 20402–9325